The UK
Scanning Directory
5th Edition

Interproducts
Publishers of Specialist Radio Books
Scotland and Eire

The UK Scanning Directory

UK Office:
8 Abbot Street, Perth, PH2 0EB, Scotland
Tel/Fax: (01738) 441199

Introduction

After nearly two years of continuous monitoring and revising by our editorial team around the country, we have finally succeeded in bringing you the most comprehensive, up-to-date edition of *The UK Scanning Directory* yet.

This 5th Edition
- continues to be Britain's most controversial radio book
- lists over 42,500 spot frequencies nationwide
- has many more duplex frequencies
- contains Low Band Skip from Eastern Europe and HF allocations
- and includes the largest police frequency list ever published

The UK Scanning Directory continues to gain more column inches and minutes of air time than any other radio book, and has been featured on both BBC and local radio stations, as well as in *Focus* magazine and *The Mirror*.

In answer to the huge growth in the hobby and an increasing demand for accurate information, the *Police Scanning Club* has been formed to provide readers with up-to- the-minute advances in Police communications. Readers will be kept up-to-date with the rapid advances in radio technology.

We have already begun collecting new frequencies, so why not send in your lists and take advantage of our new and exciting competition, details of which that can be found at the back of this edition.

Editor
June 1996

Using the UK Scanning Directory

Each page of *The UK Scanning Directory* is set out in five column; Base and Mobile frequencies, Mode, Location and User & Notes.

Base Frequency: This is the most acive frequency where most will be heard so the best one to monitor.

Mobile Frequency: In a Simplex arrangement, this frequency will be the same as the Base frequency. However, in a Duplex arrangement, this frequency will carry only signals from mobiles.

Mode: This is the mode that should be selected on your scanner for best reception.

Location: This is generally the area from where the signal originates. For example, if you are in Cambridge and you heard a signal on a particular frequency, then the location of the signal will be Cambridge.

User & Notes: This column contains details of who uses a particular frequency, their callsign, channel number and any other relevant notes.

Below is an example of a typical page.

Column 1:Base & Repeater Transmit Frequency (Duplex)
Base & Mobile Transmit Frequency (Simplex)

Column 2:Mobile Transmit Frequency (Duplex)
Mobile & Base Transmit Frequency (Simplex)

Column 3: Transmission Mode (i.e. AM, NFM, WFM, etc)

Column 4: Location (The approximate area where the signal will be heard, i.e. City, Town, District, Village, Hamlet, Settlement, County, Caravan, Forest, Ghetto, Squat, Palace, Inner City, Skip, etc)

Column 5: User, Callsign & Remarks

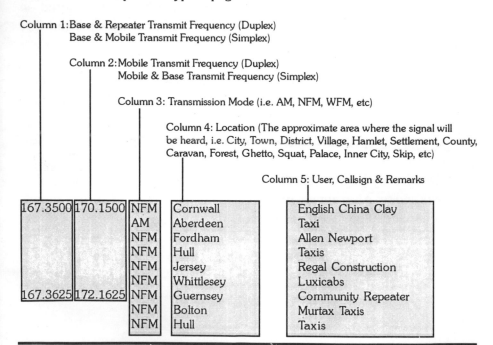

167.3500	170.1500	NFM	Cornwall	English China Clay
		AM	Aberdeen	Taxi
		NFM	Fordham	Allen Newport
		NFM	Hull	Taxis
		NFM	Jersey	Regal Construction
		NFM	Whittlesey	Luxicabs
167.3625	172.1625	NFM	Guernsey	Community Repeater
		NFM	Bolton	Murtax Taxis
		NFM	Hull	Taxis

A great deal of confusion has arisen from the gaps left after certain frequencies, for example, the gaps that follow 167.3500/170.1500 in the above extract. These gaps have been introduced to make the page less cluttered and more user friendly. Any gaps that follow a frequency indicates that the same frequency applies of all entries below the first. Therefore, the 167.3500/170.1500 group means:

167.3500	170.1500	NFM	Cornwall	English China Clay
167.3500	170.1500	AM	Aberdeen	Taxi
167.3500	170.1500	NFM	Fordham	Allen Newport
167.3500	170.1500	NFM	Hull	Taxis
167.3500	170.1500	NFM	Jersey	Regal Construction
167.3500	170.1500	NFM	Whittlesey	Luxicabs

If you are new to scanning the following list of the main users of the VHF/UHF bands will help you to quickly find their frequencies.

Due to overwhelming workload experienced by the editorial staff of *The UK Scanning Directory*, we are unable to answer queries by telephone, however, you can send them in writing.

List of Abbreviations and Terms

AA	Automobile Association
AFIS	Aerodrome Flight Information Service
AFSATCOM	US Air Force Satellite Communications
AM	Amplitude Modulation
ARA	Air Refuelling Area
ATC	Air Traffic Control or Air Training Corps
ATCC	Air Traffic Control Centre
ATIS	Aerodrome Terminal Information Service
AWACS	Airborne Warning & Control System
BAe	British Aerospace
BBC	British Broadcasting Corporation
BGS	British Geological Survey
BNFL	British Nuclear Fuels Ltd
BR	British Rail
BT	British Telecom
BTP	British Transport Police
CAC	Centralised Approach Control
CB	Citizen Band
CEGB	Central Electricity Generating Board
CMD	Command
Comms	Communications
CW	Continuous Wave (Morse)
DAB	Digital Audio Broadcasting
DATIS	Digital Aerodrome Terminal Information Service
DME	Distance Measuring Equipment
DTI	Department of Trade and Industry
DSRR	Digital Short Range Radios
FLTSATCOM	US Navy Satellite Communications
FM	Frequency Modulation
GCHQ	Government Communications Headquarters
GSM	New digital mobile phones
IBA	Independent Broadcasting Authority
IFR	Instrument Flight Rules
ILR	Independent Local Radio
ILS	Instrument Landing System
ITN	Independent Television News
ITV	Independent Television
LBS	Low Band Skip
LWT	London Weekend Television
MoD	Ministry of Defence
Mould	MoD National Home Defence Repeater Network
MRSA	Mandatory Radar Service Area

MWL	Mid-Wales Railway Line
NATO	North Atlantic Treaty Organisation
NASA	National Aeronautics and Space Administration
NB	Narrow Band
NCB	National Coal Board
NFM	Narrow Band FM
O/B	Outside Broadcast
Ops	Operations
PAR	Precision Approach Radar
PFA	Popular Flying Association
PMR	Private Mobile Radio
PR	Personal Radio
R	Runway (Left & Right)
RAF	Royal Air Force
RCA	Radiocommunications Agency
RN	Royal Navy
RTTY	Radio Teletype
SAR	Search and Rescue
SCS	Shopping Centre Security
Spec.	Specification
SRE	Surveillance Radar Element
SSB	Single-Side Band
SSTV	Slow Scan Television
Std	Standard
Surv.	Surveillance
TACAN	Tactical Air Navigation
TMA	Terminal Manoeuvring Area
TX	Transmission
UACC	Upper Air Control Centre
UHF	Ultra High Frequency (300 - 3000 MHz)
UKAEA	UK Atomic Energy Authority
USAF	US Air Force
USAFE	US Air Force Europe
USB	Upper Side Band
VFR	Visual Flight Rules
VHF	Very High Frequency (30 - 300 MHz)
VOLMET	Aviation Weather Broadcast
VOR	VHF Omni-Directional Radio Range
WFM	Wide Band FM

Longwave, Medium Wave and Shortwave Allocations

Many scanners now cover frequencies down to 100 kHz and allow access to the exciting world of Shortwave radio. Below is a list of frequency allocations, but if you want to learn more about receiving stations from around the world, turn to the back of this book for a list of publications what will introduce you fascinating subject.

148.5 - 283.5 kHz	Longwave Broadcasting AM
283.5 - 320 kHz	Maritime NDB, Aeronautical Navigation
320 - 405 kHz	Aeronautical Navigation NDB
405 - 435 kHz	Aeronautical Navigation NDB, Maritime Mobiles
435 - 495 kHz	Maritime Mobiles
495 - 505 kHz	Mobile (Distress and Calling)
505 - 526 kHz	Maritime Mobiles
526 - 1626 kHz	Medium Wave Broadcasting
1626 -2850 kHz	Maritime
2850 -2000 kHz	160 metres Amateur Radio
2300 - 2495 kHz	120 metres Tropical Braodcasting
2851 - 3019 kHz	En-Route Aeronautical Mobiles
3023 - 3152 kHz	Off-Route Aeronautical Mobiles
3155 - 3200 kHz	Fixed and Land & Maritime Mobiles
3200 - 3400 kHz	90 metres Tropical Broadcasting and Fixed & Land Mobiles
3401 - 3497 kHz	En-Route Aeronautical Mobiles
3500 - 3800 kHz	80 metres Amateur Radio
3950 - 4000 kHz	75 metres European Braodcasting
4000 - 4435 kHz	Maritime Fixed & Mobiles
4438 - 4650 kHz	Fixed and Land & Maritime Mobiles
4651 - 4696 kHz	En-Route Aeronautical Mobiles
4700 - 4995 kHz	Off-Route Aeronautical Mobiles
4750 - 5060 kHz	60 metres Tropical Broadcasting
5060 - 5450 kHz	Fixed and Land & Maritime Mobiles
5450 - 5477 kHz	Off-Route Aeronautical Mobiles
5481 - 5676 kHz	En-Route Aeronautical Mobiles
5680 - 5726 kHz	Off-Route Aeronautical Mobiles
5730 - 5960 kHz	Fixed and Land & Maritime Mobiles
5950 - 6200 kHz	49 metres Broadcasting Band
6200 - 6526 kHz	Maritime Mobiles
6526 - 6682 kHz	En-Route Aeronautical Mobiles
6685 - 6765 kHz	Off-Route Aeronautical Mobiles
6765 - 7000 kHz	Fixed and Land Mobiles
7000 - 7100 kHz	40 metres Amateur Radio
7100 - 7300 kHz	41 metres Broadcasting Band
7300 - 8100 kHz	Fixed and Land Mobiles
8100 - 8195 kHz	Fixed and Maritime Mobiles
8195 - 8812 kHz	Maritime Mobiles
8816 - 8960 kHz	En-Route Aeronautical Mobiles
8965 - 9037 kHz	Off-Route Aeronautical Mobiles
9040 - 9500 kHz	Fixed

9500 - 9900 kHz	31 metres Broadcasting Band
9900 - 9995 kHz	Fixed
10006 - 10096 kHz	En-Route Aeronautical Mobiles
10100 - 10150 kHz	30 metres Amateur Radio
10150 - 11175 kHz	Fixed and Land & Maritime Mobiles
11175 - 11271 kHz	Off-Route Aeronautical Mobiles
11276 - 11396 kHz	En-Route Aeronautical Mobiles
11400 - 12230 kHz	Fixed
11650 - 12050 kHz	25 metres Broadcasting Band
12230 - 13197 kHz	Maritime Mobiles
13200 - 13257 kHz	Off-Route Aeronautical Mobiles
13261 - 13357 kHz	En-Route Aeronautical Mobiles
13360 - 13600 kHz	Fixed and Land & Maritime Mobiles
13600 - 13800 kHz	22 metres Broadcasting Band
13800 - 14000 kHz	Fixed and Land Mobiles
14000 - 14350 kHz	20 metres Amateur Band
14350 - 14990 kHz	Fixed and Land & Maritime Mobiles
15010 - 15097 kHz	Off-Route Aeronautical Mobiles
15100 - 15600 kHz	19 metres Broadcasting Band
15600 - 16360 kHz	Fixed
16360 - 17407 kHz	Maritime Mobiles
17410 - 17550 kHz	Fixed
17550 - 17900 kHz	16 metres Broadcasting Band
17901 - 17967 kHz	En-Route Aeronautical Mobiles
17970 - 18027 kHz	Off-Route Aeronautical Mobiles
18030 - 18068 kHz	Fixed
18068 - 18168 kHz	16 metres Amateur Band
18168 - 18780 kHz	Fixed
18780 - 18900 kHz	Maritime Mobiles
18900 - 19680 kHz	Fixed
19680 - 19797 kHz	Maritime Mobiles
19800 - 21000 kHz	Fixed & Land Mobiles
21000 - 21450 kHz	15 metres Amateur Band
21450 - 21850 kHz	13 metres Broadcasting Band
21850 - 21870 kHz	Fixed
21870 - 21924 kHz	Aeronautical Fixed
21925 - 21998 kHz	En-Route Aeronautical Mobiles
22000 - 22852 kHz	Maritime Mobiles
22855 - 23000 kHz	Fixed
23000 - 23200 kHz	Fixed and Land & Maritime Mobiles
23200 - 23350 kHz	Off-Route Aeronautical Mobiles
23350 - 24890 kHz	Fixed & Land Mobiles
24890 - 24990 kHz	12 metres Amateur Band
24990 - 25070 kHz	Fixed & Land Mobiles
25070 - 25210 kHz	Maritime Mobiles
25210 - 25520 kHz	Fixed and Land & Maritime Mobiles
25550 - 25600 kHz	Radio Astronomy
25600 - 26100 kHz	11 metres Broadcasting Band
26100 - 26172 kHz	Maritime Mobiles
26175 - 26235 kHz	Fixed and Land & Maritime Mobiles

Base	Mobile	Mode	Location	User and Notes
25.0200 - 25.0700 MHz			FIXED AND LAND MOBILE USB	
25.0700 - 25.2100 MHz			MARITIME MOBILE USB & RTTY	
25.2100 - 25.5500 MHz			FIXED, LAND AND MARITIME MOBILE USB	
25.5500 - 25.6000 MHz			RADIO ASTRONOMY	
25.6000 - 26.1000 MHz			11M BROADCASTING BAND AM	
26.1000 - 26.1750 MHz			MARITIME MOBILE USB	
26.1750 - 26.2350 MHz			FIXED, LAND AND MARITIME MOBILE USB	
26.2180		NFM	Nationwide	DTI Test & Development
26.2350 - 26.8700 MHz			LOW POWER PAGING	
26.5880		NFM	Nationwide	Common Paging Channel
26.9650 - 27.4050 MHz			CEPT (UK & EUROPE) CB & CONTROLLED MODELS	
26.9650		NFM	Nationwide	Channel 01
26.9750		NFM	Nationwide	Channel 02
26.9850		NFM	Nationwide	Channel 03
26.9950		NFM	Nationwide	'Brown' Model Channel
27.0050		NFM	Nationwide	Channel 04
27.0150		NFM	Nationwide	Channel 05
27.0250		NFM	Nationwide	Channel 06
27.0350		NFM	Nationwide	Channel 07
27.0450		NFM	Nationwide	'Red' Model Channel
27.0450		NFM	Nationwide	DTI Test & Development
27.0550		NFM	Nationwide	Channel 08
27.0650		NFM	Nationwide	Channel 09
27.0750		NFM	Nationwide	Channel 10
27.0850		NFM	Nationwide	Channel 11
27.0950		NFM	Nationwide	'Orange' Model Channel
27.1050		NFM	Nationwide	Channel 12
27.1150		NFM	Nationwide	Channel 13
27.1200		NFM	Nationwide	Paging Test & Development
27.1250		NFM	Nationwide	Channel 14
27.1350		NFM	Nationwide	Channel 15
27.1450		NFM	Nationwide	'Yellow' Model Channel
27.1550		NFM	Nationwide	Channel 16
27.1625		NFM	St Helier	Jeanne Jugan Hospital Paging
27.1650		NFM	Nationwide	Channel 17
27.1750		NFM	Nationwide	Channel 18
27.1850		NFM	Nationwide	Channel 19
27.1950		NFM	Nationwide	'Green' Model Channel
27.2050		NFM	Nationwide	Channel 20
27.2150		NFM	Nationwide	Channel 21

Base	Mobile	Mode	Location	User and Notes
27.2250		NFM	Nationwide	Channel 22
27.2350		NFM	Nationwide	Channel 24
27.2450		NFM	Nationwide	'Blue' Model Channel
27.2450		NFM	Nationwide	Channel 25
27.2550		NFM	Nationwide	Channel 23
27.2650		NFM	Nationwide	Channel 26
27.2750		NFM	Nationwide	Channel 27
27.2850		NFM	Nationwide	Channel 28
27.2950		NFM	Nationwide	Channel 29
27.3050		NFM	Nationwide	Channel 30
27.3150		NFM	Nationwide	Channel 31
27.3250		NFM	Nationwide	Channel 32
27.3350		NFM	Nationwide	Channel 33
27.3450		NFM	Nationwide	Channel 34
27.3550		NFM	Nationwide	Channel 35
27.3650		NFM	Nationwide	Channel 36
27.3750		NFM	Nationwide	Channel 37
27.3850		NFM	Nationwide	Channel 38
27.3950		NFM	Nationwide	Channel 39
27.4050		NFM	Nationwide	Channel 40

27.4050 - 27.6000 MHz   MOBILES, WEATHER SONDES & LOW POWER ALARMS

27.60125 - 27.99125 MHz   UK CB

Base	Mobile	Mode	Location	User and Notes
27.60125	27.60125	NFM	Nationwide	Channel 01
27.61125	27.61125	NFM	Nationwide	Channel 02
27.62125	27.62125	NFM	Nationwide	Channel 03
27.63125	27.63125	NFM	Nationwide	Channel 04
27.64125	27.64125	NFM	Nationwide	Channel 05
27.65125	27.65125	NFM	Nationwide	Channel 06
27.66125	27.66125	NFM	Nationwide	Channel 07
27.67125	27.67125	NFM	Nationwide	Channel 08
27.68125	27.68125	NFM	Nationwide	Channel 09 Emergency
27.69125	27.69125	NFM	Nationwide	Channel 10
27.70125	27.70125	NFM	Nationwide	Channel 11
27.71125	27.71125	NFM	Nationwide	Channel 12
27.72125	27.72125	NFM	Nationwide	Channel 13
27.73125	27.73125	NFM	Nationwide	Channel 14 Calling
27.74125	27.74125	NFM	Nationwide	Channel 15
27.75125	27.75125	NFM	Nationwide	Channel 16
27.76125	27.76125	NFM	Nationwide	Channel 17
27.77125	27.77125	NFM	Nationwide	Channel 18
27.78125	27.78125	NFM	Nationwide	Channel 19 Calling
27.79125	27.79125	NFM	Nationwide	Channel 20
27.80125	27.80125	NFM	Nationwide	Channel 21
27.81125	27.81125	NFM	Nationwide	Channel 22
27.82125	27.82125	NFM	Nationwide	Channel 23
27.83125	27.83125	NFM	Nationwide	Channel 24

Base	Mobile	Mode	Location	User and Notes
27.84125	27.84125	NFM	Nationwide	Channel 25
27.85125	27.85125	NFM	Nationwide	Channel 26
27.86125	27.86125	NFM	Nationwide	Channel 27
27.87125	27.87125	NFM	Nationwide	Channel 28
27.88125	27.88125	NFM	Nationwide	Channel 29
27.89125	27.89125	NFM	Nationwide	Channel 30
27.90125	27.90125	NFM	Nationwide	Channel 31
27.91125	27.91125	NFM	Nationwide	Channel 32
27.92125	27.92125	NFM	Nationwide	Channel 33
27.93125	27.93125	NFM	Nationwide	Channel 34
27.94125	27.94125	NFM	Nationwide	Channel 35
27.95125	27.95125	NFM	Nationwide	Channel 36
27.96125	27.96125	NFM	Nationwide	Channel 37
27.97125	27.97125	NFM	Nationwide	Channel 38
27.98125	27.98125	NFM	Nationwide	Channel 39
27.99125	27.99125	NFM	Nationwide	Channel 40

28.0000 - 29.7000 MHz   10M AMATEUR BAND USB, AMATEUR SATELLITE AND LOW POWER DEVICES

Base	Mobile	Mode	Location	User and Notes
28.2000		CW	Crowborough	GB3SXE Beacon
28.2150		CW	Slough	GB3RAL Beacon
29.6000		NFM	Nationwide	FM Calling Channel

29.7000 - 29.9700 MHz   MOD TACTICAL CHANNELS 25 KHZ SIMPLEX NFM

30.0050 - 31.0250 MHz   NASA SPACE TO EARTH NFM SIMPLEX

Base	Mobile	Mode	Location	User and Notes
30.0100		NFM	Space	Downlink
30.0250	30.0250	NFM	RAF Fairford	Base Security

30.0250 - 31.7000 MHz   USAFE COMMUNICATIONS 25 KHZ SIMPLEX

Base	Mobile	Mode	Location	User and Notes
30.1750		NFM	Salisbury Plain	Army
30.2000		NFM	Salisbury Plain	Army
30.3250		NFM	Salisbury Plain	Army
30.3500		NFM	Nationwide	Army Forward Air Controllers
30.4500		NFM	Nationwide	US Military MARS Network
30.5000	30.5000	NFM	London	US Embassy Security (Eagle)
30.5500	30.5500	NFM	RAF Fairford	Base Security
30.9875	30.9875	NFM	RAF Fairford	Base Security
31.0000	31.0000	NFM	RAF Fairford	Tanker Ground Ops
31.1825	31.1825	NFM	RAF Fairford	Fence Security
31.2000	31.2000	NFM	Salisbury Plain	Army
		NFM	RAF Fairford	Ground Maintenance
31.2125		NFM	Nationwide	Digital Signalling
31.2500	31.2500	NFM	RAF Fairford	Base Security
31.3000	31.3000	NFM	RAF Fairford	Base Medical Services
31.4000	31.4000	NFM	RAF Fairford	Tanker Ground Operations
31.4375		NFM	Nationwide	Digital Signalling
31.5000	31.5000	NFM	Brighton	TA Barracks

Base	Mobile	Mode	Location	User and Notes
31.5000	31.5000	NFM	Preston	TA Barracks
31.6750		NFM	Salisbury Plain	Army
31.7000		NFM	Salisbury Plain	Army
31.7250	161.0000	NFM	Nationwide	Hospital Paging
31.7250 - 31.7750 MHz			**HOSPITAL PAGING EMERGENCY SPEECH RETURN**	
31.7500	161.0250	NFM	Nationwide	Hospital Paging
31.7750	161.0500	NFM	Nationwide	Hospital Paging
31.8000	31.8000	AM	Nationwide	RAF Cadets Channel V12
31.8000 - 34.9000 MHz			**USAFE COMMUNICATIONS 25 kHz SIMPLEX**	
31.9125		NFM	Nationwide	Digital Signalling
31.9500		NFM	Salisbury Plain	Army
32.2000	32.2000	NFM	Nationwide	USAF Base Security
32.2500		NFM	Salisbury Plain	Army
32.3000	32.3000	NFM	Brighton	TA Barracks
		NFM	Preston	TA Barracks
		NFM	RAF Fairford	Base Security
32.3250		NFM	Salisbury Plain	Army
32.3500	32.3500	NFM	Salisbury Plain	Army
		NFM	RAF Mildenhall	Security
32.4250		NFM	Salisbury Plain	Army
32.5250		NFM	Salisbury Plain	Army
32.5750		NFM	Salisbury Plain	Army
32.9000		NFM	Salisbury Plain	Army
33.1250	33.1250	NFM	Nationwide	Army Land Forces
33.2000		NFM	Salisbury Plain	Army
33.2500	33.2500	NFM	RAF Lakenheath	Birdscare Operations
		NFM	RAF Mildenhall	Birdscare Operations
33.3000	33.3000	NFM	Nationwide	USAF War Training
33.5000	33.5000	NFM	RAF Lakenheath	Birdscare Operations
		NFM	RAF Mildenhall	Birdscare Operations
33.6750	33.6750	NFM	Brighton	TA Barracks
		NFM	Preston	TA Barracks
33.7000	33.7000	NFM	RAF Mildenhall	Fire Control
33.7750		NFM	Salisbury Plain	Army
33.8625	33.8625	NFM	RAF Mildenhall	Ambulance
34.1000	34.1000	NFM	Nationwide	USAF Medical
34.1250		NFM	Salisbury Plain	Army
34.1500	34.1500	NFM	RAF Lakenheath	Crash Operations
		NFM	RAF Mildenhall	Crash Operations
34.3000		NFM	Salisbury Plain	Army
34.4000		NFM	Nationwide	Army Forward Air Controllers
34.7625	34.7625	NFM	RAF Mildenhall	Security
34.9000	34.9000	NFM	RAF Lakenheath	Base Security
		NFM	RAF Mildenhall	Security
		NFM	RAF Upper Heyford	Base Security

Base	Mobile	Mode	Location	User and Notes
34.9250 - 34.9750 MHz			**LOW POWER ALARMS FOR ELDERLY AND INFIRM**	
			ALARM FOR ELDERLY & INFIRM	
35.0000 - 35.2500 MHz			**RADIO CONTROLLED MODELS 10 KHZ (100 MW MAX)**	
35.0000		NFM	Nationwide	Channel 60
35.0100		NFM	Nationwide	Channel 61
35.0200		NFM	Nationwide	Channel 62
35.0300		NFM	Nationwide	Channel 63
35.0400		NFM	Nationwide	Channel 64
35.0500		NFM	Nationwide	Channel 65
35.0600		NFM	Nationwide	Channel 66
35.0700		NFM	Nationwide	Channel 67
35.0800		NFM	Nationwide	Channel 68
35.0900		NFM	Nationwide	Channel 69
35.1000		NFM	Nationwide	Channel 70
35.1100		NFM	Nationwide	Channel 71
35.1200		NFM	Nationwide	Channel 72
35.1300		NFM	Nationwide	Channel 73
35.1400		NFM	Nationwide	Channel 74
35.1500		NFM	Nationwide	Channel 75
35.1600		NFM	Nationwide	Channel 76
35.1700		NFM	Nationwide	Channel 77
35.1800		NFM	Nationwide	Channel 78
35.1900		NFM	Nationwide	Channel 79
35.2000		NFM	Nationwide	Channel 80
35.2100		NFM	Nationwide	Channel 81
35.2200		NFM	Nationwide	Channel 82
35.2300		NFM	Nationwide	Channel 83
35.2400		NFM	Nationwide	Channel 84
35.2500		NFM	Nationwide	Channel 85
35.2500	35.2500	NFM	Salisbury Plain	Army
35.2500 - 37.7500 MHz			**MoD TACTICAL COMMUNICATIONS 25 KHZ SIMPLEX**	
35.2750	35.2750	NFM	Salisbury Plain	Army
35.3500	35.3500	NFM	Brecon Beacons	Army
35.4000	35.4000	NFM	Brecon Beacons	Army
		NFM	RAF Upper Heyford	Ground Control
35.5750	35.5750	NFM	Salisbury Plain	Army
35.6000	35.6000	NFM	RAF Mildenhall	Security
35.6250		NFM	Salisbury Plain	Army
35.7750	35.7750	NFM	Salisbury Plain	Army
35.8250		NFM	France	PMR [LBS]
35.9000	35.9000	NFM	RAF Mildenhall	Security
35.9750	35.9750	NFM	Nationwide	Royal Signals
36.0000	36.0000	NFM	Brighton	TA Barracks
		NFM	Preston	TA Barracks
36.3500		NFM	Bovington	Army Training Camp
36.7500		NFM	Nationwide	Army Forward Air Controllers

Base	Mobile	Mode	Location	User and Notes
36.8000		NFM	Nationwide	ATC Channel V12
36.8500		NFM	Salisbury Plain	Army
37.2250	37.2250	NFM	Stanford Battle Area	Army
37.3000	37.3000	AM	Nationwide	RAF Cadets Channel V11
37.3250		NFM	Salisbury Plain	Army
37.7500 - 38.2500 MHz			**RADIO ASTRONOMY BAND**	
37.9000 - 40.1000 MHz			**MoD TACTICAL COMMUNICATIONS 25 KHz SIMPLEX**	
38.0000	38.0000	USB	Nationwide	Racal Comsec Spot
38.1000	38.1000	AM	Nationwide	RAF Cadets Channel V13
38.3200		NFM	Nationwide	Fish Tagging (Salmon)
38.4600	34.3600	NFM	Germany	Emergency Channel Ch 801
38.4800	34.3800	NFM	Germany	Emergency Channel Ch 802
38.5000	34.4000	NFM	Germany	Emergency Channel Ch 803
38.5200	34.4200	NFM	Germany	Emergency Channel Ch 804
38.5400	34.4400	NFM	Germany	Emergency Channel Ch 805
38.5600	34.4600	NFM	Germany	Emergency Channel Ch 806
38.5750		NFM	Senny Bridge	Army
38.5800	34.4800	NFM	Germany	Emergency Channel Ch 807
38.6000	34.5000	NFM	Germany	Emergency Channel Ch 808
38.6200	34.5200	NFM	Germany	Emergency Channel Ch 809
38.6250		NFM	Oakhampton	Army 657 Sqn Ops
38.6400	34.5400	NFM	Germany	Emergency Channel Ch 810
38.6600	34.5600	NFM	Germany	Emergency Channel Ch 811
38.6800	34.5800	NFM	Germany	Emergency Channel Ch 812
38.7000	34.6000	NFM	Germany	Emergency Channel Ch 813
38.7200	34.6200	NFM	Germany	Emergency Channel Ch 814
38.7400	34.6400	NFM	Germany	Emergency Channel Ch 815
38.7600	34.6600	NFM	Germany	Emergency Channel Ch 816
38.7800	34.6800	NFM	Germany	Emergency Channel Ch 817
38.8000	34.7000	NFM	Germany	Emergency Channel Ch 818
38.8200	34.7200	NFM	Germany	Emergency Channel Ch 819
38.8400	34.7400	NFM	Germany	Emergency Channel Ch 820
38.8600	34.7600	NFM	Germany	Emergency Channel Ch 821
38.8800	34.7800	NFM	Germany	Emergency Channel Ch 822
38.9000	34.8000	NFM	Germany	Emergency Channel Ch 823
38.9200	34.8200	NFM	Germany	Emergency Channel Ch 824
38.9400	34.8400	NFM	Germany	Emergency Channel Ch 825
38.9600	34.8600	NFM	Germany	Emergency Channel Ch 826
38.9800	34.8800	NFM	Germany	Emergency Channel Ch 827
39.0000	39.0000	NFM	Ludford Cove	Range Patrol Vessel
		NFM	Salisbury Plain	Army
39.0000	34.9000	NFM	Germany	Emergency Channel Ch 828
39.0200	34.9200	NFM	Germany	Emergency Channel Ch 829
39.0400	34.9400	NFM	Germany	Emergency Channel Ch 830
39.0600	34.9600	NFM	Germany	Emergency Channel Ch 831
39.0800	34.9800	NFM	Germany	Emergency Channel Ch 832

Base	Mobile	Mode	Location	User and Notes
39.1000	35.0000	NFM	Germany	Emergency Channel Ch 833
39.1200	35.0200	NFM	Germany	Emergency Channel Ch 834
39.1400	35.0400	NFM	Germany	Emergency Channel Ch 835
39.1600	35.0600	NFM	Germany	Emergency Channel Ch 836
39.1800	35.0800	NFM	Germany	Emergency Channel Ch 837
39.2000	35.1000	NFM	Germany	Emergency Channel Ch 838
39.2200	35.1200	NFM	Germany	Emergency Channel Ch 839
39.2400	35.1400	NFM	Germany	Emergency Channel Ch 840
39.2600	35.1600	NFM	Germany	Emergency Channel Ch 841
39.2800	35.1800	NFM	Germany	Emergency Channel Ch 842
39.3000	35.2000	NFM	Germany	Emergency Channel Ch 843
39.3200	35.2200	NFM	Germany	Emergency Channel Ch 844
39.3400	35.2400	NFM	Germany	Emergency Channel Ch 845
39.3600	35.2600	NFM	Germany	Emergency Channel Ch 846
39.3800	35.2800	NFM	Germany	Emergency Channel Ch 847
39.4000	35.3000	NFM	Germany	Emergency Channel Ch 848
39.4200	35.3200	NFM	Germany	Emergency Channel Ch 849
39.4400	35.3400	NFM	Germany	Emergency Channel Ch 850
39.4600	35.3600	NFM	Germany	Emergency Channel Ch 851
39.4800	35.3800	NFM	Germany	Emergency Channel Ch 852
39.5000	35.4000	NFM	Germany	Emergency Channel Ch 853
39.5000	39.5000	NFM	Nationwide	Army Tanks Channel
39.5200	35.4200	NFM	Germany	Emergency Channel Ch 854
39.5400	35.4400	NFM	Germany	Emergency Channel Ch 855
39.5600	35.4600	NFM	Germany	Emergency Channel Ch 856
39.5800	35.4800	NFM	Germany	Emergency Channel Ch 857
39.6000	39.6000	NFM	Ludford Cove	Army Patrol Vessel
39.6000	35.5000	NFM	Germany	Emergency Channel Ch 858
39.6200	35.5200	NFM	Germany	Emergency Channel Ch 859
39.6400	35.5400	NFM	Germany	Emergency Channel Ch 860
39.6500	39.6500	NFM	Nationwide	Army Tanks Channel
39.6600	35.5600	NFM	Germany	Emergency Channel Ch 861
39.6800	35.5800	NFM	Germany	Emergency Channel Ch 862
39.7000	35.6000	NFM	Germany	Emergency Channel Ch 863
39.7200	35.6200	NFM	Germany	Emergency Channel Ch 864
39.7400	35.6400	NFM	Germany	Emergency Channel Ch 865
39.7500	39.7500	NFM	Nationwide	Royal Signals Display
39.7600	35.6600	NFM	Germany	Emergency Channel Ch 866
39.7800	35.6800	NFM	Germany	Emergency Channel Ch 867
39.8000	35.7000	NFM	Germany	Emergency Channel Ch 868
39.8200	35.7200	NFM	Germany	Emergency Channel Ch 869
39.8400	35.7400	NFM	Germany	Emergency Channel Ch 870
39.8600	35.7600	NFM	Germany	Emergency Channel Ch 871
39.8800	35.7800	NFM	Germany	Emergency Channel Ch 872
39.9000	35.8000	NFM	Germany	Emergency Channel Ch 873
39.9000	39.9000	NFM	RAF Fairford	Base Security
40.0000	40.0000	NFM	Salisbury Plain	Army
40.0500	40.5000	NFM	Nationwide	Army Distress Frequency

Base	Mobile	Mode	Location	User and Notes
40.0800	40.0800	NFM	London	Sky News Link
40.2000	40.2000	AM	Nationwide	RAF Cadets Channel V14
40.2750	40.2750	NFM	London	Royal Military Police
40.6650		NFM	Nationwide	Channel 665

40.6650 - 40.9550 MHz RADIO CONTROLLED SURFACE MODELS 10 kHz

Base	Mobile	Mode	Location	User and Notes
40.6750		NFM	Nationwide	Channel 675
40.6850		NFM	Nationwide	Channel 685
40.6950		NFM	Nationwide	Channel 695
40.7000	40.7000	NFM	Bovington	Army Training Camp
		NFM	Salisbury Plain	Army
40.7050		NFM	Nationwide	Channel 705
40.7150		NFM	Nationwide	Channel 715
40.7250		NFM	Nationwide	Channel 725
40.7350		NFM	Nationwide	Channel 735
40.7450		NFM	Nationwide	Channel 745
40.7500	40.7500	NFM	Bovington	Army Training Camp
40.7550		NFM	Nationwide	Channel 755
40.7650		NFM	Nationwide	Channel 765
40.7750		NFM	Nationwide	Channel 775
40.7850		NFM	Nationwide	Channel 785
40.7950		NFM	Nationwide	Channel 795
40.8050		NFM	Nationwide	Channel 805
40.8150		NFM	Nationwide	Channel 815
40.8250		NFM	Nationwide	Channel 825
40.8350		NFM	Nationwide	Channel 835
40.8450		NFM	Nationwide	Channel 845
40.8550		NFM	Nationwide	Channel 855
40.8650		NFM	Nationwide	Channel 865
40.8750		NFM	Nationwide	Channel 875
40.8750	40.8750	NFM	Salisbury Plain	Army
40.8850		NFM	Nationwide	Channel 885
40.8950		NFM	Nationwide	Channel 895
40.9050		NFM	Nationwide	Channel 905
40.9150		NFM	Nationwide	Channel 915
40.9250		NFM	Nationwide	Channel 925
40.9350		NFM	Nationwide	Channel 935
40.9450		NFM	Nationwide	Channel 945
40.9550		NFM	Nationwide	Channel 955

41.0000 - 46.6000 MHz MoD TACTICAL COMMUNICATIONS 25 kHz SIMPLEX

Base	Mobile	Mode	Location	User and Notes
41.1250	41.1250	NFM	Salisbury Plain	Army
42.0500	42.0500	NFM	Jersey	Territorial Army
		NFM	Salisbury Plain	Army
42.1250	42.1250	NFM	Nationwide	Army War Training
42.3250	42.3250	NFM	Salisbury Plain	Army
42.5500	42.5500	NFM	Salisbury Plain	Army
43.1000	43.1000	NFM	Salisbury Plain	Army

Base	Mobile	Mode	Location	User and Notes
43.2250	43.2250	NFM	Salisbury Plain	Army
43.5500	43.5500	NFM	Salisbury Plain	Army
43.7750	43.7750	NFM	Salisbury Plain	Army
44.0000	44.0000	NFM	Bovington	Army Training Camp
		NFM	Salisbury Plain	Army
44.4250	44.4250	NFM	Salisbury Plain	Army
44.4500	44.4500	NFM	Nationwide	Army War Training
45.3000	45.3000	NFM	Salisbury Plain	Army
		NFM	Stanford Battle Area	Army
45.4000	45.4000	NFM	Senny Bridge	Army
45.4250	45.4250	NFM	Stanford Battle Area	Army
45.7000	45.7000	NFM	Wiltshire	Dunge Hill War Games
45.7125	45.7125	NFM	Nationwide	Army War Training
46.0000	46.0000	NFM	Nationwide	Royal Signals Display

46.0000 - 68.0000 MHz   TV BAND I (NOT UK, DX FROM EUROPE)

Base	Mobile	Mode	Location	User and Notes
46.1250	46.1250	NFM	Nationwide	Army War Training
46.3250	46.3250	NFM	Nationwide	Army War Training
46.6100	49.6700	NFM	Nationwide	US Specification Channel 1

46.6100 - 46.9700 MHz   US SPEC. CORDLESS TELEPHONES BASE
(SPLIT + 3.06 MHz)

Base	Mobile	Mode	Location	User and Notes
46.6300	49.8450	NFM	Nationwide	US Specification Channel 2
46.6700	49.8600	NFM	Nationwide	US Specification Channel 3
46.7100	49.7700	NFM	Nationwide	US Specification Channel 4
46.7300	49.8750	NFM	Nationwide	US Specification Channel 5
46.7700	49.8300	NFM	Nationwide	US Specification Channel 6
46.8000	46.8000	NFM	London	BBC Music Link
46.8300	49.8900	NFM	Nationwide	US Specification Channel 7
46.8700	49.9300	NFM	Nationwide	US Specification Channel 8
46.9000	46.9000	NFM	Scarborough	Cordless Telephone
46.9300	49.9900	NFM	Nationwide	US Specification Channel 9
46.9700	49.9700	NFM	Nationwide	US Specification Channel 10

47.0000 - 47.4000 MHz   FUTURE PMR ALLOCATION, CURRENTLY MoD

47.3125 - 47.36875 MHz LONG RANGE ALARMS

Base	Mobile	Mode	Location	User and Notes
47.4000		NFM	Nationwide	Car Theft Paging Alarms
47.4000	47.4000	NFM	London	BBC Music Link
47.41875	77.5500	NFM	Nationwide	Extended Range Telephone

47.41875 - 47.43125 MHz   EXTENDED RANGE CORDLESS PHONES

Base	Mobile	Mode	Location	User and Notes
47.43125	77.5125	NFM	Nationwide	Extended Range Telephone
47.45625	1.6420	NFM	Nationwide	Channel 1

47.45625 - 47.54375 MHz   DTI APPROVED CORDLESS TELEPHONES

Base	Mobile	Mode	Location	User and Notes
47.46875	1.6620	NFM	Nationwide	Channel 2
47.48125	1.6820	NFM	Nationwide	Channel 3

Base	Mobile	Mode	Location	User and Notes
47.49375	1.7020	NFM	Nationwide	Channel 4
47.50625	1.7220	NFM	Nationwide	Channel 5
47.51875	1.7420	NFM	Nationwide	Channel 6
47.53125	1.7620	NFM	Nationwide	Channel 7
47.54375	1.7820	NFM	Nationwide	Channel 8

47.5500 - 48.5500 MHz BROADCASTING LINKS

Base		Mode	Location	User and Notes
47.6450		NFM	Nationwide	BBC O/B
47.94375		NFM	Nationwide	ITV Engineers Channel 1
47.94375		NFM	Stockport	TV Engineers
47.95625		NFM	Nationwide	ITV Engineers Channel 2
47.96875		NFM	Nationwide	ITV Engineers Channel 3
48.05625		NFM	Isle of Wight	I.o.W. Radio Feeder (1242 kHz)
48.08125		NFM	London	Sky TV Talkback
48.4000		NFM	Nationwide	Channel 1

48.4000 - 48.5000 MHz CORDLESS RADIO MICROPHONES 12.5 KHZ

Base		Mode	Location	User and Notes
48.40625		NFM	Nationwide	ASP-Hi Talkback (52.85625)
48.4125		NFM	Nationwide	ASP-Hi Talkback (52.86875)
48.4125		NFM	Nationwide	Channel 2
48.4250		NFM	Nationwide	ASP-Hi Talkback (52.87125)
48.4250		NFM	Nationwide	Channel 3
48.4375		NFM	Nationwide	ASP-Hi Talkback (52.90375)
48.4375		NFM	Nationwide	Channel 4
48.4500		NFM	Nationwide	ASP-Hi Talkback (52.90625)
48.4500		NFM	Nationwide	Channel 5
48.4625		NFM	Nationwide	ASP-Hi Talkback (52.91875)
48.4625		NFM	Nationwide	Channel 6
48.4750		NFM	Nationwide	ASP-Hi Talkback (52.93125)
48.4750		NFM	Nationwide	Channel 7
48.4875		NFM	Nationwide	Channel 8
48.5000		NFM	Nationwide	ASP-Hi Talkback (52.94375)
48.9750		NFM	Nationwide	Short Term Hire Paging
48.9875		NFM	Nationwide	Short Term Hire Paging
49.0000		NFM	Nationwide	Channel 1

49.0000 - 49.4875 MHz ONE WAY NON SPEECH PAGING SYSTEMS 12.5 KHZ

Base		Mode	Location	User and Notes
49.0125		NFM	Nationwide	Channel 2
49.0250		NFM	Nationwide	Channel 3
49.0375		NFM	Nationwide	Channel 4
49.0500		NFM	Nationwide	Channel 5
49.0625		NFM	Nationwide	Channel 6
49.0750		NFM	Nationwide	Channel 7
49.0875		NFM	Nationwide	Channel 8
49.1000		NFM	Nationwide	Channel 9
49.1125		NFM	Nationwide	Channel 10
49.1250		NFM	Nationwide	Channel 11
49.1375		NFM	Nationwide	Channel 12

Base	Mobile	Mode	Location	User and Notes
49.1500		NFM	Nationwide	Channel 13
49.1625		NFM	Nationwide	Channel 14
49.1750		NFM	Nationwide	Channel 15
49.1875		NFM	Nationwide	Channel 16
49.2000		NFM	Nationwide	Channel 17
49.2125		NFM	Nationwide	Channel 18
49.2250		NFM	Nationwide	Channel 19
49.2375		NFM	Nationwide	Channel 20
49.2500		NFM	Nationwide	Channel 21
49.2625		NFM	Nationwide	Channel 22
49.2750		NFM	Nationwide	Channel 23
49.2875		NFM	Nationwide	Channel 24
49.3000		NFM	Nationwide	Channel 25
49.3125		NFM	Nationwide	Channel 26
49.3250		NFM	Nationwide	Channel 27
49.3375		NFM	Nationwide	Channel 28
49.3500		NFM	Nationwide	Channel 29
49.3625		NFM	Nationwide	Channel 30
49.3750		NFM	Nationwide	Channel 31
49.3875		NFM	Nationwide	Channel 32
49.4000		NFM	Nationwide	Channel 33
49.4125		NFM	Nationwide	Channel 34
49.4250		NFM	Bournemouth	Hospital Paging
49.4250		NFM	Nationwide	Hospital Channel 35
49.4375		NFM	Nationwide	Hospital Channel 36
49.4500		NFM	Jersey	Hospital Cardiac Bleep & Voice
49.4500		NFM	Nationwide	Hospital Channel 37
49.4625		NFM	Nationwide	Hospital Channel 38
49.4750		NFM	Nationwide	Hospital Channel 39
49.4875		NFM	Nationwide	Channel 40

49.5000 - 49.7875 MHz   BBC CORDLESS MICROPHONES NFM

49.6700 - 49.9700 MHz   US SPEC. CORDLESS 'PHONES BASE
(SPLIT + 3.06 MHz)

49.8200 - 49.9875 MHz   WALKIE TALKIES, RADIO MICS AND BABY MONITORS

Base	Mobile	Mode	Location	User and Notes
49.8200		NFM	Nationwide	Channel 1
49.8300		NFM	Nationwide	Channel 2
49.8300		NFM	Nationwide	Channel A
49.8300		NFM	Nationwide	Maxan Channel 1
49.8400		NFM	Nationwide	Channel 3
49.8400		NFM	Nationwide	Channel UK1
49.8450		NFM	Nationwide	Channel B
49.8450		NFM	Nationwide	Maxan Channel 2
49.8500		NFM	Nationwide	Channel 4
49.8600		NFM	Nationwide	Channel 5
49.8600		NFM	Nationwide	Channel C

Base	Mobile	Mode	Location	User and Notes
49.8600		NFM	Nationwide	Maxan Channel 3
49.8700		NFM	Nationwide	Channel 6
49.8750		NFM	Nationwide	Channel D
49.8750		NFM	Nationwide	Maxan Channel 4
49.8800		NFM	Nationwide	Channel UK2
49.8900		NFM	Nationwide	Channel 7
49.8900		NFM	Nationwide	Channel E
49.8900		NFM	Nationwide	Maxan Channel 5
49.9000		NFM	Nationwide	Channel 8
49.9100		NFM	Nationwide	Channel 9
49.9200		NFM	Nationwide	Channel 10
49.9300		NFM	Nationwide	Channel 11
49.9400		NFM	Nationwide	Channel 12
49.9500		NFM	Nationwide	Channel 13
49.9600		NFM	Nationwide	Channel 14
49.9600		NFM	Nationwide	Channel UK3
49.9700		NFM	Nationwide	Channel 15
49.9800		NFM	Nationwide	Channel 16

50.0000 - 52.0000 MHz   6M UK AMATEUR RADIO BAND ALL MODES

Base	Mobile	Mode	Location	User and Notes
50.0000		CW	Buxton	Beacon (GB3BUX)
50.0200		CW	Anglesey	Beacon (GB3SIX)
50.0420		CW	St Austell	Beacon (GB3CTC)
50.0500		CW	London	Beacon (GB3NHQ)
50.0600		CW	Inverness	Beacon (GB3RMK)
50.0640		CW	Lerwick	Beacon (GB3LER)
50.0650		CW	St Helier	Beacon (GB3IOJ)
50.2000	50.2000	USB	Nationwide	SSB Calling
51.5100	51.5100	NFM	Nationwide	FM Calling

52.0000 - 52.3875 MHz   BROADCASTING LINKS NFM

52.8500 - 52.9500 MHz   CORDLESS RADIO MICROPHONES 12.5 KHZ

Base	Mobile	Mode	Location	User and Notes
52.8500		NFM	Nationwide	Channel 1
52.8625		NFM	Nationwide	ASP Talkback Sound Links
52.8625		NFM	Nationwide	Channel 2
52.8750		NFM	Nationwide	ASP Talkback Sound Links
52.8750		NFM	Nationwide	Channel 3
52.8875		NFM	Nationwide	Channel 4
52.9000		NFM	Nationwide	ASP Talkback Sound Links
52.9000		NFM	Nationwide	Channel 5
52.9125		NFM	Nationwide	ASP Talkback Sound Links
52.9125		NFM	Nationwide	Channel 6
52.9250		NFM	Nationwide	ASP Talkback Sound Links
52.9250		NFM	Nationwide	Channel 7
52.9375		NFM	Nationwide	ASP Talkback Sound Links
52.9375		NFM	Nationwide	Channel 8
52.9500		NFM	Nationwide	ASP Talkback Sound Links

Base	Mobile	Mode	Location	User and Notes
53.5250		NFM	Nationwide	BBC O/B Continuity
53.5750		NFM	Taunton	BBC O/B Mics (Somerset Sound)

53.7500 - 55.7500 MHz   BBC 5W CORDLESS MICROPHONES

Base	Mobile	Mode	Location	User and Notes
53.7500		NFM	Nationwide	BBC O/B Microphone Ch. 1
53.8500		NFM	Nationwide	BBC O/B Microphone Ch. 2
53.9500		NFM	Nationwide	BBC O/B Microphone Ch. 3

54.0000 - 60.0000 MHz   MoD TACTICAL COMMUNICATIONS 25 KHz SIMPLEX

Base	Mobile	Mode	Location	User and Notes
54.0000		NFM	Nationwide	BBC O/B Microphone
54.0500		NFM	Nationwide	BBC O/B Microphone Ch. 4
54.1500		NFM	Nationwide	BBC O/B Microphone Ch. 5
54.2000		NFM	Nationwide	BBC O/B Microphone
54.2500		NFM	Nationwide	BBC O/B Microphone Ch. 6
54.3500		NFM	Nationwide	BBC O/B Microphone Ch. 7
54.4000		NFM	Nationwide	BBC O/B Microphone
54.4500		NFM	Nationwide	BBC O/B Microphone Ch. 8
54.5500		NFM	Nationwide	BBC O/B Microphone Ch. 9
54.6000		NFM	Nationwide	BBC O/B Microphone
54.6500		NFM	Nationwide	BBC O/B Microphone Ch. 10
54.7600		NFM	Nationwide	BBC O/B Microphone Ch. 11
54.8500		NFM	Nationwide	BBC O/B Microphone Ch. 12
54.9500		NFM	Nationwide	BBC O/B Microphone Ch 13
55.0000		NFM	Nationwide	BBC O/B Microphone
55.0500		NFM	Nationwide	BBC O/B Microphone Ch. 14
55.1500		NFM	Nationwide	BBC O/B Microphone Ch. 15
55.2000		NFM	Nationwide	BBC O/B Microphone
55.2500		NFM	Nationwide	BBC O/B Microphone Ch. 16
55.3500		NFM	Nationwide	BBC O/B Microphone Ch. 17
55.4000		NFM	Nationwide	BBC O/B Microphone
55.4500		NFM	Nationwide	BBC O/B Microphone Ch. 18
55.5000		NFM	Nationwide	BBC O/B Microphone
55.5500		NFM	Nationwide	BBC O/B Microphone Ch. 19
56.6250		NFM	Nationwide	Royal Signals Public Displays
56.9750		NFM	Nationwide	BBC O/B Continuity
60.2950		NFM	Nationwide	BBC O/B Continuity

60.7500 - 62.7500 MHz   BBC 5W CORDLESS AND OUTSIDE BROADCAST MICS

Base	Mobile	Mode	Location	User and Notes
60.7500		NFM	Nationwide	BBC O/B Microphone Ch. 20
60.8000		NFM	Nationwide	BBC O/B Microphone
60.8500		NFM	Nationwide	BBC O/B Microphone Ch. 21
60.9000		NFM	Nationwide	BBC O/B Microphone
60.9500		NFM	Nationwide	BBC O/B Microphone Ch. 22
61.0000		NFM	Nationwide	BBC O/B Microphone
61.0500		NFM	Nationwide	BBC O/B Microphone Ch. 23
61.1000		NFM	Nationwide	BBC O/B Microphone
61.1500		NFM	Nationwide	BBC O/B Microphone Ch. 24
61.2500		NFM	Nationwide	BBC O/B Microphone Ch. 25

Base	Mobile	Mode	Location	User and Notes
61.3000		NFM	Nationwide	BBC O/B Microphone
61.3500		NFM	Nationwide	BBC O/B Microphone Ch. 26
61.4000		NFM	Nationwide	BBC O/B Microphone
61.4500		NFM	Nationwide	BBC O/B Microphone Ch. 27
61.5000		NFM	Nationwide	BBC O/B Microphone
61.5500		NFM	Nationwide	BBC O/B Microphone Ch. 28
61.6500		NFM	Nationwide	BBC O/B Microphone Ch. 29
61.7000		NFM	Nationwide	BBC O/B Microphone
61.7500		NFM	Nationwide	BBC O/B Microphone Ch. 30
61.8000		NFM	Nationwide	BBC O/B Microphone
61.8500		NFM	Nationwide	BBC O/B Microphone Ch. 31
61.9000		NFM	Nationwide	BBC O/B Microphone
61.9500		NFM	Nationwide	BBC O/B Microphone Ch. 32
62.0500		NFM	Nationwide	BBC O/B Microphone Ch. 33
62.1500		NFM	Nationwide	BBC O/B Microphone Ch. 34
62.2000		NFM	Nationwide	BBC O/B Microphone
62.2500		NFM	Nationwide	BBC O/B Microphone Ch. 35
62.3500		NFM	Nationwide	BBC O/B Microphone Ch. 36
62.4500		NFM	Nationwide	BBC O/B Microphone Ch. 37
62.5500		NFM	Nationwide	BBC O/B Microphone Ch. 38
62.6000		NFM	Nationwide	BBC O/B Microphone
62.9250		NFM	Nationwide	BBC O/B Microphones (Spare)
63.3875		NFM	London	Courier Service North London

64.0000 - 68.0000 MHz MoD Tactical Communications 25 kHz Simplex

Base	Mobile	Mode	Location	User and Notes
64.0375		NFM	Nationwide	BBC O/B Microphones
65.9600		WFM	Zalau, Romania	Radioteleviziunea Romana [LBS]
		WFM	Gheorgheni, Romania	Radioteleviziunea Romana [LBS]
66.0200		WFM	Miskolc, Hungary	Magyar Radio [LBS]
66.1400		WFM	Kemadi, Hungary	Magyar Radio [LBS]
66.1700		WFM	P. Neant, Romania	Radioteleviziunea Romana [LBS]
66.2000		WFM	Brno, Czech Republic	Cesko Rozhlas [LBS]
66.2900		WFM	Szentes, Hungary	Magyar Radio [LBS]
66.3200		WFM	Ostrava, Czech Republic	Cesko Rozhlas [LBS]
66.3600		WFM	Birlad, Romania	Radioteleviziunea Romana [LBS]
66.3800		WFM	Kosice, Slovakia	Slovensky Rozhlas [LBS]
66.4400		WFM	Sibiu, Romania	Radioteleviziunea Romana [LBS]
		WFM	Hradec Kralove, Czech Republic	Cesko Rozhlas [LBS]
66.4700		WFM	Siedice, Poland	Polskie Radio I Telewizja [LBS]
66.5600		WFM	Poznan, Poland	Polskie Radio I Telewizja [LBS]
		WFM	Baia Mare, Romania	Radioteleviziunea Romana [LBS]
66.6200		WFM	Budapest, Hungary	Magyar Radio [LBS]
66.6800		WFM	Zamosc, Poland	Polskie Radio I Telewizja [LBS]
66.7600		WFM	Cluj, Romania	Radioteleviziunea Romana [LBS]
66.8000		WFM	Miskolc, Hungary	Magyar Radio [LBS]
66.8300		WFM	Praha, Czech Republic	Cesko Rozhlas [LBS]
66.9200		WFM	Kemadi, Hungary	Magyar Radio [LBS]
66.9500		WFM	Koszalin, Poland	Polskie Radio I Telewizja [LBS]

Base	Mobile	Mode	Location	User and Notes
67.0100		WFM	Bacau, Romania	Radioteleviziunea Romana [LBS]
67.0125		NFM	Nationwide	BBC O/B Control
67.0250		NFM	Nationwide	BBC O/B Control
67.0400		WFM	Gyor, Hungary	Magyar Radio [LBS]
67.1000		WFM	Jesenik, Czech Republic	Cesko Rozhlas [LBS]
67.1900		WFM	Pecs, Hungary	Magyar Radio [LBS]
67.2500		WFM	Olsztyn, Poland	Polskie Radio I Telewizja [LBS]
		WFM	Vilcea, Romania	Radioteleviziunea Romana [LBS]
67.2800		WFM	Poprad, Slovakia	Slovensky Rozhlas [LBS]
67.3400		WFM	Varatec, Romania	Radioteleviziunea Romana [LBS]
		WFM	Pizen, Czech Republic	Cesko Rozhlas [LBS]
67.4000		WFM	Poznan, Poland	Polskie Radio I Telewizja [LBS]
		WFM	Budapest, Hungary	Magyar Radio [LBS]
67.4600		WFM	Luban, Poland	Polskie Radio I Telewizja [LBS]
67.6100		WFM	Zamosc, Poland	Polskie Radio I Telewizja [LBS]
		WFM	Ceske Budejovice, Czech Republic	Cesko Rozhlas [LBS]
67.6400		WFM	Klodzko, Poland	Polskie Radio I Telewizja [LBS]
67.6700		WFM	Zalau, Romania	Radioteleviziunea Romana [LBS]
		WFM	Bratislava, Slovakia	Slovensky Rozhlas [LBS]
67.7900		WFM	Constanta, Romania	Radioteleviziunea Romana [LBS]
67.8500		WFM	Szentes, Hungary	Magyar Radio [LBS]
67.8800		WFM	Focsania, Romania	Radioteleviziunea Romana [LBS]
		WFM	Ostrava, Czech Republic	Cesko Rozhlas [LBS]
67.9400		WFM	Warszawa, Poland	Polskie Radio I Telewizja [LBS]
		WFM	Kosice, Slovakia	Slovensky Rozhlas [LBS]
67.9700		WFM	Pecs, Hungary	Magyar Radio [LBS]
68.0000 - 69.5000 MHz			**MoD, MOULD & TACTICAL COMMUNICATIONS 25 KHZ**	
68.0000		WFM	Hradec Kralove, Czech Republic	Cesko Rozhlas [LBS]
68.0250	68.0250	AM	Cheltenham	MoD Transport
		AM	Nationwide	UKAEA Transport Movements
68.0300		WFM	Siedice, Poland	Polskie Radio I Telewizja [LBS]
68.0600		WFM	Poprad, Slovakia	Slovensky Rozhlas [LBS]
68.1200		WFM	Baia Mare, Romania	Radioteleviziunea Romana [LBS]
68.1250	68.1250	NFM	Brecon Beacons	Army Range Ops
68.1500	68.1500	NFM	Nationwide	Army Pye Channel 6
68.1500	79.3500	NFM	Camberely	Army Stores
		NFM	Maidenhead	Army Stores
		NFM	Nationwide	Army Stores
68.2000		NFM	Isle of Man	Highways & Transport
68.2000	68.2000	NFM	Nationwide	HM Customs & Excise
68.2000	78.4000	NFM	Nationwide	Army Pye Channel 4
68.2400		WFM	Luban, Poland	Polskie Radio I Telewizja [LBS]
		WFM	Bucuresti, Romania	Radioteleviziunea Romana [LBS]
		WFM	Kemadi, Hungary	Magyar Radio [LBS]
68.2500	68.2500	NFM	Nationwide	HM Customs & Excise
68.2625	68.2625	NFM	Nationwide	HM Customs & Excise
68.2750		NFM	Dartmoor	Military Range

Base	Mobile	Mode	Location	User and Notes
68.2750	68.2750	NFM	Nationwide	HM Customs & Excise
68.2875	68.2875	NFM	Nationwide	HM Customs & Excise
68.3000	79.2250	NFM	Nationwide	Army Pye Channel 1
68.3500		NFM	Dartmoor	Military Range
68.3500	68.3500	NFM	Nationwide	Army Pye Channel 5
68.3600		WFM	Cluj, Romania	Radioteleviziunea Romana [LBS]
		WFM	Nagykanizsa, Hungary	Magyar Radio [LBS]
68.3625		NFM	Nationwide	Army Cadet Force Ch 1
68.3875		NFM	Bristol	MoD Transport
68.4000	79.2500	NFM	Nationwide	Army Pye Channel 2
68.4250		NFM	Dartmoor	Military Range
		NFM	Northern Ireland	British Army
68.4250	79.2750	NFM	Nationwide	Army Pye Channel 3
68.4800		WFM	Miskolc, Hungary	Magyar Radio [LBS]
68.5000		NFM	RN Rosyth	Dockyard Ops
68.5000	79.8000	NFM	Nationwide	Army Pye Channel 7
68.5100		WFM	Kudowa, Poland	Polskie Radio I Telewizja [LBS]
68.5200		WFM	Resita, Romania	Radioteleviziunea Romana [LBS]
68.5250	79.7000	NFM	Nationwide	Army Pye Channel 8
68.5500	68.5500	NFM	Nationwide	HM Customs & Excise
68.5625		AM	RAE Farnborough	Emergency Services
68.6000	79.9500	NFM	Nationwide	Army Pye Channel 9
		WFM	Gheorgheni, Romania	Radioteleviziunea Romana [LBS]
68.6125		AM	RAE Farnborough	Tractor Control
68.6250		NFM	Larkhill	Army Range
68.6375		AM	RAE Farnborough	ATC Ch 6
		AM	Nationwide	Army Pye Channel 1
		NFM	Northern Ireland	British Army
68.6600		WFM	Jesenik, Czech Republic	Cesko Rozhlas [LBS]
68.6875		AM	Cheltenham	MoD Transport
		AM	RAE Farnborough	Ground Services
		AM	Hampshire	MoD transport
68.6938		AM	RAE Farnborough	Repair Workshop
68.7200		NFM	Machynlleth	ManWeb
		WFM	Topolog, Romania	Radioteleviziunea Romana [LBS]
		WFM	Szentes, Hungary	Magyar Radio [LBS]
68.7625		NFM	Salisbury Plain	Army Transport (Tenor Base)
68.7800		WFM	Jelenia Góra, Poland	Polskie Radio I Telewizja [LBS]
68.7875		AM	Cheltenham	MoD Transport
68.8400		WFM	Bratislava, Slovakia	Slovensky Rozhlas [LBS]
68.8688		AM	RAE Farnborough	Fire
68.8700		WFM	Bacau, Romania	Radioteleviziunea Romana [LBS]
		WFM	Comanesti, Romania	Radioteleviziunea Romana [LBS]
		WFM	Kosice, Slovakia	Slovensky Rozhlas [LBS]
68.9063		AM	RAE Farnborough	Medical
68.9600		WFM	Praha, Czech Republic	Cesko Rozhlas [LBS]
68.9875		NFM	Brecon Beacons	Mould
69.0750	69.0750	NFM	Okehampton	Military Range

Base	Mobile	Mode	Location	User and Notes
69.0800		WFM	Ostrava, Czech Republic	Cesko Rozhlas [LBS]
69.1100		WFM	Varatec, Romania	Radioteleviziunea Romana [LBS]
69.1250		NFM	Isle of Man	Highways & Transport
		NFM	Northern Ireland	British Army
69.1550		NFM	Northern Ireland	British Army .
69.1750	69.1750	NFM	Okehampton	Military Range
69.2000		NFM	Northern Ireland	British Army
		WFM	Poprad, Slovakia	Slovensky Rozhlas [LBS]
69.2500		NFM	Northern Ireland	British Army
69.2500		WFM	Usti nad Labem, Czech Republic	Cesko Rozhlas [LBS]
69.3250		NFM	Brecon Beacons	Army
		NFM	Northern Ireland	British Army
69.3500		AM	Brecon Beacons	Army Cadets Hike Control
		WFM	Sibiu, Romania	Radioteleviziunea Romana [LBS]
		WFM	Hradec Kralove, Czech Republic	Cesko Rozhlas [LBS]
69.3750		NFM	Northern Ireland	British Army
69.3800		WFM	Zamosc, Poland	Polskie Radio I Telewizja [LBS]
		WFM	Budapest, Hungary	Magyar Radio [LBS]
69.4000		WFM	Nationwide	Eastern European LBS
69.4000		NFM	Northern Ireland	British Army
69.4000	69.4000	NFM	RAC Network Q Rally	Rally Control
69.4500	69.4500	NFM	RAC Network Q Rally	Rally Control
69.4750	84.5250	NFM	Nationwide	39 Inf Bgd/Sig Chan A9
69.4875	69.4875	NFM	RAC Network Q Rally	Rally Control

69.5000 - 69.8000 MHz   MoD Tactical Communications 25 kHz Simplex

Base	Mobile	Mode	Location	User and Notes
69.5000		WFM	Zilina, Slovakia	Slovensky Rozhlas [LBS]
69.5000	69.5000	NFM	Okehampton	Military Range
		NFM	RN Rosyth	Security
69.5500	69.5500	NFM	Northern Ireland	British Army
69.5600		WFM	Luban, Poland	Polskie Radio I Telewizja [LBS]
		WFM	Olsztyn, Poland	Polskie Radio I Telewizja [LBS]
		WFM	Pizen, Czech Republic	Cesko Rozhlas [LBS]
69.6500		WFM	Timisoara, Romania	Radioteleviziunea Romana [LBS]
69.6800		WFM	T. Severin, Romania	Radioteleviziunea Romana [LBS]
		WFM	Banska Bystrica, Slovakia	Slovensky Rozhlas [LBS]
69.7000		WFM	Nationwide	Eastern European LBS
69.7400		WFM	Klodzko, Poland	Polskie Radio I Telewizja [LBS]
		WFM	Bistrita, Romania	Radioteleviziunea Romana [LBS]
69.7500	69.7500	NFM	Northern Ireland	British Army
69.7750	69.7750	NFM	Isle of Man	Highways & Transport
69.8000	69.8000	NFM	Northern Ireland	British Army

69.8250 - 69.9625 MHz   BBC TV O/B "System One" CMCR Studio Manager
Talkback & MoD Tactical Communications

Base	Mobile	Mode	Location	User and Notes
69.8225	74.7000	NFM	Nationwide	BBC Studio Manager Ch. 3
69.8250		NFM	Manchester	ITN Studio Link
		NFM	Nationwide	BBC CMCR Channel 7

Base	Mobile	Mode	Location	User and Notes
		NFM	Northern Ireland	British Army
69.8350	75.2688	NFM	Nationwide	BBC Studio Manager Ch. 4
69.8375		NFM	Nationwide	BBC CMCR Channel 8
		NFM	Scotland	BBC Scotland CMCR
69.8450		AM	Salisbury Plain	Army
69.8475		NFM	Nationwide	BBC Studio Manager Ch. 5
69.8500		NFM	Nationwide	BBC CMCR Channel 9
		NFM	Northern Ireland	British Army
69.8600		NFM	Nationwide	BBC Studio Manager Ch.l 6
		WFM	Oradea, Romania	Radioteleviziunea Romana [LBS]
		WFM	Brno, Czech Republic	Cesko Rozhlas [LBS]
69.8625		NFM	Nationwide	BBC CMCR Channel 10
69.8725		NFM	Nationwide	BBC Studio Manager Ch.l 7
69.8750		NFM	Nationwide	BBC CMCR Channel 11
69.8850		NFM	Nationwide	BBC Studio Manager Ch. 8
69.8975		NFM	Nationwide	BBC Studio Manager Ch. 9
69.9000		NFM	Goodwood	BBC Glorious Goodwood OB
		NFM	Haydock Park	TV OB
		NFM	Isle of Man	Highways & Transport
		NFM	Scotland	BBC Scotland Channel 12
69.9000	75.29375	NFM	Swansea	BBC Wales O/B
69.9075	75.2875	NFM	Nationwide	BBC Studio Manager Ch. 2
69.9200		WFM	Iasi, Romania	Radioteleviziunea Romana [LBS]
69.9250		NFM	Nationwide	BBC Studio Continuity
69.9500		NFM	Northern Ireland	British Army
69.9625	75.2625	NFM	Nationwide	BBC Studio Manager Ch. 1

69.9650 - 70.0000 MHz   MOD TACTICAL COMMUNICATIONS 25 KHZ

Base	Mobile	Mode	Location	User and Notes
69.9800		WFM	Liberec, Czech Republic	Cesko Rozhlas [LBS]
		WFM	Nagykanizsa, Hungary	Magyar Radio [LBS]
69.9875		NFM	Nationwide	RAC Network Q Rally

70.0000 - 70.5000 MHz   4M AMATEUR RADIO BAND

Base	Mobile	Mode	Location	User and Notes
70.0000		CW	Buxton	Beacon (GB3BUX)
70.0100		WFM	Constanta, Romania	Radioteleviziunea Romana [LBS]
70.0180		CW	Dundee	Beacon (GB3ANG)
70.0220		CW	Jersey	Beacon (GB3MCB)
70.0285		NFM	Chelmsford	Mid Essex Gravel Pits
70.0300		CW	St Austell	Beacon (GB3CTC)
70.0400		CW	Chatham	Beacon (GB3REB)
		WFM	Novaci, Romania	Radioteleviziunea Romana [LBS]
70.0600		CW	Dundee	Beacon (GB3ANG)
70.0700		WFM	Ceske Budejovice, Czech Republic	Cesko Rozhlas [LBS]
70.1000		WFM	Kekes, Hungary	Magyar Radio [LBS]
70.1300		CW	Slane	Beacon (EI4RF)
70.1600		WFM	Jesenik, Czech Republic	Cesko Rozhlas [LBS]
70.2000	70.2000	CW	Nationwide	CW Calling Channel
		SSB	Nationwide	SSB Calling Channel

Base	Mobile	Mode	Location	User and Notes
70.2200		WFM	Siedice, Poland	Polskie Radio I Telewizja [LBS]
		WFM	Focsania, Romania	Radioteleviziunea Romana [LBS]
70.2600	70.2600	AM	Nationwide	AM Calling Channel
70.3000		WFM	Nationwide	Eastern European LBS
70.3000		NFM	Merseyside	Fire Brigade
		NFM	Salisbury Plain	Army
70.3000	70.3000	NFM	Nationwide	FAX Calling Channel
		NFM	Nationwide	RTTY Calling Channel
70.3125	70.3125	NFM	Nationwide	Packet Channel
70.3250	70.3250	NFM	Nationwide	Packet Channel
70.3400		WFM	Pizen, Czech Republic	Cesko Rozhlas [LBS]
70.3500		NFM	Nationwide	Raynet Channel
70.3750		NFM	Nationwide	Raynet Channel
70.4000		NFM	Nationwide	Raynet Channel
		WFM	Bucuresti, Romania	Radioteleviziunea Romana [LBS]
		WFM	Sopron, Hungary	Magyar Radio [LBS]
70.4300		WFM	Tokaj, Hungary	Magyar Radio [LBS]
70.4500	70.4500	NFM	Nationwide	FM Calling Channel
70.4875	70.4875	NFM	Nationwide	Packet Channel
70.5000		AM	Galashiels	Fire Brigade (ZF)

70.5125 - 71.5000 MHz Fire Brigades (England & Wales) 12.5 kHz
[Mobile 80.5000 - 81.5000 MHz]

Base	Mobile	Mode	Location	User and Notes
70.5125	80.1875	NFM	Northumberland	Fire Brigade (M2LJ)
70.5125	80.4375	AM	West Midlands	Fire Brigade (FBW)
70.5250		AM	Ipswich	Fire Brigade
		AM	Manchester	Fire Brigade
70.5250	80.7375	AM	Manchester	Fire Brigade (FT) Ch 2
70.5250	80.9625	AM	London	Fire Brigade (FH) Ch 1
70.5375	80.1125	AM	North Yorkshire	Fire Brigade (M2LY)
70.5375	80.1875	AM	Nottinghamshire	Fire Brigade (M2NZ)
70.5500	80.0000	AM	Manchester	Fire Brigade HQ (FT) Ch 1
70.5600		NFM	Lincoln	Fire Brigade
70.5625	80.6000	AM	Mid Glamorgan	Fire Brigade (WF)
70.5625	80.9875	AM	Lincolnshire	Fire Brigade (NV)
70.5750	80.4625	AM	West Midlands	Fire Brigade (FBW) Ch 3
70.5800		WFM	Usti nad Labem, Czech Republic	Cesko Rozhlas [LBS]
70.5875	80.1875	AM	Hampshire	Fire Brigade (HX) Ch 2
70.5875	80.7625	AM	Manchester	Fire Brigade (FT) Ch 3
70.6000	80.0000	AM	Derbyshire	Fire Brigade (M2ND)
70.6000	81.2625	NFM	Warwickshire	Fire Brigade (M2YS)
70.6100		WFM	Suceava, Romania	Radioteleviziunea Romana [LBS]
70.6125		NFM	West Yorkshire	Fire Brigade (M2XF)
70.6125	80.1250	AM	Dyfed	Fire Brigade (WD)
		NFM	Surrey	Fire Brigade (HF)
70.6250		AM	Merseyside	Fire Brigade (M2FO) Ch 3
70.6250	80.6125	AM	Essex	Fire Brigade (VD) Ch 1
70.6375	80.0000	AM	Doncaster	Fire Brigade (M2XV)

Base	Mobile	Mode	Location	User and Notes
70.6375	80.1125	AM	South Yorkshire	Fire Brigade (XV)
70.6375	80.2125	AM	East Sussex	Fire Brigade (KD)
70.6400		WFM	Deva, Romania	Radioteleviziunea Romana [LBS]
		WFM	Kabhegy, Hungary	Magyar Radio [LBS]
70.6500		AM	Swindon	Fire Brigade
70.6500	80.9875	AM	Wiltshire	Fire Brigade (QM)
70.6625	81.0000	AM	Leicestershire	Fire Brigade (M2NK)
70.6750		AM	Liverpool	Fire Brigade
70.6750	80.5250	AM	South Glamorgan	Fire Brigade (WD)
70.6750	80.5500	NFM	Lancashire	Fire Brigade (BE) Ch 1
70.6875	81.1250	AM	Hereford & Worcester	Fire Brigade (YB)
70.7000		WFM	Nationwide	Eastern European LBS
70.7000	80.0000	NFM	Merseyside	Fire Brigade (M2FO) Ch 4
		NFM	Norwich City	Fire Brigade (M2VF)
70.7000	80.2000	AM	Merseyside	Fire Brigade (M2FO)
		AM	Norfolk	Fire Brigade (M2VF)
70.7000	81.1250	NFM	Gwent	Fire Brigade (WP) Ch 4
70.7125		AM	Manchester	Fire Brigade
70.7125	80.3500	AM	East Sussex	Fire Brigade Ch 2
70.7125	80.8000	AM	Derbyshire	Fire Brigade (M2ND)
70.7250	80.0375	AM	Devon	Fire Brigade (M2QD)
70.7250	80.6750	AM	Essex	Fire Brigade (VD) Ch 2
70.7500	80.7500	AM	Northamptonshire	Fire Brigade (NO)
70.7624	80.1500	AM	East London	Fire Brigade (M2FE) Ch3
70.7625	80.9875	NFM	West Yorkshire	Fire Brigade (M2XF)
70.7750	80.5000	AM	Cheshire	Fire Brigade (M2CF)
		AM	Hampshire	Fire Brigade (HX) Ch 1
70.7875	80.8000	AM	Cornwall	Fire Brigade (QA)
70.7900		WFM	Olsztyn, Poland	Polskie Radio I Telewizja [LBS]
		WFM	Arad, Romania	Radioteleviziunea Romana [LBS]
70.8000	80.5125	NFM	West Sussex	Fire Brigade (KW)
70.8125	81.2125	AM	Gwynedd	Fire Brigade (WC)
70.8200		WFM	Zilina, Slovakia	Slovensky Rozhlas [LBS]
70.8250	80.3250	AM	Devon	Fire Brigade (M2QD)
70.8250	80.7875	AM	Manchester	Fire Brigade (FT) Ch 4
70.8375		AM	Cumbria	Fire Brigade
		AM	Galashiels	Fire Brigade (ZF)
70.8375	80.0000	AM	Cambridgeshire	Fire Brigade
70.8375	80.0375	NFM	Cumbria	Fire Brigade (BC)
70.8375	80.1250	AM	Kent	Fire Brigade (KF)
70.8500	80.9625	AM	Powys	Fire Brigade (WB)
		WFM	Cimpulung, Romania	Radioteleviziunea Romana [LBS]
		WFM	Praha, Czech Republic	Cesko Rozhlas [LBS]
70.8625	80.5500	AM	Dorset	Fire Brigade (QK)
70.8750	80.6625	NFM	West Yorkshire	Fire Brigade (M2XF)
70.8875	80.2125	AM	Durham	Fire Brigade (LF)
70.8875	80.9375	AM	Staffordshire	Fire Brigade (YG)
70.8875		AM	Hertfordshire	Fire Brigade (M2KP)

Base	Mobile	Mode	Location	User and Notes
70.9000	80.0375	AM	Hertfordshire	Fire Brigade (M2VI)
70.9000	80.4000	NFM	Suffolk	Fire Brigade (VN)
70.9000	80.6000	NFM	Lancashire	Fire Brigade (BE) Ch 2
70.9125		AM	London	Fire Brigade Data Channel
70.9125	80.0000	NFM	Essex	Fire Brigade (M2VD) Ch3
70.9375		NFM	England & Wales	Fire Brigade Data Channel
70.9400		WFM	Banska Bystrica, Slovakia	Slovensky Rozhlas [LBS]
70.9500	80.0000	AM	West Glamorgan	Fire Brigade (WZ)
70.9625	80.1125	AM	London	Fire Brigade (FS)
70.9625	81.0875	AM	Merseyside	Fire Brigade (M2FO) Ch 2
70.9750		NFM	Stockport	Fire Brigade
70.9750	80.6500	AM	Shropshire	Fire Brigade (YU)
70.9875	80.0000	NFM	Gwynedd	Fire Brigade (M2WC)
71.0000		WFM	Oradea, Romania	Radioteleviziunea Romana [LBS]
71.0125		AM	Bristol	Fire Brigade
71.0125	80.1750	AM	Avon	Fire Brigade (M2QG)
71.0300		WFM	Nagykanizsa, Hungary	Magyar Radio [LBS]
71.0375	81.0625	AM	Merseyside	Fire Brigade (M2FO)
71.0600		WFM	P. Neant, Romania	Radioteleviziunea Romana [LBS]
		WFM	Petrosani, Romania	Radioteleviziunea Romana [LBS]
71.0750		AM	Bristol	Fire Brigade
71.0750	80.1500	AM	Humberside	Fire Brigade (XT)
71.0750	80.6250	AM	Gloucester	Fire Brigade (QF)
71.1000		AM	Oxford	Fire Brigade
71.1000	80.3750	AM	Humberside	Fire Brigade (XT)
71.1000	80.6625	AM	Oxfordshire	Fire Brigade (M2HI)
71.1125	80.0000	AM	Bedfordshire	Fire Brigade (M2VM)
		AM	Cleveland	Fire Brigade (LT)
71.1200		WFM	Suwalki, Poland	Polskie Radio I Telewizja [LBS]
		WFM	Bratislava, Slovakia	Slovensky Rozhlas [LBS]
71.1250	80.1125	AM	Somerset	Fire Brigade (QI)
71.1375	80.4375	AM	North Yorkshire	Fire Brigade (LY)
		AM	Scarborough	Fire Brigade
71.1375	80.4500	AM	Buckinghamshire	Fire Brigade (HK)
71.1500	80.5125	AM	West Midlands	Fire Brigade (FBW)
71.1625	80.8750	AM	Clwyd	Fire Brigade (M2WK)
71.1750	80.0000	AM	North Yorkshire	Fire Brigade (LY)
71.1750	80.2125	AM	North London	Fire Brigade (FN) Ch 4
71.1800		WFM	Liberec, Czech Republic	Cesko Rozhlas [LBS]
71.2000	80.0000	NFM	Lancashire	Fire Brigade (M2BE) Ch2
71.2000	80.2250	NFM	Berkshire	Fire Brigade (M2HD)
71.2100		WFM	Kekes, Hungary	Magyar Radio [LBS]
71.2500	80.0000	NFM	Gloucester	Fire Brigade (M2YP)
71.2750	81.0625	AM	Isle of Wight	Fire Brigade (HP)
71.2750	81.0875	NFM	Suffolk	Fire Brigade (VN)
71.3000		AM	Tyne and Wear	Fire Brigade (LP) Ch 1
		WFM	Ploesti, Romania	Radioteleviziunea Romana [LBS]
71.3125		NFM	England & Wales	Fire Brigade Data Channel

Base	Mobile	Mode	Location	User and Notes
71.3300		WFM	Tokaj, Hungary	Magyar Radio [LBS]
71.3375		AM	London	Fire Brigade 1200 Baud Data
		NFM	England & Wales	Fire Brigade Data Channel
71.3375	80.0000	NFM	London	Fire Brigade (M2FHO) Ch5
		NFM	Tyne and Wear	Fire Brigade (LP) Ch 2
71.3875		AM	Gloucestershire	Fire Brigade (QC)
71.3875	80.0000	NFM	Lancashire	Fire Brigade (BE) Ch 3
71.4000	81.2500	NFM	Nationwide	RW Radio Engineers
71.4125		NFM	Nationwide	Police Radio Engineering
71.4125	60.6000	NFM	Nationwide	MetPol Secure Radio Testing
71.4200		WFM	Kabhegy, Hungary	Magyar Radio [LBS]
71.4250	80.5250	AM	Cambridgeshire	Fire Brigade (VC)
71.4500		AM	Nottinghamshire	Fire Brigade (NZ)
		WFM	Warszawa, Poland	Polskie Radio I Telewizja [LBS]
71.4750		NFM	Nationwide	Police Radio Engineering
71.5000		NFM	Portsmouth	PMR

71.5125 - 72.7875 MHz PMR Low Band Mobiles 12.5 kHz
(Base + 10.5 MHz)

Base	Mobile	Mode	Location	User and Notes
71.5125		NFM	Birmingham	National Breakdown
71.5500		NFM	Cambridge	Bidwells
		NFM	Ipswich	Water Board
		NFM	London	Baron Cars
71.6000		WFM	Zilina, Slovakia	Slovensky Rozhlas [LBS]
71.6300		WFM	Ceske Budejovice, Czech Republic Cesko Rozhlas [LBS]
71.6500		NFM	Nationwide	DTI Engineers Channel
71.7200		WFM	Jelenia Góra, Poland	Polskie Radio I Telewizja [LBS]
		WFM	Zielona Góra, Poland	Polskie Radio I Telewizja [LBS]
		WFM	Timisoara, Romania	Radioteleviziunea Romana [LBS]
71.7250		AM	Cleveland	Fire Brigade
71.8100		WFM	Lublin, Poland	Polskie Radio I Telewizja [LBS]
		WFM	Pecs, Hungary	Magyar Radio [LBS]
71.8250		NFM	Chelmsford	Water Board
71.8400		WFM	Bydgoszcz, Poland	Polskie Radio I Telewizja [LBS]
		WFM	Iasi, Romania	Radioteleviziunea Romana [LBS]
71.8600		WFM	Sopron, Hungary	Magyar Radio [LBS]
71.8700		WFM	Brno, Czech Republic	Cesko Rozhlas [LBS]
71.9000		AM	Nationwide	Selective Call
		WFM	Novaci, Romania	Radioteleviziunea Romana [LBS]
71.9600		WFM	Topolog, Romania	Radioteleviziunea Romana [LBS]
71.9875		NFM	Nationwide	AA
72.0200		WFM	Bialystok, Poland	Polskie Radio I Telewizja [LBS]
		WFM	Pila, Poland	Polskie Radio I Telewizja [LBS]
		WFM	Namestovo, Slovakia	Slovensky Rozhlas [LBS]
72.0800		WFM	Sopron, Hungary	Magyar Radio [LBS]
72.1100		WFM	Tokaj, Hungary	Magyar Radio [LBS]
72.1750	85.6750	NFM	Barrow	Barrow Five Taxis
72.2000		WFM	Deva, Romania	Radioteleviziunea Romana [LBS]

Base	Mobile	Mode	Location	User and Notes
		WFM	Cimpulung, Romania	Radioteleviziunea Romana [LBS]
		WFM	Usti nad Labem, Czech Republic	Cesko Rozhlas [LBS]
72.2250		NFM	Nationwide	BBC/IBA Microwave Links Setup
72.2750	85.7750	NFM	Blackpool	Red Cabs Taxis
72.3200		WFM	Birlad, Romania	Radioteleviziunea Romana [LBS]
72.3250		NFM	Southampton	Taxis
72.3375	72.3375	AM	Jersey	Ideal Hire Cars Channel 2
72.3600		WFM	Resita, Romania	Radioteleviziunea Romana [LBS]
72.3875	85.8875	AM	Blackpool	Tower Taxis
72.4250	85.9250	AM	Blackpool	Radio Cabs
72.4375	85.9375	AM	Blackpool	Progress Taxis
72.4400		WFM	Klodzko, Poland	Polskie Radio I Telewizja [LBS]
		WFM	Bistrita, Romania	Radioteleviziunea Romana [LBS]
72.5000		WFM	Banska Bystrica, Slovakia	Slovensky Rozhlas [LBS]
72.5375		AM	Methley Park	Private Hospital
72.5600		WFM	Arad, Romania	Radioteleviziunea Romana [LBS]
72.5750		AM	Lochaber	Ambulance Repeater
72.5900		WFM	Lublin, Poland	Polskie Radio I Telewizja [LBS]
72.6200		WFM	Bydgoszcz, Poland	Polskie Radio I Telewizja [LBS]
72.6500		NFM	Kent	Tour de France French PMR
72.6800		WFM	Suwalki, Poland	Polskie Radio I Telewizja [LBS]
		WFM	Vilcea, Romania	Radioteleviziunea Romana [LBS]
72.7100		WFM	T. Severin, Romania	Radioteleviziunea Romana [LBS]
72.7400		WFM	Liberec, Czech Republic	Cesko Rozhlas [LBS]
72.7700		WFM	Kekes, Hungary	Magyar Radio [LBS]

72.8000 - 73.9250 MHz   MoD TACTICAL COMMUNICATIONS 25 kHz DUPLEX

Base	Mobile	Mode	Location	User and Notes
72.8000		NFM	Brecon Beacons	Army Range Ops
		WFM	Bialystok, Poland	Polskie Radio I Telewizja [LBS]
		WFM	Pila, Poland	Polskie Radio I Telewizja [LBS]
		WFM	Petrosani, Romania	Radioteleviziunea Romana [LBS]
72.8000	74.8000	NFM	Nationwide	Secure Government Mobiles
72.8125		NFM	Southampton	Royal Navy Loading
72.8250		NFM	RAF Fairford	Base Ops
72.9200		WFM	Ploesti, Romania	Radioteleviziunea Romana [LBS]
72.9800		WFM	Suceava, Romania	Radioteleviziunea Romana [LBS]
		WFM	Bihor, Romania	Radioteleviziunea Romana [LBS]
		WFM	Kabhegy, Hungary	Magyar Radio [LBS]
72.9875	72.9875	NFM	HMS Drake	Naval Provost
73.0000		NFM	Brecon Beacons	Army Range Ops
73.0000	78.9000	NFM	Nationwide	Army Pye Equipment Ch. 7
73.0250	78.6500	NFM	Nationwide	Army Pye Equipment Ch. 8
73.1000		NFM	Aldershot	Military Police
73.1250	78.4000	NFM	Nationwide	Army Pye Equipment Ch. 1
73.1500	78.4250	NFM	Nationwide	Army Pye Equipment Ch.2
73.2000		NFM	DRA Farnborough	Ground Movements
73.2000	78.4500	NFM	Nationwide	Army Pye Equipment Ch. 3
73.2125		NFM	Southampton	Royal Navy Transport

Base	Mobile	Mode	Location	User and Notes
73.2250	78.4750	NFM	Nationwide	Army Pye Equipment Ch. 4
73.2500	78.5000	NFM	Nationwide	Army Pye Equipment Ch. 5
73.2560		NFM	Midlands	Army Base Security
73.2750		NFM	Kent	Tour de France French PMR
73.3250	78.8000	NFM	Nationwide	Army Pye Equipment Ch. 6
73.3250		NFM	Plymouth	Royal Marines
73.3375		NFM	RN Portsdown	Base Ops
73.3500		NFM	Nationwide	MoD Security Police
		NFM	RAF High Wycombe	Security
73.3500	73.3500	NFM	West Midlands	USAF Police
73.3875		NFM	Nationwide	Sea Cadets
73.4000		NFM	Plymouth	MoD Operations
73.4250		NFM	RN Faslane	Transport
73.4375		AM	RAE Farnborough	Ground Control
73.4500		NFM	RN Portsdown	Security
73.4625		AM	RAE Farnborough	Ground Vehicles
73.46875		AM	RAE Farnborough	Workshop Ch 5
73.4750		NFM	RAF Greenham Common	Security
73.4750		NFM	RAF Molesworth	Security
73.4750	73.4750	NFM	Nationwide	MoD Police
73.4875		NFM	RAE Farnborough	Ground Service Ch 1
73.5000	78.6500	NFM	Nationwide	Army Pye Equipment Ch. 1
73.5250	78.7250	NFM	Nationwide	Army Pye Equipment Ch. 2
73.5375		NFM	Plymouth	MoD Operations
73.5500		NFM	RAF Scampton	Ops
73.5500	78.7750	NFM	Nationwide	Army Pye Equipment Ch. 9
73.5625		NFM	RN Faslane	Security (Alpha Control)
73.5675		NFM	RN Poole	Royal Marines
73.5750		NFM	Plymouth	Military Police
73.5750		NFM	RN Dartmouth	Navy Ops
73.6125		NFM	Plymouth	MoD Police
73.6250		NFM	RAF Molesworth	Securit Ch 2
73.6375		NFM	Plymouth	MoD Police
		NFM	RAE Farnborough	Movements Control Ch 6
73.6500		NFM	London	MoD Police
		NFM	RAF Molesworth	Security Ch 3
73.66875		NFM	RAE Farnborough	Fire Ch 4
73.6750		NFM	RAF Molesworth	Security Ch 4
73.7000		NFM	Nationwide	Army Cadet Force
		NFM	RN Faslane	MoD Police
73.7000	84.1250	NFM	Nationwide	61 Sig Sqn Channel 1
73.70625		NFM	RAE Farnborough	Medical Ch 2
73.7250	84.1500	NFM	Nationwide	61 Sig Sqn Channel 2
73.7500	84.1750	NFM	Nationwide	61 Sig Sqn Channel 3
73.7750	84.2500	NFM	Nationwide	61 Sig Sqn Channel 4
73.8000		NFM	Brecon Beacons	Army Range Control
73.8000	84.2750	NFM	Nationwide	61 Sig Sqn Channel 5
73.8250	84.3250	NFM	Nationwide	61 Sig Sqn Channel 6

Base	Mobile	Mode	Location	User and Notes
73.8500		NFM	Nationwide	Army Cadet Force
		NFM	Nationwide	MOD Police ch5
		NFM	RAF Molesworth	Security
73.8500	84.3500	NFM	Nationwide	61 Sig Sqn Channel 7
73.8750	84.3750	NFM	Nationwide	61 Sig Sqn Channel 8
73.9000	84.4250	NFM	Nationwide	61 Sig Sqn Channel 9

73.9250 - 74.1000 MHz   MoD Mould Repeaters 12.5 kHz Duplex

Base	Mobile	Mode	Location	User and Notes
73.9250	84.4750	NFM	Nationwide	61 Sig Sqn Channel 10
74.0125		NFM	Northamptonshire	Mould
74.0125	74.0125	NFM	Scarborough	Mould
74.0250	79.0125	NFM	Hampshire	Mould
		NFM	Lincolnshire	Mould
		NFM	West Midlands	Mould
74.0375		NFM	Shropshire	Mould
		NFM	Wiltshire	Mould
74.0500		NFM	Brecon Beacons	Mould
		NFM	Northamptonshire	Mould
		NFM	Nottinghamshire	Mould
		NFM	West Midlands	Mould
74.0625		NFM	Manchester	Mould
		NFM	Northamptonshire	Mould
		NFM	West Midlands	Mould
		NFM	West Yorkshire	Mould
74.0750		NFM	Devon	Mould
		NFM	Gwent	Mould
74.0875		NFM	Gwent	Mould
		NFM	Manchester	Mould
		NFM	Tayside	Mould
		NFM	West Midlands	Mould

74.1000 - 74.7875 MHz   MoD Mould & Tactical Channels 12.5 kHz

Base	Mobile	Mode	Location	User and Notes
74.1125		NFM	Colchester	Barracks
		NFM	Gwent	Mould Ch 1
		NFM	Manchester	Mould
		NFM	West Midlands	Mould
74.1250		NFM	Brecon Beacons	Mould
		NFM	West Midlands	Mould
74.1375		NFM	Brecon Beacons	Mould
74.1500		NFM	Shropshire	Mould
		NFM	West Midlands	Mould
74.1625		NFM	Manchester	Mould
		NFM	Strathclyde	Mould
		NFM	West Midlands	Mould
74.1875		NFM	West Yorkshire	Mould
74.2000	79.3000	NFM	Nationwide	RAF Police Transport
		NFM	Nationwide	Military Transport Security
		NFM	Norfolk	Mould

Base	Mobile	Mode	Location	User and Notes
74.2125		NFM	Strathclyde	Mould
74.2125	79.2125	NFM	Gwent	Mould
74.2250		NFM	Colchester	Mould
		NFM	Lincolnshire	Mould
		NFM	Nationwide	Royal Ordnance Corps
		NFM	Nottinghamshire	Mould
		NFM	RAF Upper Heyford	Mould
		NFM	West Midlands	Mould
74.2375		NFM	Lincolnshire	Mould
		NFM	Shropshire	Mould
		NFM	Tayside	Mould
74.2500	79.2875	NFM	Colchester	Barracks
74.2500	79.3500	NFM	Norfolk	Mould
		NFM	Suffolk	Mould
74.2625		NFM	Gwent	Mould
74.2750		NFM	Strathclyde	Mould
74.3125		NFM	Gwent	Mould
		NFM	Shropshire	Mould
74.3375		NFM	Manchester	Mould
74.3500	79.4500	NFM	Brecon Beacons	Mould
74.3625		NFM	Chester	Mould
		NFM	Hampshire	Mould
74.3750		NFM	Brecon Beacons	Mould
74.3875	79.4125	NFM	Devon	Mould
		NFM	Gwent	Mould
74.4000		NFM	Brecon Beacons	Mould
		NFM	Cambridge	Marshalls Ltd Fire Channel
74.4125		NFM	Brecon Beacons	Mould
		NFM	Shropshire	Mould
		NFM	West Yorkshire	Mould
74.4375		NFM	Strathclyde	Mould
74.4375	79.6625	NFM	Norfolk	Mould
		NFM	West Midlands	Mould
74.4500	79.4500	NFM	Brecon Beacons	Mould
74.4625		NFM	Gwent	Mould
74.4675	79.7125	NFM	Gwent	Mould
74.4875	79.9265	NFM	Hampshire	Mould
		NFM	Norfolk	Mould
		NFM	Wiltshire	Mould
74.5125		NFM	Brecon Beacons	Mould
		NFM	West Midlands	Mould
74.5250		NFM	Brecon Beacons	Mould
74.5375		NFM	Brecon Beacons	Mould
		NFM	Lincolnshire	Mould
		NFM	West Midlands	Mould
74.5500	79.5500	NFM	Nationwide	RAF Police
74.5625		NFM	Brecon Beacons	Mould
74.5750		NFM	Brecon Beacons	Mould

Base	Mobile	Mode	Location	User and Notes
		NFM	Manchester	Mould
		NFM	Shropshire	Mould
		NFM	West Yorkshire	Mould
74.5875		NFM	Devon	Mould
		NFM	Gwent	Mould
		NFM	Hampshire	Mould
		NFM	Wiltshire	Mould
74.6000		NFM	Kent	Tour de France French PMR
		NFM	West Midlands	Mould
74.6125		NFM	Brecon Beacons	Mould
		NFM	West Midlands	Mould
74.6250		NFM	Brecon Beacons	Mould
		NFM	Devon	Mould
74.6500	79.6125	NFM	Hampshire (Crabwood Farm)	Mould
74.6625		NFM	Brecon Beacons	Mould
74.6750		NFM	Strathclyde	Mould
74.6750	79.7125	NFM	Gwent	Mould
74.6875	79.6875	NFM	Cambridgeshire	Mould Ch 15
74.7000		NFM	Gwent	Mould
		NFM	Tayside	Mould
74.7000	79.7125	NFM	Brecon Beacons	Mould
74.7125		NFM	Oxfordshire	Mould
74.7250		NFM	Brecon Beacons	Mould
		NFM	Manchester	Mould
		NFM	Shropshire	Mould
74.7375		NFM	Hampshire	Mould
		NFM	London	Mould
74.7500		NFM	Devon	Mould
		NFM	Manchester	Mould
		NFM	Shropshire	Mould
		NFM	Wiltshire	Mould
74.7625		NFM	Gwent	Mould
74.7875		NFM	Gwent	Mould

Base	Mobile	Mode	Location	User and Notes
74.8000 - 75.2500 MHz			**CIVIL AVIATION OUTER, MIDDLE & INNER RUNWAY MARKERS**	
75.0000		AM	Nationwide	Runway Marker Beacons
		NFM	RAF Lakenheath	Security
		NFM	RAF Mildenhall	Security

Base	Mobile	Mode	Location	User and Notes
75.2500 - 75.3000 MHz			**BBC O/B TALKBACK & MoD TACTICAL COMMS**	
75.2500		AM	Pendine (MoD)	Range Ops
		AM	West Midlands	USAF Police
75.2625	69.9625	NFM	Nationwide	BBC O/B Talkback Ch 1
75.2686	69.8350	NFM	Nationwide	BBC O/B Talkback Ch 4
75.2813	69.8725	NFM	Nationwide	BBC O/B Talkback Ch 7
75.2875	69.9075	NFM	Nationwide	BBC O/B Talkback Ch 2
75.2938	69.8975	NFM	Nationwide	BBC O/B Talkback Ch 9

Base	Mobile	Mode	Location	User and Notes
75.3000 - 76.7000 MHz			**MoD POLICE, MOULD & USAFE SECURITY 12.5 kHz**	
75.3000	75.3000	AM	Pendine (MoD)	Range Ops
		AM	Porton Down	Security
		AM	Suffolk	USAF Police
75.3250	75.3250	NFM	Nationwide	USAF Ground Common
		NFM	RAF Lakenheath	Ground Ops
		NFM	RAF Mildenhall	Ground Ops
75.3500	75.3500	NFM	RAF Upper Heyford	Security
75.4000	75.4000	AM	Pendine (MoD)	Range Ops
		AM	Suffolk	USAF Police
75.4250	75.4250	NFM	RAF Upper Heyford	Ground
75.4500	75.4500	NFM	Nationwide	USAF Base Security
		NFM	RAF Upper Heyford	Security
75.4750		NFM	Brecon Beacons	Mould
		NFM	RAF Molesworth	Security Ch 1
75.4950	75.9150	NFM	Holland	Wegenwacht
75.5000		AM	Christchurch	Military
		AM	Glasgow	RAF Security
		NFM	Gwent	Royal Air Force
		NFM	Northamptonshire	Security
75.5000	75.5000	NFM	RAF Upper Heyford	Security
75.5250	75.5250	NFM	RAF Upper Heyford	Ground
75.5500	75.5500	NFM	RAF Upper Heyford	Security
75.5750	75.5750	NFM	Nationwide	USAF Ground Common
		NFM	RAF Lakenheath	Ground Ops
		NFM	RAF Mildenhall	Ground Ops
75.5875	75.5875	NFM	RAF Greenham Common	Base Commander
		NFM	RAF Upper Heyford	Security
75.6000		NFM	Plymouth	MoD
75.6750		NFM	Plymouth	MoD Dockyard Ops
75.6750	75.6750	NFM	RAF Lakenheath	Security
		NFM	RAF Mildenhall	Security
75.7125		NFM	Hampshire	Mould
		NFM	Oxfordshire	Mould
75.7375		NFM	London	Mould
		NFM	Nationwide	Military Close Protection Ch 11
75.7500		NFM	Devon	Mould
		NFM	Gwent	Mould
		NFM	Wiltshire	Mould
75.7625	75.7625	NFM	Salisbury Plain	Close Support Group
75.7875		NFM	Gwent	Mould
		NFM	Lothian and Borders	Mould
75.8000	75.8000	NFM	RAF Upper Heyford	Security
75.8125		NFM	Brecon Beacons	Army
75.8250		NFM	Nationwide	Military Close Protection Ch 12
		NFM	Nationwide	T19 Tactical Support Team.
75.8250	75.8250	NFM	Nationwide	USAF Special Agents
75.8375		NFM	RN Faslane	Security (Charlie Control)

Base	Mobile	Mode	Location	User and Notes
75.8375	75.8375	NFM	RAF Mildenhall	Security
75.8625		NFM	Oxfordshire	Mould
75.8750		NFM	Devon	Mould
		NFM	Dorset	Territorial Army Mould
		NFM	Gwent	Mould
		NFM	London	Mould
		NFM	Nationwide	Military Close Protection Ch 10
75.9000		NFM	Gwent	Mould
75.9125		NFM	Gwent	Mould
75.9375		NFM	Fife	Mould
		NFM	Gwent	Mould
		NFM	Hampshire	Mould
		NFM	Tayside	Mould
75.9400		NFM	Salisbury Plain	Army
75.9500		NFM	South Wales	Mould
75.9625		NFM	Hampshire	Mould
75.9750		NFM	Nationwide	Royal Signals
76.0000		NFM	Taunton	Deane Borough Council
76.0000	76.0000	NFM	Nationwide	USAF Police
76.0000	78.0000	NFM	Sweden	Mobile Manual Phones
76.0125		NFM	Gwent	Mould
		NFM	Hampshire	Mould
		NFM	Plymouth	MoD Dockyard Ops
		NFM	West Midlands	Mould
76.0500		NFM	West midlands	USAF Maintenance Ch 6
76.0500	76.0500	NFM	RAF Lakenheath	Security
76.0625		NFM	Devon	Mould
		NFM	Gwent	Mould
		NFM	Nationwide	Military Close Protection Ch 15
76.0750		NFM	Hampshire	USAF
		NFM	Wiltshire	USAF
76.1125		NFM	Gwent	Mould
		NFM	Hampshire	Mould
76.1250		NFM	Gwent	Mould
		NFM	West Midlands	Mould
76.1625		NFM	Hampshire	Mould
76.2250		NFM	Devon	Mould
		NFM	Gwent	Mould
		NFM	Nationwide	Military Close Protection Ch 16
76.2250	76.2250	NFM	Nationwide	USAF Base to Mobile
		NFM	RAF Mildenhall	Security
76.2500		NFM	Brecon Beacons	Army
76.2500	76.2500	NFM	RAF Mildenhall	Security
76.2625		NFM	Gwent	Army
76.3000		NFM	RNAS Culdrose	Ground Services
		NFM	RNAS Yeovilton	Navy Provosts
76.3000	76.3000	NFM	RAF Upper Heyford	Security
76.3250		NFM	Devon	Mould

Base	Mobile	Mode	Location	User and Notes
		NFM	Hampshire	Mould
		NFM	Lothian and Borders	Mould
		NFM	Nationwide	Military Close Protection Ch 14
		NFM	Tayside	Mould
76.3250	76.3250	NFM	London	MoD Police Ruislip
		NFM	RAF Lakenheath	Security
		NFM	RAF Mildenhall	Security
		NFM	RAF Upper Heyford	Maintenance Ch 4
76.3500	76.3500	NFM	RAF Lakenheath	Crystal Palace
		NFM	RAF Alconbury	Security
76.3625		NFM	Northamptonshire	Mould
		NFM	West Midlands	Mould
76.3875		NFM	Hampshire	Mould
76.4000	76.4000	NFM	RAF Greenham Common	Security Fence Control
76.4375		NFM	Hampshire	Mould
		NFM	London	Mould
		NFM	Nationwide	Military Close Protection Ch 09
		NFM	Oxfordshire	Mould
		NFM	Salisbury Plain	Army
		NFM	West Midlands	Mould
76.4400		NFM	Salisbury Plain	Army
76.4500	76.4500	NFM	RAF Fairford	Security
76.4750		NFM	Hampshire	USAF
		NFM	London	Mould
		NFM	South Wales	Mould
76.5000		NFM	Nationwide	Military Close Protection Ch 13
76.5000	76.5000	NFM	London	MoD Police Ruislip
76.5250	76.5250	NFM	Camberley	WRAC Gate Security
		NFM	RAF Lakenheath	Security
76.5500	76.5500	NFM	RAF Alconbury	Security
		NFM	RAF Greenham Common	Security
		NFM	RAF Upper Heyford	Security
76.5625		NFM	Kent	Tour de France (French)
76.5750	76.5750	NFM	RAF Lakenheath	Security Ch 2
76.6000	76.6000	NFM	Cumbria	Range Control
76.6125		NFM	Hampshire	USAF
76.6250	76.6250	NFM	RAF Greenham Common	Security
76.6500	76.6500	NFM	RAF Alconbury	Security
		NFM	RAF Greenham Common	Security
		NFM	RAF Upper Heyford	Security
76.6750	76.6750	NFM	RAF Greenham Common	Security
		NFM	RAF Lakenheath	Security
		NFM	RAF Upper Heyford	Maintenance

76.7000 - 76.9500 MHz   HM CUSTOMS, BT, & USAFE COMMS 12.5 KHZ

Base	Mobile	Mode	Location	User and Notes
76.7000		NFM	Cumbria	Range Control
		NFM	Ipswich	HM Customs Ch 4
		NFM	Nationwide	British Telecom Channel A

Base	Mobile	Mode	Location	User and Notes
		NFM	Nationwide	Customs & Excise Channel 4
		NFM	Nationwide	USAF Police
76.7000	86.7125	NFM	Manchester	HM Customs (Magpie) Ch 1
76.7125		NFM	Manchester	HM Customs (Magpie) Ch 5
		NFM	Nationwide	Customs & Excise Channel 5
76.7250		NFM	Ipswich	HM Customs Ch 6
		NFM	London	HM Customs Ch 6
		NFM	Nationwide	Customs & Excise Channel 6
		NFM	RAF Leeming	Ground
76.7250	86.7125	NFM	Manchester	HM Customs (Magpie) Ch 2
76.7375		NFM	Ipswich	HM Customs Ch 7
		NFM	London	HM Customs Ch 7
		NFM	Manchester	HM Customs (Magpie) Ch 7
		NFM	Manchester	HM Customs (Magpie) Ch 9
		NFM	Nationwide	British Telecom Channel B
		NFM	Nationwide	Customs & Excise Ch 9
76.7375	86.7375	NFM	Ipswich	HM Customs Ch 9
76.7375	86.9375	NFM	Manchester	HM Customs (Magpie) Ch 3
76.7500		NFM	Nationwide	British Telecom Channel C
		NFM	Nationwide	Customs & Excise
76.7625		NFM	Nationwide	British Telecom Channel D
76.8250	86.8250	NFM	Nationwide	Thames TV Talkback
76.9000		NFM	West Midlands	USAF Base Gate Security
76.9250		NFM	West Midlands	USAF Base Gate Security
76.9375	76.9375	NFM	Nationwide	Customs & Excise Channel 7
76.9500	76.9500	NFM	Ipswich	HM Customs Ch 8
		NFM	Manchester	HM Customs (Magpie) Ch 4
		NFM	Plymouth	HM Customs
		NFM	Nationwide	Customs & Excise Channel 8
76.9625 - 77.5000 MHz			**PMR Low Band Mobiles 12.5 kHz Duplex**	
77.1375		NFM	Hampshire	Motorway Surveyors
77.2125		NFM	Hampshire	Netley Country Park Rangers
77.2375		NFM	Hampshire	New Forest Council
77.2500		NFM	Hampshire	Motorway Surveyors
		NFM	RNAS Culdrose	Ground Services
77.2500	87.2500	NFM	Stockton	Borough Council
77.2625	87.2625	NFM	Stockton	Borough Council
77.2875		NFM	Galway	Tone Repeater
77.7000		NFM	Swansea City	Royal Mail
77.8000 - 79.0000 MHz			**MoD & USAFE, BBC O/B Networks 12.5 kHz**	
77.8750	77.8750	NFM	Nationwide	ITN O/B Film Mobiles
77.9875		NFM	Hampshire	Marchwood Miltary Port
78.0000	78.0000	NFM	Hampshire	Army Ops
		NFM	RAF Finningley	ATC Air Show Stewards
78.0000	80.0000	NFM	Sweden	Ambulance & Fire Services
78.0250	78.0250	NFM	RAF Greenham Common	USAF Security Foot Patrols

Base	Mobile	Mode	Location	User and Notes
78.0500		NFM	London	Military
78.1000		AM	Nationwide	ATC Channel V3
		NFM	Nationwide	BBC O/B
		NFM	RAF Finningley	Ground Services
78.1000	78.1000	AM	Nationwide	RAF Cadets Channel V1
78.1125		NFM	RN Faslane	Security (Papa Control)
78.1250		NFM	Guilford	Army
78.1375	78.1375	NFM	Blandford	Royal Signals Security
78.1500		NFM	Nationwide	BBC O/B Talkback Channel 1
78.1500	84.5000	NFM	Okehampton	Military Range
78.1625		NFM	Salisbury Plain	MOD Police (Hippy Surveillance)
78.1625	73.6125	NFM	Plymouth	MoD Police
		NFM	RN Faslane	Security (Bravo Control)
78.1625	84.6625	NFM	Okehampton	Military Range
78.1750	84.6750	NFM	Okehampton	Military Range
78.1875	78.1875	NFM	Nationwide	BBC O/B Camera Channel 1
78.2000	78.2000	NFM	Nationwide	BBC O/B Camera Channel 2
78.2125	78.2125	NFM	Nationwide	BBC O/B Engineering Ch. 3
78.2155		NFM	Nationwide	BBC O/B
78.2250		NFM	RAF Finningley	Ground Services
78.2250	78.2250	AM	Avon	Air Training Corps
		NFM	Nationwide	BBC O/B Engineering Ch. 4
		NFM	RAF Greenham Common	Security
78.2275		NFM	Nationwide	BBC O/B
		NFM	Nationwide	BBC O/B Rigging
78.2315		NFM	DRA Farnborough	DRA Security
78.2375		NFM	Salisbury Plain	MOD Police (Hippy Surveillance)
78.2375	78.2375	NFM	Nationwide	BBC Microwave Link Setup
		NFM	Nationwide	BBC O/B Engineering Ch. 5
78.2400		NFM	Nationwide	BBC O/B Rigging
78.2500	78.2500	NFM	Nationwide	BBC O/B Lighting Channel 6
78.2525		NFM	Nationwide	BBC O/B
78.2750		NFM	Bovington	Army Camp Ch 3
78.2750	78.2750	NFM	Colchester	Barracks
		NFM	Hampshire	Army Ops
		NFM	Waterbeach	Security
78.2875	78.2875	NFM	Colchester	Barracks Ch 4
78.3000		NFM	AAC Middle Wallop	Military Police
		NFM	Bovington	Army Camp Ch 4
		NFM	Nationwide	Combined Cadet Force
78.3000	78.3000	NFM	Colchester	Barracks Ch 2
		NFM	Nationwide	Combined Cadet Force
		NFM	Stanford Battle Area	Stanford Ops
		NFM	Waterbeach	Security
78.3125		NFM	Aldershot	Military Police
78.3125	78.3125	NFM	Salisbury Plain	Military Police
78.3250		NFM	West Moors	Army Ch 3
78.3250	78.3250	NFM	Colchester	Barracks Ch 3

Base	Mobile	Mode	Location	User and Notes
		NFM	Hampshire	Military Police
		NFM	London	Military Police
		NFM	Stanford Battle Area	Stanford Ops
		NFM	Waterbeach	Security
78.3375		NFM	London	MoD Police
78.3375	78.8875	NFM	Finland	Traffic Police
78.3500		NFM	RAF Fairford	Base Ops
78.3625		NFM	Bovington	Army Camp Ch 6
78.3675		NFM	Portsmouth	RN Police
78.3750		NFM	Aldershot	Army Camp Security
78.3875		NFM	London	MoD Police
		NFM	Portsmouth	RN Police
78.4000	73.1250	NFM	London	MoD Police
		NFM	Nationwide	Army Equipment Channel 1
78.4125		NFM	AAC Middle Wallop	Ops
		NFM	Knightsbridge	Bomb Squad
		NFM	London	Chelsea Barracks
		NFM	London	MoD Police
		NFM	RAF Northolt	Security
78.4250	73.1500	NFM	Nationwide	Army Equipment Channel 2
78.4375		NFM	Bovington	Army Camp Ch 6
78.4500		NFM	AAC Middle Wallop	Crash
78.4500	73.2000	NFM	Nationwide	Army Equipment Channel 3
78.4750	73.2250	NFM	Nationwide	Army Equipment Channel 4
78.4875		NFM	Aldershot Camp	Army Security
		NFM	Guildford	Military Police
78.4875	78.4875	NFM	Colchester	Military Police
78.5000		NFM	Nationwide	Army Equipment Channel 5
78.5250		NFM	RAF Greenham Common	USAF Police
		NFM	Welford	USAF Bomb Disposal Units
78.5375		NFM	Bovington	Army Camp Ch 1
78.5500		NFM	Shropshire	Army Fire Channel
78.5750		NFM	RAF Fairford	IAT Tanker Ops
		NFM	RNAS Culdrose	Base Ops
		NFM	RNAS Yeovilton	Crash Ops Ch 4
78.6000		NFM	RAF Wittering	RAF Police Ch 52
78.6125		NFM	Bovington	Army Camp Ch 2
78.6375		NFM	Hampshire	MOD Police
78.6500	73.5000	NFM	Nationwide	Army Equipment Channel 1
78.6750		NFM	RAF Wittering	RAF Police Ch 53
78.6750	73.2500	NFM	Nationwide	Army Equipment Channel 8
78.6875		NFM	Portsmouth	RN Security
78.6975	78.6975	NFM	Nationwide	RAF Police
78.7000		NFM	RAF Fairford	Base Ops
78.7750		NFM	London	Military Police
		NFM	London	MoD Police
		NFM	NFM	Ternhill Army Fire Channel
		NFM	Ternhill	Army Fire

Base	Mobile	Mode	Location	User and Notes
78.7750	73.5500	NFM	Hampshire	Army
		NFM	Nationwide	Army Equipment Channel 9
		NFM	RNAS Portland	Tower
78.8000		NFM	Great Malvern	RSRE Base Security
		NFM	Hampshire	Army
		NFM	Poole	Royal Marines
78.8000	149.5000	NFM	London	MoD Police
78.8000	73.3500	NFM	Nationwide	Army Equipment Channel 6
78.8125		NFM	Newbury	Army
78.8250		NFM	AAC Middle Wallop	Ops
		NFM	Donington	Army Ordnance Depot Fire
		NFM	London	MoD Police
78.0375	78.8375	NFM	Killdenhall	MoD police
78.8500		NFM	AAC Middle Wallop	Ops
		NFM	Brecon Beacons	Army
		NFM	RAF Wittering	RAF Police Ch 54
78.9000		NFM	RN Lee-On-Solent	Crash Ops
		NFM	RNAS Lee-on-Solent	Tower Rescue
		NFM	RNAS Yeovilton	Fuel & Maintenance
78.9000	73.0000	NFM	Nationwide	Army Equipment Channel 7
78.9500		NFM	AAC Middle Wallop	Tower-Ground
		NFM	RNAS Culdrose	Base Ops
		NFM	RNAS Culdrose	Ops
		NFM	RNAS Merryfield	Ops
78.9750		NFM	Cheltenham	GCHQ Security and Transport
79.0000 - 80.0000 MHz			**MoD and RAF Ground Services 12.5 kHz**	
79.0000	79.0000	NFM	RNAS Yeovilton	Tower-Ground Ch 3
		NFM	RAF Coningsby	56(R) Squadron Ops
		NFM	RAF Leeming	Air Defence Channel
		NFM	RAF Odiham	Ops
		NFM	RAF Uxbridge	Ops
		NFM	RNAS Yeovilton	Ground
79.0000	80.0000	NFM	Sweden	Scandanavian Police
79.0250		NFM	RAF Finningley	Ground Vehicles
		NFM	RAF Manston	Tower-Ground
		NFM	RAF Valley	Q Control
		NFM	Salisbury Plain	Army
79.0250	79.0250	NFM	RAF Cottesmore	Tower
		NFM	RAF Marham	Security
79.0500		NFM	RAF Lyneham	Crew Buses
79.0500	79.0500	AM	RAF Machrihanish	Tower
		NFM	RAF Coningsby	Tower
		NFM	RAF Leuchars	Felix Control
		NFM	RAF Lyneham	Crew Buses
		NFM	RAF Northolt	Paintbox Control
79.0750		NFM	RAF Church Fenton	Tower-Ground
		NFM	RAF Cosford	Tower-Ground

Base	Mobile	Mode	Location	User and Notes
79.0750	79.0750	NFM	RAF Cosford	ATC
		NFM	RAF Northolt	Tower Crash Tenders
		NFM	RAF Wyton	Ops
79.1000		NFM	RAF Valley	Tower-Ground
79.1000	79.1000	NFM	Nationwide	RAF Police Channel 1
		NFM	RAF Valley	Tower
79.1250		NFM	RAF Brize Norton	Ground
		NFM	RAF Manston	Maintenance
		NFM	RAF St Mawgan	Personnel Services
79.1250	79.1250	NFM	RAF Brize Norton	Ground Services
		NFM	RAF Cottesmore	Ratchet Control/Line
		NFM	RAF Manston	RAF Police (Seagull)
		NFM	RAF Marham	Engineering
		NFM	RAF St Athan	Loadmaster and Ground
79.1375	79.1375	NFM	RAF Leuchars	Ground Services
79.1500	79.1500	NFM	Nationwide	RAF Police Channel 2
		NFM	RAF Abingdon	Tower Ch 2
		NFM	RAF Linton-on-Ouse	Ground Services
79.1750		NFM	RAF Lyneham	Tower-Ground
		NFM	RAF Wattisham	74 Sqn
79.1750	79.1750	NFM	RAF Lyneham	Tower Ground
		NFM	RAF Northolt	Forward Control
		NFM	RAF Wyton	Ops
79.1875	79.1875	NFM	RAF Northolt	Link Repeater
79.2000		NFM	RAF Leeming	Saracen
		NFM	RAF Wattisham	Network Ch 3
79.2000	79.2000	NFM	Nationwide	RAF Police Channel 3
		NFM	RAF Coningsby	Ground Services
		NFM	RAF Newton	Police Training
79.2125	74.1125	NFM	Gwent	Mould
		NFM	Manchester	Mould
		NFM	Norfolk	Mould
		NFM	RAE Aberporth	MoD Police
79.2250		NFM	RAF Waddington	RAF Police (Whitecap Control)
79.2250	79.2250	NFM	RAF Abingdon	RAF Police
		NFM	RAF Cottesmore	Ops (Bravo)
		NFM	RAF Kinloss	Ops (Moonshine Control)
		NFM	RAF Leuchars	Ops (Zulu Control)
		NFM	RAF Spadeadam	Ops
		NFM	RAF Wittering	RAF Police Ch 3/13
79.2250	68.3000	NFM	Nationwide	Army Channel 1
79.2500		NFM	RAF Church Fenton	Marshallers
		NFM	RAF Wittering	Ops
79.2500	79.2500	NFM	Nationwide	RAF Police Channel 4
		NFM	RAF Leuchars	Ground Ops
		NFM	RAF Linton-on-Ouse	Ground Services
		NFM	RAF Marham	Security
		NFM	RAF Wittering	RAF Police

Base	Mobile	Mode	Location	User and Notes
79.2500	68.4000	NFM	Nationwide	Army Channel 2
79.2625	79.2625	NFM	RAF Leeming	Ground
79.2750		NFM	RAF Finningley	Base Security
		NFM	RAF Finningley	RAF Police (Bravo)
		NFM	RAF Lyneham	Ground Control
		NFM	RAF St Athan	Ground & Transport
		NFM	RAF St Mawgan	RAF Police
		NFM	RAF Valley	RAF Police (Livid Control)
		NFM	RAF Wittering	Ops
79.2750	79.2750	NFM	RAF Lyneham	Ground Control
		NFM	RAF Marham	Tower
		NFM	RAF Northolt	Ground Control
		NFM	RAF St Athan	Transport and Ground
		NFM	RAF Wittering	RAF Police
79.2750	68.4250	NFM	Nationwide	Army Channel 3
79.3000	79.3000	NFM	Nationwide	RAF Police Channel 5
		NFM	RAF Coltishall	RAF Police (Whitecap Control)
		NFM	RAF Coltishall	Tower
		NFM	RAF Odiham	Tower
		NFM	RAF Wittering	RAF Police
79.3250	79.3250	NFM	RAE Farnborough	Ground
		NFM	RAF Cosford	Ops
		NFM	Farnborough	Ground Control
		NFM	Galway	Galway Heating Oil Co.
		NFM	Nationwide	RAF Police
		NFM	RAF Cosford	Ground Control
		NFM	RAF Leeming	Ground
		NFM	RAF Linton-on-Ouse	Ground Services
		NFM	RAF Lossiemouth	Tower
		NFM	RAF Scampton	Tower
		NFM	RAF Waddington	Ground Services
79.3500	79.3500	NFM	RAF Manston	RAF Police
		NFM	RAF Waddington	Channel One
		NFM	RAF Wittering	Ch I/11/51
		NFM	Nationwide	RAF Police Channel 6
		NFM	RAF Coningsby	Ground Services
		NFM	RAF Kemble	Tower
		NFM	RAF Leuchars	Crash Ops
		NFM	Nationwide	Royal Signals
		NFM	RAF Manston	RAF Police (Seagull)
79.3750	79.3750	NFM	RAF Church Fenton	RAF Police (Whitecap Control)
		NFM	Gosport	RN Security (Tanzy Control)
		NFM	RAF Leuchars	Crash Ops
		NFM	RAF Marham	Elfin
		NFM	RAF Odiham	Ruler
79.3875	79.3875	NFM	RAF Leuchars	Ground Services
79.4000	79.4000	NFM	RAF Lyneham	Ops
		NFM	RAF Northolt	RAF Police (Mayfly Control)

Base	Mobile	Mode	Location	User and Notes
		NFM	RAF Wattisham	Ops
		NFM	Nationwide	Army Channel 4
		NFM	Nationwide	RAF Police Channel 7
		NFM	RAF Coningsby	Ground Services
		NFM	RAF Leeming	Air Defence Channel
		NFM	RAF Leuchars	Ground Services
		NFM	RAF Tain	Range Control
		NFM	RAF Wittering	RAF Police Ch 7/17
79.4125	74.3875	NFM	Gwent	Mould
79.4250	79.4250	NFM	RAF Waddington	Tower-Ground
		NFM	RAF Brize Norton	Tower-Ground
		NFM	RAF Kinloss	Tower
79.4500	79.4500	NFM	RAF Cosford	Charlie Control
		NFM	Nationwide	RAF Police Channel 8
		NFM	RAF Binbrook	Ground Services
		NFM	RAF Coltishall	Ops (Zero)
		NFM	RAF Cosford	Charlie Control
		NFM	RAF Leeming	Air Defence Channel
		NFM	RAF Wittering	RAF Police
79.4750	79.4750	NFM	Lydd	Army Camp Security
		NFM	RAF Coningsby	Line
		NFM	RAF Cranwell	Ground Services
		NFM	RAF Northolt	Ops (Papa Control)
		NFM	Nationwide	RAF Police
79.4875		NFM	Northern Ireland	RAF Repeater
		NFM	Southend on Sea	MoD Repeater
79.5000	79.5000	NFM	RAF Waddington	Channel Four
		NFM	RAF Wittering	Ops
		NFM	Lydd	Army Camp Security
		NFM	RAE Aberporth	MoD Police
		NFM	Nationwide	RAF Police Channel 9
		NFM	RAF Kemble	Tower Ch 2
		NFM	RAF Mildenhall	Security
		NFM	RAF Neatishead	Security
		NFM	RAF Wittering	RAF Police Ch 9/19
		NFM	RAF Wyton	RAF Police
79.5250	79.5250	NFM	RAF Wattisham	Network
		NFM	RAF Wittering	Ops
		NFM	RAF Lossiemouth	Ops
		NFM	RAF Newton	Ops (Tempo)
		NFM	RAF Wittering	RAF Police
79.5375		NFM	RAE Farnborough	Medical Ops
79.5500	79.5500	NFM	RAF Wattisham	56Sqn (Basil Control)
		NFM	Nationwide	RAF Police Channel 10
		NFM	RAF Coningsby	Ground Services
79.5625	79.5625	NFM	Ternhill	Army Staff Cars
79.5750	79.5750	NFM	RAF Wattisham	Police (Silicon Control)
		NFM	RAF Leeming	Air Defence Channel

Base	Mobile	Mode	Location	User and Notes
		NFM	RAF Lossiemouth	Ops (Epoch Control)
79.6000	79.6000	NFM	Nationwide	RAF Police Channel 11
		NFM	RAF Brize Norton	Ops (Brize Ops)
		NFM	RAF Lossiemouth	Ops (Oxide Control)
		NFM	RAF Manston	RAF Police (Seagull)
79.6125	79.6125	NFM	Cambridgeshire	Mould Ch 4
79.6250	79.6250	NFM	RAF Wittering	Ground Services
79.6500	79.6500	NFM	Nationwide	RAF Police Channel 12
		NFM	RAF Brize Norton	Loadmasters
		NFM	RAF Benson	Tower
		NFM	RAF Brize Norton	Tower-Ground
		NFM	RAF Coningsby	Ground Services
		NFM	RAF Lyneham	Tower
79.6750	79.6750	NFM	RAF Valley	F Control
		NFM	RAF Brize Norton	Loadmaster
		NFM	RAF Newton	Tower
		NFM	RAF Northolt	Ops
79.6800	79.6800	NFM	RAF Waddington	Channel Five
79.7000	79.7000	NFM	RAF Coningsby	Ground Services
		NFM	RAF Leeming	Air Defence Channel
		NFM	RAF Marham	Line
79.7000	68.1500	NFM	Nationwide	Army Channel 6
		NFM	Nationwide	BBC Engineering Channel
79.7125	79.7125	NFM	Colchester	Barracks
		NFM	Stanford Battle Area	Stanford Ops
79.7125	74.4000	NFM	Gwent	Mould
79.7125	74.4675	NFM	Gwent	Mould
79.7250	74.7250	NFM	RAF Cottesmore	Grady Control
79.7625	74.2625	NFM	Gwent	Mould
79.7625	74.6750	NFM	Gwent	Mould
79.7750	79.7750	NFM	Colchester	Barracks
		NFM	Nationwide	RAF Fire Channel
		NFM	RAF Binbrook	Fire
		NFM	RAF Leeming	Air Defence Channel
		NFM	RAF Northolt	Ops
79.8000	79.8000	NFM	Nationwide	Army Channel 7
		NFM	RAF Coningsby	Ground Services
79.8250	79.8250	NFM	RAF Wittering	RAF Police
		NFM	Nationwide	RAF Police Convoys
		NFM	RAF Wittering	RAF Police
79.8500	79.8500	NFM	RAF Abingdon	Salvage Transport
79.8750	79.8750	NFM	RAF Odiham	Line 33 Squadron
79.9000	68.5250	NFM	Nationwide	Army Channel 8
79.9500	68.6000	NFM	Nationwide	Army Channel 9
79.9500	79.9500	NFM	RAF Wittering	Ground Services
79.9875	79.9750	NFM	RAF Coningsby	56(R) Squadron Ops

80.0000 - 82.5000 MHz   RADIO ASTRONOMY

Base	Mobile	Mode	Location	User and Notes
80.0000 - 81.5000 MHz			**FIRE BRIGADES (ENGLAND & WALES)**	
			[BASE 70.5000 - 71.5000 MHz]	
80.0000	87.0000	NFM	Sweden	Business Communications
80.0125		AM	London	Fire Tender to Tender Ch 21
		NFM	Lancashire	Fire Brigade Ch 9
80.0750		AM	London	Fire Tender to Tender Ch 22
80.2000		NFM	Norfolk	Fire Brigade
80.2250		NFM	West Yorkshire	Fire Brigade Mobiles Ch3
80.4000		AM	Suffolk	Fire Brigade
80.4125	71.1125	AM	Bedfordshire	Fire Brigade
80.5500		NFM	Southend on Sea	Council
81.0000		NFM	Denmark	Fire/Ambulance
		NFM	Nationwide	Police CID/RCS
81.0375		NFM	Suffolk	Fire Brigade
81.0875		NFM	Suffolk	Fire Brigade
81.1125		NFM	Welling	Taxis
81.1250		NFM	Nationwide	Fire Brigade Channel
81.1625		NFM	Plymouth	BT
81.2500		NFM	Galway	Tone Repeater
81.2625		NFM	Tayside	Link
81.3125		NFM	Tayside	Link
81.3500		NFM	Tayside	Link
81.5000 - 83.5000 MHz			**LOW BAND PMR (SIMPLEX & DUPLEX)**	
			[SPLIT - 10.5 MHz]	
81.5750		NFM	England & Wales	Police Radio Engineering
81.7000	68.2000	NFM	Nationwide	HM Customs & Excise
		NFM	London	HM Customs & Excise
81.7375		NFM	London	HM Customs & Excise
81.7500	68.2500	NFM	Nationwide	HM Customs & Excise
		NFM	London	HM Customs & Excise
		NFM	Dover	HM Customs (Dingo Control)
81.7625	68.2625	NFM	Nationwide	HM Customs & Excise
		NFM	London	HM Customs & Excise
81.7750	68.2750	NFM	Nationwide	HM Customs & Excise
		NFM	Immingham	HM Customs
81.7750		NFM	Nationwide	Network Q RAC Rally Marshall
81.7875	68.2875	NFM	Nationwide	HM Customs & Excise
		NFM	Immingham	HM Customs
		NFM	London	HM Customs & Excise
		NFM	Oban	HM Customs
81.8000		NFM	Poole	Repeater
81.8250	81.8250	AM	Nationwide	Motorway Police Units
81.8500	68.3500	NFM	Glasgow	Taxis
81.8875	68.3875	NFM	Sussex	PMR Repeater
81.9125	68.4125	NFM	Slough	Taxis
81.9250	68.4250	NFM	Birmingham	Taxi Service
		NFM	Redcar	Taxis

Base	Mobile	Mode	Location	User and Notes
81.9375	68.4375	NFM	Southall	Sky Cars
81.9500	81.9500	NFM	London	Fire Brigade HQ Ops Room
81.9625	68.4625	AM	Plymouth	Plymouth Taxis
81.9875	68.4875	NFM	Portsmouth	PMR
		NFM	Kent	Courier Service
		NFM	Kent	Doctors
		NFM	Grimsby	Marine Gas and Oil
82.0000	68.5000	NFM	Sussex	PMR Repeater
82.0250		NFM	Bexley Heath	Taxis
82.0375		NFM	London	London Car Hire
82.0500	68.5500	NFM	Nationwide	HM Customs & Excise
		NFM	Liverpool	HM Customs
		NFM	Manchester	HM Customs
82.0625	68.5625	NFM	Glasgow	Taxis
82.1000	68.6000	NFM	Glasgow	Taxis
82.1125	68.6125	NFM	Glasgow	Taxis
		NFM	Edinburgh	Taxis
82.1375	68.6375	NFM	London	Building Supplier
		NFM	Tonbridge	Medicall
82.1875	68.6875	NFM	London	Contract Dustcart
82.2250	68.7250	NFM	Newcastle	PMR
82.3000	68.8000	NFM	Leicester	PMR
		NFM	Sussex	PMR Repeater
		NFM	Tunbridge Wells	Medicall
82.4375	68.9375	NFM	Glasgow	Taxis
		NFM	Gravesend	Taxis
82.5250	69.0250	NFM	Nationwide	Road Construction Recovery
82.5375		NFM	Walsall	Taxi
82.5500		NFM	Lincoln	PMR
82.7875		NFM	Nationwide	RAC Network Q Rally
82.8000	82.8000	NFM	RAC Network 'Q' Rally	Rally Control
82.8125	82.8125	NFM	RAC Network 'Q' Rally	Rally Channel 3
82.9000	82.9000	NFM	RAC Network 'Q' Rally	Ford Team
82.9250	69.4250	NFM	RAC Network 'Q' Rally	Subara Team
82.9500		NFM	Nationwide	Network Q RAC Rally Recovery
82.9875	69.4875	NFM	RAC Network 'Q' Rally	Toyota Channel 2
83.2450		NFM	Dublin	Electricity Board
83.5000 - 84.0000 MHz			**FIRE BRIGADES (ENGLAND & WALES)**	**12.5 KHz**
84.0000	85.0000	NFM	Denmark	Police
84.0150	74.2150	NFM	Germany	Emergency Channel Ch 347
84.0350	74.2350	NFM	Germany	Emergency Channel Ch 348
84.0500		NFM	Lothian & Borders	Tweed Valley MR
84.0550	74.2550	NFM	Germany	Emergency Channel Ch 349
84.0750	74.2750	NFM	Germany	Emergency Channel Ch 350
84.0875		NFM	Nationwide	Military Close Protection Ch 3
84.0950	74.2950	NFM	Germany	Emergency Channel Ch 351
84.1150	74.3150	NFM	Germany	Emergency Channel Ch 352

Base	Mobile	Mode	Location	User and Notes
84.1250 - 84.9750 MHz			MoD POLICE COMMUNICATIONS 25 KHZ	
84.1250		NFM	Nationwide	Army Cadet Force
84.1350	74.3350	NFM	Germany	Emergency Channel Ch 353
84.1500		NFM	Nationwide	Military Close Protection Ch 4
84.1550	74.3550	NFM	Germany	Emergency Channel Ch 354
84.1750	74.3750	NFM	Germany	Emergency Channel Ch 355
84.1950	74.3950	NFM	Germany	Emergency Channel Ch 356
84.2150	74.4150	NFM	Germany	Emergency Channel Ch 357
84.2250	84.2250	NFM	Nationwide	RAF
84.2350	74.4350	NFM	Germany	Emergency Channel Ch 358
84.2550	74.4550	NFM	Germany	Emergency Channel Ch 359
84.2625		NFM	Nationwide	Military Close Protection Ch 7
84.2750	74.4750	NFM	Germany	Emergency Channel Ch 360
84.2950	74.4950	NFM	Germany	Emergency Channel Ch 361
84.3000	84.3000	NFM	Brecon Beacons	RAF Mountain Rescue Ch1
		NFM	Nationwide	RAF Mountain Rescue Ch.1
84.3150	74.5150	NFM	Germany	Emergency Channel Ch 362
84.3250	84.3250	NFM	Nationwide	RAF Mountain Rescue Ch.2
84.3350	74.5350	NFM	Germany	Emergency Channel Ch 363
84.3500	74.1250	NFM	Ireland	Fire Brigade
84.3500	84.3500	NFM	Nationwide	Military Police
84.3550	74.5550	NFM	Germany	Emergency Channel Ch 364
84.3625		NFM	Nationwide	Military Close Protection Ch 6
84.3625	84.3625	NFM	Nationwide	Military Police
84.3750	74.1500	NFM	Ireland	Fire Brigade
84.3750	74.5750	NFM	Germany	Emergency Channel Ch 365
84.3750	84.3750	NFM	Nationwide	Military Police
84.3875	84.3875	NFM	Nationwide	Military Police
84.3950	74.5950	NFM	Germany	Emergency Channel Ch 366
84.4000	74.1750	NFM	Ireland	Fire Brigade
84.4000	84.4000	NFM	Nationwide	Military Police
84.4125	84.4125	NFM	Nationwide	Military Police
84.4150	74.6150	NFM	Germany	Emergency Channel Ch 367
84.4250	74.2000	NFM	Ireland	Fire Brigade
84.4250	84.4250	NFM	Nationwide	Military Police
84.4350	74.6350	NFM	Germany	Emergency Channel Ch 368
84.4375	84.4375	NFM	Nationwide	Military Police
84.4500	74.2250	NFM	Ireland	Fire Brigade
84.4500	84.4500	NFM	Nationwide	Military Police
84.4550	74.6550	NFM	Germany	Emergency Channel Ch 369
84.4625	84.4625	NFM	Nationwide	Military Police
84.4750	74.2500	NFM	Ireland	Fire Brigade
84.4750	74.6750	NFM	Germany	Emergency Channel Ch 370
84.4750	84.4750	NFM	Castlemartin	RAC Range
		NFM	Nationwide	Military Police
84.4875	84.4875	NFM	Nationwide	Military Police Escorts
84.4950	74.6950	NFM	Germany	Emergency Channel Ch 371
84.5000	74.2750	NFM	Ireland	Fire Brigade

Base	Mobile	Mode	Location	User and Notes
84.5000	84.5000	NFM	Nationwide	Military Police Escorts
84.5125	84.5125	NFM	Nationwide	Military Police
84.5150	74.7150	NFM	Germany	Emergency Channel Ch 372
84.5250	74.3000	NFM	Ireland	Fire Brigade
84.5250	84.5250	NFM	Aldershot	Military Police Data
84.5350	74.7350	NFM	Germany	Emergency Channel Ch 373
84.5375	84.5375	NFM	Nationwide	Military Police
84.5500	74.3250	NFM	Ireland	Fire Brigade
84.5500	84.5500	NFM	London	Military Police
84.5550	74.7550	NFM	Germany	Emergency Channel Ch 374
84.5625	84.5625	NFM	Nationwide	Military Police
84.5750	74.3500	NFM	Ireland	Ambulance Service
84.5750	74.7750	NFM	Germany	Emergency Channel Ch 375
84.5750	84.5750	NFM	Nationwide	Military Police
84.5875	84.5875	NFM	Nationwide	Military Police
84.5950	74.7950	NFM	Germany	Emergency Channel Ch 376
84.6000	74.3750	NFM	Ireland	Ambulance Service
84.6000	84.6000	NFM	Nationwide	Military Mountain Rescue
		NFM	Southampton	Royal Navy
84.6150	74.8150	NFM	Germany	Emergency Channel Ch 377
84.6250	74.4000	NFM	Ireland	Ambulance Service
84.6350	74.8350	NFM	Germany	Emergency Channel Ch 378
84.6400		NFM	Salisbury Plain	Defence Land Services
84.6500	72.8500	NFM	RN Faslane	Medics
84.6500	74.4250	NFM	Ireland	Ambulance Service
84.6550	74.8550	NFM	Germany	Emergency Channel Ch 379
84.6750	74.4500	NFM	Ireland	Ambulance Service
84.6750	74.8750	NFM	Germany	Emergency Channel Ch 380
84.6950	74.8950	NFM	Germany	Emergency Channel Ch 381
84.7000	74.4750	NFM	Ireland	Ambulance Service
84.7125		NFM	Nationwide	Military Close Protection Ch 2
84.7150	74.9150	NFM	Germany	Emergency Channel Ch 382
84.7250	74.5000	NFM	Ireland	Ambulance Service
84.7350	74.9350	NFM	Germany	Emergency Channel Ch 383
84.7500	74.5250	NFM	Ireland	Ambulance Service
84.7550	74.9550	NFM	Germany	Emergency Channel Ch 384
84.7625		NFM	Nationwide	Military Close Protection Ch 1
84.7750	74.5500	NFM	Ireland	Ambulance Service
84.7750	74.9750	NFM	Germany	Emergency Channel Ch 385
84.7750	84.7750	NFM	Southampton	Royal Navy
84.7950	74.9950	NFM	Germany	Emergency Channel Ch 386
84.8000	74.5750	NFM	Ireland	Ambulance Service
84.8150	75.0150	NFM	Germany	Emergency Channel Ch 387
84.8250	74.6000	NFM	Ireland	Ambulance Service
84.8250	84.8250	NFM	Nationwide	RAF
		NFM	Nationwide	RAF Helicopter Winchmen
84.8350	75.0350	NFM	Germany	Emergency Channel Ch 388
84.8375		NFM	Nationwide	Military Close Protection Ch 6

Base	Mobile	Mode	Location	User and Notes
84.8375	84.8375	NFM	Perth	Territorial Army
84.8500		NFM	Nationwide	Military Close Protection Ch 5
84.8550	75.0550	NFM	Germany	Emergency Channel Ch 389
		NFM	Germany	Emergency Channel Ch 390
84.8950	75.0950	NFM	Germany	Emergency Channel Ch 391
84.9150	75.1150	NFM	Germany	Emergency Channel Ch 392
84.9250	84.9250	NFM	Southampton	Royal Navy
84.9350	75.1350	NFM	Germany	Emergency Channel Ch 393
84.9550	75.1550	NFM	Germany	Emergency Channel Ch 394
		NFM	Germany	Emergency Channel Ch 395
84.9750	84.9750	NFM	Ludford Cove	Army Range Control Ch 1
84.9950	75.1950	NFM	Germany	Emergency Channel Ch 396

85.0125 - 86.2875 MHz PMR Low Band Base Repeaters 12.5 kHz [Split - 13.5 MHz]

Base	Mobile	Mode	Location	User and Notes
85.0125	71.5125	AM	Jersey	Jersey Telecom
		NFM	Avon	Severn Trent Water
		NFM	Brighton	Focsa Street Cleaners
		NFM	Ealing	Trade PMR
		NFM	Perth	Tayside Water Board
85.0150	75.2150	NFM	Germany	Emergency Channel Ch 397
85.0250	71.5250	NFM	Pickering	Council
		NFM	Ipswich	Council
		NFM	Norfolk	County Highways
		NFM	Gedling	Gedling Borough Council
85.0350	75.2350	NFM	Germany	Emergency Channel Ch 398
85.0375	71.5375	NFM	Aberdeen	Roads Department
		AM	Leeds	Gritters/snow ploughs
		AM	St Austell	Chris Perry Motors
		AM	Killwinning	Roads Department
		NFM	Dumfries	Council Roads Department
		NFM	Dumfries	Council Roads Dept
		NFM	Easington	Works Dept
		NFM	Hastings	Council
		NFM	Ipswich	Council Repeater
		NFM	Strathclyde	Strathclyde Council
		NFM	Cambridge	Regency Cars
85.0500	71.5500	NFM	Aylsham	East Coast Grain
		NFM	Southampton	Taxis
		NFM	Peterborough	Royal Taxis
		NFM	Romford	Atlas Minicabs
		AM	Jersey	Abbey
		NFM	Benington	Braceys
		NFM	Cambridge	Trumpington Farms
		NFM	Cleveland	Mastercare
		NFM	Ipswich	Anglia Water
		NFM	Ipswich	Cubitt Holdings
		NFM	London	Baron Transport

Base	Mobile	Mode	Location	User and Notes
		NFM	Norfolk	Farm Feed Co.
		NFM	Perth	Tayside Water Board
		NFM	Reepham	Salle Farm Co.
		NFM	Suffolk	Farm Feed Co.
85.0550	75.2550	NFM	Germany	Emergency Channel Ch 399
85.0625	71.5625	NFM	Cleveland	Mastercare
		NFM	Caerphilly	Coddy Cabs
		NFM	Hull	Moss Tyres
		NFM	West Midlands	Ambulances Transferals
		NFM	Kettering	A-Z Taxis
		NFM	London	Diamond Cars
		NFM	London	Lee Vans
		NFM	Norfolk	James Abbotts Ltd
		NFM	Suffolk	James Abbotts Ltd
		NFM	Swansea	Bryan Twyn Taxis
		NFM	West Midlands	Mastercare
		NFM	Witham	Anglia Land Drainage
85.0750	71.5750	AM	Derbyshire	Tilcon
		AM	Leeds	Gritter/Snow Ploughs
		NFM	Scunthorpe	Taxis
		NFM	Great Yarmouth	Wolsey Taxis
		NFM	Ipswich	Anglia Water
		NFM	Lakenheath	H. Palmer
		NFM	Little Downham	W.B. Chambers.
		NFM	London	David Marshall
		NFM	Perth	Taxi
		NFM	Wrexham	Trafford Estate
85.0750	75.2750	NFM	Germany	Emergency Channel Ch 400
85.0875	71.5875	NFM	Balbdock	Winifred Express
		AM	Cornwall	County Council
		NFM	Hillingdon	Sky Radio Cars
		NFM	Baldock	Winifred Express
		NFM	Cambridge	Regency Cars
		NFM	Colchester	Wooldridge
		NFM	Guernsey	Guernsey Gas Co.
		NFM	Newmarket	Six Mile Bottom Estate
85.0950	75.2950	NFM	Germany	Emergency Channel Ch 401
85.1000	71.6000	NFM	Brecon	Welsh Water
		NFM	Glasgow	Water Department
		NFM	Nottingham	Trent Water
		NFM	South Grampian	Water Board
		NFM	Ipswich	Anglia Water
85.1125	71.6125	NFM	Abergavenny	Welsh Water
		AM	Leeds	Yorkshire Water
		NFM	Manchester	PMR
		NFM	North-West	PMR
		NFM	Colchester	Roadworks Depot
		NFM	Ipswich	Roadworks Depot

Base	Mobile	Mode	Location	User and Notes
		NFM	Norwich	Anglian Water
		NFM	Stanway	Roadworks Depot
		NFM	Thames Valley	Thames Valley Water
		NFM	West Yorkshire	British Pipeline
85.1150	75.3150	NFM	Germany	Emergency Channel Ch 402
85.1250	71.6250	NFM	Essex	British Pipeline
		NFM	Jersey	Jersey Electricity Company Ch 3
		NFM	Nationwide	British Pipeline
		NFM	Strathclyde	Strathclyde Council
85.1350	75.3350	NFM	Germany	Emergency Channel Ch 403
85.1375	71.6375	NFM	Edinburgh	British Telecom
		NFM	Nationwide	British Telecom Channel 6
85.1500	71.6500	NFM	Nationwide	British Telecom Channel 2
85.1550	75.3550	NFM	Germany	Emergency Channel Ch 404
85.1625	71.6625	NFM	Glasgow	Data Link
		NFM	Nationwide	British Telecom Channel 4
		NFM	Perth	British Telecom
		NFM	Lancaster	British Telecom
		NFM	Morecambe	British Telecom
85.1750	75.3750	NFM	Germany	Emergency Channel Ch 405
85.1750	71.6750	NFM	Dundee	BT Data Link
		NFM	Jersey	Jersey Electricity Company Ch 2
		NFM	Nationwide	British Telecom Channel 1
		NFM	Perth	British Telecom
85.1875	71.6875	NFM	Edinburgh	British Telecom Voice Link
		NFM	Nationwide	British Telecom Channel 5
		NFM	Perth	British Telecom Data Link
85.1950	75.3950	NFM	Germany	Emergency Channel Ch 406
85.2000	71.7000	NFM	Nationwide	British Telecom Channel 3
		AM	Liverpool	Taxis
		AM	York	British Telecom
		NFM	Manchester	Airport Police
85.2125	71.7125	NFM	Bishop Stortford	Water Board
		AM	Swansea City	South Wales Water Board
		NFM	Glossop	Water Board
		NFM	Hampshire	Water Board Ch 2
		NFM	Dundee	Tayside Water Board
		NFM	Folkestone	Water Board
		NFM	Gwent	South Wales Water
		NFM	Ipswich	Anglia Water
		NFM	Lea Valley	Southern Water Channel 2
		NFM	Lancaster	Water Board
		NFM	Morecambe	Water Board
		NFM	Montgomery	Severn Trent Water
		NFM	Saffron Waldon	Water Board
85.2150	75.4150	NFM	Germany	Emergency Channel Ch 407
85.2250	71.7250	AM	Cornwall	County Council
		AM	Cardiff	South Glamorgan Council

Base	Mobile	Mode	Location	User and Notes
		NFM	Dumbarton	Council
		NFM	Dumfries	Water Board
		NFM	Lea Valley	Southern Water Channel 4
		NFM	London	Chelsea Council
		NFM	London	Westminster Council
		NFM	Thames Valley	Thames Valley Water
85.2350	75.4350	NFM	Germany	Emergency Channel Ch 408
85.2375	71.7375	NFM	Borders	Water Board
		NFM	Walsall	Water Board
		NFM	Nottingham	Trent Water
		NFM	Aberdeen	Water Board
		NFM	Essex	Wessex Water
		NFM	Gwynedd	Welsh Water
		NFM	Perth	Tayside Water Board
		NFM	Suffolk	Suffolk Water
		NFM	Thames Valley	Thames Valley Water
85.2500	71.7500	NFM	Barrow	Water Board
		AM	York	Yorkshire Water
		NFM	Newcastle	Water Board
		NFM	Frimley	Surrey Water
		NFM	Hampshire	Portsmouth Water
		NFM	Jersey	Jersey Milk
		NFM	Lea Valley	Water Board
		NFM	Leeds	Automobile Association
		NFM	Letchwood	Water Board
		NFM	Lancaster	Water Board
		NFM	Morecambe	Water Board
		NFM	Norfolk	Anglia Water
		NFM	Perth	Tayside Water Board (PerWat)
		NFM	Suffolk	Anglia Water
		NFM	Surrey	Thames Water
		NFM	West Yorkshire	Automobile Association
		NFM	Scarborough	Water Authority
85.2550	75.4550	NFM	Germany	Emergency Channel Ch 409
85.2625	71.7625	NFM	Avon	Severn Trent Water
		AM	York	Yorkshire Water
		NFM	Kent	Water Board
		NFM	Nottinghamshire	Severn Trent Water
		NFM	Hampshire	Portsmouth Water
		NFM	Kent	Kent Water
		NFM	Thames Valley	Thames Valley Water
85.2750	75.4750	NFM	Germany	Emergency Channel Ch 410
85.2750	71.7750	NFM	Cornwall	South West Water
		AM	Driffield	Yorkshire Water
		NFM	Manchester	North West Water
		NFM	North-West	PMR
		NFM	Somerset	Council Housing
		NFM	Ipswich	Anglia Water

Base	Mobile	Mode	Location	User and Notes
		NFM	Kent	Kent Water
		NFM	Norfolk	Anglia Water
		NFM	Perth	Tayside Water Board (PerWat)
		NFM	Suffolk	Anglia Water
		NFM	Tayside	Tayside Water Board
		NFM	West Yorkshire	Yorkshire Water
85.2875	71.7875	NFM	Anglia	Anglia Water Ch 13
		AM	Gwynedd	Welsh Water
		AM	Sussex	Water Board
		NFM	Ballachulish	Water Board
		NFM	Peterborough	Anglia Water
		NFM	Tayside	Water Board
		NFM	Yorkshire	Water Board
		NFM	Brighton	Southern Water (Red Base)
85.2950	75.4950	NFM	Germany	Emergency Channel Ch 411
85.3000	71.8000	NFM	Aberdeen	Council Dog Catcher
		NFM	Hampshire	Council Drainage
		NFM	North-West	PMR
		WFM	Maidenhead	BBC Southern Counties
		NFM	Breckland	Council HQ
		NFM	Ipswich	Community Repeater
		NFM	London	Brent Council
		NFM	Thames Valley	Thames Valley Water Ch 5
85.3125	71.8125	NFM	Brighton	Southern Water (Distribution)
		NFM	Bristol	Water Authority
		NFM	Humberside	Council
		NFM	Huntingdon	Anglia Water
		NFM	Newmarket	PMR
		NFM	Sheffield	Yorkshire Water Board
		NFM	Tayside	Tayside Water Board
		NFM	W Sussex	Wessex Water Ch 6
85.3150	75.5150	NFM	Germany	Emergency Channel Ch 412
85.3250	71.8250	AM	Ayr	Water Board
		AM	Sheffield	Yorkshire Water
		NFM	Co. Durham	Electricians
		NFM	Merseyside	PMR
		NFM	Aberdeen	British Gas
		NFM	Bournemouth	Dorset Water
		NFM	Brighton	Southern Water (Green Base)
		NFM	Burnley	North West Water
		NFM	Doncaster	Yorkshire Water
		NFM	Edinburgh	Water Board
		NFM	Folkestone	Community Repeater
		NFM	Gloucester	Gloucester Water
		NFM	Ipswich	Anglia Water
		NFM	Northampton	Anglia Water
85.3350	75.5350	NFM	Germany	Emergency Channel Ch 413
		NFM	Aberdeen	Water Board

Base	Mobile	Mode	Location	User and Notes
		NFM	Carlisle	Water Board
		NFM	Mold	Clwyd Water Board
		AM	Huntingdon	Anglia Water
		NFM	Gwent	Severn Trent Water
		NFM	Humberside	Humberside Water
		NFM	Ipswich	Anglia Water
		NFM	Kidderminster	Worcestershire Water
		NFM	Perth	Tayside Water Board (PerWat)
		NFM	Plymouth	South West Water
		NFM	Sheffield	Yorkshire Water Board
85.3500	71.8500	NFM	Belfast	Water Board
		NFM	Hampshire	Bottle Bank Collection
		NFM	Clwyd	Clwyd Council
		NFM	Portsmouth	City Council
		NFM	Saddleworth	Highways
		NFM	Swansea City	Council
		AM	Wiltshire	Water Board Ch 2
		NFM	Guernsey	Civil Defence
		NFM	Kent	Kent Water
		NFM	Renfrew	Council
		NFM	Stowmarket	Council Highways
85.3550	75.5550	NFM	Germany	Emergency Channel Ch 414
85.3625	71.8625	NFM	Chester	Car Transporters
		NFM	Yorkshire	Water Board
		AM	Glamorgan	Water Board
		NFM	North Tayside	Water Board
		NFM	Essex	Wessex Water
		NFM	Huntingdon	Anglia Water
85.3750	71.8750	NFM	Belfast	NI Electricity Service
		NFM	London	Thames Water Authority
		NFM	Barnsley	Yorkshire Water
		NFM	Bury St Edmunds	Council Highways
85.3750	75.5750	NFM	Germany	Emergency Channel Ch 415
85.3875	71.8875	NFM	Belfast	Newtownabbey Council
		NFM	Cambridge	Anglia Water
		AM	Co. Durham	Water Board
		NFM	Huntingdon	Anglia Water
		NFM	Nottinghamshire	Severn Trent Water
		NFM	Perth	Tayside Construction
		NFM	Perth	Tayside Water Board
85.3950	75.5950	NFM	Germany	Emergency Channel Ch 416
85.4000	71.9000	NFM	Hounslow	Council (162.2Hz)
		NFM	Somerset	Tarmac Topmix
		NFM	Yorkshire	Water Board
		NFM	Kent	Kent Water
		NFM	London	Hounslow CTCSS
		NFM	Perth	Tayside Water Board
		NFM	Sheffield	Council (162.2Hz)

Base	Mobile	Mode	Location	User and Notes
85.4125	71.9125	NFM	Brighton	Southern Water (Drainage)
		AM	Caernarfon	Welsh Water
		NFM	Manchester	PMR
		NFM	Stoke-on-Trent	Water Board
		AM	Manningtree	Water Board
		AM	Tendring Hundreds	Water Board
		NFM	West Sussex	Water Board
		NFM	Ipswich	Anglia Water
		NFM	Perth	Tayside Water Board (PerWat)
		NFM	West Midlands	Midland Water
		NFM	Wye	Welsh Water Channel 33
85.4150	75.6150	NFM	Germany	Emergency Channel Ch 417
85.4250	71.9250	NFM	Guernsey	Fire Service
		NFM	Wales	Council Repeater
		NFM	Ipswich	Community Repeater
		NFM	Kent	Council (162.2Hz)
		NFM	Tayside	Tayside Water Board
85.4350	75.6350	NFM	Germany	Emergency Channel Ch 418
85.4375	71.9375	NFM	Alford	Roads Department
		AM	Scunthorpe	Water Board
		NFM	Leeds	Roadworks
		NFM	Merseyside	PMR
		NFM	Cornwall	South West Water
		NFM	Eastbourne	Eastbourne Water
		NFM	Gloucestershire	Cotswolds Water
		NFM	Gowerton	Welsh Water
		NFM	Lea Valley	Southern Water
		NFM	Surrey	Thames Water
85.4500	71.9500	AM	Bedford	Bedford Sewage
		NFM	North-West	PMR
		NFM	Cumnock	SRC Local Council Services
		NFM	Gwynedd	Welsh Water
		NFM	Kent	Kent Water
		NFM	Minehead	Somerset Water
		NFM	Norfolk	Anglia Water
		NFM	Pitcaple	Roads Department
		NFM	Suffolk	Anglia Water
		NFM	Swansea	Dyfed Council
		NFM	Newport	Council Ch 3
85.4550	75.6550	NFM	Germany	Emergency Channel Ch 419
85.4625	71.9625	AM	Ayr	Water Board
		NFM	Barrow	PMR
		NFM	Avon	Severn Trent Water
		NFM	Haverfordwest	Welsh Water
		NFM	Manchester	North West Water
		NFM	Norfolk	Anglia Water
		NFM	Suffolk	Anglia Water
		NFM	West Sussex	Southern Water Ch 3

Base	Mobile	Mode	Location	User and Notes
85.4750	71.9750	NFM	Broadstairs	Chauffeur Service
		NFM	Gatwick	Capital Coaches
		NFM	Grampian	Transport
		NFM	Germany	Emergency Channel Ch 420
		NFM	Bristol	Automobile Association
		NFM	Hastings	Hastings Water
		NFM	Kings Lynn	Dow Chemicals
85.4875	71.9875	AM	Dumfries	Automobile Association
		NFM	London	Automobile Association
		NFM	Nationwide	Automobile Association Ch. 6
85.4950	75.6950	NFM	Germany	Emergency Channel Ch 421
05.5000	72.0000	NFM	Cardiff	Automobile Association
		NFM	London	Automobile Association
		NFM	Midlands	Automobile Association
		NFM	Nationwide	Automobile Association Ch. 2
		NFM	Nottingham	Automobile Association
85.5125	72.0125	NFM	Brim	Automobile Association
		NFM	Ipswich	Automobile Association
		NFM	London	Automobile Association
		NFM	Nationwide	Automobile Association Ch. 4
		NFM	Perth	Automobile Association
85.5150	75.7150	NFM	Germany	Emergency Channel Ch 422
85.5250	72.0250	NFM	Aberdeen	Automobile Association
		NFM	Belfast	AA Channel 1
		NFM	Anglia	Automobile Association
		NFM	Glasgow	Automobile Association
		NFM	Guernsey	Automobile Association
		NFM	London	Automobile Association
		NFM	Nationwide	Automobile Association Ch. 1
		NFM	Perth	Automobile Association
		NFM	West Midlands	Automobile Association
85.5350	75.7350	NFM	Germany	Emergency Channel Ch 423
85.5375	72.0375	NFM	Brighton	Automobile Association
		NFM	Blackpool	Council Beach Patrol
		NFM	Milton Keynes	AA
		NFM	Exeter	Automobile Association
		NFM	London	Automobile Association
		NFM	Nationwide	Automobile Association Ch. 5
		NFM	Oakhampton	Automobile Association
		NFM	Perth	Automobile Association
85.5500	72.0500	NFM	Aberdeen	Automobile Association
		NFM	Bristol	Automobile Association
		NFM	Ipswich	Automobile Association
		NFM	London	Automobile Association
		NFM	Nationwide	Automobile Association Ch. 3
		NFM	Norwich	Automobile Association
85.5550	75.7550	NFM	Germany	Emergency Channel Ch 424
85.5625	72.0625	NFM	Edinburgh	Automobile Association

Base	Mobile	Mode	Location	User and Notes
		NFM	Guernsey	Water Board
		NFM	Ipswich	Automobile Association
		NFM	Liverpool	Automobile Association
		NFM	London	Automobile Association
		NFM	Nationwide	Automobile Association Ch. 7
		NFM	Perth	Automobile Association
85.5750	75.7750	NFM	Germany	Emergency Channel Ch 425
85.5750	72.0750	NFM	Belfast	NI Electricity Service
		NFM	Jersey	Jersey Electricity Company Ch 1
		NFM	Thames Valley	Thames Water Ch 3
85.5875	72.0875	AM	Cumbria	Automobile Association
		AM	Lancashire	Automobile Association
		NFM	Ipswich	Automobile Association
		NFM	London	Automobile Association
		NFM	Nationwide	Automobile Association Ch. 8
		NFM	Perth	Automobile Association Data
85.5950	75.7950	NFM	Germany	Emergency Channel Ch 426
85.6000	72.1000	NFM	Belfast	NI Electricity Service
		NFM	Exeter	Council
		NFM	Forest Heath	Council
		NFM	Scarborough	Council
		NFM	Blackpool	Council Parks
		NFM	Jersey	Civil Defence Link to France
		NFM	Norfolk	Royal Automobile Club
		NFM	Suffolk	Royal Automobile Club
85.6125	72.1125	NFM	Humberside	Community Repeater
		NFM	London	Concord Ltd
		NFM	Poole	Poole Adventure Centre
85.6150	75.8150	NFM	Germany	Emergency Channel Ch 427
85.6250	72.1250	NFM	Bath	Silversails Taxis
		NFM	Uxbridge	Cabline
		NFM	Abbotts Ripton	Fellows Estate
		NFM	Colchester	J. Collie Ltd
		NFM	London	Battersea Cars
		NFM	London	Globe Bikes
		NFM	London	Haden Carriers
		NFM	Norfolk	Automobile Association
		NFM	Suffolk	Automobile Association
85.6350	75.8350	NFM	Germany	Emergency Channel Ch 428
85.6375	72.1875	NFM	Exeter	TNT
		NFM	Aberdeen	Taxi
		NFM	Guernsey	Fruit Export
		NFM	Solent	Solent Waters Rescue
85.6500	72.1500	AM	Altricham	Trafftax
		AM	Portsmouth	Taxis
		NFM	Ealing	Trade Centre Ch 1
		NFM	Jersey	Civil Defence Link to France
		NFM	London	Chequers Transport

Base	Mobile	Mode	Location	User and Notes
		NFM	London	Riva Communications Ltd
		NFM	Norfolk	Royal Automobile Club
		NFM	St Ives	Tyrell Contractors
		NFM	Suffolk	Royal Automobile Club
85.6550	75.8550	NFM	Germany	Emergency Channel Ch 429
85.6625	72.1625	NFM	Lochaber	Caledonian Canal
		NFM	Maidenhead	U-Want Taxis
		NFM	Maidenhead	Valley Taxis
		NFM	London	Westland Market Tower
		NFM	London	Wide Fulham
		NFM	London	Anderson Young Ltd
		NFM	Norfolk	M. Crouch Ltd
		NFM	Suffolk	M. Crouch Ltd
85.6750	75.8750	NFM	Germany	Emergency Channel Ch 430
85.6750	72.1750	AM	Colchester	Eastern Tractors
		NFM	Milton Keynes	Harper Cars
		NFM	Chatteris	Allpress Farms
		NFM	Walsall Wood	Claridge TV & Radio
		NFM	Aberdeen	Taxi
		NFM	Colchester	Eastern Tractors
		NFM	Jersey	LuxiCabs Ch 1
		NFM	London	Petchey & Velite Cars
		NFM	Norfolk	Hughes TV Servicing
		NFM	Suffolk	Hughes TV Servicing
		NFM	Brighton	Streamline Taxis
		NFM	Thetford	Lloyd & Marriot Vets
85.6875	72.1875	NFM	Exeter	TNT Carriers
		NFM	Milton Keynes	Skyline Taxis
		NFM	Slough	Castle Radio Cars
		NFM	London	Belsize Ltd
		NFM	Norfolk	Royal Automobile Club
		NFM	Suffolk	Royal Automobile Club
		NFM	Wishaw	Myles Taxis
85.6950	75.8950	NFM	Germany	Emergency Channel Ch 431
85.7000	72.2000	NFM	Grimsby	Stoneledge Haulage
		AM	Hull	Redune Taxis
		NFM	London	Echo Cars
		NFM	Scarborough	R&C Company
		NFM	Aberdeen	Shanks Transport
85.7125	72.2125	NFM	West Mersea	Grey
		NFM	London	AA M25 Recovery
		NFM	London	Summit Cars
		NFM	Nationwide	Curry's Master Care
85.7150	75.9150	NFM	Germany	Emergency Channel Ch 432
85.7250	72.2250	NFM	Ipswich	RAC Motor Recovery
		NFM	Nationwide	Sitaclear Technology Ltd
		NFM	Weasenham	Farms (94.8Hz)
		NFM	Bedford	Carlow Radio

Base	Mobile	Mode	Location	User and Notes
		NFM	Brighton	Rediffusion
		NFM	London	Ascot & Bracknell
		NFM	Norfolk	AA A12 Recovery
		NFM	Shrewsbury	Taxis
		NFM	Suffolk	AA Recovery (A12)
85.7350	75.9350	NFM	Germany	Emergency Channel Ch 433
85.7375	72.2375	NFM	Colchester	Fieldspray Ltd
		AM	St Austell	Haul-U-Waste
		NFM	North Yorkshire	Taxis
		NFM	Dundee	Deliveries
		NFM	Edinburgh	Garage
		NFM	Glasgow	Plant Hire
		NFM	London	Swift & Safe
85.7500	72.2500	NFM	A55	Automobile Association
		NFM	Manchester	Taxi
		NFM	Royton	Borough Taxis
		NFM	Guernsey	Warry's Bakery
		NFM	Hitchin	Rorall Taxis
		NFM	Lakenheath	Trevor Cobbold
		NFM	London	American Cars
		NFM	London	Putney Cars
		NFM	Oldham	Taxis
85.7550	75.9550	NFM	Germany	Emergency Channel Ch 434
85.7625	72.2625	NFM	Culzean	NTS Rangers
		NFM	Jersey	Regent Radio
		NFM	Aberdeen	Port Maintenence
		NFM	Cambridge	Plant Growing Institute
		NFM	London	Galaxy Cars
		NFM	Long Stratton	C.P.S Fuels
		NFM	Norfolk	Automobile Association
		NFM	Suffolk	Automobile Association
85.7750	72.2750	NFM	Alloa	Taxi
		AM	Levenshulme	Premier Cars
		NFM	Leigh-on-Sea	Taxis
		NFM	Manchester	Premier Taxis
		NFM	Manchester	Wheelclampers
		NFM	Slough	Scorpio Radio Cars
		NFM	Warrington	Wheel Clampers
		AM	Perth	Taxi
		NFM	Blackpool	Red Cabs
		NFM	Guernsey	Le Pelley Taxi
		NFM	London	Allways Ltd
		NFM	Norfolk	Automobile Association
		NFM	Norwich	R.C. Snelling
		NFM	Oxford	LuxiCabs
		NFM	Sheffield	Hargreaves Clearwaste Co.
		NFM	Stoke on Trent	Lucky Seven Taxis
		NFM	Suffolk	Automobile Association

Base	Mobile	Mode	Location	User and Notes
		NFM	Warrington	Wheel Clampers
85.7750	75.9750	NFM	Germany	Emergency Channel Ch 435
85.7875	72.2875	NFM	Edinburgh	Taxi
		NFM	Nationwide	Automobile Association Ch. 9
		NFM	Ipswich	Automobile Association
		NFM	London	Automobile Association
		NFM	Brighton	Automobile Association
85.7950	75.9950	NFM	Germany	Emergency Channel Ch 436
85.8000	72.3000	NFM	Anglia	Parcline Ltd
		NFM	Hull	Security Express
		NFM	Cardiff	Cardiff Garage Services
		NFM	Guilford	RAC
		NFM	Aberdeen	City Council
		NFM	Nationwide	Express Security Vans
		NFM	Nationwide	Parceline Ltd
		NFM	Plymouth	City Council Cleansing Dept
		NFM	Brighton	Express Security Vans
		NFM	Surrey	Automobile Association
85.8125	72.3125	NFM	Aberdeen	Taxi
		NFM	Nationwide	DTI Channel L0065
		NFM	Haverfordwest	Vet Service
85.8150	76.0150	NFM	Germany	Emergency Channel Ch 437
85.8250		NFM	Guernsey	Huelin
		NFM	Southampton	Taxis
		NFM	Letchwood	Joe's Taxis
		NFM	London	Kwik Cars
		NFM	Norwich	Beeline Taxis
		NFM	Soham	P. Lyon
		NFM	Cornwall	Pye Transport
85.8350	76.0350	NFM	Germany	Emergency Channel Ch 438
85.8375	72.3375	AM	St Austell	Haul-U-Waste
		NFM	Blantyre	Ariel & Art Cabs
		NFM	Guernsey	Falles Hire Cars
		NFM	Jersey	Ideal Cars Channel 1
		NFM	Jersey	Rank Taxis Channel 3
		NFM	Littleport	J.C. Rains Ltd
		NFM	London	Belsize Ltd
		NFM	London	Courier 83 Ltd
		NFM	Luton	James Early Ltd
		NFM	Cornwall	English China Clay
85.8500	72.3500	NFM	Kirkby	Taxis
		NFM	Skelmersdale	Taxi
		NFM	Tyneside	Taxis
		NFM	Widnes	Taxis
		NFM	Wigan	Taxi
		NFM	Newtown	Taxis
		NFM	Widnes	Taxis
		NFM	Cornwall	English China Clay

Base	Mobile	Mode	Location	User and Notes
		NFM	Nationwide	Philips Transport Scheme
		NFM	Nationwide	Pye Telecom Channel 2
85.8550	76.0550	NFM	Germany	Emergency Channel Ch 439
85.8625	72.3625	NFM	Lanarkshire	Doctor Deputy Service
		NFM	Guernsey	J.H. Mahy & Sons Ltd
		NFM	London	Fisher Sylvester Ltd
		NFM	London	G & R Tyres
		NFM	London	Pronto Cars
85.8750	76.0750	NFM	Germany	Emergency Channel Ch 440
85.8750	72.3750	NFM	Nationwide	DTI 28 Day Hire
		NFM	Nationwide	Pye Telecom Channel 1
85.8875	72.3875	NFM	Aylsham	Aylsham Produce
		NFM	Burnley	Delta Cabs
		NFM	Neath	Car Rallying
85.8875	72.3875	NFM	Blackpool	Tower Taxis
		AM	Perth	Tay Transport
		NFM	Burnley	Taxis
		NFM	Diss	East Coast Grain
		NFM	London	Teleportation Ltd
		NFM	Norfolk	East Coast Grain
		NFM	Suffolk	Aylsham Produce
85.8950	76.0950	NFM	Germany	Emergency Channel Ch 441
85.9000	71.4000	NFM	Burnley	Delta Cabs
		NFM	Newcastle	Taxis
		AM	Jersey	Rank Taxis
		NFM	Cambridge	John's of Cambridge
		NFM	Diss	G.W. Padley
		NFM	Edinburgh	TV Repairs
		NFM	Jersey	Rank Taxis
		NFM	London	Sensechoice
		NFM	Spalding	Glen Heat and Irrigation
		AM	Kettering	Headlands Taxis
85.9125	72.4125	NFM	Aberdeen	Breakdown Services
		NFM	Brigg	Gallowswood Recovery Service
		NFM	Edinburgh	TV Repairs
		NFM	Ipswich	Taxi
		NFM	London	Anglo Spanish
		NFM	London	Arrival Couriers
		NFM	London	Central Motors
		NFM	London	K Cars
		NFM	Perth	Local Deliveries
		NFM	Perth	Tay Breakdown Service
85.9150	76.1150	NFM	Germany	Emergency Channel Ch 442
85.9250	72.4250	NFM	Blackpool	Radio Cabs
		NFM	Birmingham	Star Cars
		NFM	Jersey	LuxiCabs Ch 2
		NFM	London	Laurie Buxton
		NFM	London	Town & Country

Base	Mobile	Mode	Location	User and Notes
85.9350	76.1350	NFM	Germany	Emergency Channel Ch 443
85.9375	72.4375	NFM	Bury	Moorside Taxis
		NFM	Kent	Porlant Car Hire
		NFM	London	Action Cars
85.9500	72.4500	AM	Chichester	Taxi
		NFM	Leigh-on-Sea	Taxis
		NFM	Guernsey	Crossways Agricultural
		NFM	London	Action Cars
		NFM	London	Galaxy Bikes
		NFM	London	Super Express
85.9550	76.1550	NFM	Germany	Emergency Channel Ch 444
85.9625	72.4625	NFM	Great Massingham	Gilman Ltd
		NFM	London	Globe Cars
		NFM	Norfolk	Don Robin Farms
85.9750	76.1750	NFM	Germany	Emergency Channel Ch 445
		NFM	Hamilton	Bridge Cars
		AM	Leeds	Amber Cars
		NFM	Guernsey	Stan Brouard Ltd
		NFM	Nationwide	Tarmac Roadstone
		NFM	Norfolk	Stanway Taxis
		NFM	Suffolk	Stanway Taxis
		NFM	Sutton	Darby Plant
		NFM	Woodbridge	Wm Kerr Farms (103.5Hz)
85.9875	72.4875	NFM	London	Avery Cars
		NFM	London	City & Suburban
		NFM	London	Commutercars
		NFM	London	Parkward Ltd
		NFM	London	Southampton Way Cars
		NFM	Jersey	Fetch & Carry
		NFM	St. Neots	Eyrsbury Plant Hire
85.9950	76.1950	NFM	Germany	Emergency Channel Ch 446
86.0000	72.5000	NFM	Nationwide	Community Repeater
		NFM	Aberdeen	Rig Maintenence
		NFM	London	Kilburn Cars
		NFM	London	Windmill Cars
86.0125	72.5125	NFM	Jersey	Blue Coaches
		NFM	Milton Keynes	Washing Machine Repairs
		NFM	York	Hotpoint
		NFM	Leeds	Automobile Association
		NFM	Leeds	Hotpoint
86.0150	76.2150	NFM	Germany	Emergency Channel Ch 447
86.0250	72.5250	AM	Ayr	Scottish Ambulance Service
		AM	Haddington	Scottish Ambulance Service
		AM	Nationwide	Scottish Ambulance Ch L82
		NFM	Bedfordshire	Bedford Social Services
		NFM	Humberside	Community Repeater
		NFM	Spay Valley	Scottish Ambulance
86.0350	76.2350	NFM	Germany	Emergency Channel Ch 448

Base	Mobile	Mode	Location	User and Notes
86.0375	72.5375	AM	Barhead	Scottish Ambulance Service
		AM	Dundee	Scottish Ambulance
		AM	Glasgow	Scottish Ambulance
		AM	Guernsey	Public Works
		AM	Lincolnshire	Community Repeater
		AM	London	Medicall
		AM	Nationwide	Scottish Ambulance Ch L83
		AM	Nationwide	St Johns Private Ambulance
86.0500	72.5500	AM	Nationwide	Scottish Ambulance Ch L84
		NFM	Peterborough	CBS Repeater
		NFM	Southampton	Taxis
		AM	Elgin	Scottish Ambulance Ch L84
		AM	Fort Augustus	Scottish Ambulance Ch L84
		NFM	Lincolnshire	Comunity Repeater
		NFM	London	Medicall
86.0550	76.2550	NFM	Germany	Emergency Channel Ch 449
86.0625	72.5625	AM	Nationwide	Scottish Ambulance Ch. L85
		NFM	Anglesey	Yns Mon Council
		NFM	Gt. Ashfield	G. Miles
		NFM	Norfolk	Sandringham Estate
86.0750	72.5750	AM	Aberdeen	Scottish Ambulance
		AM	Dumfries and Galloway	Scottish Ambulance Service
		AM	Edinburgh	Scottish Ambulance Service
		AM	Inverness	Scottish Ambulance
		AM	Nationwide	Community Repeater
		AM	Nationwide	Scottish Ambulance Ch.L86
86.0750	76.0750	NFM	Wiltshire	Water Board Ch 1
86.0750	76.2750	NFM	Germany	Emergency Channel Ch 450
86.0750	77.6750	NFM	Netherlands	Police Ch 804
86.0875	77.6875	NFM	Netherlands	Police Ch 805
86.0875	72.5875	AM	Nationwide	Scottish Ambulance Ch. L87
		AM	Braemar	Scottish Ambulance
		AM	Edinburgh	Scottish Ambulance Service
		NFM	Norfolk	Cabban Breeze
		NFM	Norfolk	Douglas Framlingham
86.0950	76.2950	NFM	Germany	Emergency Channel Ch 451
86.1000	77.7000	NFM	Netherlands	Police Ch 806
86.1000	72.6000	AM	Motherwell	Scottish Ambulance
		NFM	Hadleigh	Lemon & Sutherland
		AM	Nationwide	Scottish Ambulance Ch. L88
		NFM	Hadleigh	Lemon & Sutherland
		NFM	Newmarket	PMR
86.1125	77.7125	NFM	Netherlands	Police Ch 807
		NFM	Humberside	Tyre Co.
		AM	Dumfermline	Scottish Ambulance
		AM	Lincolnshire	Community Repeater
		AM	Nationwide	Scottish Ambulance Ch. L89
86.1150	76.3150	NFM	Germany	Emergency Channel Ch 452

Base	Mobile	Mode	Location	User and Notes
86.1250	72.6250	AM	Airdrie	Scottish Ambulance Service
		NFM	Cheshire	Courier Service
		NFM	Edinburgh	Ambulance Service
		AM	Coatbridge	Scottish Ambulance Service
		AM	Dumfries and Galloway	Scottish Ambulance Service
		AM	Edinburgh	Scottish Ambulance Service
		AM	Kilmarnock	Scottish Ambulance Service
		AM	Nationwide	Scottish Ambulance Ch. L90
		NFM	Guernsey	Guernsey Telecoms
		NFM	Norfolk	E.P.H. Radio Repeater
		NFM	Sheffield	Community Repeater
		NFM	Cardiff	F.W. Morgan Builders
86.1250	77.7250	NFM	Netherlands	Police Ch 808
86.1350	76.3350	NFM	Germany	Emergency Channel Ch 453
86.1375	77.7375	NFM	Netherlands	Police Ch 809
86.1375	72.6375	AM	Jersey	De Gruchy Vets
		AM	Perth	Scottish Ambulance
		NFM	Mid Wales	British Waterways
		NFM	Norfolk	Storno Radio Telephone Co
		NFM	Suffolk	Storno Radio Telephone Co
86.1500	77.7500	NFM	Netherlands	Police Ch 810
86.1500	72.6500	AM	Nationwide	Scottish Ambulance Ch. L91
86.1550	76.3550	NFM	Germany	Emergency Channel Ch 454
86.1625	77.7625	NFM	Netherlands	Police Ch 811
86.1625	72.6625	AM	Glasgow	Scottish Ambulance
		AM	Kent	County Council
		AM	Lancashire	Regional Health Ambulance
		AM	Nationwide	Car Radio Telephone Hire
		AM	Nationwide	Scottish Ambulance Ch. L92
		AM	Powys	Welsh Water
		AM	Radnor	County Council
		NFM	Nationwide	Radiofone Channel
86.1750	76.3750	NFM	Germany	Emergency Channel Ch 455
86.1750	77.7750	NFM	Netherlands	Police Ch 812
86.1750	72.6750	NFM	Newmarket	PMR
		NFM	Belfast	NI Electricity Service
		NFM	Norfolk	Ipswich Transport Ltd
		NFM	Suffolk	Ipswich Transport Ltd
86.1875	77.7875	NFM	Netherlands	Police Ch 813
86.1875	72.6875	AM	Falkirk	Scottish Ambulance
		AM	Nationwide	Scottish Ambulance Ch.L93
		NFM	Nationwide	Automobile Assoc. Channel 10
86.1950	76.3950	NFM	Germany	Emergency Channel Ch 456
86.2000	77.8000	NFM	Netherlands	Police Ch 814
86.2000	72.7000	NFM	Bristol	Automobile Assoc. Channel 11
		NFM	Oban	Ambulances
		NFM	Ipswich	Automobile Assoc. Channel 11
		NFM	Nationwide	Automobile Assoc. Channel 11

Base	Mobile	Mode	Location	User and Notes
86.2125	77.8125	NFM	Netherlands	Police Ch 815
86.2125	72.7125	NFM	East Sussex	County Council
		NFM	London	Enterprise Ltd
		NFM	Norfolk	William Cory Heating
		NFN	Needham Market	Quinton Skip Hire
86.2150	76.4150	NFM	Germany	Emergency Channel Ch 457
86.2250	77.8250	NFM	Netherlands	Police Ch 816
86.2250	72.7250	NFM	Burnley	Breakdown Recovery
		NFM	Belfast	NI Electricity Service
		NFM	Carnforth	PMR
		NFM	Ipswich	Doctors on Call
		NFM	Scunthorpe	Humberside Highways
		NFM	Peterborough	Watchdog
		NFM	Portsmouth	Taxi
		NFM	Ipswich	Doctor's Night Call
		NFM	Norfolk	Ipswich Transport Ltd
		NFM	Perth	Amtrac Delivery Service
		NFM	Suffolk	Ipswich Transport Ltd
86.2350	76.4350	NFM	Germany	Emergency Channel Ch 458
86.2375	77.8375	NFM	Netherlands	Police Ch 817
86.2375	72.7375	NFM	Ipswich	Deliveries
		NFM	Armagh	Road Construction
		NFM	Perth	Deliveries
		NFM	Great Yarmouth	Container Depot
		NFM	Great Oakley	Oakley Skip Hire
		NFM	Kettering	Farmers
86.2500	77.8500	NFM	Netherlands	Police Ch 818
86.2500	72.7500	NFM	East Sussex	County Council
		NFM	Hull	Hotpoint
		NFM	Aberdeen	Snowploughs
		NFM	Nationwide	Hotpoint Channel 1
86.2550	76.4550	NFM	Germany	Emergency Channel Ch 459
86.2625	77.8625	NFM	Netherlands	Police Ch 819
86.2625	72.7625	NFM	Grampian	Taxis
		AM	Aberdeen	Council
		AM	Humberside	Council
		AM	Nationwide	Hotpoint Channel 2
86.2750	72.7750	NFM	Bournemouth	Cryston Comms
		NFM	Belfast	NI Electricity Service
		NFM	Dumfries	Council
		NFM	East Sussex	Wealdon (162.2Hz)
		NFM	Humber	Cryston Comms
		NFM	Leeds	Cryston Comms
		NFM	Nationwide	Cryston Communications
86.2750	76.4750	NFM	Germany	Emergency Channel Ch 460
86.2750	77.8750	NFM	Netherlands	Police Ch 820
86.2875	77.8875	NFM	Netherlands	Police Ch 821
86.2875	72.7875	NFM	Great Yarmouth	Container Depot

Base	Mobile	Mode	Location	User and Notes
		NFM	Leeds	RSPCA
		NFM	Wilmston	Vets
		NFM	Ipswich	RSPCA
		NFM	Perth	Tayside Water Board
86.2950	76.4950	NFM	Germany	Emergency Channel Ch 461
86.3000 - 86.7000 MHz			**PMR Low Band 12.5 kHz**	
86.3000	72.8000	NFM	East Sussex	County Council
86.3000	76.8000	NFM	Nationwide	Vibroplant Plc
86.3000	77.9000	NFM	Netherlands	Police Ch 822
86.3000	86.3000	NFM	Nationwide	IBA Aerial Riggers
86.3125	77.9125	NFM	Netherlands	Police Ch 823
86.3125	86.3125	AM	Nationwide	Park Ranger Service Ch 2
		AM	Nationwide	St Johns Ambulance Channel 1
		NFM	North Yorkshire Moors	Rangers
		NFM	Nationwide	Mountain Rescue Channel 1
86.3150	76.5150	NFM	Germany	Emergency Channel Ch 462
86.3250	77.9250	NFM	Netherlands	Police Ch 824
86.3250	86.3250	NFM	Nationwide	Mountain Rescue Reserve
		AM	Blackpool	Gino's Pizza Deliveries
		NFM	Nationwide	National Parks Ch 2
86.3350	76.5350	NFM	Germany	Emergency Channel Ch 463
86.3375	77.9375	NFM	Netherlands	Police Ch 825
86.3375	86.3375	NFM	Cumbria	Lakes Mountain Rescue Ch. 2
		NFM	Norwich	Sir Robin Lee
86.3500	77.9500	NFM	Netherlands	Police Ch 826
86.3500	86.3500	AM	Nationwide	St Johns Ambulance Channel 3
86.3500	86.3500	NFM	Cairngorm	Ski Lifts
		NFM	Cumbria	Lakes Mountain Rescue Ch. 3
		NFM	Jersey	D. E. Payn Electrics
		NFM	Jersey	TV Aerial Erectors
		NFM	Nationwide	Mountain Rescue Channel 3
		NFM	Sutherland	Seafield Estate Gamekeepers
		NFM	Nationwide	Red Cross
		NFM	Scotland	The Scottish Office
86.3550	76.5550	NFM	Germany	Emergency Channel Ch 464
86.3625	77.9625	NFM	Netherlands	Police Ch 827
86.3625	86.3625	NFM	Nationwide	Boy Scouts Channel 1
86.3750	76.5750	NFM	Germany	Emergency Channel Ch 465
86.3750	77.9750	NFM	Netherlands	Police Ch 828
86.3750	86.3750	NFM	Jersey	Jersey Building Firm
		NFM	Nationwide	REACT CB Emergency
		NFM	Scotland	The Scottish Office
		NFM	Wakefield	Stamnley Royal Hospital
86.3875	77.9875	NFM	Netherlands	Police Ch 829
86.3875	86.3875	NFM	France	Nuclear Alert Frequency
		NFM	Nationwide	National Parks Ch 1
86.3950	76.5950	NFM	Germany	Emergency Channel Ch 466

Base	Mobile	Mode	Location	User and Notes
86.4000	78.0000	NFM	Netherlands	Police Ch 830
86.4000	86.4000	NFM	Nationwide	National Park Rangers
		NFM	Yorkshire	Yorkshire Dales Warden
		NFM	Felixstowe	Docks
		NFM	North Yorkshire Moors	Rangers
86.4125	78.0125	NFM	Netherlands	Police Ch 831
86.4125	86.4125	AM	Nationwide	St Johns Ambulance Channel 2
		NFM	Berkshire	Council Ch 3
		NFM	Nationwide	Mountain Rescue Channel 2
		NFM	Nationwide	Peak National Parks
86.4150	76.6150	NFM	Germany	Emergency Channel Ch 467
86.4250	78.0250	NFM	Netherlands	Police Ch 832
86.4250	86.4250	NFM	Nationwide	Forestry Commission Channel 3
		NFM	Ettrick & Lauderdale	District Council
86.4350	76.6350	NFM	Germany	Emergency Channel Ch 468
86.4375	78.0375	NFM	Netherlands	Police Ch 833
86.4375	86.4375	NFM	Jersey	Jersey Rally Control
		NFM	Isle of Man	Tudor Manx Rally
		NFM	Nationwide	RAC Rally Medical/Safety
86.4500	78.0500	NFM	Netherlands	Police Ch 834
86.4500	86.4500	NFM	Avon	Severn Trent Water
		AM	Blackpool	Private Ambulance
		NFM	Nationwide	Forestry Commission Channel 2
		NFM	Nationwide	Wimpey Construction Ch. 1
86.4550	76.6550	NFM	Germany	Emergency Channel Ch 469
86.4625	78.0625	NFM	Netherlands	Police Ch 835
86.4625	86.4625	NFM	Nationwide	Local Authority Common
86.4750	76.6750	NFM	Germany	Emergency Channel Ch 470
86.4750	78.0750	NFM	Netherlands	Police Ch 836
86.4750	86.4750	NFM	Linton	T.B. Fairy
		NFM	Cheshire	Gallifords Civil Engineers
		NFM	Jersey	Public Health Ambulance
		NFM	Yorkshire	British Rail
		NFM	Nationwide	BR Incidents
		NFM	Nationwide	British Rail Incidents
		NFM	Nationwide	Forestry Commission Channel 1
86.4875	78.0875	NFM	Netherlands	Police Ch 837
86.4950	76.6950	NFM	Germany	Emergency Channel Ch 471
86.5000	72.5000	NFM	Swindon	Radio Taxis
86.5000	78.1000	NFM	Netherlands	Police Ch 838
86.5000	86.5000	NFM	Luton Airport	McAlpine Aviation
		NFM	Nationwide	BNFL Nuclear Incident Ch 1
		NFM	Nationwide	CEGB Nuclear Incidents Ch. 1
		NFM	Nationwide	IBA Aerial Riggers
		NFM	Suffolk	Suffolk County Council
86.5125	78.1125	NFM	Netherlands	Police Ch 839
86.5125	86.5125	NFM	Guernsey	St John Ambulance Link
86.5150	76.7150	NFM	Germany	Emergency Channel Ch 472

Base	Mobile	Mode	Location	User and Notes
86.5250	73.1250	NFM	Netherlands	Police Ch 840
86.5250	86.5250	NFM	Nationwide	BBC O/B Riggers
		NFM	Nationwide	BNFL Nuclear Incident Ch 2
		NFM	Nationwide	CEGB Nuclear Incidents Ch. 2
		NFM	Dunstable	Taleds Motors Co
		NFM	Enfield	Weston Ltd
86.5350	76.7350	NFM	Germany	Emergency Channel Ch 473
86.5375	78.1375	NFM	Netherlands	Police Ch 841
86.5375	86.5375	NFM	Derbyshire	Middleton Top Rangers
		NFM	North-West	PMR
86.5500	78.1500	NFM	Netherlands	Police Ch 842
86.5500	86.5500	NFM	Guernsey	Cobo Surgery
		NFM	Nationwide	BNFL Nuclear Incident Ch.I 3
		NFM	Nationwide	CEGB Nuclear Incidents Ch. 3
86.5550	76.7550	NFM	Germany	Emergency Channel Ch 474
86.5625	78.1625	NFM	Netherlands	Police Ch 843
86.5625	86.5625	NFM	Aberdeen	Robert Gordon Univ. of Tech
		NFM	Nationwide	DHL International
86.5750	76.7750	NFM	Germany	Emergency Channel Ch 475
86.5750	78.1750	NFM	Netherlands	Police Ch 844
86.5750	86.5750	NFM	Nationwide	CEGB Mine Rescue
86.5875	78.1875	NFM	Netherlands	Police Ch 845
86.5950	76.7950	NFM	Germany	Emergency Channel Ch 476
86.6000	78.2000	NFM	Netherlands	Police Ch 846
86.6125	78.2125	NFM	Netherlands	Police Ch 847
86.6150	76.8150	NFM	Germany	Emergency Channel Ch 477
86.6250	78.2250	NFM	Netherlands	Police Ch 848
86.6250	86.6250	NFM	Nationwide	Boy Scouts Channel 2
		NFM	Nationwide	Wimpey Construction Ch. 2
		AM	Sheffield	Council Repairs
		NFM	RAF Marham	Wimpey Construction Ch. 2
86.6350	76.8350	NFM	Germany	Emergency Channel Ch 478
86.6375	78.2375	NFM	Netherlands	Police Ch 849
86.6375	86.6375	NFM	Bedford	RSPB
		NFM	Jersey	Telefitters
		NFM	Nationwide	Wimpey Construction Ch. 3
		NFM	RAF Marham	Wimpey Construction Ch. 3
86.6500	78.2500	NFM	Netherlands	Police Ch 850
86.6550	76.8550	NFM	Germany	Emergency Channel Ch 479
86.6625		NFM	Nationwide	Vickers Sesimic Surveys
86.6625	78.2625	NFM	Netherlands	Police Ch 851
86.6750	76.6750	NFM	Jersey	Dinard Emergency Link
86.6750	76.8750	NFM	Germany	Emergency Channel Ch 480
86.6750	78.2750	NFM	Netherlands	Police Ch 852
86.6750	86.6750	NFM	Nationwide	UKAEA Radiation Survey
86.6875	78.2875	NFM	Netherlands	Police Ch 853
86.6950	76.8950	NFM	Germany	Emergency Channel Ch 481
86.7000	78.3000	NFM	Netherlands	Police Ch 854

Base	Mobile	Mode	Location	User and Notes
86.7000	86.7000	NFM	Nationwide	AA Emergency
		NFM	Nationwide	UK Emergency Channel 999
		NFM	Nationwide	UKAEA Health Physics
		NFM	Dungeness	Power Station
86.7125 - 87.5000 MHz		**PMR Low Band Base Duplex (Mobiles - 10.5 MHz)**		
86.7125	76.7125	NFM	Nationwide	HM Customs & Excise Ch 1
86.7125	78.3125	NFM	Netherlands	Police Ch 855
86.7150	76.9150	NFM	Germany	Emergency Channel Ch 482
86.7250	78.3250	NFM	Netherlands	Police Ch 856
86.7250	76.2250	NFM	North Tayside	Tayside Water Board (AmWat)
		NFM	Swansea Docks	HM Customs
		NFM	Nationwide	HM Customs & Excise Ch 2
86.7350	76.9350	NFM	Germany	Emergency Channel Ch 483
86.7375	76.7375	NFM	Ipswich	Repeater
		NFM	London	HM Customs Drugs Squad
		NFM	Nationwide	HM Customs & Excise Ch 9
86.7375	78.3375	NFM	Netherlands	Police Ch 857
86.7500	76.2500	NFM	Burnley	Plant Hire
		NFM	Hornsea	East Coast Caravan Security
		NFM	Lowestoft	Hughes TV Rentals
		NFM	Cwnbran	Gwent Council Ch 8
86.7500	78.3500	NFM	Netherlands	Police Ch 858
86.7550	76.9550	NFM	Germany	Emergency Channel Ch 484
86.7625	78.3625	NFM	Netherlands	Police Ch 859
86.7625	76.7625	NFM	Ipswich	Traffic
		NFM	Saddleworth	PMR
		NFM	Suffolk	Traffic
		NFM	Wrenthan	Traffic
		NFM	Tayside	Community Repeater
86.7750	76.2750	NFM	Merseyside	Plant Hire Company
		NFM	North-West	PMR
		NFM	Portsmouth	City Council
		NFM	York	Yorkshire Parcels Group
86.7750	76.9750	NFM	Germany	Emergency Channel Ch 485
86.7750	78.3750	NFM	Netherlands	Police Ch 860
86.7875	78.3875	NFM	Netherlands	Police Ch 861
86.7950	76.9950	NFM	Germany	Emergency Channel Ch 486
86.8000	76.8000	NFM	Brighton	Community Repeater
		NFM	Bradford	Community Transport
		NFM	Dyfed	Vets
		NFM	Hampshire	Council (162.2Hz)
		NFM	London	Datapost
		NFM	London	Post Office Tower
		NFM	Sussex	Community Repeater
		NFM	Sussex	STS Truleigh Hill
		NFM	Cheltenham	Yagi-Dish Security
86.8000	76.3000	NFM	Nationwide	Vibroplant

Base	Mobile	Mode	Location	User and Notes
86.8000	78.4000	NFM	Netherlands	Police Ch 862
86.8125	78.4125	NFM	Netherlands	Police Ch 863
86.8150	77.0150	NFM	Germany	Emergency Channel Ch 487
86.8250	78.4250	NFM	Netherlands	Police Ch 864
86.8250	76.8250	NFM	Thames Valley	ITN Ch 4
		NFM	Bristol	ITV Broadcast Link
		NFM	Manchester	Granada TV Talkback
86.8350	77.0350	NFM	Germany	Emergency Channel Ch 488
86.8375	78.4375	NFM	Netherlands	Police Ch 865
86.8500	76.8500	NFM	Perth	Tayside Water Board
		NFM	Clwyd	Delivery Company
		NFM	Telford	InterRam Couriers Ch 1
		NFM	Co Durham	BT Aerial Riggers
86.8500	78.4500	NFM	Netherlands	Police Ch 866
86.8550	77.0550	NFM	Germany	Emergency Channel Ch 489
86.8625	78.4625	NFM	Netherlands	Police Ch 867
86.8625	76.8250	NFM	Manchester	Amtrak Express Parcels
		NFM	Plymouth	Plymouth Vets
		NFM	Nationwide	RSPCA (71.9Hz)
86.8750	76.8750	NFM	Lochaber	Council Roads Dept
86.8750	77.0750	NFM	Germany	Emergency Channel Ch 490
86.8750	78.4750	NFM	Netherlands	Police Ch 868
86.8875	76.8875	NFM	Ballachulish	HRC Roads/Snow Ploughs
		NFM	Lothian & Borders	Water Board
86.8875	78.4875	NFM	Netherlands	Police Ch 869
86.8950	77.0950	NFM	Germany	Emergency Channel Ch 491
86.9000	76.9000	NFM	Southwold	Suffolk Traffic
		NFM	Merseyside	Skip Hire
		NFM	Merseyside	Transport Company
		NFM	North-West	PMR
		NFM	Hull	Limerick Construction
86.9000	78.5000	NFM	Netherlands	Police Ch 870
86.9125	78.5125	NFM	Netherlands	Police Ch 871
86.9125	76.4125	NFM	Lochaber	HRC Roads
		NFM	North-West	PMR
86.9150	77.1150	NFM	Germany	Emergency Channel Ch 492
86.9250	78.5250	NFM	Netherlands	Police Ch 872
86.9350	77.1350	NFM	Germany	Emergency Channel Ch 493
86.9375	78.5375	NFM	Netherlands	Police Ch 873
86.9375	76.9375	NFM	Nationwide	HM Customs Ch 3
		NFM	London	HM Customs Drugs Squad
		NFM	Perth	Water Board
86.9500	78.5500	NFM	Netherlands	Police Ch 874
86.9500	76.4500	NFM	Nationwide	HM Customs Ch 4
		NFM	Dover	HM Customs
		NFM	Fishguard Docks	HM Customs
		NFM	Dundee	Tayside Water Board
86.9550	77.1550	NFM	Germany	Emergency Channel Ch 494

Base	Mobile	Mode	Location	User and Notes
86.9625	76.8625	NFM	Nationwide	RSPCA Channel
		NFM	Lochaber	Forestry Commission
		NFM	Gwynedd	Forestry Commission
		NFM	Newtown	Wayside Forestry Commission
		NFM	Brighton	RSPCA
86.9625	78.5625	NFM	Netherlands	Police Ch 875
86.9750		NFM	Holland	Water Companies
86.9750	76.8625	NFM	Manchester	Water Board
		NFM	North-West	PMR
86.9750	77.1750	NFM	Germany	Emergency Channel Ch 495
		NFM	Manchester	Water Board
86.9750	78.5750	NFM	Netherlands	Police Ch 876
86.9875	78.5875	NFM	Netherlands	Police Ch 877
86.9875	76.9875	NFM	London	Guarda Security
		NFM	London	Curzon Asylum
86.9950	77.1950	NFM	Germany	Emergency Channel Ch 496
87.0000	77.0000	NFM	Nationwide	RAC Channel 2
		NFM	Berkshire	Council
		NFM	Cumbria	RAC Data Link
		NFM	Lancashire	RAC Data Link
		NFM	Guernsey	RAC
		NFM	Edinburgh	Data Link
		NFM	Wymondham	Ayton Asphalt
87.0000	78.6000	NFM	Netherlands	Police Ch 878
87.0125	77.0125	NFM	Nationwide	RAC Channel 4
		NFM	Glasgow	RAC Data Link
		NFM	Ipswich	RAC Data Link
		NFM	Newcastle	RAC Data Link
		NFM	York	RAC Data Link
		AM	Stirling	RAC Data Link
		NFM	Bristol	RAC Data Link
87.0125	78.6125	NFM	Netherlands	Police Ch 879
87.0150	77.2150	NFM	Germany	Emergency Channel Ch 497
87.0250	77.0250	NFM	Nationwide	RAC Channel 1
		NFM	Glasgow	Data Link
		AM	Stirling	Royal Automobile Club
		NFM	Ipswich	RAC
		NFM	Newmarket	RAC Data Link
		NFM	Perth	RAC Data Link
87.0250	78.6250	NFM	Netherlands	Police Ch 880
87.0350	77.2350	NFM	Germany	Emergency Channel Ch 498
87.0375	77.0375	NFM	Nationwide	RAC Channel 5
		NFM	East Durham	Private Message
		NFM	Kent (Euro Tunnel)	Trans Manche Ltd
87.0375	78.6375	NFM	Netherlands	Police Ch 881
87.0500	77.0500	NFM	Nationwide	RAC Channel 3
		NFM	North-West	PMR
		NFM	Perth	Data Link

Base	Mobile	Mode	Location	User and Notes
		NFM	Grimsby	Raylor Ltd
		NFM	Leeds	Raylor Ltd
		NFM	Skelmersdale	Taxis
		NFM	Teeside	Raylor Ltd
		NFM	York	Raylor Ltd
		NFM	Leeds	Armor Guard
		NFM	Lothian and Borders	RAC
87.0500	78.6500	NFM	Netherlands	Police Ch 882
87.0550	77.2550	NFM	Germany	Emergency Channel Ch 499
87.0625	78.6625	NFM	Netherlands	Police Ch 883
87.0625	77.0625	NFM	Bishop Stortford	Rougewell Ltd
		NFM	Wrexham	Derek's Taxis
		NFM	Haywards Heath	Station Taxis
		NFM	Jersey	RAC
		NFM	London	Statisted Containers Ltd
		NFM	Gwent	Forestry Commission
		NFM	Perth	Taxi
87.0750	77.0750	NFM	Bristol	Ace Taxis
		NFM	Bury	Red Rose Taxis
		NFM	Glasgow	Taxi
		AM	Jersey	Taxi Rank
		AM	London	Concorde Minicabs Wembley
		NFM	Glasgow	Taxis
		NFM	Ipswich	Council
		NFM	St Ives	ARC
		NFM	St Ives	Bowlers Taxis
87.0750	77.2750	NFM	Germany	Emergency Channel Ch 500
87.0750	78.6750	NFM	Netherlands	Police Ch 884
87.0875	78.6875	NFM	Netherlands	Police Ch 885
87.0875	77.0875	NFM	Chichester	Council Refuse
		NFM	Lancashire	Haulage Contractor
		NFM	Morecambe	PMR
		NFM	Heysham	PMR
		NFM	Jersey	Jersey Evening Post
		NFM	London	Savoy Rolls Royce
		NFM	London	Stanstead Containers Ltd
		NFM	Nationwide	RSPCA Channel Ch 2
87.0950	77.2950	NFM	Germany	Emergency Channel Ch 501
87.1000	78.7000	NFM	Netherlands	Police Ch 886
87.1000	77.1000	NFM	Brighton	Taxis
		NFM	Barrow	PMR
		NFM	Bolton	Road Maintenance
		NFM	Telford	InterRam Couriers Ch 2
		NFM	Preston	Taxis
		NFM	Hove	Hove Streamline Taxis
		NFM	London	J.R. Cars
		NFM	Morecambe	PMR
		NFM	Heysham	PMR

Base	Mobile	Mode	Location	User and Notes
		NFM	Warrington	Cell Security Group
		NFM	Montrose	Council Housing
		NFM	Guernsey	Gilroy's
		NFM	Leicester	ABC Taxis
		NFM	London	B.J. Transport
87.1150	77.3150	NFM	Germany	Emergency Channel Ch 502
87.1250	77.1250	NFM	Ayr	SRC Building & Works Depart.
		NFM	Badergh	Council
		NFM	Toxteth	Ethic Funfare Organisers
		NFM	Powys	Forestry Commission
		NFM	Strathclyde	Strathclyde Council
87.1350	77.3350	NFM	Germany	Emergency Channel Ch 503
87.1375	71.1375	NFM	Cardiff	Community Repeater
		NFM	Leeds	Construction Co.
		AM	Kent	Kent Council Highways Dept.
		NFM	Hampshire	Council
		NFM	Fishguard	Highways Council
		NFM	Kent	Council (Tour de France)
		NFM	City of London	Paddy's Fireworks Co.
87.1500	72.6500	AM	Lancashire	Websters Cable & Jointing Co
		NFM	Kent	Tour de France
		NFM	Fishguard	District Council
		NFM	Stirling	PMR
		NFM	Nationwide	Radiofone Channel Ch 1
		NFM	Lancashire	County Highways Ch 1
87.1550	77.3550	NFM	Germany	Emergency Channel Ch 504
87.1625	77.1625	NFM	Aberdeen	Council
		AM	Kent	Kent Council Highways Dept.
		NFM	Lincolnshire	Highways
		NFM	N Yorkshire	Highways
		NFM	Buckinghamshire	Council
		NFM	Dumfermline	Fife Regional Council
		NFM	Shropshire	County Council Emer. Planning
87.1750	77.1750	NFM	Avon	Highways
		NFM	Glasgow	Underground Control
		NFM	Nottinghamshire	Comunity Repeater
		NFM	Lancashire	County Park Rangers
87.1750	77.3750	NFM	Germany	Emergency Channel Ch 505
87.1875	77.1875	NFM	Cambridgeshire	Council
		NFM	Chichester	W Sussex Council
		NFM	Fife	Fife Regional Council Roads
		NFM	Morecambe	PMR
		NFM	Heysham	PMR
		NFM	Lancashire	Snowploughs & Gritters Ch 2
		NFM	Oxford	Council
		NFM	Radnor	Powys Council Highways
		NFM	Surrey	Council Ch 2
		AM	W Yorkshire	Highways

Base	Mobile	Mode	Location	User and Notes
87.1950	77.3950	NFM	Germany	Emergency Channel Ch 506
87.2000	77.2000	NFM	County Durham	County Council
		NFM	Cumbria	Quarry
		NFM	Foreham	Council
		NFM	North-West	PMR
		NFM	Lewes	Council
		NFM	Surrey	Council (110.9Hz)
		NFM	Waveney	Council
87.2125	77.2125	NFM	Aberfeldy	Council Gritters
		NFM	Buckinghamshire	Council
		NFM	Hertfordshire	Council
		NFM	Hull	Council
		NFM	North Humberside	Council
		NFM	Rushmoor	Council (162.2Hz)
		NFM	Scotland	Council
		NFM	Sheffield	Council Highways
		NFM	Staffordshire	Council
		NFM	Nationwide	Council Common
87.2150	77.4150	NFM	Germany	Emergency Channel Ch 507
87.2250	77.2250	NFM	Kent	Tour de France
		NFM	London	Met Police Clamping
		NFM	Oxford	City Council Ch 3 (162.2Hz)
87.2350	77.4350	NFM	Germany	Emergency Channel Ch 508
87.2375	77.2375	NFM	Dundee	Tayside Water Board
		AM	Gwynedd	Gwynedd Council
		NFM	Manchester	Sheltered Housing Wardens
		NFM	North-West	PMR
		NFM	Eastbourne	Council
		NFM	Fife	Fife Regional Council
		NFM	Morecambe	PMR
		NFM	Heysham	PMR
		NFM	Lancashire	County Council Ch 3
		NFM	Oxfordshire	County Council Ch 1
		NFM	Perth	Tayside Regional Council
87.2500	77.2500	NFM	Birmingham	City Council Engineers
		NFM	West Midlands	Snowploughs & Gritters
		NFM	East Sussex	Emergency Centre
		NFM	Brecon	Powys County Highways
		NFM	Hertfordshire	Council
		NFM	Hampshire	Council (162.2Hz)
87.2550	77.4550	NFM	Germany	Emergency Channel Ch 509
87.2625	77.2625	NFM	Ayr	Local Council Services
		AM	West Sussex	County Council (162.2Hz)
		AM	Yorkshire	Trading Standards Office
		NFM	Stockton	CCC Engineers
		NFM	England & Wales	Council Common
		NFM	Gwent	Council
		NFM	Leicester	Council

Base	Mobile	Mode	Location	User and Notes
		NFM	Oxfordshire	County Council
		NFM	Perth	Tayside Regional Council
		NFM	Slough	Council
87.2750	77.4750	NFM	Germany	Emergency Channel Ch 510
		NFM	Edinburgh	Council Inroads
		NFM	Hanley	Security
		NFM	Lothian and Borders	Lothian Reg. Council (V)
		NFM	West Yorkshire	Bus Inspectors
		NFM	Blackpool	Illuminations
87.2875	77.2875	NFM	Fife	Fife Regional Council Drainage
87.3000	77.3000	NFM	Anglia	Breckland District Council
		NFM	Mold	Clwyd County Council
		AM	Dumfries	Snowploughs & Gritters
		NFM	Derbyshire	Derbyshire Council Roads
		NFM	Hertfordshire	Council
		NFM	Jersey	Waterworks
		NFM	Norfolk	Breckland District Council
		NFM	Perth	Tayside Water Board
87.3125	77.3125	NFM	Cardiff	Parcel Force Ch 2
		NFM	Perth	Tayside Regional Council
		NFM	Windsor	Royal Parks
87.3250	77.3250	NFM	Derbyshire	Council
		NFM	Perth	Tayside Regional Council
		NFM	South Yorkshire	Council
87.3375	77.3375	NFM	Cardiff	Parcel Force Ch 1
		NFM	Edinburgh	Highways Control
		NFM	Lancaster	Vet Service
		NFM	Morecambe	Vet Service
87.3500	77.3500	NFM	Castle Douglas	Stewartry Council
		NFM	Edinburgh	MacGas
		NFM	North-West	PMR
		NFM	Oxford	Heseltine Asylum Security
		NFM	Stoke	Civil Engineers
		NFM	Guernsey	Gaudion Skip Hire
87.3625	77.3625	NFM	Castle Douglas	Forestry Commission
		NFM	North-West	PMR
		NFM	Saddleworth	Haulage Firm
		NFM	Glen Falloch	West Roads Department
		NFM	Perth	Tayside Regional Council
		NFM	Strathclyde	Forestry Commission
		NFM	Tayside	Forestry Commission
87.3750	77.3750	NFM	Linconshire	Community Repeater
		NFM	Yorkshire	RSPCA
		AM	Jersey	Dr Scott Warren
87.3875	87.3875	AM	France	Nuclear Alert Channel
87.3875	77.3875	NFM	Cardiff	Thorn Homeserve TV Repairs
		NFM	Stoke	Garage
		NFM	Ipswich	Community Repeater

Base	Mobile	Mode	Location	User and Notes
		NFM	Perth	Community Repeater
87.4000	77.4000	NFM	Aberdeen	Aberdeen Skip Hire
		NFM	Huntington	Doctors Scheme
		NFM	Nationwide	Doctor Scheme
		NFM	Perth	Tayside Water Board
87.4125	77.4125	NFM	Avon	Ace Skip Hire
		NFM	Bristol	P.D.G Courier Service
		NFM	Elvington	A1 Haulage
		NFM	Elvington	Elvington Plant Hire
		NFM	Elvington	Silverseal Auto Windscreens
		NFM	Lochaber	Council Roads Dept
		NFM	Staffordshire	JCB Drivers
		NFM	London	Onyx Cleansing Services
		NFM	Perth	Tayside Regional Council
		NFM	Scotland	Council Highways Common
87.4250	77.4250	NFM	Stirling	County Council (B)
		NFM	Guernsey	Remote Gas Detectors
		NFM	Blackpool	County Highways
87.4375	77.4375	NFM	Bedford	County Surveyors Ch 1
		NFM	Coris Mid Wales	Forestry Commission
		NFM	Plymouth	City Engineers
		NFM	West Midlands	Council
		NFM	Bedford	County Surveyors
		NFM	Scotland	Council Highways Common
87.4500	77.4500	AM	Avon	Sub Council Control
		NFM	Belfast	Dept. of Environment
		NFM	London	Infomation Service
		NFM	Berkshire	Council Ch 1 (162.2Hz)
		NFM	Cambridge	Highways Ch 3
		NFM	Haverfordwest	Preseli Pembroke Council
		NFM	Peterborough	Cotton Television
87.4625	77.4625	NFM	Berkshire	Council Surveyor Ch 2
		AM	Lincolnshire	Highways
		NFM	Lothian & Borders	Roads Dept
		NFM	Essex	Highways Ch 2
		NFM	N.C. Emlyn	Highways Council
		NFM	Hereford	Council
		NFM	West Midlands	Snowploughs & Gritters
		NFM	West Sussex	West Sussex Council
		NFM	Worcester	Council
87.4750	77.4750	NFM	Peterborough	Cotton TV
		NFM	Buckinghamshire	County Council
		NFM	Morecambe	PMR
		NFM	Heysham	PMR
		NFM	Birmingham	Bin Bomb Pub
		NFM	Pembrokeshire	MoD Castlemartin
87.4875	77.4875	NFM	Gainsbrough	Grimsby Council
		NFM	Peterborough	Royal Taxis

	Mobile	Mode	Location	User and Notes
00	77.5000	NFM	Cambridge	John Grieves
		NFM	Guernsey	States Telecom
		NFM	Leeds	Skip Hire
7000	77.7000	WFM	Nationwide	RSL 28 Day Stations
.8000	77.8000	WFM	Nationwide	RSL 28 Day Stations
57.9000	77.9000	WFM	London	Energy
		WFM	Nottingham	Heatwave Radio

88.0000 - 90.2000 MHz NATIONWIDE BBC RADIO 2

88.1000	WFM	Cirencester	
	WFM	Ffestiniog	
	WFM	Grantham	
	WFM	Gwynedd	
	WFM	Isle of Skye	
	WFM	Llanidloes	
	WFM	Poseys	
	WFM	Western Isles	
	WFM	Ballachulish Area	
	WFM	Border Counties	
	WFM	Devon & East Cornwall	
	WFM	Guildford & Farnham Area	
	WFM	Llandloes Area	
	WFM	Mallaig Area	
	WFM	Manningtree Area	
	WFM	North Cumbria Area	
	WFM	South West Devon & Plymouth	
	WFM	West Islay	
88.2000	WFM	Bexhill	
	WFM	Mid Glamorgan	
	WFM	Newbury	
	WFM	Truskmore	RTE Radio 1
	WFM	Wiltshire	
	WFM	Betws-Y-Coed Area	
	WFM	Elgin Area	
	WFM	Knock More Area	
	WFM	Nailsworth Area	
88.3000	WFM	Castletownbere	RTE Radio 1
	WFM	Co Down	
	WFM	Dunbartonshire	
	WFM	Forfar Area	
	WFM	Galashiels	
	WFM	Gwynedd	
	WFM	Kilmarnock Area	
	WFM	Leicestershire	
	WFM	Leven & Renton Area	
	WFM	Lochgilphead Area	
	WFM	Melody FM North Normandy	
	WFM	Midland Counties	

Base	Mobile	Mode	Location	User and Notes
		WFM	Moville	RTE Radio 1
		WFM	Ness of Lewis	
		WFM	Shetland Isles	
		WFM	Staffordshire & Shorpshire Area	
		WFM	Sutton Coldfield	
		WFM	Trowbridge Area	
		WFM	Ullapool	
		WFM	Wensleydale Area	
		WFM	Westwood	
		WFM	Windermere Area	
88.4000		WFM	Ammanford Area	
		WFM	Campbeltown Area	
		WFM	Colwyn Bay	
		WFM	Dyfed	
		WFM	Ebbw Vale Area	
		WFM	Folkestone Area	
		WFM	Hebden Bridge Area	
		WFM	Isle Of Man	
		WFM	London	Unity FM
		WFM	Mid Glamorgan	
		WFM	Peebles Area	
		WFM	South London	
		WFM	Surrey	
		WFM	Walsden Area	
		WFM	Wharfdale Area	
88.5000		WFM	Barnstaple Area	
		WFM	Blaenavon Area	
		WFM	Central South of England	
		WFM	Cowal Peninsular & Rothesay Area	
		WFM	Devon	
		WFM	Dungarvan	RTE Radio 1
		WFM	Isle of Wight	
		WFM	North Eastern Counties	
		WFM	Three Rock	RTE Radio 1
		WFM	West Glamorgan	
		WFM	West Skye	
		WFM	West Yorkshire	
88.6000		WFM	Sheffield	BBC Radio Sheffield
		WFM	Bedford Area	
		WFM	Berwick	
		WFM	Co Armagh	
		WFM	Eastbourne	
		WFM	Hereford & Welsh Borders	
		WFM	Inveraray Area	
		WFM	Mid Glamorgan	
		WFM	North West Lancashire	
		WFM	Ross On Wye Area	
		WFM	Warrenpoint Area	

Base	Mobile	Mode	Location	User and Notes
88.7000		WFM	Abergavenny Area	
		WFM	Aberystwyth Area & Cardigan Bay	
		WFM	Ayr Area	
		WFM	Creetown Area	
		WFM	Grampian Area	
		WFM	Kirkconnel Area	
		WFM	Londonderry Area	
		WFM	Okehampton Area	
88.7500		WFM	London	Sunrise FM
88.8000		WFM	Jersey	BBC Radio Jersey
		WFM	Cambridgeshire	
		WFM	Chippenham Area	
		WFM	Co An trim	
		WFM	Cornwall	
		WFM	County Mayo	RTE Radio 1
		WFM	Crystal Palace	
		WFM	Gower Peninisular	
		WFM	Isles of Scilly	
		WFM	Lincolnshire	
		WFM	London	Giriz FM
		WFM	Maghera	RTE Radio 1
		WFM	Newark	
		WFM	Penaligon Downs	
		WFM	Wiltshire	
88.9000		WFM	A yrshire	
		WFM	Ballycastle Area	
		WFM	Brecon	
		WFM	Cambridge Area	
		WFM	Carmarthen Area	
		WFM	Chard	
		WFM	Gwent	
		WFM	Keighley Area	
		WFM	Llangollen	
		WFM	Northampton Area	
		WFM	Oban Area	
		WFM	Todmorden Area	
		WFM	Ystalyfera Area	
89.0000		WFM	Abertillery	
		WFM	Bath City Area	
		WFM	Chesterfield	
		WFM	Exeter Area	
		WFM	Kendal Area	
		WFM	Isle of Man	Manx Radio
		WFM	Minehead	
		WFM	North Gloucestershire	
		WFM	Perth Area	
		WFM	South Islay	
		WFM	Swindon	

Base	Mobile	Mode	Location	User and Notes
		WFM	West Glamorgan	
89.1000		WFM	Border Counties	
		WFM	Brigport	
		WFM	Conwy	
		WFM	Devon	
		WFM	Dorset	
		WFM	Greater London	
		WFM	Home Counties	
		WFM	Humberside	
		WFM	Kent	
		WFM	Kingussie Area	
		WFM	Kippure	RTE Radio 1
		WFM	Larne Area	
		WFM	Llandrindod Wells Area	
		WFM	Llanfyllin	
		WFM	Poseys	
		WFM	Rosneath Area	
		WFM	Somerset	
		WFM	Ullapool & Lewis Area	
89.2000		WFM	Aberdare Area	
		WFM	Cork City	RTE Radio 1
		WFM	Dunbartonshire	
		WFM	France	Culture Cherbourg
		WFM	Holywell Hill	RTE Radio 1
		WFM	Mid Glamorgan	
		WFM	Pitlochry Area	
		WFM	Pontypool Area	
		WFM	Stroud Area	
89.3000		WFM	Achill	RTE Radio 1
		WFM	Argyll	
		WFM	Bristol City Area	
		WFM	Cheshire Area	
		WFM	County Galway	RTE Radio 1
		WFM	Derbyshire	
		WFM	Fort William Area	
		WFM	Greater Manchester	
		WFM	Gwent	
		WFM	Haverfordwest	
		WFM	Lancashire	
		WFM	Merseyside	
		WFM	Nottinghamshire	
		WFM	Orkney Isl	
		WFM	Perthshire	
		WFM	South West Wales	
		WFM	Westem Isles	
		WFM	Wrexham & Deeside Area	
		WFM	Yorkshire	
89.4000		WFM	Avon	

Base	Mobile	Mode	Location	User and Notes
		WFM	Gwynedd	
		WFM	Isle of Wight	
		WFM	Limerick City	RTE Radio 1
		WFM	Newry	
		WFM	Northumberland	
		WFM	Enniskillen Area	
		WFM	France	MusiqueBrest
		WFM	Kincardine Area	
		WFM	Machynlleth Area	
		WFM	Ventnor	
89.5000		WFM	Ayrshire	
		WFM	Cahirciveen	RTE Radio 1
		WFM	Darwen	
		WFM	Devon	
		WFM	East Skye	
		WFM	Grantham Area	
		WFM	Greenholm & Darvel Area	
		WFM	Innerleithin Area	
		WFM	Isle of Mull	
		WFM	Oxfordshire & Wiltshire	
		WFM	Pennar	
		WFM	South Knapdale	
		WFM	Swansea Area	
		WFM	Tobermoray	
89.6000		WFM	Channel Islands	
		WFM	Fermdale	
		WFM	Hastings	
		WFM	Inverness Area	
		WFM	Keswick	
		WFM	Lancashire	
		WFM	Limavady	
		WFM	Londonderry	
		WFM	Ludlow Area	
		WFM	Mid Glamorgan	
		WFM	Mount Leinster	RTE Radio 1
		WFM	North East Scotland	
		WFM	North Wales Coast & Anglesey	
		WFM	Poseys	
		WFM	Rossshire	
		WFM	Welshpool Area	
		WFM	Whitby Area	
89.7000		WFM	Berwick	
		WFM	Cornholme Area	
		WFM	Dyfed	
		WFM	Kinlochleven Area	
		WFM	Lampeter Area	
		WFM	Lancashire	
		WFM	Llanbydder Area	

Base	Mobile	Mode	Location	User and Notes
		WFM	London	Station FM Brixton/Tottenham
		WFM	Lyme Regis	
		WFM	Newhaven Area	
		WFM	Norfolk	
		WFM	Saddleworth Area	
		WFM	South East London	
		WFM	Stranraer Area	
		WFM	Suffolk	
		WFM	Surrey	
		WFM	Wearsdale Area	
		WFM	West Cornwall	
		WFM	Whitehaven	
89.8000		WFM	Anglesey	
		WFM	Caversham	
		WFM	Clwyd	
		WFM	Croaghmoyle, Mayo	RTE Radio 1
		WFM	Fanad	RTE Radio 1
		WFM	Grampian	
		WFM	Grantown Area	
		WFM	Isle of Lewis	
		WFM	Leeds	
		WFM	Matlock Area	
		WFM	Newcastle-upon-Tyne	
		WFM	Pudsey Area	
		WFM	Salisbury Area	
		WFM	Sheffield Area	
		WFM	South Devon	
		WFM	Stornaway	
		WFM	West of Oswestry & Welshpool	
89.9000		WFM	Athlone	RTE Radio 1
		WFM	Cardiff	
		WFM	County Mayo	RTE Radio 1
		WFM	Forth Valley	
		WFM	France Musique Rennes	
		WFM	Girvan Area	
		WFM	Gloucester & Somerset Area	
		WFM	Haslingden Area	
		WFM	High Wycombe Area	
		WFM	Lowland Scotland	
		WFM	N Bristol	
		WFM	Scarborough Area	
		WFM	Scottish Central Lowlands	
		WFM	Sheffield	
		WFM	Somerest & North Devon	
		WFM	South & East Wales	
90.0000		WFM	Buxton Area	
		WFM	Dover	

Base	Mobile	Mode	Location	User and Notes
		WFM	High Wycombe	
		WFM	London	Charity FM
		WFM	Morecambe Bay Area	
		WFM	Mullaghanish	RTE Radio 1
		WFM	South Cumbria	
		WFM	South East Kent	
		WFM	Weymonth Area	
90.1000		WFM	Aberdeenshire	
		WFM	Basingstoke	
		WFM	Belfast & East Counties	
		WFM	Berwick & Borders	
		WFM	Brighton Area	
		WFM	Caithness	
		WFM	Deeside Area	
		WFM	Dolgellau Area	
		WFM	Llandtfriog Area	
		WFM	Marlborough	
		WFM	Newcastle Emlyn Area	
		WFM	Newton Area	
		WFM	Northumberland	
		WFM	Peterborough	
		WFM	Powys	
		WFM	Wick Area	
90.2000		WFM	Lancashire	
		WFM	North Yorkshire	
		WFM	Poseys	BBC Radio 3

90.3000 - 92.4000 MHz   NATIONWIDE BBC RADIO 3

Base	Mobile	Mode	Location	User and Notes
90.3000		WFM	Ballachulish Area	
		WFM	Border Counties	
		WFM	Cirencester	
		WFM	Devon & East Cornwall	
		WFM	Festiniog Area	
		WFM	Grantham Area	
		WFM	Guildford & Farnham Area	
		WFM	Isle of Islay	
		WFM	Llandloes Area	
		WFM	Mallaig Area	
		WFM	Manchester	I-Tel FM
		WFM	Manningtree Area	
		WFM	North Cumbria	
		WFM	South West Devon & Plymouth	
		WFM	West Skye	
		WFM	Western Isles	
90.4000		WFM	Betws-Y-Coed Area	
		WFM	County Mayo	RTE Radio 2
		WFM	Elgin Area	
		WFM	Knock More Area	

Base	Mobile	Mode	Location	User and Notes
		WFM	Mid Glamorgan	
		WFM	Nailsworth Area	
		WFM	Newbury	
		WFM	Wiltshire	
90.5000		WFM	Co Down	
		WFM	Dunbartonshire	
		WFM	Forfar Area	
		WFM	Glasgow	
		WFM	Gywnedd	
		WFM	Kilmarnock Area	
		WFM	Leicestershire	
		WFM	Leven & Renton Area	
		WFM	Lockgilphead Area	
		WFM	Midland Counties	
		WFM	Normandy	Radio Manche
		WFM	Shetland Isl	
		WFM	Staffordshire & Shorpshire Area	
		WFM	Stornaway	
		WFM	Trowbridge Area	
		WFM	Ullapool	
		WFM	Wensleydale Area	
		WFM	Westwood	
		WFM	Windermere Area	
90.6000		WFM	Ammanford Area	
		WFM	Campbeltown Area	
		WFM	Clwyd	
		WFM	Dyfed	
		WFM	Ebbw Vale Area	
		WFM	Folkestone Area	
		WFM	Hebden Bridge Area	
		WFM	Isle of Man	
		WFM	London	Pulse FM
		WFM	Mid Glamorgan	
		WFM	Peebles Area	
		WFM	South London	
		WFM	Surrey	
		WFM	Walsden Area	
		WFM	Wharfdale Area	
90.7000		WFM	Argyll	
		WFM	Barnstaple Area	
		WFM	Blaenavon Area	
		WFM	Central South of England	
		WFM	Cowal Peninsular & Rothesay Area	
		WFM	Gwent	
		WFM	Isle of Wight	
		WFM	London	Local Community Radio
		WFM	North Eastern Counties	
		WFM	Scarborough Area	

Base	Mobile	Mode	Location	User and Notes
		WFM	West Glamorgan	
		WFM	West Skye	
		WFM	West Yorkshire	
90.8000		WFM	Bedford Area	
		WFM	Berwick	
		WFM	Co Armagh	
		WFM	Eastbourne	
		WFM	Hereford & Welsh Borders	
		WFM	Inveraray Area	
		WFM	Kinross Area	
		WFM	Mid Glamorgan	
		WFM	North West Lancashire	
		WFM	Ross On Wye Area	
		WFM	Warrenpoint Area	
90.9000		WFM	Aberdeenshire	
		WFM	Abergavenny Area	
		WFM	Aberystwyth Area & Cardigan Bay	
		WFM	Argyll	
		WFM	Ayr Area	
		WFM	Cambridgeshire	
		WFM	Creetown Area	
		WFM	Grampian Area	
		WFM	Gwent	
		WFM	Kirkconnel Area	
		WFM	Lincolnshire	
		WFM	Londonderry Area	
		WFM	Newark Area	
		WFM	Normandy	CFM
		WFM	Okehampton Area	
		WFM	Stirling	
		WFM	Stranraer Area	
		WFM	West Yorkshire	
91.0000		WFM	Ballycastle Area	
		WFM	Chippenham Area	
		WFM	Cornwall	
		WFM	County Mayo	RTE Radio 2
		WFM	Crystal Palace	
		WFM	Galway	RTE Radio 2
		WFM	Gower Peninsular	
		WFM	Isles of Scilly	
		WFM	Penaligon Downs	
91.1000		WFM	Brecon	
		WFM	Cambridge Area	
		WFM	Carmarthen Area	
		WFM	Channel Islands	
		WFM	Girvan Area	
		WFM	Gwent	
		WFM	Keighley Area	

Base	Mobile	Mode	Location	User and Notes
		WFM	Llangollen Area	
		WFM	Northampton Area	
		WFM	Oban Area	
		WFM	Somerset	
		WFM	Todmorden Area	
		WFM	Ystalyfera Area	
91.2000		WFM	Abertillery Area	
		WFM	Bath City Area	
		WFM	Chesterfield Area	
		WFM	Exeter Area	
		WFM	Kendal Area	
		WFM	Kingussie Area	
		WFM	Minehead	
		WFM	North Gloucestershire	
		WFM	Perth Area	
		WFM	South Islay	
		WFM	Swindon	
		WFM	West Glamorgan	
91.3000		WFM	Ashkirk	
		WFM	Border Counties	
		WFM	Brigport	
		WFM	Conwy	
		WFM	Devon	
		WFM	Dorset	
		WFM	Greater London	
		WFM	Home Counties	
		WFM	Kent	
		WFM	Kingussie Area	
		WFM	Larne Area	
		WFM	Llandrindod Wells Area	
		WFM	Llanfyllin Area	
		WFM	Rossshire	
		WFM	Somerset	
		WFM	Ullapool & Lewis Area	
		WFM	West Kilbride	
91.4000		WFM	Aberdare Area	
		WFM	Pitlochry Area	
		WFM	Pontypool Area	
		WFM	Rosneath Area	
		WFM	Stroud Area	
91.5000		WFM	Bristol City Area	
		WFM	Cheshire Area	
		WFM	County Galway	RTE Radio 2
		WFM	Derbyshire	
		WFM	Fort William Area	
		WFM	France	Culture Caen
		WFM	Greater Manchester	
		WFM	Haverfordwest	

Base	Mobile	Mode	Location	User and Notes
		WFM	Humberside	
		WFM	Lancashire	
		WFM	Merseyside	
		WFM	Nottinghamshire	
		WFM	Orkney Isl	
		WFM	Perthshire	
		WFM	South Kanpdale	
		WFM	South West Wales	
		WFM	Western Isles	
		WFM	Wrexham & Deeside Area	
		WFM	Yorkshire	
91.6000		WFM	Avon	
		WFM	Co Down	
		WFM	Enniskillen Area	
		WFM	Gwynedd	
		WFM	Kincardine Area	
		WFM	London	Genesis FM
		WFM	Machynlleth Area	
		WFM	Northumberland	
91.7000		WFM	Darwen	
		WFM	East Devon	
		WFM	East Skye	
		WFM	Grantham Area	
		WFM	Greenholme & Darvel Area	
		WFM	Innerleithin Area	
		WFM	Isle Of Mull	
		WFM	Isle of Wight	
		WFM	Oxfordshire & Wiltshire	
		WFM	Pennar	
		WFM	Swansea Area	
		WFM	Tobermoray	
		WFM	Ventnor	
91.8000		WFM	Fermdale	
		WFM	Hastings	
		WFM	France	Fun Radio
		WFM	Inverness Area	
		WFM	Keswick Forest	
		WFM	Lancashire	
		WFM	Limavady Area	
		WFM	Ludlow Area	
		WFM	Mid Glamorgan	
		WFM	North East Scotland	
		WFM	North Wales Coast & Anglesey	
		WFM	Poseys	
		WFM	Tayside	
		WFM	Welshpool Area	
		WFM	Whitby Area	
91.9000		WFM	Berwickshire	

Base	Mobile	Mode	Location	User and Notes
		WFM	Cornholme Area	
		WFM	Dyfed	
		WFM	France	RFL
		WFM	Kinlochleven Area	
		WFM	Lancashire	
		WFM	Lampeter Area	
		WFM	Llanybydder Area	
		WFM	Lyme Regis	
		WFM	Newhaven Area	
		WFM	Norfolk	
		WFM	Saddleworth Area	
		WFM	South East London	
		WFM	Stranraer	
		WFM	Suffolk	
		WFM	Surrey	
		WFM	Wearsdale Area	
		WFM	West Cornwall	
		WFM	Whiteha ven	
92.0000		WFM	Anglesey	
		WFM	Brittany	Nostalgie
		WFM	Caversham	
		WFM	Clwyd	
		WFM	County Mayo	RTE Radio 2
		WFM	Grampian	
		WFM	Granton Area	
		WFM	London	PowerJam
		WFM	Matlock Area	
		WFM	Newcastle Area	
		WFM	Pudsey Area	
		WFM	Salisbury Area	
		WFM	South Devon	
		WFM	Stornaway	
		WFM	West of Oswestry & Welshpool	
92.1000		WFM	Forth Valley	
		WFM	Galashiels	BBC Radio Scotland
		WFM	Gloucester & Somerset Area	
		WFM	Haslingden Area	
		WFM	High Wycome Area	
		WFM	Lowland Scotland	
		WFM	N Bristol	
		WFM	Scarborough Area	
		WFM	Scottish Central Lowlands	
		WFM	Sheffield Area	
		WFM	Somerset & North Devon	
		WFM	South & East Wales	
92.2000		WFM	Berwick & Borders	
		WFM	Bexhill	
		WFM	Buxton Area	

Base	Mobile	Mode	Location	User and Notes
		WFM	High Wycombe	
		WFM	Morecambe Bay Area	
		WFM	North Yorkshire	
		WFM	Peterborough	
		WFM	South Cumbria	
		WFM	Weymouth Area	
92.3000		WFM	Aberdeenshire	
		WFM	Basingstoke	
		WFM	Belfast & East Counties	
		WFM	Brighton Area	
		WFM	Caithness	
		WFM	Deeside Area	
		WFM	Dolgellau Area	
		WFM	France MusiqueCherbourg	
		WFM	Llandyfriog Area	
		WFM	London	Weekend Rush
		WFM	Marlborough	
		WFM	Newcastle Emlyn Area	
		WFM	Newton Area	
		WFM	Northumberland	
		WFM	Peterborough Area	
		WFM	Poseys	
		WFM	Wick Area	
92.4000 -94.6000 MHz			**NATIONWIDE BBC RADIO 4**	
92.4000		WFM	BBC Radio Leeds	
		WFM	Dover	
		WFM	Holme Moss	BBC Radio Leeds
		WFM	Poseys	BBC Radio Cymru
		WFM	South East Kent	
92.5000		WFM	BBC Radio Scotland Ballachulish Area	
		WFM	BBC Radio Scotland Mallaig Area	
		WFM	BBC Radio Scotland W Islay	
		WFM	Border Counties	
		WFM	Cirencester	
		WFM	Devon & East Cornwall	
		WFM	Ffestiniog	BBC Radio Cymru
		WFM	Grantham Area	
		WFM	Guildford & Farnham Area	
		WFM	Isle of Skye	BBC Radio Scotland
		WFM	Manningtree Area	
		WFM	North Cumbria	
		WFM	South West Devon & Plymouth	
92.5500		WFM	Clettraval	BBC Radio Scotland
92.6000		WFM	Newbury	
		WFM	Truskmore	Raidio Na Gaeltachta
		WFM	Wiltshire	
		WFM	Elgin Area	BBC Radio Scotland

Base	Mobile	Mode	Location	User and Notes
		WFM	Knock More Area	BBC Radio Scotland
		WFM	County Mayo	RTE Radio 3
		WFM	Galway	RTE Radio 3
		WFM	Nailsworth Area	
92.7000		WFM	Castletownbere	Raidio Na Gaeltachta
		WFM	Nottinghamshire	
		WFM	Westwood	
		WFM	Forfar Area	BBC Radio Scotland
		WFM	Kilmarnock Area	BBC Radio Scotland
		WFM	Leven & Renton Area	BBC Radio Scotland
		WFM	Lochgilphead Area	BBC Radio Scotland
		WFM	Ness of Lewis	BBC Radio Scotland
		WFM	Shetland Isl	BBC Radio Scotland
		WFM	Leicestershire	
		WFM	Midland Counties	
		WFM	Staffordshire & Shorpshire Area	
		WFM	Trowbridge Area	
		WFM	Wensleydale Area	
		WFM	Windermere Area	
92.8000		WFM	Campbeltown Area	BBC Radio Scotland
		WFM	Peebles Area	BBC Radio Scotland
		WFM	Clwyd	BBC Radio Cymru
		WFM	Eastbourne	
		WFM	Hebden Bridge Area	
		WFM	Isle Of Man	
		WFM	Mid Glgmorgan	
		WFM	South London	
		WFM	Surrey	
		WFM	Walsden Area	
		WFM	Ebbw Vale	
		WFM	Wharfdale Area	
92.9000		WFM	Cowal Peninsular	BBC Radio Scotland
		WFM	West Skye	BBC Radio Scotland
		WFM	Central South of England	
		WFM	Croaghmoyle, Mayo	Raidio Na Gaeltachta
		WFM	Devon	
		WFM	Gwent	
		WFM	Isle of Wight	
		WFM	Moville	Raidio Na Gaeltachta
		WFM	North Eastern Counties	
		WFM	Three Rock	Raidio Na Gaeltachta
		WFM	West Glamorgan	
		WFM	West Yorkshire	
93.0000		WFM	Inveraray Area	BBC Radio Scotland
		WFM	Bedford Area	
		WFM	Berwick	
		WFM	Brittany	France Bretagne Ouest
		WFM	Hereford & Welsh Borders	

Base	Mobile	Mode	Location	User and Notes
		WFM	Mid Glamorgan	
		WFM	North West Lancashire	
		WFM	Warrenpoint Area	Radio Ulster
		WFM	Ross On Wye Area	
93.1000		WFM	Aberystwyth	BBC Radio Cymru
		WFM	Ayr Area	BBC Radio Scotland
		WFM	Grampian Area	BBC Radio Scotland
		WFM	Kirkconnel Area	BBC Radio Scotland
		WFM	Cambridgeshire	
		WFM	Folkestone Area	
		WFM	Gwent	
		WFM	Lincolnshire	
		WFM	Newark Area	
		WFM	Normandy	Fun Radio
		WFM	Okehampton Area	
		WFM	Londonderry	Radio Foyle
93.2000		WFM	Ballycastle Area	
		WFM	Guernsey	BBC Radio Guernsey
		WFM	Brighton	Pure FM
		WFM	Chippenham Area	
		WFM	Co Antrim	
		WFM	Cornwall	
		WFM	County Mayo	RTE Radio 3
		WFM	Crystal Palace	
		WFM	Galway	RTE Radio 3
		WFM	Isles of Scilly	
		WFM	Maghera	Raidio Na Gaeltachta
		WFM	Penaligon Downs	
		WFM	Ton Petre	BBC Radio Cymru
93.3000		WFM	Girvan Area	BBC Radio Scotland
		WFM	Kinross Area	BBC Radio Scotland
		WFM	Oban Area	BBC Radio Scotland
		WFM	Brecon	BBC Radio Cymru
		WFM	Cambridge Area	
		WFM	Carmarthen	BBC Radio Cymru
		WFM	Chard	
		WFM	Gwent	BBC Radio Cymru
		WFM	Keighley Area	
		WFM	Llangollen	
		WFM	Northampton Area	
		WFM	Todmorden	
93.4000		WFM	Abertillery	
		WFM	Bath City Area	
		WFM	Perth Area	BBC Radio Scotland
		WFM	South Islay	BBC Radio Scotland
		WFM	Chesterfield	
		WFM	Dungarvan	Raidio Na Gaeltachta
		WFM	Exeter Area	

Base	Mobile	Mode	Location	User and Notes
		WFM	Kendal Area	
		WFM	Minehead	
		WFM	Normandy	Radio Manche
		WFM	North Gloucestershire	
		WFM	South Glamorgan	BBC Radio Cymru
		WFM	Swindon	
93.5000		WFM	Border Counties	BBC Radio Scotland
		WFM	Kingussie Area	BBC Radio Scotland
		WFM	Ullapool & Lewis Area	BBC Radio Scotland
		WFM	Brigport	
		WFM	Bristol City Area	
		WFM	Conwy	BDC Radio Cymru
		WFM	Devon	
		WFM	Dorset	
		WFM	France	Inter Rennes
		WFM	Greater London	
		WFM	Home Counties	
		WFM	Kent	
		WFM	Kippure	Raidio Na Gaeltachta
		WFM	Llandrindod Wells	BBC Radio Cymru
		WFM	Poseys	
		WFM	Radio Ulster Larne Area	
		WFM	Somerset	
		WFM	West Kilbride	BBC Radio Scotland
93.6000		WFM	Aberdare	BBC Radio Cymru
		WFM	Pitlochry	BBC Radio Scotland
		WFM	Rosneath Area	BBC Radio Scotland
		WFM	Cork City	Raidio Na Gaeltachta
		WFM	Holywell Hill	Raidio Na Gaeltachta
		WFM	Mid Glamorgan	
		WFM	Pontypool	BBC Radio Cymru
		WFM	Stroud Area	
93.7000		WFM	Achill	Raidio Na Gaeltachta
		WFM	Alderney	Island FM
		WFM	Fort William Area	BBC Radio Scotland
		WFM	Orkney Isl	BBC Radio Scotland
		WFM	South Knapdale	BBC Radio Scotland
		WFM	Bristol	BBC Radio 4
		WFM	Bristol	BBC Radio 4
		WFM	Cheshire Area	
		WFM	County Galway	RTE Radio 3
		WFM	Daliburgh	BBC Radio Scotland/Highland
		WFM	Derbyshire	
		WFM	Galway	RTE Radio 3
		WFM	Greater Manchester	
		WFM	Gwent	
		WFM	Humberside	
		WFM	Lancashire	

Base	Mobile	Mode	Location	User and Notes
		WFM	Merseyside	
		WFM	Nottinghamshire	
		WFM	Perthshire	BBC Radio Scotland/Tayside
		WFM	Wrexham & Deeside Area	
		WFM	Yorkshire	
93.8000		WFM	Avon	
		WFM	Kincardine Area	BBC Radio Scotland
		WFM	France	France Inter
		WFM	Gwynedd	
		WFM	London	Vibes FM
		WFM	Newry	BBC Radio Ulster
		WFM	Northumberland	
		WFM	Poseys	BBC Radio Cymru
		WFM	Enniskillen Area	Radio Ulster
		WFM	Ventnor	
93.9000		WFM	East Skye	BBC Radio Scotland
		WFM	Greenholm & Darvel	BBC Radio Scotland
		WFM	Innerleithen Area	BBC Radio Scotland
		WFM	Tobermoray	BBC Radio Scotland
		WFM	Isle Of Mull	BBC Radio Scotland
		WFM	Britanny	Nostalgie
		WFM	Cahirciveen	Raidio Na Gaeltachta
		WFM	Devon	
		WFM	Grantham Area	
		WFM	Oxfordshire & Wiltshire	
		WFM	Pennar	
		WFM	Swansea	BBC Radio Cymru
		WFM	Todmorden Area	
		WFM	Welshpool	
94.0000		WFM	Inverness	BBC Radio Scotland
		WFM	North East Scotland	BBC Radio Scotland
		WFM	W. Midlands	Black County Sounds
		WFM	Fermdale	
		WFM	Keswick Forest	
		WFM	Lancashire	
		WFM	Limavady Area	
		WFM	London	Juice-94
		WFM	Ludlow Area	
		WFM	Mid Glamorgan	
		WFM	Mount Leinster	Raidio Na Gaeltachta
		WFM	Whitby Area	
94.1000		WFM	Kinlochleven Area	BBC Radio Scotland
		WFM	Stranraer	BBC Radio Scotland
		WFM	Berwickshire	BBC Radio Scotland/Tweed
		WFM	Cornholme Area	
		WFM	France	InterCherbourg
		WFM	Lyme Regis	
		WFM	Newhaven Area	

Base	Mobile	Mode	Location	User and Notes
		WFM	Norfolk	
		WFM	Redruth	
		WFM	Saddleworth Area	
		WFM	South East London	
		WFM	Suffolk	
		WFM	Surrey	
		WFM	Wearsdale Area	
		WFM	West Cornwall	
		WFM	Whitehaven	
94.1500		WFM	London	Touchdown Radio
94.2000		WFM	Anglesey	BBC Radio Cymru
		WFM	Brittany	France Culture
		WFM	Derby	BBC Radio Derby
		WFM	Stornaway	BBC Radio Scotland
		WFM	Caversham	
		WFM	Clwyd	
		WFM	County Mayo	RTE Radio 3
		WFM	Fanad	Raidio Na Gaeltachta
		WFM	Galway	RTE Radio 3
		WFM	Hastings	
		WFM	Matlock Area	
		WFM	Newcastle Area	
		WFM	Pudsey Area	
		WFM	Salisbury Area	
		WFM	South Devon	
		WFM	Wolverhampton	Skyline Radio
94.3000		WFM	Forth Valley	BBC Radio Scotland
		WFM	Lowland Scotland	BBC Radio Scotland
		WFM	Bristol	
		WFM	Gloucester & Somerset Area	
		WFM	Haslingden Area	
		WFM	High Wycombe Area	
		WFM	London	Sky
		WFM	Scarborough Area	
		WFM	Sheffield	
		WFM	Somerset & North Devon	
		WFM	South & East Wales	
94.4000		WFM	Buxton Area	
		WFM	High Wycombe	
		WFM	Morecambe Bay Area	
		WFM	Mullaghanish	Raidio Na Gaeltachta
		WFM	France	France Inter
		WFM	North Yorkshire	
		WFM	South Cumbria	
		WFM	South East Kent	
		WFM	Weymouth Area	
94.5000		WFM	Basingstoke	
		WFM	Deeside Area	BBC Radio Scotland

Base	Mobile	Mode	Location	User and Notes
		WFM	Wick Area	BBC Radio Scotland
		WFM	Berwick & Borders	
		WFM	Brighton Area	
		WFM	Normandy	Fun Radio
		WFM	Chatton	
		WFM	Dolgellau	BBC Radio Cymru
		WFM	Llandyfriod	BBC Radio Cymru
		WFM	London	Kool FM
		WFM	Marlborough	
		WFM	Peterborough Area	
		WFM	Poseys	
		WFM	Belfast & East Counties	Radio Ulster

94.6000 -97.6000 MHz   NATIONWIDE INDEPENDENT RADIO

Base	Mobile	Mode	Location	User and Notes
94.6000		WFM	Granton	BBC Radio Scotland
		WFM	Cheshire	BBC Radio Stoke On Trent
		WFM	Henley	BBC Radio Surrey & Berkshire
		WFM	Bexhill	BBC Radio 4
		WFM	Pendle Forest	BBC Radio 4
		WFM	Brittany	Fun Radio
94.7000		WFM	Argyll	BBC Radio 4
		WFM	Hereford	BBC Radio Hereford & Worc's
		WFM	Solway	BBC Radio Solway
		WFM	Chesterfield	BBC Radio Sheffield
		WFM	Glasgow	Radio Scotland
		WFM	Invernessshire	BBC Radio 4
		WFM	Isle of Islay	BBC Radio 4
94.8000		WFM	Jersey	BBC Radio 4
		WFM	Huntshaw Cross	BBC Radio Devon
		WFM	Isle of Skye	BBC Radio 4
		WFM	Knock More	BBC Radio 4
		WFM	Meriden	BBC CWR
94.9000		WFM	Ayrshire	BBC Radio 4
		WFM	Coventry	BBC CWR
		WFM	Londonderry	BBC Radio 4
		WFM	Bristol City	BBC Radio Bristol
		WFM	Lincolnshire	BBC Radio Lincolnshire
		WFM	Perth	BBC Radio Scotland
		WFM	Forfar	BBC Radio 4
		WFM	London	Greater London Radio
		WFM	Shetland	BBC Radio 4
95.0000		WFM	Teesside	BBC Radio Cleveland
		WFM	Stroud	BBC Radio Gloucestershire
		WFM	Leicester	BBC Radio Leicestershire
		WFM	Ludlow	BBC Radio Shropshire
		WFM	Newhaven	BBC Radio Sussex
		WFM	Peebles	BBC Radio 4
95.1000		WFM	Argyll	BBC Radio 4

Base	Mobile	Mode	Location	User and Notes
		WFM	South Wales	BBC Radio Gwent
		WFM	Norfolk	BBC Radio Norfolk
		WFM	Horsham	BBC Radio Sussex
		WFM	G Manchester	Greater Manchester Radio
		WFM	Gwent	BBC Radio Wales
		WFM	Isle of Lewis	BBC Radio 4
		WFM	Ballycastle	Radio Ulster
		WFM	Western Isles	BBC Radio 4
		WFM	Normandy	France Normandie-Rouen
		WFM	France	Cherie-FM
95.2000		WFM	Argyll	BBC Radio 4
		WFM	E Cornwall	BBC Radio Cornwall
		WFM	Kendal	BBC Radio Cumbria
		WFM	Oxfordshire	BBC Radio Oxford
		WFM	Clermont Carn	RTE Radio 1
		WFM	Nromandy	Radio Manche
95.3000		WFM	Aberdeenshire	BBC Radio 4
		WFM	Argyll	BBC Radio 4
		WFM	Ayrshire	BBC Radio 4
		WFM	Matlock	BBC Radio Derby
		WFM	Southend	BBC Radio Essex
		WFM	Wharfdale	BBC Radio Leeds
		WFM	Brighton	BBC Radio Sussex
		WFM	Dumfriesshire	BBC Radio 4
		WFM	Kirkcudbrightshire	BBC Radio 4
		WFM	Perthshire	BBC Radio 4
95.3250		WFM	London	Function FM
95.4000		WFM	Tyneside	BBC Radio Newcastle
		WFM	Windsor	BBC Radio Surrey & Berkshire
		WFM	Limavady	Radio Ulster
		WFM	Brittany	France Inter
95.5000		WFM	Bedford	BBC Radio Bedfordshire
		WFM	Taunton	BBC Radio Bristol
		WFM	E Lancashire	BBC Radio Lancashire
		WFM	Mansfield	BBC Radio Nottinghamshire
		WFM	Scarborough	BBC Radio York
		WFM	Bristol	BBC Radio Bristol
		WFM	Carmarthen	BBC Radio 4
		WFM	Brest	France Inter
		WFM	Lowestoft	BBC Suffolk
		WFM	Newark	BBC Radio Nottinghamshire
		WFM	Somerset	Somerset Sound
		WFM	Tayside	BBC Radio 4
		WFM	Wiltshire	Somerset Sound
95.6000		WFM	Argyll	BBC Radio 4
		WFM	Cumbria	BBC Radio Cumbria
		WFM	W Midlands	BBC Radio West Midlands
		WFM	Co Fermanagh	BBC Radio 4

Base	Mobile	Mode	Location	User and Notes
		WFM	Caen	France Musique
95.7000		WFM	Peterborough	BBC Radio Cambridge
		WFM	Dorset	BBC Radio Dorset
		WFM	Invernessshire	BBC Radio 4
		WFM	Isle of Islay	BBC Radio 4
95.8000		WFM	Exeter	BBC Radio Devon
		WFM	Merseyside	BBC Radio Merseyside
		WFM	Berkshire	Capital Radio
		WFM	London	Capital 95.8 FM
		WFM	Glasgow	BBC Radio 4
		WFM	Lanarkshire	BBC Radio 4
		WFM	London	Capital 95.8 FM
		WFM	Surrey	Capital Radio
		WFM	St Malo	Radio Force 7
95.9000		WFM	Aberdeenshire	BBC Radio 4
		WFM	SW Wales	BBC Radio 4
		WFM	South Wales	BBC Radio Gwent
		WFM	Yorkshire	BBC Radio Humberside
		WFM	Borders	BBC Radio Newcastle
		WFM	Fort William	BBC Radio 4
		WFM	Thanet	Invicta FM
		WFM	Orkney	BBC Radio 4
		WFM	Western Isles	BBC Radio 4
		WFM	France	France Musique
96.0000		WFM	Cambridgeshire	BBC Radio Cambridge
		WFM	Scilles	BBC Radio Cornwall
		WFM	Okehampton	BBC Radio Devon
		WFM	Shropshire	BBC Radio Shropshire
		WFM	Belfast	BBC Radio 4
		WFM	Belfast	Radio Ulster
		WFM	Weymouth	Wessex FM
		WFM	France	Radio Boule
96.1000		WFM	SW Cumbria	BBC Radio Furness
		WFM	S Hampshire	BBC Radio Solent
		WFM	Berkshire	Hits 96 Radio
		WFM	Buckinghamshire	Hits 96 Radio
		WFM	Colchester	SGR
		WFM	Colchester	SGR
		WFM	County Mayo	MWR FM
		WFM	Rotherham	Hallam FM
		WFM	Innerleithen	BBC Radio 4
		WFM	Ashford	Invicta FM
		WFM	Isle of Mull	BBC Radio 4
		WFM	Isle of Skye	BBC Radio 4
		WFM	Isle of Lewis	BBC Radio 4
		WFM	London	Zoom FM
		WFM	Oxfordshire	Hits 96 Radio
		WFM	Poseys	BBC Radio Cymru

Base	Mobile	Mode	Location	User and Notes
		WFM	Ullapool	BBC Radio 4
96.2000		WFM	Aylesbury	Mix 96
		WFM	Coventry	Kix 96
		WFM	North Devon	Lantern Radio
		WFM	Scarborough	Yorkshire Coast Radio
		WFM	Shetland	SIBC
		WFM	Trent FM	Notts & Derby
		WFM	Tyneside	Century Radio
		WFM	France	Radio Cote d'Armor
96.3000		WFM	Colwyn Bay	Marcher Coast FM
		WFM	Llandudno	Marcher Coast FM
		WFM	N Wales	Coast FM
		WFM	North Wales	Marcher Coast FM
		WFM	Parsley	Q96 FM
		WFM	Southend	Essex Radio
		WFM	Avon	GWR
		WFM	Leeds	Radio Aire
		WFM	Normnady	France Inter
96.4000		WFM	Birmingham	BRMB Radio
		WFM	Carlisle	CFM Radio
		WFM	County Mayo	RTE 3
		WFM	Guildford	County Sound
		WFM	Torbay	Devonalr Radio
		WFM	Limavady	Downtown Radio
		WFM	Galway	County Clare Radio
		WFM	Premier Radio	NW Surrey
		WFM	Perth	Radio Tay
		WFM	Bury St Edmonds	Saxon Radio
		WFM	S Cheshire	Signal Cheshire
		WFM	Surrey	Mercury
		WFM	Swansea	Swansea Sound
		WFM	Torbay	Gemini FM
		WFM	Normandy	Nostalgie
96.5000		WFM	Blackpool	Radio Wave
		WFM	Marlborough	GWR
		WFM	Lancashire	Radio Wave
		WFM	Mansfield	Trent Local Radio
		WFM	Nottingham	Trent FM
		WFM	Taunton	Orchard FM
		WFM	St. Brieux	NRJ
96.6000		WFM	Aberystwyth	Radio Ceredigion
		WFM	Enniskillen	Downtown Radio
		WFM	Fort William	Nevis Radio
		WFM	Inverness	Moray Firth Radio
		WFM	Northampton	Northants 96
		WFM	Tavistock	Radio In Tavistock
		WFM	St Albans	Oasis Radio
		WFM	Teesside	TFM Radio

Base	Mobile	Mode	Location	User and Notes
		WFM	France	Radio France Mayenne
96.7000		WFM	North Kent	BBC Radio Kent
		WFM	Belfast	BCR
		WFM	Stirling	Centresound
		WFM	Merseyside	City FM
		WFM	Kings Lynn	KLFM
		WFM	N Hampshire	Light FM
		WFM	Ayrshire	West Sound
96.8000		WFM	Bristol	BBC Radio Cymru
		WFM	County Mayo	Galway Bay Radio
		WFM	Selkirk	Radio Borders
		WFM	Wenvoe	BBC Radio Cymru
96.9000		WFM	Blackpool	The Bay FM
		WFM	Blackpool	Wave FM
		WFM	Bedford	Chiltern Radio
		WFM	Brixton	Choice FM
		WFM	Isle of Man	Manx Radio
		WFM	Morecambe	The Bay
		WFM	Aberdeen	North Sound
		WFM	S Staffordshire	Signal Stafford
		WFM	Newhaven	Southern Sound
		WFM	Surrey	Southern FM
		WFM	Humberside	Viking FM
97.0000		WFM	Exeter	Devonair Radio
		WFM	Exeter	Gemini FM
		WFM	Glasgow	Clyde 1
		WFM	Dover	Invicta FM
		WFM	Ireland	RTE 2
		WFM	Coventry	Mercia Sound
		WFM	Plymouth	Plymouth Sound
		WFM	Thames Valley	Radio 210
97.1000		WFM	Jersey	BBC Radio 1
		WFM	County Galway	MWR FM
		WFM	Haslemere	Delta Radio
		WFM	Galway	MWR FM
		WFM	Ipswich	SGR FM
		WFM	Tyneside	Metro FM
		WFM	N Wales	Marcher Sound
		WFM	Yeovil	Orchard FM
		WFM	Ipswich	Radio Orwell
		WFM	Wrexham	MFM
97.2000		WFM	Wolverhampton	Beacon West Midlands
		WFM	Bristol	Galaxy Radio
		WFM	Dorchester	Wessex FM
		WFM	Bristol	For The People
		WFM	Swindon	GWR
		WFM	Harrogate	Stray FM
		WFM	Isle of Man	Manx Radio

Base	Mobile	Mode	Location	User and Notes
		WFM	SW Scotland	South West Sound
97.3000		WFM	London	Crown FM
		WFM	London	London News
		WFM	Edinburgh	Radio Forth RFM
97.4000		WFM	Cambridge	Q103
		WFM	Luton	Chiltern Radio
		WFM	Belfast	Cool FM
		WFM	Banbury	Fox FM
		WFM	Sheffield	Hallam FM
		WFM	Inverness	Moray Firth Radio
		WFM	Bradford	Pennine FM
		WFM	St. Malo	Radio Force 7
		WFM	South Wales	Red Dragon Radio
		WFM	Lancashire	Red Rose Radio
97.5000		WFM	Bradford	The Pulse
		WFM	E Solent	Ocean Sound
		WFM	Pitlochry	Heartland FM
		WFM	Berwick	Radio Borders
		WFM	Horsham	Radio Mercury
		WFM	Hastings	Southern Sound
		WFM	Girvan	West Sound
		WFM	Normandy	France Normandie-Caen
97.6000 -99.8000 MHz			**NATIONWIDE BBC RADIO 1**	
97.6000		WFM	Luton	Chiltern Radio
		WFM	Edinburgh	Forth FM
		WFM	Folkestone	BBC Radio Kent
		WFM	Kent	BBC Kent
		WFM	Hereford	Radio Wyvern
97.7000		WFM	Ballachulish	
		WFM	Border Counties	
		WFM	Cirencester	
		WFM	Devon & East Cornwall	
		WFM	East Cornwall	
		WFM	Ffestiniog	
		WFM	Grantham Area	
		WFM	Guildford & Farnham Area	
		WFM	Gwynedd	
		WFM	Hastings	
		WFM	Isle of Islay	
		WFM	Isle of Skye	
		WFM	Llanidloes	
		WFM	Mallaig	
		WFM	Manningtree	
		WFM	North Cumbria	
		WFM	South West Devon & Plymouth	
		WFM	Western Isles	
97.8000		WFM	Betws-y-Coed	

Base	Mobile	Mode	Location	User and Notes
		WFM	Knock More	
		WFM	Mid Glamorgan	
		WFM	Newbury	
		WFM	Pendle Forest	
		WFM	Wiltshire	
		WFM	France CultureBrest	
		WFM	Midland Counties Area	
		WFM	Nailsworth Area	
		WFM	Staffordshire & Shropshire	
97.9000		WFM	Ayrshire	
		WFM	Co. Down	
		WFM	Dunbartonshire	
		WFM	Gwynedd	
		WFM	Lochgilphead	BBC Radio Nan Gaidheal
		WFM	Midlands	
		WFM	Ness of Lewis	
		WFM	Shetland	
		WFM	Ullapool	
		WFM	Wensleydale	
		WFM	Westwood	
		WFM	Windermere	
		WFM	Forfar Area	
		WFM	Leicestershire	
		WFM	Perth Area	
		WFM	Trowbridge Area	
98.0000		WFM	Campbeltown	
		WFM	Clwyd	
		WFM	Dyfed	
		WFM	Ebbw Vale	
		WFM	Hebden Bridge	
		WFM	Isle of Man	
		WFM	Mid Glamorgan	
		WFM	Peebles	
		WFM	Surrey	
		WFM	Walsden	
		WFM	Wharfedale	
		WFM	South London	
		WFM	Brittany	NRJ
98.1000		WFM	Argyll	
		WFM	Devon	
		WFM	Eastbourne	
		WFM	Isle of Skye	
		WFM	Mid Glamorgan	
		WFM	West Glamorgan	
		WFM	West Yorkshire	
		WFM	Dublin	98 FM Dublin
		WFM	North Eastern Counties	
98.2000		WFM	Argyll	

The UK Scanning Directory

Base	Mobile	Mode	Location	User and Notes
		WFM	Berwick	
		WFM	Buckinghamshire	
		WFM	Co Armagh	
		WFM	Herefordshire	
		WFM	Isle of Wight	
		WFM	London	De-ja-vu
		WFM	Mid Glamorgan	
		WFM	Inveraray Area	BBC Radio 4
		WFM	Kinross Area	BBC Radio 4
		WFM	Bedford Area	
		WFM	Central South of England	
		WFM	North West Lancashire	
98.3000		WFM	Aberdeenshire	
		WFM	Abergavenny	
		WFM	Argyll	
		WFM	Kirkcudbrightshire	
		WFM	London	Unique
		WFM	Londonderry	
		WFM	Okehampton	
		WFM	West Yorkshire	
		WFM	Aberystwyth Area & Cardigan Bay	
		WFM	Cambridgeshire	
		WFM	Folkestone Area	
		WFM	France Culture Rennes	
		WFM	Grampian Area	
		WFM	Lincolnshire	
		WFM	Newark Area	
98.4000		WFM	Co An trim	
		WFM	Comwall	
		WFM	Devon	
		WFM	Isles of Scilly	
		WFM	Penaligon Downs	
		WFM	Ton Petre	
		WFM	Chippenham Area	
98.5000		WFM	Brecon	
		WFM	Cambridge	
		WFM	Carmarthen	
		WFM	Chard	
		WFM	Crystal Palace	
		WFM	Girvan	
		WFM	Gwent	
		WFM	Keighley	
		WFM	Llangollen	
		WFM	London	Elite
		WFM	Northampton	
		WFM	Oban	
		WFM	Todmorden	
		WFM	Brittany	France Musique

Base	Mobile	Mode	Location	User and Notes
98.6000		WFM	Chesterfield	
		WFM	Exeter	
		WFM	Gloucestershire	
		WFM	Isle of Islay	
		WFM	Kendal	
		WFM	Minehead	
		WFM	Swindon	
		WFM	West Glamorgan	
		WFM	Abertillery	
		WFM	Bath City Area	
		WFM	County Mayo	RTE Radio 3
		WFM	Perth	
98.7000		WFM	Ashkirk	
		WFM	Brigport	
		WFM	Conwy	
		WFM	Devon	
		WFM	Dorset	
		WFM	Kingussie	
		WFM	Lame	
		WFM	Llandrindod Wells	
		WFM	Poseys	
		WFM	Rossshire	
		WFM	Somerset	
		WFM	West Kilbride	
		WFM	Border Counties Area	
98.8000		WFM	Mid Glamorgan	
		WFM	Pitlochry	
		WFM	Pontypool	
		WFM	Greater London	
		WFM	Home Counties	
		WFM	Radio Profile Normandy	
		WFM	Rosneath Area	
		WFM	Stroud Area	
		WFM	Wrexham & Deeside Area	
98.9000		WFM	Bristol	
		WFM	Fort William	
		WFM	Gwent	
		WFM	Orkney	
		WFM	Perthshire	
		WFM	South Knapdale	
		WFM	Western Isles	
		WFM	Cheshire Area	
		WFM	Derbyshire	
		WFM	Greater Manchester	
		WFM	Humberside	
		WFM	Lancashire	
		WFM	Merseyside	
		WFM	Nottinghamshire	

Base	Mobile	Mode	Location	User and Notes
		WFM	South East Wales	
		WFM	Yorkshire	
		WFM	Brittany	France Musique
		WFM	Normandy	CFM
99.0000		WFM	Aberdeenshire	
		WFM	Avon	
		WFM	Co Fermanagh	
		WFM	Gwynedd	
		WFM	Isle of Wight	
		WFM	Machynlleth	
		WFM	Newry	
		WFM	Northumberland	
99.1000		WFM	Ayrshire	
		WFM	Darwen	
		WFM	Devon	
		WFM	Gwent	
		WFM	Innerleithen	
		WFM	Isle of Mull	
		WFM	Swansea	
		WFM	Greenholm & Darvel Area	
		WFM	Oxfordshire & Wiltshire	
		WFM	France	Radio Boule
99.2000		WFM	Bexhill	
		WFM	Co Londonderry	
		WFM	Fermdale	
		WFM	Keswick Forest	
		WFM	Lancashire	
		WFM	London	Irie
		WFM	Ludlow	
		WFM	Mid Glamorgan	
		WFM	Welshpool	
		WFM	Whitby	
		WFM	Inverness	
		WFM	North East Scotland	
		WFM	Pennar	
99.3000		WFM	Berwickshire	
		WFM	Dyfed	
		WFM	Kinlochleven	
		WFM	Lancashire	
		WFM	Lyme Regis	
		WFM	Newhaven	
		WFM	Redruth	
		WFM	Stranraer	
		WFM	Surrey	
		WFM	Weardale	
		WFM	West Yorkshire	
		WFM	Whitehaven	
		WFM	Saddleworth Area	

Base	Mobile	Mode	Location	User and Notes
		WFM	South East London	
		WFM	Suffolk & Norfolk Area	
		WFM	Normandy	NRJ
99.4000		WFM	Caversham	
		WFM	Clwyd	
		WFM	Derbyshire	
		WFM	Isle of Lewis	
		WFM	Newcastle upon Tyne	
		WFM	South Devon	
		WFM	North Wales Coast & Anglesey	
		WFM	Pudsey Area	
		WFM	Salisbury Area	
		WFM	France	RFM
99.5000		WFM	Dover	
		WFM	Haslingden	
		WFM	N Bristol	
		WFM	Sheffield	
		WFM	Central Lowlands	
		WFM	Forth Valley	
		WFM	Gloucester Area	
		WFM	Lowland Scotland	
		WFM	Scarborough Area	
		WFM	Somerset & North Devon	
		WFM	South & East Wales	
99.6000		WFM	High Wycombe	
		WFM	London	Ragga FM
		WFM	North Yorkshire	
		WFM	Buxton Area	
		WFM	France InterCaen	
		WFM	Morecambe Bay Area	
		WFM	South Cumbria	
		WFM	Weymouth Area	
99.7000		WFM	Aberdeenshire	
		WFM	Basingstoke	
		WFM	Belfast	
		WFM	Caithness	
		WFM	Dolgellau	
		WFM	Llandyfriog	
		WFM	Marlborough	
		WFM	Northumberland	
		WFM	Powys	
		WFM	Brighton Area	
		WFM	Peterborough Area	
99.7500		WFM	Manchester	Love Energy
99.8000		WFM	Powys	

99.8000 - 103.8000 MHz NATIONWIDE INDEPENDENT RADIO

Base	Mobile	Mode	Location	User and Notes
99.9000		WFM	Cumbria	Classic FM
		WFM	Cherbourg	France Cherbourg

Base	Mobile	Mode	Location	User and Notes
100.0000		WFM	London	Kiss FM
		WFM	Surrey	Kiss FM
		WFM	Berkshire	Kiss FM
		WFM	Plymouth	Classic FM
		WFM	Devon	Classic FM
100.1000		WFM	Perth	Classic FM
		WFM	Edinburgh	Scot FM
		WFM	Midlands	Classic FM
		WFM	Manchester	Classic FM
		WFM	Normandy	France-Normandie-Rouen
100.2000		WFM	St Lo	Radio Manche
100.3000		WFM	Glasgow	Scot FM
		WFM	Tyneside	Classic FM
		WFM	Gosport	Classic FM
		WFM	North East	Classic FM
		WFM	Isle of Wight	Classic FM
100.4000		WFM	North West	Jazz FM
		WFM	Manchester	Jazz FM
		WFM	London	Pressure FM
		WFM	Normandy	France Cherbourg
100.5000		WFM	London	JBC FM
		WFM	Aberdeenshire	Classic FM
		WFM	Londonderry	Classic FM
		WFM	Lincolnshire	Classic FM
		WFM	Nationwide	RSL 28 Day stations
		WFM	St Malo	RPV
100.6000		WFM	London Hendon	Tottenham ComRadio
100.7000		WFM	North East	Century FM
		WFM	Gwynedd	Classic FM
		WFM	Midlands	Heart FM
		WFM	Normandy	France Cherbourg
100.8000		WFM	Oxfordshire	Classic FM
100.8500		WFM	Berkshire	Classic FM
		WFM	Buckinghamshire	Classic FM
100.9000		WFM	London	Classic FM
		WFM	Kent	Classic FM
101.0000		WFM	Bristol	Galaxy FM
		WFM	Bristol	Galaxy FM
		WFM	Calne	Galaxy 101
101.1000		WFM	Holme Moss	Classic FM
		WFM	Edinburgh	Scot FM
		WFM	Normandy	NRJ
101.3000		WFM	Oxford	Classic FM
		WFM	Oxford	Classic FM
		WFM	A yrshire	Classic FM
		WFM	Swansea	Classic FM
		WFM	London	Eruption
101.4500		WFM	Manchester	Frontline

Base	Mobile	Mode	Location	User and Notes
101.5000		WFM	Norwich	Classic FM
101.6000		WFM	London	Star FM
		WFM	Anglesey	Classic FM
		WFM	Gwynedd	Classic FM
		WFM	Alton	Wey Valley Radio
		WFM	Brittany	RTL
101.7000		WFM	Central Scotland	Classic FM
		WFM	Bristol	Classic FM
		WFM	Sheffield	Classic FM
		WFM	Harlow	Ten 17
		WFM	Wenvoe	Classic FM
		WFM	Normandy	France Culture
101.8000		WFM	Tyneside	Century Radio
		WFM	North East	Century FM
		WFM	Dover	Classic FM
		WFM	London	Phreak FM
101.9000		WFM	Peterborough	Classic FM
		WFM	Belfast	Classic FM
		WFM	Normandy	NRJ
102.0000		WFM	Sunset Radio	Manchester
102.0000		WFM	London	London Jazz Radio
		WFM	Hastings	Southern FM
		WFM	Salisbury	Spire FM
		WFM	Alton	Wey Valley Radio
		WFM	Manchester	Kiss 102
102.1000		WFM	Inverurie	North East Community Radio
		WFM	Cherbourg	Radio Force 7
102.2000		WFM	Wiltshire	GWRW
		WFM	Greater London	London Jazz Radio
		WFM	E Cornwall	Pirate FM
		WFM	Lincoln	Lincs FM Radio
		WFM	London	JFM
		WFM	Plymouth	Pirate FM
		WFM	Lincolnshire	Lincs Local Radio
		WFM	Birmingham	Choice FM
		WFM	London	Jazz FM
		WFM	Comwafl	Pirate FM
		WFM	Shetland	SIBC
102.3000		WFM	Dundee	Radio Tay
		WFM	E Dorest	Two Counties Radio
		WFM	Windermere	The Bay
		WFM	Normandy	NRJ
102.4000		WFM	Birmingham	Buzz FM
		WFM	Londonderry	Downtown Radio
		WFM	Norfolk	BroadsRadio Broadland
		WFM	Cheltenham	Severn Sound
		WFM	N Sussex	Southern Sound
		WFM	Newark	Lincs FM

Base	Mobile	Mode	Location	User and Notes
		WFM	Normandy	France Musique
102.5000		WFM	Glasgow	Clyde FM
		WFM	County Mayo	MWR FM
		WFM	Oxford	Fox FM
		WFM	Halifax	Pennine FM
		WFM	Penrith	CFM Radio
		WFM	Carlisle	CFM
		WFM	Huddersfield	The Pulse
102.6000		WFM	Chelms	Essex Radioford
		WFM	Mendips	Orchard FM
		WFM	Coventry	Radio Harmony
		WFM	N Staff	Signal Radio s
		WFM	Berkshire	Fox FM
		WFM	Oxfordshire	Fox FM
		WFM	Buckinghamshire	Fox FM
		WFM	Wiltshire	Fox FM
		WFM	Oxford	Fox FM
		WFM	NStaffordshire	Signal One
		WFM	Oxford	Fox FM
		WFM	Caen	France Normandie-Caen
102.7000		WFM	Peterborough	Hereward Radio
		WFM	Reigate	Radio Mercury
		WFM	Clermont Carn	Raidio Na Gaeltachta
		WFM	Kelghley	BBC Radio Leeds
102.8000		WFM	SE Kent	Invicta FM
		WFM	Worcester	Radio Wyvern
		WFM	Perth	Radio Tay
		WFM	West Cornwall	Pirate FM
		WFM	Redruth	Pirate FM
		WFM	Derby	Ram FM
		WFM	Derby	Trent FM 945
102.9000		WFM	Barnsley	Hallam FM
		WFM	Leamington	Mercia Sound
		WFM	Londonderry	102.9
		WFM	Andover	Radio 210
		WFM	Normandy	NRJ
103.0000		WFM	W Dorset	Devonair Radio
		WFM	Bath Cit	GWRy
		WFM	Peebles	Radio Borders
		WFM	Isle of Wight	Classic FM
		WFM	Tyneside	Metro FM
		WFM	East Devon	Gemini FM
		WFM	Newcastle upon Tyne	Metro FM
		WFM	Cambridge	Q103
		WFM	Stroud	Severn Sound
		WFM	Peterhead	NorthSound 1
		WFM	Newmarket	CN FM 103
		WFM	Manches	Key 103ter

Base	Mobile	Mode	Location	User and Notes
		WFM	Cambridge	CN FM 103
103.1000		WFM	Shropshire	Beacon Shropshire
		WFM	Medway	Invicta FM
		WFM	Rennes	France Armorique
		WFM	Stirling	Central FM
		WFM	Peebles	Radio Borders
		WFM	Scarborough	Yorkshire Coast Radio
103.2000		WFM	Bradford	Bradford City Radio
		WFM	Solent	Power FM
		WFM	Cardiff	Red Dragon Radio
		WFM	Leicester	Sound FM
		WFM	Kendal	The Bay
		WFM	Bradford	Sunrise FM
		WFM	Morecambe	The Bay
103.3000		WFM	Milton Keynes	Horizon Radio
		WFM	Haringey	London Greek Radio
		WFM	Donegal	Hi-Land Radio
		WFM	Milton Keynes	Horizon FM
		WFM	Aberystwvth	Radio Ceredigion
		WFM	Glasgow	Clyde 1
103.4000		WFM	Devon	BBC Radio Devon
		WFM	Doncaster	Hallam FM
		WFM	Wrexham	Marcher Sound MFM
		WFM	Eyemouth	Radio Borders
		WFM	Sunderland	Wear FM
		WFM	Sunderland	Sun City 103.4
103.5000		WFM	Chelmsford	BBC Radio Essex
		WFM	Glasgow	East End Radio
		WFM	Brighton	Southern Sound
		WFM	Salisbury	Wiltshire Sound
		WFM	Isle of Mull	BBC Radio Nan Gaidheal
		WFM	Birmingham	PCRL
		WFM	Ffestiniog	BBC Radio 4
		WFM	West Kilbride	BBC Radio 4
		WFM	Gwent	BBC Radio 4
		WFM	Larne	BBC Radio 4
		WFM	Brittany	Fun Radio
103.5500		WFM	London	Flex
103.6000		WFM	Leicester	BBC Radio Northampton
		WFM	Swindon	Wiltshire Sound
		WFM	Birmingham	BBC CWR
		WFM	Wiltshire	BBC Radio Wiltshire
		WFM	Oxfordshire	BBC Radio Wiltshire
		WFM	Welshpool	BBC Radio Cymru
		WFM	Isle of Islay	BBC Radio Nan Gaidheal
		WFM	Anglesey	BBC Radio 4
		WFM	W Islay	BBC Radio 4
		WFM	Anglesey	BBC Radio 4

Base	Mobile	Mode	Location	User and Notes
		WFM	Rossshire	BBC Radio 4
		WFM	Machynlleth	BBC Radio 4
		WFM	Dolgellau	BBC Radio 4
		WFM	Stranraer	BBC Radio 4
		WFM	West Glamorgan	BBC Radio 4
103.7000		WFM	Yorkshire	BBC Radio York
		WFM	Coventry	BBC CWR
		WFM	Mid Glamorgan	BBC Radio Cymru
		WFM	Pennar	BBC Radio Cymru
		WFM	Clettraval	BBC Radio Nan Gaidheal
		WFM	Argyll	BBC Radio Nan Gaidheal
		WFM	Isle of Man	Manx Radio
		WFM	Manchester	Sting FM
		WFM	Dyfed	BBC Radio 4
		WFM	Jersey	Channel 103
103.8000		WFM	Luton	BBC Radio Bedfordshire
		WFM	Notts	BBC Radio Nottinghamshire
		WFM	Thamesmead	Independent Radio
		WFM	Donegal	North Atlantic Radio
		WFM	Dorset	BBC Dorset FM
		WFM	Clwyd	BBC Radio Cymru
		WFM	Hertfordshire	BBC 3CR
		WFM	Llandrindod Wells	BBC Radio 4
		WFM	Dunbartonshire	BBC Radio 4
103.8500		WFM	Glasgow	Freedom FM
103.9000		WFM	W Cornwall	BBC Radio Cornwall
		WFM	Central Lancs	BBC Radio Lancashire
		WFM	S Suffolk	BBC Radio Suffolk
		WFM	West Yorkshire	BBC Radio Leeds
		WFM	Rossshire	BBC Radio Nan Gaidheal
		WFM	Ashkirk	BBC Radio 4
		WFM	Pitlochry	BBC Radio 4
		WFM	Newry	BBC Radio 4
104.0000		WFM	N Sussex	BBC Radio Sussex
		WFM	Newcastle	BBC Radio Newcastle
		WFM	Nuneaton	BBC CWR
		WFM	Great Malvern	BBC Hereford & Worcester
		WFM	Perth Area	BBC Radio 4
		WFM	Normandy	RFM
104.1000		WFM	S Yorks	BBC Radio Sheffield
		WFM	W Berks	BBC Radio Surrey & Berkshire
		WFM	Oxfordshire	BBC Radio Berkshire
		WFM	Buckinghamshire	BBC Radio Berkshire
		WFM	Surrey	BBC Radio Berkshire
		WFM	Stafford	BBC Radio Stoke-on-Trent
		WFM	Dunbartonshire	BBC Radio 4
		WFM	Gwynedd	BBC Radio 4
		WFM	Dinard	Radio Force 7

Base	Mobile	Mode	Location	User and Notes
104.2000		WFM	Windermere	BBC Radio Cumbria
		WFM	Dover	BBC Radio Kent
		WFM	Northants	BBC Radio Northampton
		WFM	Dover	BBC Radio Kent
		WFM	Northamptonshire	BBC Radio Northampton
		WFM	Windermere	BBC Radio Cumbria
		WFM	Fort William	BBC Radio Nan Gaidheal
		WFM	Daliburgh	BBC Radio Nan Gaidheal
		WFM	Argyll	BBC Radio Nan Gaidheal
		WFM	London	Nation
		WFM	Swansea	BBC Radio 4
		WFM	Grampian	BBC Radio 4
104.3000		WFM	Northallerton	BBC Radio York
		WFM	Wiltshire	Wiltshire Sound
		WFM	Llangollen	BBC Radio Cymru
		WFM	Abertillery	BBC Radio Cymru
		WFM	Isle of Lewis	BBC Radio Nan Gaidheal
		WFM	Mallaig	BBC Radio Nan Gaidheal
		WFM	Isle of Skye	BBC Radio Nan Gaidheal
		WFM	Ayrshire	BBC Radio 4
		WFM	Ton Petre	BBC Radio 4
		WFM	France	RTL
104.4000		WFM	Gateshead	BBC Radio Newcastle
		WFM	Norfolk	BBC Radio Norfolk
		WFM	Reading	BBC Radio Surrey & Berkshire
		WFM	Gateshead	BBC Radio Newcastle
		WFM	W Norfolk	BBC Radio Norfolk
		WFM	Powys	BBC Radio Cymru
		WFM	Kinlochleven	BBC Radio Nan Gaidheal
		WFM	Llandyfriog	BBC Radio 4
		WFM	Conwy	BBC Radio 4
		WFM	St Lo	Radio Manche
104.5000		WFM	Milton Keynes	BBC Radio Bedfordshire
		WFM	Derbyshire	BBC Radio Derby
		WFM	Lancaster	BBC Radio Lancashire
		WFM	Mid Sussex	BBC Radio Sussex
		WFM	Berkshire	Three Counties Radio
		WFM	Wiltshire	Three Counties Radio
		WFM	Oxfordshire	Three Counties Radio
		WFM	Mid Glamorgan	BBC Radio Cymru
		WFM	West Glamorgan	BBC Radio Cymru
		WFM	North Bucks	BBC 3CR
		WFM	Perth	BBC Radio 4
		WFM	Caithness	BBC Radio 4
		WFM	Perthshire	BBC Radio 4
		WFM	Aberdeenshire	BBC Radio 4
104.6000		WFM	Bath City	BBC Radio Bristol
		WFM	N Suffolk	BBC Radio Suffolk

Base	Mobile	Mode	Location	User and Notes
		WFM	Guildford	BBC Radio Surrey
		WFM	Kidderminster	BBC Hereford & Worcester
		WFM	Ebbw Vale	BBC Radio Cymru
		WFM	Mid Glamorgan	BBC Radio Cymru
		WFM	Oban	BBC Radio Nan Gaidheal
		WFM	Manchester	Soul Nation
		WFM	Co Armagh	BBC Radio 4
		WFM	Dyfed	BBC Radio 4
		WFM	Berwickshire	BBC Radio 4
		WFM	Clwyd	BBC Radio 4
104.7000		WFM	Severn Valley	BBC Radio Gloucestershire
		WFM	Guernsey	Island FM
		WFM	Grantham	BBC Radio Lincolnshire
		WFM	Isle of Skye	BBC Radio Nan Gaidheal
		WFM	York	Minster FM
		WFM	Aberdare	BBC Radio 4
		WFM	Brecon	BBC Radio 4
104.8000		WFM	South Knapdale	BBC Radio Nan Gaidheal
		WFM	Burton Down	BBC Southern Counties Radio
		WFM	Gwynedd	BBC Radio 4
		WFM	Pontypool	BBC Radio 4
		WFM	Llanidloes	BBC Radio 4
		WFM	Mid Glamorgan	BBC Radio 4
		WFM	France	Europe 1
104.9000		WFM	Manningtree	BBC Radio Essex
		WFM	Coalville	BBC Radio Leicestershire
		WFM	High Wycombe	BBC Radio Surrey & Berkshire
		WFM	Stockport	KFM Radio
		WFM	Greater London	Melody Radio
		WFM	Manningtree	BBC Radio Essex
		WFM	Stockport	KFM Radio
		WFM	Cheshire	Signal Cheshire
		WFM	Fermdale	Radio Cymru
		WFM	Newark	Local Radio
		WFM	Gwynedd	BBC Radio Cymru
		WFM	Gwent	BBC Radio Cymru
		WFM	Rosshire	BBC Radio Nan Gaidheal
		WFM	Ness of Lewis	BBC Radio Nan Gaidheal
		WFM	Islay	BBC Radio Nan Gaidheal
		WFM	Argyll	BBC Radio Nan Gaidheal
		WFM	Marlborough	BBC Wiltshire Sound
		WFM	Stockport	Signal Cheshire
		WFM	South Islay	BBC Radio 4
		WFM	Haverfordwest	BBC Radio 4
		WFM	Stirling	BBC Radio 4
		WFM	Betws-y-Coed	BBC Radio 4
		WFM	Poseys	BBC Radio 4
		WFM	Mid Glamorgan	BBC Radio 4

Base	Mobile	Mode	Location	User and Notes
		WFM	Granville	Radio Force 7
105.0000		WFM	Milton Keynes	Frequency FM
105.1000		WFM	Bradford	Paradise FM
		WFM	France	NRJ
105.2000		WFM	Portsmouth	Angel FM
		WFM	Merseyside	Merseyland Alternative Radio
		WFM	London	Scandal FM
		WFM	Nationwide	RSL 28 Day stations
		WFM	France	Nostalgie
105.2300		WFM	Tameside	Radio Lightning
105.3450		WFM	London	Chance FM
105.3700		WFM	London	Local Community Radio
105.4000		WFM	London	Melody FM
		WFM	London	Melody Radio
		WFM	London	Melody FM
		WFM	Merseyside	Pure FM
		WFM	Nationwide	RSL 28 Day stations
105.5000		WFM	Leicester	Fresh FM
		WFM	Macclesfield	Radio Galaxy Massive
		WFM	Normandy	France Info
105.6000		WFM	Tamworth	Palace FM
		WFM	Berkshire	Direction
		WFM	Leeds	People's FM
		WFM	London	Radio Unknown
		WFM	Merseyside	Raw FM
		WFM	London	Zone FM
		WFM	Nationwide	RSL 28 Day stations
		WFM	Normandy	France Info
105.6750		WFM	London	The Don FM Brixton/Tottenham
		WFM	London	The Twiz
105.7000		WFM	Merseyside	Groove FM
		WFM	West Midlands	Sangeet
105.8000		WFM	Slough	Acropolis FM
		WFM	London	Virgin
		WFM	Leeds	Joy FM
		WFM	London	Point Blank FM
		WFM	Merseyside	Radio Tarqua
		WFM	London	Trance FM
		WFM	London	Virgin Radio
		WFM	Nationwide	RSL 28 Day stations
105.8200		WFM	London	Local Community Radio
105.9000		WFM	London	The Dream
106.0000		WFM	Bradford	Asian Paradise Radio
		WFM	Merseyside	Radio Caroline
		WFM	Leeds	Underground FM
		WFM	Nationwide	RSL 28 Day stations
106.0300		WFM	London	Local Community Radio
106.1000		WFM	Slough	Scandal FM

Base	Mobile	Mode	Location	User and Notes
		WFM	West Midlands	Kaos
		WFM	Normandy	RTL2
106.2000		WFM	Nationwide	RSL 28 Day stations
		WFM	London	Heart 106.2 FM
		WFM	Normandy	RTL2
106.3000		WFM	Birmingham	Frontline
106.4000		WFM	Portsmouth	Good Vibes FM
106.5000		WFM	Oldham	Ambient FM
		WFM	Sheffield	Fresh FM
106.6000		WFM	Slough	Star FM
		WFM	Nationwide	RSL 28 Day stations
		WFM	Normandy	Nostaglie
106.7000		WFM	Brixton	Rose FM
		WFM	Stockport	FAB FM
		WFM	France	Europe 1
106.8000		WFM	Sheffield	Foulmouth FM
		WFM	Leeds	Radio Apni Awaaz
106.9000		WFM	London	Maria London Community Radio
107.0000		WFM	Midlands	Midlands Underground FM
		WFM	Leeds	Unity FM
		WFM	Nationwide	RSL 28 Day stations
107.0500		WFM	London	The Dream
107.2000		WFM	Leicester	Genetic Community Radio
		WFM	Sheffield	Sheffield Community Radio
107.3000		WFM	London	Transmission 1
107.4000		WFM	Stockport	Power FM Radio
		WFM	Hull	Sweet FM
		WFM	Nationwide	RSL 28 Day stations
107.5000		WFM	Leicester	Kickin' FM
		WFM	Sheffield	Dance FM
		WFM	Leicester	Fresh FM
		WFM	Hickley	Kickin' FM
		WFM	Berkshire	Radio Active
107.6000		WFM	Merseyside	Commodore FM
107.7000		WFM	Tameside	Wild 1077
107.8000		WFM	Leeds	Dream FM
		WFM	Nationwide	RSL 28 Day stations

108.0000 - 112.0000 MHz TACAN AND DME IDENTS, ILS LOCALISERS AND

Base	Mobile	Mode	Location	User and Notes
108.0000		AM	RAF Greenham Common	TACAN Ident (GCN)
		AM	Belfast	DME (I-BFH)
		AM	Dundee Airport	DME Ident (DDE)
		AM	RAF Cottesmore	TACAN Ident (CTM)
		AM	Guernsey Airport	ILS Localiser Runway 09 (I-UY)
		AM	RAF Mildenhall	ILS Localiser Runway 11 (I-MIL)
		AM	Guernsey Airport	ILS Localiser Runway 27 (I-GH)
		AM	RAF Chivenor	ILS Localiser Runway 28 (CV)
		AM	RAF Mildenhall	ILS Localiser Runway 29 (I-MLD)

Base	Mobile	Mode	Location	User and Notes
		AM	RAF Abingdon	ILS Localiser Runway 36 (AB)
108.1500		AM	Blackpool Airport	DME Ident
		AM	Lydd Airport	DME Ident
		AM	Lydd Airport	ILS Localiser Runway 22 (I-LYX)
		AM	Blackpool Airport	ILS Localiser Runway 28 (I-BPL)
108.2000		AM	Boscombe Down (MoD)	TACAN Ident (BDN)
108.3000		AM	RAF Lakenheath	ILS Localiser Runway 24 (I-LKH)
		AM	Londonderry	ILS/DME Rwy 26 (EGT)
		AM	Bedford (MoD Airfield)	ILS Localiser Runway 27 (BQ)
		AM	Deauville	ILS Localiser Runway 30 (DV)
108.4000		AM	RAF Valley	TACAN Ident (VYL)
108.5000		AM	Sumburgh Airport	DME Ident
		AM	Teesside Airport	DME Ident
		AM	Teesside Airport	ILS Localiser Runway 05 (I-TSE)
		AM	Sumburgh Airport	ILS Localiser Runway 09 (SUB)
		AM	RAF Benson	ILS Localiser Runway 19 (BO)
		AM	Teesside Airport	ILS Localiser Runway 23 (I-TD)
		AM	Sumburgh Airport	ILS Localiser Runway 27 (I-SG)
108.6000		AM	Kirkwall Airport	VOR/DME Ident (KWL)
108.7000		AM	Newton Point	TACAN Ident (NTP)
		AM	RAF Shawbury	ILS Localiser Runway 19 (SY)
		AM	RAF Leuchars	ILS Localiser Runway 27 (LU)
		AM	RAF St Mawgan	ILS Localiser Runway 31 (SM)
108.7500		AM	Humberside Airport	DME Ident
		AM	Humberside Airport	ILS Localiser Runway 21 (I-HS)
108.8000		AM	Weathersfield	TACAN Ident (WET)
108.9000		AM	Edinburgh Airport	DME Ident
		AM	Ventnor	TACAN Ident (VNR)
		AM	Kerry	DME/ILS R25 KER
		AM	Edinburgh Airport	ILS Localiser Runway 07 (I-VG)
		AM	Dublin	ILS/DME Rwy 10
		AM	Cranfield	ILS Localiser Runway 22 (I-CR)
		AM	Edinburgh Airport	ILS Localiser Runway 25 (I-TH)
		AM	Dublin	ILS/DME Rwy 28
108.9500		AM	Woodford	DME Ident (I-WU)
		AM	Woodford	ILS Localiser Runway 25 (I-WU)
109.0500		AM	Yeovil Aerodrome	DME Ident (YVL)
109.1000		AM	Southampton Airport	ILS Localiser Runway 20 (I-SN)
109.1500		AM	Luton Airport	DME Ident
		AM	Luton Airport	ILS Localiser Rwy 08 (I-LTN)
		AM	Luton Airport	ILS Localiser Runway 26 (I-LJ)
109.2000		AM	Inverness Airport	VOR/DME Ident (INS)
		AM	Swansea Aerodrome	DME Ident (SWZ)
109.3000		AM	RAF Wattisham	TACAN Ident (WTM)
		AM	Glasgow Airport	ILS Localiser Runway 23 (I-OO)
		AM	RAF Church Fenton	ILS Localiser Runway 24 (CF)
		AM	RAF Wyton	ILS Localiser Runway 27 (WT)
109.3500		AM	East Midlands	ILS Localiser Runway 09 (I-BMW)

Base	Mobile	Mode	Location	User and Notes
		AM	Biggin Hill	ILS Localiser Runway 21 (I-BGH)
		AM	East Midlands	ILS Localiser Runway 27 (I-EME)
109.4000		AM	Barrow Airport	DME Ident (WL)
		AM	Guernsey Airport	VOR/ATIS (GUR)
109.5000		AM	London Heathrow	DME Ident
		AM	Manchester Airport	DME Ident
		AM	Plymouth Airport	DME Ident
		AM	Manchester Airport	ILS Localiser Runway 06 (I-MM)
		AM	London Heathrow	ILS Localiser Runway 09R (I-BB)
		AM	Manchester Airport	ILS Localiser Runway 24 (I-NN)
		AM	Shannon Airport	ILS Runway 24 (SA)
		AM	Ostend Airport	ILS Localiser Rwy 26 (IOS)
		AM	London Heathrow	ILS Localiser Runway 27L (I-LL)
		AM	Plymouth Airport	ILS Localiser Runway 31 (I-PLY)
109.6000		AM	RAF Odiham	TACAN Ident (ODH)
		AM	RAF Linton-on-Ouse	TACAN Ident (LOZ)
109.7000		AM	RAF Lyneham	ILS Localiser Runway (LA)
		AM	RAF Valley	ILS Localiser Runway 14 (VY)
		AM	Belfast/Aldergrove	ILS Localiser Runway 25 (I-AG)
		AM	RAF Cranwell	ILS Localiser Runway 26 (CW)
		AM	RAF Kinloss	ILS Localiser Runway 26 (KS)
		AM	Beauvais	ILS Localiser Runway 31 (BV)
		AM	Dinard	ILS Localiser Runway 36 (DR)
109.7500		AM	Coventry Airport	ILS Localiser Runway 23 (I-CT)
109.8000		AM	RAF Kinloss	TACAN Ident (KSS)
		AM	RAF Lyneham	TACAN (LYE)
109.8500		AM	Fair Oaks Aerodrome	DME Ident (FRK)
109.9000		AM	Warton (MoD)	DME Ident
		AM	East Midlands Airport	ILS Localiser Runway 09 (I-EMW)
		AM	Aberdeen/Dyce Airport	ILS Localiser Runway 16 (I-AX)
		AM	Cork Airport	ILS Runway 17 (ICA)
		AM	Stornoway Airport	ILS Localiser Runway 18 (I-SV)
		AM	Exeter Airport	ILS Localiser Runway 26 (I-XR)
		AM	Warton (MoD)	ILS Localiser Runway 26 (WQ)
		AM	East Midlands Airport	ILS Localsier Runway 27 (I-EME)
		AM	Cherbourg	ILS Runway 29 (MP)
		AM	Aberdeen/Dyce Airport	ILS Localiser Runway 34 (I-ABD)
		AM	Cork Airport	ILS Runway 35 (ICN)
110.0000		AM	Galway	DME (CRN)
110.1000		AM	Birmingham Airport	DME Ident
		AM	Glasgow Airport	ILS Localiser Runway 05 (I-UU)
		AM	Birmingham Airport	ILS Localiser Runway 15 (I-BIR)
		AM	RAF Marham	ILS Localiser Runway 24 (MR)
		AM	Rennes Airport	ILS Runway 29 (RS)
		AM	Birmingham Airport	ILS Localiser Runway 33 (I-BM)
110.1500		AM	Bristol Airport	ILS Localiser Runway 09 (I-BON)
		AM	Bristol Airport	ILS Localiser Runway 27 (I-BTS)
110.2000		AM	RAF Lakenheath	TACAN Ident (LKH)

Base	Mobile	Mode	Location	User and Notes
110.3000		AM	London Heathrow	DME Ident
		AM	London Heathrow	ILS Localiser Runway 09L (I-AA)
		AM	Prestwick Airport	ILS Localiser Runway 13 (I-PP)
		AM	RAF Leeming	ILS Localiser Runway 16 (LI)
		AM	RAF Cottesmore	ILS Localiser Runway 23 (CM)
		AM	Jersey Airport	ILS Localiser Runway 27 (I-DD)
		AM	London Heathrow	ILS Localiser Runway 27R (I-RR)
		AM	Prestwick Airport	ILS Localiser Runway 31 (I-KK)
110.4000		AM	Perth Aerodrome	VOR (PTH)
110.5000		AM	Bournemouth Airport	DME Ident
		AM	RAF Leuchars	TACAN Ident (LUK)
		AM	Stansted Airport	DME Ident
		AM	Stansted Airport	ILS Localiser Runway 05 (I-SED)
		AM	Bournemouth Airport	ILS Localiser Runway 08 (I-BMH)
		AM	Stansted Airport	ILS Localiser Runway 23 (I-SX)
		AM	Bournemouth Airport	ILS Localiser Runway 26 (I-BH)
110.5500		AM	Filton (BAe)	ILS Localiser Runway 10 (I-BRF)
		AM	Filton (BAe)	ILS Localiser Runway 28 (I-FB)
110.7000		AM	Cardiff Airport	DME Ident
		AM	Carlisle Airport	DME Ident (CO)
		AM	London Heathrow	DME Ident (HHT)
		AM	Cardiff Airport	ILS Localiser Runway 12 (I-CDF)
		AM	RAF Linton-on-Ouse	ILS Localsier Runway 22 (LO)
		AM	London Heathrow	ILS Localiser Runway 23 (I-CC)
		AM	RAF Coningsby	ILS Localiser Runway 26 (CY)
		AM	Connaught Airport	ILS Localsier Rwy 27 (I-CK)
		AM	Cardiff Airport	ILS Localiser Runway 30 (I-CWA)
110.9000		AM	Leeds/Bradford Airport	ILS Localiser Runway 09 (I-LBF)
		AM	Leeds/Bradford Airport	ILS Localiser Runway 32 (I-LF)
		AM	Gatwick	DME Ident
		AM	Jersey Airport	DME Ident (I-JJ)
		AM	Ronaldsway	DME Ident
		AM	Gatwick	ILS Localiser Runway 08R (I-GG)
		AM	Jersey Airport	ILS Localiser Runway 09 (I-JJ)
		AM	Norwich Airport	ILS Localiser Runway 14 (I-NH)
		AM	Belfast/Aldergrove	ILS Runway 17 (I-FT)
		AM	Gatwick	ILS Localiser Runway 26L (I-WW)
		AM	Ronaldsway	ILS Localiser Runway 27 (I-RY)
111.0000		AM	RNAS Yeovilton	TACAN Ident (VLN)
111.1000		AM	RAF Coningsby	TACAN Ident (CGY)
		AM	RAF Fairford	ILS Localiser Runway 09 (I-FFA)
		AM	RAF Waddington	ILS Localiser Runway 21 (WA)
		AM	RAF Lossiemouth	ILS Localiser Runway 23 (LM)
		AM	RAF Wattisham	ILS Localiser Runway 23 (WT)
		AM	RAF Fairford	ILS Localiser Runway 27 (I-FFD)
111.3000		AM	Perth Aerodrome	ILS Localiser Runway 21 (I-PRF)
		AM	Hatfield Aerodrome	ILS Localiser Runway 24 (I-HD)
111.3500		AM	Southend Airport	DME Ident

Base	Mobile	Mode	Location	User and Notes
		AM	Southend Airport	ILS Localiser Runway 24 (I-ND)
111.4000		AM	RAF Binbrook	TACAN Ident (BNK)
111.5000		AM	London Docklands	DME Ident
		AM	Newcastle Airport	DME Ident
		AM	RAF Fairford	TACAN Ident (FFA)
		AM	Newcastle Airport	ILS Localiser Runway 07 (I-NC)
		AM	London Docklands	ILS Localiser Runway 10 (LST)
		AM	Dublin	ILS/DME Rwy 16
		AM	RAF Coltishall	ILS Localiser Runway 22 (CS)
		AM	Newcastle Airport	ILS Localiser Runway 25 (I-NWC)
		AM	London Docklands	ILS Localiser Runway 28 (LST)
111.6000		AM	RAF Chivenor	TACAN Ident (CVR)
111.7000		AM	Boscombe Down (MoD)	ILS Localiser Runway 24 (BD)
111.7500		AM	Liverpool Airport	DME Ident
		AM	Liverpool Airport	ILS Localiser Runway 09 (LVR)
		AM	Liverpool Airport	ILS Localiser Runway 27 (I-LQ)
111.9000		AM	RAF Brize Norton	TACAN Ident (BZN)
		AM	RAF Brize Norton	ILS Localiser Runway 08 (BZA)
		AM	RAF Brize Norton	ILS Localiser Runway 26 (BZB)
		AM	RAF Honington	ILS Localiser Runway 27 (HT)

112.0000 - 117.9750 MHz TACAN And DME Idents, ATIS And VOR Aero

Base	Mobile	Mode	Location	User and Notes
112.1000		AM	Pole Hill	VOR/DME Ident (POL)
112.2000		AM	Jersey Airport	VOR/ATIS (JSY)
		AM	Ronaldsway	VOR/DME Ident (IOM)
112.3000		AM	London Heathrow	Heathrow Arrival Information
112.5000		AM	St Abbs	VOR/DME Ident (SAB)
		AM	Cherbourg	VOR (CBG)
112.6000		AM	RAF St Mawgan	TACAN Ident (SMG)
112.7000		AM	Berry Head	VOR/DME Ident (BHD)
		AM	Donegal Aerodrome	DME Ident (CFN)
		AM	Berry Head	VOR/DME (BHD)
		AM	Donegal (Carrickfin)	DME (CFN)
112.8000		AM	Gamston Aerodrome	VOR/DME Ident (GAM)
		AM	Rennes Airport	VOR (RNE)
113.1000		AM	Strumble	VOR/DME Ident (STU)
113.2000		AM	Warton (MoD)	TACAN Ident (WTN)
113.3000		AM	Shannon Airport	DVOR/DME (SHA)
113.3500		AM	Southampton Airport	VOR/ATIS (SAM)
113.5500		AM	Manchester Airport	VOR/DME Ident (MCT)
113.6000		AM	Wick Aerodrome	TACAN Ident (WIZ)
		AM	Wick Aerodrome	VOR (WIK)
		AM	London Heathrow	VOR/DME Ident (LON)
113.6500		AM	Honiley	VOR/DME Ident (HON)
113.7000		AM	RAF Upper Heyford	TACAN Ident (UPH)
113.7500		AM	Bovingdon	VOR/DME Ident (BNN)
113.8000		AM	Talla	VOR/DME Ident (TLA)
113.9000		AM	Ottringham	VOR/DME Ident (OTR)

Base	Mobile	Mode	Location	User and Notes
114.0000		AM	Midhurst	VOR/DME Ident (MID)
114.0500		AM	Lydd Airport	VOR (LYD)
114.1000		AM	Wallasey	VOR/DME Ident (WAL)
114.2000		AM	Land's End Airport	VOR/DME Ident (LND)
114.2500		AM	Newcastle Airport	VOR/ATIS (NEW)
114.3000		AM	Aberdeen/Dyce Airport	ATIS
		AM	Aberdeen/Dyce Airport	VOR/DME Ident (ADN)
		AM	Dinard	VOR (DIN)
114.3500		AM	Compton	VOR/DME Ident (CPT)
114.4000		AM	Benbecula Airport	TACAN Ident (BEZ)
		AM	Benbecula Airport	VOR (BEN)
114.5000		AM	Koksijde	VOR/DME Ident (KOK)
114.5500		AM	Clacton Aerodrome	VOR/DME Ident (CLN)
114.6000		AM	Cork Airport	DVOR/DME Ident (CRK)
114.7500		AM	Chichester/Goodwood Aerodrome	VOR (GWC)
114.8000		AM	RAF Sculthorpe	TACAN Ident (SKT)
114.9000		AM	Vallafield	TACAN Ident (VFD)
		AM	Dublin	VOR/DME Ident (DUB)
		AM	Dublin	VOR/DME (DUB)
114.9500		AM	Dover	VOR/DME Ident (DVR)
115.1000		AM	Stornoway Airport	TACAN Ident (STZ)
		AM	Stornoway Airport	VOR (STN)
		AM	Biggin Hill	VOR/DME Ident (BIG)
115.2000		AM	Dean Cross	VOR/DME Ident (DCS)
115.3000		AM	Ockham	VOR/DME Ident (OCK)
115.4000		AM	Glasgow Airport	VOR/ATIS/DME Ident (GOW)
115.5500		AM	Gloucester Airport	DME Ident (GOS)
115.6000		AM	Lambourne	VOR/DME Ident (LAM)
115.7000		AM	Stoke on Trent	VOR/DME Ident (TNT)
115.8000		AM	Baldonnel	VOR Ident (BAL)
115.9000		AM	RAF Mildenhall	TACAN Ident (MLD)
		AM	Beauvais	VOR Ident (BVS)
116.0000		AM	RAF Machrihanish	DVOR (MAC)
		AM	RAF Machrihanish	TACAN Ident (MAZ)
116.1000		AM	RAF Church Fenton	TACAN Ident (CHF)
116.2000		AM	Blackbushe Aerodrome	DME Ident (BLC)
116.2500		AM	Barkway	VOR/DME Ident (BKY)
116.4000		AM	Daventry	VOR/DME Ident (DTY)
116.5000		AM	Cranfield	VOR Ident (CFD)
		AM	RAF Coltishall	TACAN Ident (CSL)
116.6000		AM	RAF Brawdy	TACAN Ident (BDY)
		AM	Abbeville	VOR Ident (ABB)
116.7500		AM	Cambridge Airport	DME Ident (CAB)
117.0000		AM	Seaford	VOR/DME Ident (SFD)
117.1000		AM	Burnham	VOR (BUR)
117.2000		AM	Belfast	VOR/DME Ident (BEL)
117.3000		AM	Detling	VOR/DME Ident (DET)
117.3500		AM	Sumburgh Airport	VOR/DME Ident (SUM)

Base	Mobile	Mode	Location	User and Notes
117.4000		AM	RAF Cranwell	TACAN Ident (CWZ)
		AM	Connaught Airport	VOR/DME Ident (CON)
117.4500		AM	Brecon	VOR/DME Ident (BCN)
117.5000		AM	Brookmans Park	VOR/DME Ident (BPK)
		AM	Turnberry	VOR/DME Ident (TRN)
117.6000		AM	RAF Wittering	TACAN Ident (WIT)
117.7000		AM	Tiree	VOR/DME Ident (TIR)
		AM	Oxford/Kidlington Airport	DME Ident (OX)
117.9000		AM	Mayfield	VOR/DME Ident (MAY)

117.9750 - 136.9750 MHz International Civil Aviation Band 50 kHz

Base	Mobile	Mode	Location	User and Notes
118.0000	118.0000	AM	Natiownide	Civilian Air-Air
		AM	Nationwide	Air-Air Display Coordination
		AM	Nationwide	Marlboro Aerobatic Display
		AM	Yeovil	Westland Helicopter Tests
118.0250		AM	Leeds/Bradford Airport	ATIS
118.0500	118.0500	AM	Birmingham Airport	Radar
		AM	Birmingham Airport	Approach
		AM	Manchester	ATC
		AM	Manchester	ATC
118.0750	118.0750	AM	London Docklands	Tower
118.1000	118.1000	AM	Farnborough	Air Show Tower
		AM	Aberdeen/Dyce Airport	Tower
		AM	Calais	Tower
		AM	Granville	Tower
		AM	Liverpool Airport	Tower
		AM	Penzance Heliport	Tower
118.1000		AM	Scilly Isles	Tower
118.1500	118.1500	AM	London Stansted	Tower
		AM	Prestwick Airport	Tower
		AM	Sumburgh	Radar
118.2000	118.2000	AM	Ronaldsway	Radar
		AM	Southampton Airport	Tower
118.2250	118.2250	AM	Brough Aerodrome	Approach & SRE
		AM	Paris	Area Radar
118.2500		AM	Dublin	ATIS
118.2500	118.2500	AM	Sumburgh Airport	Tower
		AM	Brittas Bay	Air-Ground
118.2750	118.2750	AM	Fishburn	Air-Ground
118.3000	118.3000	AM	Belfast/Aldergrove	Tower
		AM	Birmingham Airport	Tower
		AM	Deauville	Tower
		AM	Kirkwall Airport	Tower
		AM	Le Touquet	Tower
118.3250	118.3250	AM	Ipswich Airport	Tower
118.3500	118.3500	AM	Urnaston	Tower
		AM	Derby	Air-Ground
		AM	Brest	ACC

Base	Mobile	Mode	Location	User and Notes
		AM	Burnaston Aerodrome	Tower
118.3750	118.3750	AM	Bedford (MoD Airfield)	Radar
		AM	RAF West Drayton	Air Traffic Control
118.4000	118.4000	AM	Blackpool Airport	Tower
		AM	London City Airport	Tower
118.4250	118.4250	AM	Biggin Hill	AFIS
		AM	RAF Lyneham	Approach
118.4500	118.4500	AM	Liverpool Airport	Radar
118.4750	118.4750	AM	Norwich Airport	Radar
		AM	RAF West Drayton	London ATC
118.5000	118.5000	AM	Dublin Airport	Radar
		AM	London Heathrow	Tower
		AM	Newcastle Airport	Radar
118.5250	118.5250	AM	RAF Manston	Radar
118.5500	118.5500	AM	Stornaway	Radar
		AM	Humberside Airport	Tower
		AM	Jersey Airport	Radar
118.5750	118.5750	AM	Ashcroft Farm	Air-Ground
		AM	Manchester Airport	Radar Standby
118.6000	118.6000	AM	Gatwick	Radar
		AM	Dublin Airport	Tower
118.6250	118.6250	AM	Manchester Airport	Tower
118.6500	118.6500	AM	Bournemouth Airport	Radar
118.7000	118.7000	AM	Edinburgh Airport	Tower
		AM	London Heathrow	Tower
		AM	Ostend Airport	Tower
		AM	Shannon Airport	Tower
118.7250	118.7250	AM	Dublin	ATIS
118.8000	118.8000	AM	Barra	Tower
		AM	Cork Airport	Radar
		AM	Glasgow Airport	Tower
118.8250	118.8250	AM	Dunsfold Aerodrome	Radar
		AM	RAF West Drayton	London ATC
118.8500	118.8500	AM	Teesside Airport	Approach
118.8750	118.8750	AM	Oxford/Kidlington Airport	Tower
118.9000	118.9000	AM	Norwich	Tower
		AM	Ronaldsway	Tower
		AM	RAF Kemble	Tower
		AM	Guernsey Airport	Radar
		AM	RAF Lossiemouth	Tower
		AM	Ronaldsway	Tower
118.9500	118.9500	AM	Gatwick	Radar
119.0000	119.0000	AM	Shetlands	East Shetland Information.
		AM	Dieppe	AFIS
		AM	RAF Brize Norton	Approach
		AM	RAF Cranwell	Approach
		AM	RAF Fairford	Approach
		AM	Nationwide	RAF Common

Base	Mobile	Mode	Location	User and Notes
119.0500	119.0500	AM	Exeter Airport	Radar
119.1000	119.1000	AM	Glasgow Airport	Approach
		AM	RAF Cosford	Tower
119.1250	119.1250	AM	RAF Newton	Tower
119.1500	119.1500	AM	RAF Fairford	Tower
119.2000	119.2000	AM	Heathrow	Approach/Radar
		AM	Benbecula Airport	Approach/Tower
119.2500	119.2500	AM	Coventry Airport	Approach
		AM	Sumburgh Airport	Approach
119.2750	119.2750	AM	RAF Manston	Tower
119.3000	119.3000	AM	Cork Airport	Tower
		AM	Glasgow Airport	Radar
		AM	Hatfield Aerodrome	Radar
		AM	Toussus	Tower
119.3500	119.3500	AM	Norwich Airport	Approach
		AM	Norwich Airport	Radar
		AM	RAF Kinloss	Approach
		AM	RAF Lossiemouth	Approach
119.4000	119.4000	AM	Manchester Airport	Approach
		AM	StBrieuc	Tower
119.4250	119.4250	AM	London Docklands	Tower
119.4500	119.4500	AM	Jersey Airport	Tower
		AM	Prestwick Airport	Approach
		AM	Hinto on the Edges	Air-Ground
119.4750		AM	Cardiff Airport	ATIS
119.5000	119.5000	AM	Exeter	Approach
		AM	Heathrow	Approach/Radar
119.5500	119.5500	AM	Shipdam	Information
		AM	Dublin Airport	Radar
119.6000	119.6000	AM	Prestwick Airport	Approach
		AM	Gatwick	Radar
119.6250	119.6250	AM	Bournemouth Airport	Approach
		AM	Bournemouth Airport	Radar
119.6500	119.6500	AM	East Midlands Airport	Approach
119.7000	119.7000	AM	Chichester/Goodwood	Tower
		AM	Dinard	Radar
		AM	Newcastle Airport	Tower
		AM	Swansea Aerodrome	Tower
		AM	Toussus	Approach
		AM	Wick Aerodrome	Tower
119.7250	119.7250	AM	London Heathrow	Approach
119.7500	119.7500	AM	Woodvale Aerodrome	Tower
		AM	Perranporth	Air-Ground
119.7750	119.7750	AM	RAF West Drayton	London TMA
119.8000	119.8000	AM	Exeter Airport	Tower
		AM	Gatwick	Police Helicopter Ops
		AM	Perth Aerodrome	Tower
		AM	Teesside Airport	Tower

Base	Mobile	Mode	Location	User and Notes
		AM	Exeter	Tower
119.8250	119.8250	AM	Dunsfold Aerodrome	Radar
119.8500	119.8500	AM	Burtonwood	US Army Helicopter Ops
		AM	Liverpool Airport	Approach
119.8750	119.8750	AM	Prestwick Airport	Scottish Air Traffic Control
119.9000	119.9000	AM	RAF Odiham	Helicopter Ops
		AM	Beauvais	Approach
		AM	Cork Airport	Approach
		AM	London Heathrow	Radar
119.9250	119.9250	AM	RAF Manston	Radar
119.9500	119.9500	AM	Blackpool Airport	Radar
		AM	Guernsey Airport	Tower
119.9750	119.9750	AM	Luton Airport	Tower
		AM	RAF Coningsby	Tower
120.0000	120.0000	AM	Belfast/Aldergrove	Approach
		AM	Bognor Regis Aerodrome	Tower
		AM	Malvern (MoD)	Navy Helicopter Ops
120.0250	120.0250	AM	RAF West Drayton	Air Traffic Control
120.0500	120.0500	AM	Cardiff Airport	Radar
120.1000	120.1000	AM	Brussels	Radar
120.1250	120.1250	AM	Castledon	Radar
		AM	East Midlands Airport	Radar
120.1500	120.1500	AM	Dinard	Approach
		AM	North Cotes	Air-Ground
120.1750	120.1750	AM	RAF West Drayton	Air Traffic Control
120.2000	120.2000	AM	Luton	Tower
		AM	Shannon Airport	Approach
120.2250	120.2250	AM	Southampton Airport	Solent Radar
120.2500	120.2500	AM	Panshanger	Air-ground
		AM	Dinard	Tower
120.2750	120.2750	AM	Redhill Aerodrome	Tower/AFIS
120.3000	120.3000	AM	Baxterley Field	Air-Ground
		AM	Jersey Airport	Approach
		AM	Leeds/Bradford Airport	Tower
120.3250	120.3250	AM	RAF Northolt	Radar
120.3500	120.3500	AM	Deauville	Approach
120.4000	120.4000	AM	Aberdeen/Dyce Airport	Approach
		AM	London Heathrow	Approach
120.4500	120.4500	AM	Great Yarmouth	Tower
		AM	Jersey Airport	Air Traffic Control (Radar)
		AM	North Denes	Tower
		AM	North Sea	Oil Rig Heliport Common
120.4750	120.4750	AM	RAF West Drayton	Air Traffic Control
120.5000	120.5000	AM	Rennes Airport	Tower
		AM	Sunderland	Air Show
120.5250	120.5250	AM	Biggin Hill	Speedbird Ops
		AM	RAF West Drayton	London TMA
120.5500	120.5500	AM	Bristol Airport	Tower

Base	Mobile	Mode	Location	User and Notes
		AM	Prestwick Airport	Approach
		AM	Prestwick Airport	Radar
120.5750		AM	Luton Airport	ATIS
120.6000	120.6000	AM	Bristol Lulsgate	LARS
		AM	Cumbernauld Airport	Tower
		AM	Ostend Airport	Approach
120.6250	120.6250	AM	London Stansted	Radar/Approach
120.6500	120.6500	AM	Woodvale	Approach
		AM	Chichester/Goodwood	Tower
		AM	Hamble Aerodrome	Tower
		AM	Stavanger Airport	Radar
120.6750	120.6750	AM	Prestwick Airport	Scottish Air Traffic Control
120.7000	120.7000	AM	Lydd Airport	Approach
120.7250		AM	Birmingham Airport	ATIS
120.7500	120.7500	AM	Swansea Aerodrome	Radar
		AM	Toussus	Approach
120.7750	120.7750	AM	Ternhill	Army Approach
120.8000	120.8000	AM	RAF Coningsby	Approach
		AM	RAF Leuchars	Ground
		AM	Nationwide	Battle Of Britain Flight
120.8250	120.8250	AM	Amsterdam Schipol	Dutch Military
120.8500	120.8500	AM	Ronaldsway	Approach
120.9000	120.9000	AM	Belfast/Aldergrove	Radar
		AM	RAF Abingdon	Approach
		AM	RAF Benson	Approach
120.9250	120.9250	AM	Duxford	Air-Ground
		AM	Fowlemere	Air-Ground
		AM	Cork	ATIS
120.9500	120.9500	AM	Paris Airport	ACC/UACC
120.9750	120.9750	AM	Gloucester Airport	Radar
121.0000	121.0000	AM	London Heathrow	Tower
		AM	Woodvale Aerodrome	Approach
121.0250	121.0250	AM	RAF West Drayton	Air Traffic Control
121.0500	121.0500	AM	Leeds/Bradford Airport	Radar
121.0750	121.0750	AM	RAF North Weald	Fighter Grouping meet
		AM	Ascot	Tower
		AM	Cheltenham Racecourse	Heliport
		AM	Epsom	Tower
		AM	Duxford Aerodrome	Air Display Channel
		AM	Silverstone	Tower
121.1000	121.1000	AM	Dublin Airport	Approach
		AM	RAF Odiham	Odiham Information
121.1500	121.1500	AM	Bordeaux	Approach
121.2000	121.2000	AM	Cardiff	Tower
		AM	Edinburgh Airport	Approach
121.2250	121.2250	AM	RAF West Drayton	London ATC
121.2500	121.2500	AM	RAF Mansion	Tower
		AM	Aberdeen/Dyce Airport	Radar

Base	Mobile	Mode	Location	User and Notes
121.2750	121.2750	AM	RAF West Drayton	Air Traffic Control
121.3000	121.3000	AM	Southampton	Radar
		AM	Glasgow Airport	Radar
		AM	Lochaber	Air Ambulance
121.3250	121.3250	AM	RAF West Drayton	London TMA
121.3500	121.3500	AM	Manchester Airport	Radar
121.4000	121.4000	AM	Leavesden	Radar
		AM	Shannon Airport	Approach
		AM	Beauvais	Tower
121.5000	121.5000	AM	Nationwide	Civil Aviation Distress Channel
		AM	Nationwide	Distress & Emergency
121.6000	121.6000	AM	Booker/Wycombe	Ground
		AM	Aberdeen/Dyce Airport	Fire Channel
		AM	Kerry	Ground
		AM	Nationwide	Airfield Fire & Rescue
		AM	East Midlands	Aifield Fire Service
		AM	Manchester	Aifield Fire Service
		AM	Birmingham	Aifield Fire Service
121.7000	121.7000	AM	Aberdeen/Dyce Airport	Ground
		AM	Bournemouth Airport	Ground
		AM	Cork Airport	Tower
		AM	Coventry Airport	Ground
		AM	Glasgow Airport	Ground
		AM	London Heathrow	Tower
		AM	Manchester Airport	Delivery
		AM	Shannon	Oceanic Clearance
121.7250	121.7250	AM	Stansted Airport	Ground
121.7250		AM	Humberside Airport	ATIS
121.7500	121.7500	AM	Gatwick	Ground
121.7500		AM	Shoreham Aerodrome	ATIS
		AM	Shoreham	ATIS
		NFM	Space	Soyuz Space Station/Mir
121.7500	121.7500	AM	Belfast/Aldergrove	Ground
		AM	Edinburgh Airport	Ground
		AM	Luton Airport	Ground
		AM	Oxford/Kidlington	Ground
		AM	Blackpool	Weather Volmet
121.7750	121.7750	AM	Booker/Wycombe	Ground
121.8000		AM	Southend Airport	ATIS
121.8000	121.8000	AM	Prestwick	Ground
		AM	Birmingham Airport	Ground
		AM	Cork Airport	Ground
		AM	Dublin Airport	Ground/Tower
		AM	Gatwick	Ground
		AM	Guernsey Airport	Ground
		AM	Shannon Airport	Ground
121.8500		AM	Gloucester Airport	ATIS
		AM	Aberdeen/Dyce Airport	ATIS

Base	Mobile	Mode	Location	User and Notes
121.8500	121.8500	AM	London Heathrow	Departure
		AM	Manchester Airport	Ground
		AM	Wroughton	PFA Delivery
121.8750		AM	Biggin Hill	ATIS
		AM	RAF Cranfield	ATIS
121.9000	121.9000	AM	Connaught Airport	Ground
		AM	East Midlands Airport	Ground
		AM	Jersey Airport	Ground
		AM	London Heathrow	Ground
		AM	Ostend Airport	Ground
121.9250	121.9250	AM	Redhill	Ground (Airshows Only)
		AM	Wroughton	PFA Ground
121.9500		AM	Bournemouth Airport	ATIS
		AM	Oxford/Kidlington	ATIS
121.9500	121.9500	AM	Gatwick	Delivery
		AM	Halfpenny Green	Ground
121.9750	121.9750	AM	Heathrow	Ground
122.0000		AM	RAF Mona	ATIS
122.0000	122.0000	AM	Baldonnel Airport	Approach
		AM	Coventry Airport	Radar
		AM	Headcorn Aerodrome	Tower
		AM	North Sea	BP Buchan Field
		AM	North Sea	BP Cyprus Field
		AM	North Sea	BP Forties Field
		AM	North Sea	BP Gyda Field
122.0500	122.0500	AM	Aberdeen/Dyce Airport	British Airways
		AM	North Sea	Britoil Thistle Field
		AM	North Sea	Chevron Ninian Field
		AM	North Sea	Conoco Murchison Field
		AM	North Sea	Hamilton Argyll Field
		AM	North Sea	Ninian Field
		AM	North Sea	Shell/Esso Auk Field
		AM	North Sea	Shell/Esso Fulmar Field
		AM	North Sea	Shell/Esso Kittiwake Field
		AM	Nottingham	Hutchins Crop Sprayers
		AM	Nuthampstead	Tower
		AM	London	Jersey Air Ops
		AM	Liverpool	Keenair Ops
		AM	Nationwide	Brymon Airways
		AM	Southend	Heavilift Ops
122.0750	122.0750	AM	Duxford Aerodrome	Duxford Information
		AM	Tilstock	Tilstock Radio
122.1000	122.1000	AM	Falmouth Aerodrome	Radar
		AM	Middle Wallop Army	Tower
		AM	RAF Abingdon	Radar
		AM	RAF Benson	Tower
		AM	RAF Brawdy	Tower
		AM	RAF Chivenor	Tower

Base	Mobile	Mode	Location	User and Notes
		AM	RAF Church Fenton	Tower
		AM	RAF Coltishall	Tower
		AM	RAF Coningsby	Tower
		AM	RAF Cosford	Approach
		AM	RAF Cottesmore	Tower
		AM	RAF Cranwell	Tower
		AM	RAF Dishforth	Tower
		AM	RAF Greenham Common	Tower
		AM	RAF Kinloss	Tower
		AM	RAF Lakenheath	Tower
		AM	RAF Leeming	Tower
		AM	RAF Leuchars	Tower
		AM	RAF Linton-on-Ouse	Tower
		AM	RAF Lossiemouth	Tower
		AM	RAF Lyneham	Tower
		AM	RAF Manston	Tower
		AM	RAF Marham	Tower
		AM	RAF Newton	Tower
		AM	RAF Northolt	Tower
		AM	RAF Odiham	Tower
		AM	RAF Shawbury	Tower
		AM	RAF St Athan	Tower
		AM	RAF Spadeadam	SRE
		AM	RAF St Mawgan	Tower
		AM	RAF Swinderby	Tower
		AM	RAF Topcliffe	Tower
		AM	RAF Valley	Tower
		AM	RAF Waddington	Tower
		AM	RAF Wittering	Tower
		AM	RAF Wyton	Tower
		AM	RNAS Culdrose	Tower
		AM	RNAS Portland	Tower
		AM	RNAS Yeovilton	Tower
		AM	Nationwide	Military Tower Common
		AM	Ternhill	Army Approach
		AM	Wattisham	Tower
		AM	N of 56N	Fisheries Protection
122.1250	122.1250	AM	Leicester Aerodrome	Tower
		AM	Flotta Airfield	Tower
		AM	RNAS Aberporth	AFIS
122.1750	122.1750	AM	North Sea	Mobil Beryl Field
		AM	Turweston Aerodrome	Tower
122.2000	122.2000	AM	Cambridge Airport	Tower
		AM	Huddersfield Aerodrome	Tower
		AM	Tatenhill Aerodrome	Tower
		AM	Haverfordwest	Tower
		AM	Milford Haven	Ground-Air
		AM	IAC Gormanstown	Military App

Base	Mobile	Mode	Location	User and Notes
122.2500	122.2500	AM	Caernarfon Aerodrome	Tower
		AM	North Sea	Shell/Esso Brent Field
		AM	Rochester Aerodrome	Tower
122.2750	122.2750	AM	Nationwide	CAA Calibrator Aircraft
122.3000	122.3000	AM	Alderney	Aurigny Airlines
		AM	Blackbushe Aerodrome	AFIS
		AM	Perth Aerodrome	Approach
		AM	Peterborough	Tower (Sibson Radio)
		AM	IAC Baldonnel	Military Radar
122.3250	122.3250	AM	Clacton Aerodrome	Tower
		AM	North Sea	Hamilton Esmond Field
		AM	North Sea	Hamilton Forbes Field
		AM	North Sea	Hamilton Gordon Field
122.3500	122.3500	AM	Audley End Aerodrome	Tower
		AM	Brookland	Tower
		AM	Cardiff Airport	Operations
		AM	Channel Islands	Aurigny Operations
		AM	Cuxwold Aerodrome	Ground
		AM	East Midlands Airport	Air Bridge Carriers Ops
		AM	Edinburgh Airport	Execair Operations
		AM	Glasgow Airport	Execair
		AM	Grimsby Aerodrome	Tower
		AM	Guernsey	Aurigny Air Services
		AM	Hitchin (Rush Green)	Tower
		AM	Luton Airport	Reed Aviation
		AM	Manchester	Air Kilroe Ops
		AM	North Sea	Total Alwyn Field
		AM	Teesside Airport	Air Cam
		NFM	Lochaber	PLM Helicopters
		AM	Liverpool	Cheshire Air Training Ops
		AM	London Heathrow	Gulf Air Terminal 3
122.3750	122.3750	AM	Morecambe Bay	BP Field Helicopters
		AM	Humberside	Bond Helicopters
		AM	North Sea	BP Magnus Field
		AM	Peterhead/Langside	Tower
		AM	Plockton Airfield	Tower
		AM	Strubby Aerodrome	Tower
122.4000	122.4000	AM	Westen	Air-Ground
		AM	Dounreay Aerodrome	Tower
		AM	Elstree Aerodrome	Tower
		AM	Little Snoring Aerodrome	Tower
		AM	Scatsa Aerodrome	Radar
		AM	Westen-on-the-Green	AFIS
		AM	Bantry	Air-Ground
		AM	Weston	Air-Ground
122.4250	122.4250	AM	Earls Colne	Tower
122.4500	122.4500	AM	Belfast/Aldergrove	Approach
		AM	Chichester	Military Police Heli Ops

Base	Mobile	Mode	Location	User and Notes
		AM	Chichester/Goodwood	Approach
		AM	North Sea	Claymore & Tartan
		AM	North Sea	Occidental Claymore Field
		AM	North Sea	Piper
		AM	North Sea	Texaco Tartan Field
		AM	Sleap Aerodrome	Tower
		AM	Wickenby Aerodrome	Tower
122.4750	122.4750	AM	Nationwide	Hot Air Ballooning
122.5000	122.5000	AM	Bitteswell Aerodrome	Approach
		AM	Brussels Airport	ACC
		AM	Farnborough	Tower
		AM	Llanbedr (MoD)	Approach
		AM	Weston-super-Mare	Tower
122.5250	122.5250	AM	North Sea	Hamilton Pipe Field
		AM	Newcastle, Eire	Air-Ground
122.5500	122.5500	AM	Dunsfold Aerodrome	Approach
122.5500	122.5500	AM	Holme-next-the-Sea	Approach
		AM	RAF Mildenhall	Tower
		AM	West Freugh (MoD)	Tower
122.6000	122.6000	AM	Abbeyshrule	Air-Ground
		AM	Castlebar	Tower
		AM	Deptford Aerodrome	Tower
		AM	Dingwall Aerodrome	Tower
		AM	Inverness Airport	Approach/Tower
		AM	Kerry	Tower
		AM	Lerwick	Tower
		AM	Plymouth Airport	Tower
		AM	Seething Aerodrome	Tower
		AM	Sherburn-in-Elmet	Tower
		AM	White Waltham	Tower
122.6250	122.6250	AM	North Sea	Conoco Viking Field
122.6750	122.6750	AM	Scotland	Bonzai Sqn Air-Air
122.7000	122.7000	AM	Barton Aerodrome	Tower
		AM	Bodmin Aerodrome	Tower
		AM	Calais	Approach
		AM	Compton Abbas	Tower
		AM	Northampton (Sywell)	AFIS
		AM	Silverstone	Tower
		AM	Tiree	Tower/AFIS
		AM	IAC Gormanstown	Military Tower
122.7250	122.7250	AM	Filton (BAe)	Approach
		AM	RAF Lyneham	Approach
122.7500		AM	RAF Tain	Range Control
		AM	Le Bourget	Universal Ops
		AM	Salisbury Plain	Ops
		AM	Amsterdam	Fokker Flight Tests
122.7500	122.7500	AM	Cowden Range	Range Control
122.7750	122.7750	AM	Crowfield Aerodrome	Tower

Base	Mobile	Mode	Location	User and Notes
122.8000	122.8000	AM	Baldonnel Airport	Approach
		AM	Brest	VFR Control
		AM	North Sea	Unionoil Heather Field
		AM	Nottingham Aerodrome	Tower
		AM	Stapleford Aerodrome	Tower
122.8250	122.8250	AM	Bruntingthorpe	Tower
122.8500	122.8500	AM	Cranfield	Approach
		AM	Londonderry	Approach
122.8750	122.8750	AM	Lasham Aerodrome	Dan Air
		AM	North Sea	Phillips Hewett Field
122.9000	122.9000	AM	Connaught Airfield	Tower
		AM	Doncaster Aerodrome	Tower
		AM	Dundee Airport	Tower
		AM	Gloucester Airport	Tower
		AM	London	Battersea Heliport Tower
		AM	Long Marston	Tower
		AM	Old Sarum Aerodrome	Tower
		AM	Kilkenny	Air-Ground
122.9250	122.9250	AM	Beccles Heliport	Tower
		AM	North Sea	Phillip Ekofisk Field
122.9500	122.9500	AM	Birr Aerodrome	Air-Ground
		AM	Aberdeen/Dyce Airport	Bristow Helicopters
		AM	London	Air Ambulance Ops
		AM	North Sea	Nam Nam Field
		AM	North Sea	Nam Noordwinning
		AM	North Sea	Penzoil Noordwinning Field
		AM	North Sea	Petroland Petroland Field
		AM	North Sea	Placid Placid Field
		AM	North Sea	Zanddijk
		AM	Nationwide	Freemans Aviation
122.9750	122.9750	AM	Marston Moor	Tower
123.0000	123.0000	AM	Conington Aerodrome	Tower
		AM	Halfpenny Green	AFIS
		AM	Connemara	Tower
		AM	Inisheer	Air-Ground
		AM	Inishman	Air-Ground
		AM	Inishmore	Air-Ground
123.0250	123.0250	AM	North Sea	Hamilton Ravenspurnn
123.0500	123.0500	AM	Gigha	Gigha Radio
		AM	North Sea	Brent
		AM	North Sea	Cormorant
		AM	North Sea	Shell/Esso Eider Field
		AM	North Sea	Shell/Esso Tern Field
		AM	North Sea	Shell/Esso Dunlin Field
		AM	North Sea	Cormorant
		AM	North Sea	North Cormorant
		AM	Nuthampstead	Tower
		AM	Old Warden Aerodorme	Tower

Base	Mobile	Mode	Location	User and Notes
		AM	Peterhead/Langside	Tower
		AM	RAF Leconfield	Leconfield Rescue
		AM	Shipdham Aerodrome	Tower
		AM	Stevenage Aerodrome	British Aerospace
		AM	Wigtown	Tower
123.1000	123.1000	AM	Baldonnel Airport	Ground
		AM	Nationwide	Scotland Air Mountain Rescue
		AM	Nationwide	Search And Rescue
123.1500	123.1500	AM	Humberside Airport	Humberside Radar
		AM	Islay Airport	AFIS
		AM	Scillies	Approach/Tower
		AM	Shoreham Aerodrome	Approach
		AM	Sumburgh Airport	Radar
123.2000	123.2000	AM	Barrow Airport	Tower
		AM	Cranfield	Tower
		AM	Eniskillen	Tower
		AM	Old Sarum	Air/Ground
		AM	St Angelo	Tower
		AM	Walney Island	Lakes Gliding Club
123.2250	123.2250	AM	Fadmoor Aerodrome	Tower
		AM	North Sea	Arco Thames Field
		AM	Wroughton	Tower
123.2500	123.2500	AM	Bagby Aerodrome	Tower
		AM	Bantry	Tower
		AM	Bembridge Aerodrome	Tower
		AM	Bitteswell Aerodrome	Tower
		AM	Bridlington Aerodrome	Tower
		AM	Fowlmere Aerodrome	Fowlmere Radio
		AM	Grindale Aerodrome	Tower
		AM	Welshpool	Air-Ground
123.3000	123.3000	AM	Dublin Airport	Dublin Military ATC
		AM	RAF Benson	Radar
		AM	RAF Brawdy	Radar
		AM	RAF Brize Norton	Radar
		AM	RAF Chivenor	Radar
		AM	RAF Coltishall	Radar
		AM	RAF Coningsby	Radar
		AM	RAF Cottesmore	Radar
		AM	RAF Cranwell	Radar
		AM	RAF Honington	Radar
		AM	RAF Kinloss	Radar
		AM	RAF Lakenheath	Radar
		AM	RAF Leuchars	Radar
		AM	RAF Linton-on-Ouse	Radar
		AM	RAF Lossiemouth	Radar
		AM	RAF Lyneham	Radar
		AM	RAF Manston	Radar
		AM	RAF Marham	Radar

Base	Mobile	Mode	Location	User and Notes
		AM	RAF Odiham	Radar
		AM	RAF Shawbury	Radar
		AM	RAF St Athan	Radar
		AM	RAF St Mawgan	Radar
		AM	RAF Topcliffe	Radar
		AM	RAF Valley	Radar
		AM	RAF Waddington	Radar
		AM	RAF Wattisham	Radar
		AM	RAF Wittering	Radar
		AM	RAF Wyton	Radar
		AM	RNAS Culdrose	Radar
		AM	RNAS Yeovilton	Radar
		AM	Nationwide	Military Airfield Radar
		AM	Manchester	ATC
123.3500	123.3500	AM	Chester Aerodrome	Tower
		AM	Hatfield Aerodrome	Approach
		AM	Hawarden Aerodrome	Approach
123.3750	123.3750	AM	Morecambe Bay	British Gas Helicopters
		AM	RAF St Mawgan	Tower
		AM	Prestwick	ATC
123.4000	123.4000	AM	RAF Lyneham	Radar
123.4250	123.4250	AM	Fairoaks	Tower/AFIS
123.4500	123.4500	AM	Cark	Cark Radio
		AM	Dornoch Aerodrome	Tower
		AM	Errol Aerodrome	DZ Control
		AM	Mull	Mull Traffic
		AM	Fair Oaks Aerodrome	Tower
		AM	North Sea	Amoco Indefatigable Field
		AM	North Sea	Dab Duc Dan Field
		AM	North Sea	Dab Duc Gorm Field
		AM	North Sea	Dab Duc Skjold Field
		AM	North Sea	Marathon West Kinsale
		AM	North Sea	Mobil Camelot Field
		AM	North Sea	Shell/Esso Clipper Field
		AM	Nationwide	Air-Air Common
123.4750	123.4750	AM	Dunkeswell Aerodrome	Tower
123.5000	123.5000	AM	Baldonnel Airport	Tower
		AM	Banff Aerodrome	Tower
		AM	Coal Aston Aerodrome	Tower
		AM	Eggesford Aerodrome	Tower
		AM	Felthorpe Aerodrome	Tower
		AM	Newtownards	Tower
		AM	Sandown Aerodrome	Tower
		AM	Shobdon Aerodrome	Tower
		AM	Stornoway Airport	Tower
		AM	Berwick-on-Tweed	Winfield Radio
		AM	Swanton Morley	Tower
123.5250	123.5250	AM	North Weald	North Weald Radio

Base	Mobile	Mode	Location	User and Notes
123.5500	123.5500	AM	North Sea	Phillips Maureen Field
		AM	North Sea	Sun Balmoral Field
		AM	RAF Brize Norton	Brize Radar
123.5750	123.5750	AM	North Sea	Viking Conoco Common
		AM	Old Sarum Aerodrome	Tower
123.6000	123.6000	AM	Belmullet Aerodrome	Tower
		AM	Cambridge Airport	Approach
		AM	Carlisle Airport	Approach/Tower
		AM	Scatsa Aerodrome	Approach/Tower
123.6250	123.6250	AM	Londonderry	Approach
		AM	North Sea	Amoco Indefatigable Field
		AM	North Sea	Amoco Leman Field
		AM	North Sea	Shell/Esso Indefatigable
		AM	North Sea	Shell/Esso Leman Field
		AM	North Sea	Shell/Esso Sean Field
123.6500	123.6500	AM	Gamston Aerodrome	Tower
		AM	Hatfield Aerodrome	Hatair Ops
		AM	London Heathrow	British Airways
		AM	North Sea	Britoil Beatrice Field
		AM	North Sea	Marathon Beryl Field
		AM	Nationwide	Brymon Airways
		AM	S of 56N	Fisheries Protection
123.7000	123.7000	AM	Amsterdam Schipol	ACC
123.7250	123.7250	AM	Epson Aerodrome	Tower
123.7500	123.7500	AM	Leeds/Bradford Airport	Approach
123.8000	123.8000	AM	Stansted Airport	Tower
123.8500	123.8500	AM	Amsterdam Schipol	ACC
123.9000	123.9000	AM	RAF West Drayton	Air Traffic Control London TMA
123.9500	123.9500	AM	Shannon Airport	Shanwick Oceanic ACC
124.0000	124.0000	AM	East Midlands Airport	Tower
		AM	Paris Airport	ACC/UACC
124.0500	124.0500	AM	Paris Airport	ACC/UACC
		AM	Prestwick Airport	Scottish Air Traffic Control
124.1000		AM	Cardiff Airport	Radar
124.1000	124.1000	AM	Kerry	Air-Ground
124.1500	124.1500	AM	RAF Shawbury	Approach
		AM	RNAS Portland	Approach
		AM	Ternhill	Army Approach
		AM	Nationwide	Army Helicopter Common
124.1500	124.1500	AM	RAF Marham	Approach
124.2000	124.2000	AM	Manchester Airport	Manchester Air Traffic Control
124.2250	124.2250	AM	Gatwick	Tower
124.2500	124.2500	AM	Norwich Airport	Tower
124.2750	124.2750	AM	RAF West Drayton	Air Traffic Control
124.3000	124.3000	AM	RAF Lakenheath	Radar
		AM	Amsterdam Schipol	ACC
124.3250	124.3250	AM	Dunsfold Aerodrome	Tower
124.3500	124.3500	AM	Bristol Airport	Radar

Base	Mobile	Mode	Location	User and Notes
		AM	Chester Aerodrome	Tower
124.3750	124.3750	AM	Newcastle	Approach
124.4000	124.4000	AM	RAF Brawdy	Approach
		AM	Bedford (MoD Airfield)	Approach
124.4500	124.4500	AM	Warton (MoD)	Approach
124.4750	124.4750	AM	London Heathrow	Stand-by Ground
124.5000	124.5000	AM	Guernsey Airport	Radar
		AM	Prestwick Airport	Scottish Air Traffic Control
124.5250		AM	Dublin	ATIS
124.5500	124.5500	AM	Cranfield	Approach
124.6000	124.6000	AM	RAF West Drayton	London FIR Information
124.6500	124.6500	AM	Dublin Airport	Area Control Centre
124.6750	124.6750	AM	Humberside Airport	Approach
124.7000	124.7000	AM	Shannon Airport	ACC
		AM	Stavanger Airport	Radar
124.7500	124.7500	AM	RAF West Drayton	London FIR Information
124.8000	124.8000	AM	Coventry Airport	Tower
		AM	Rennes Airport	Approach
124.8500	124.8500	AM	Paris Airport	ACC/UACC
124.8750	124.8750	AM	Amsterdam Schipol	ACC
124.9250	124.9250	AM	Wattishan	MATZ
124.9500	124.9500	AM	Chester Garrison	Army Helicopter
		AM	Filton (BAe)	Tower
		AM	Hawarden Aerodrome	Tower
124.9750	124.9750	AM	RAF Northolt	Radar
		AM	RAF Northolt	Tower
125.0000	125.0000	AM	Brussels Airport	ACC
		AM	Cardiff Airport	Tower
		AM	Hamble Aerodrome	Approach
		AM	RAF Topcliffe	Approach
125.0500	125.0500	AM	Southend Airport	Radar
125.1000	125.1000	AM	Manchester Airport	Manchester Air Traffic Control
125.1500		AM	Paris	Paris VOLMET
125.2000	125.2000	AM	Jersey Airport	Air Traffic Control (Zone)
125.2250	125.2250	AM	Shannon	ATC
125.2500	125.2500	AM	Farnborough	Approach
		AM	RAF Odiham	Approach
125.3000	125.3000	AM	Ronaldsway	Radar
		AM	Le Touquet	Approach
125.3250	125.3250	AM	Oxford/Kidlington	Approach
125.3500	125.3500	AM	Alderney Airport	Tower
		AM	RAF Binbrook	Tower
125.4000	125.4000	AM	Chalgrove Aerodrome	Tower
		AM	Shoreham Aerodrome	Tower
		AM	Yeovil Aerodrome	Tower
125.4500	125.4500	AM	Paris	Control
125.4750	125.4750	AM	RAF West Drayton	Air Traffic Control
125.5000	125.5000	AM	Moscow	Control

Base	Mobile	Mode	Location	User and Notes
		AM	Brest	Control
		AM	RAF Faiford	IAT Base Ops
125.5500	125.5500	AM	Andrewsfield	Approach
		AM	Bournemouth Airport	Tower
		AM	Brest	IFR Control
		AM	Stansted Airport	Approach
125.6000	125.6000	AM	Bournemouth Airport	Tower
125.6250	125.6250	AM	London Heathrow	Approach Standby
125.6500	125.6500	AM	Gloucester Airport	Approach
		AM	RAF St Mawgan	Radar
125.6750	125.6750	AM	Prestwick	Scottish ATC
125.7000	125.7000	AM	Paris Airport	VFR Control
125.7250		AM	Prestwick Airport	Scottish VOLMET
125.7500	125.7500	AM	Amsterdam Schipol	ACC
125.8000	125.8000	AM	RAF West Drayton	Air Traffic Control/TMA
125.8500	125.8500	AM	Sumburgh Airport	ATIS
		AM	Cardiff Airport	Approach
		AM	RAF St Athan	Radar
125.8750	125.8750	AM	Gatwick	Radar
		AM	RAF Northolt	Talkdown
125.9000	125.9000	AM	RAF Coltishall	Approach
		AM	RAF Marham	Ground
125.9500	125.9500	AM	RAF West Drayton	London TMA
126.0000		AM	Paris	Paris VOLMET
126.0250		AM	Bristol Lulsgate	ATIS
126.0750	126.0750	AM	RAF West Drayton	ATC
126.1000	126.1000	AM	RAF Buchan	Highland Radar
126.1500	126.1500	AM	Booker/Wycombe	Air Park
		AM	Nationwide	RAF Flight Checker
126.2500	126.2500	AM	Prestwick Airport	Scottish Air Traffic Control
126.2750		AM	Birmingham Airport	ATIS
126.3000	126.3000	AM	RAF West Drayton	London TMA
126.3500	126.3500	AM	Newcastle Airport	Approach
		AM	RAF Manston	Approach/LARS
126.4000		AM	Bordeaux	VOLMET
126.4500	126.4500	AM	RAF West Drayton	London TMA
126.5000	126.5000	AM	RAF Brize Norton	Tower/Ground
		AM	RAF Church Fenton	Approach
		AM	RAF Elvington	Approach
		AM	RAF Fairford	Tower (Airshows Only)
		AM	RAF Leuchars	Approach
		AM	RAF St Mawgan	Approach
126.5500	126.5500	AM	Booker/Wycombe	Tower/AFIS
126.6000		AM	RAF West Drayton	London VOLMET North
126.6500	126.6500	AM	Manchester Airport	Manchester Air Traffic Control
126.7000	126.7000	AM	RAF Greenham Common	Radar
		AM	Boscombe Down (MoD)	Approach
		AM	Lydd Airport	Tower

Base	Mobile	Mode	Location	User and Notes
		AM	Middle Wallop Army	Army Air-Ground
126.7250	126.7250	AM	Luton	Approach/Radar
126.7500	126.7500	AM	Brussels Airport	ACC
126.8250	126.8250	AM	Gatwick	Approach
		AM	RAF West Drayton	London TMA
126.8500	126.8500	AM	Prestwick Airport	Scottish Air Traffic Control
126.8750	126.8750	AM	RAF West Drayton	London ATC
126.9000	126.9000	AM	Brussels Airport	ACC
126.9250	126.9250	AM	Woodford	Tower
126.9500	126.9500	AM	Stansted Airport	Approach
127.0000		AM	Dublin Airport	Dublin VOLMET
127.0500	127.0500	AM	Nationwide	CAA Test Flights
127.1000	127.1000	AM	RAF West Drayton	Air Traffic Control
127.1250		AM	Prestwick Airport	ATIS (Information)
127.1750		AM	Stansted Airport	ATIS
127.2500	127.2500	AM	RAF Brize Norton	Brize Radar
127.2750	127.2750	AM	Prestwick Airport	Scottish Air Traffic Control
127.3000	127.3000	AM	Cherbourg	Approach/Tower
		AM	Luton Airport	Approach
127.3500	127.3500	AM	RAF Digby	Approach
		AM	RAF Waddington	Approach
		AM	RNAS Yeovilton	Approach
127.4250	127.4250	AM	RAF West Drayton	ATC
127.4500	127.4500	AM	RAF West Drayton	London Military
127.5000	127.5000	AM	Shannon Airport	ACC
127.5250	127.5250	AM	London Heathrow	ATC
127.5500	127.5500	AM	London Heathrow	Approach
127.6250	127.6250	AM	London Heathrow	Approach
		AM	Maastricht	Eurocontrol
127.6500	127.6500	AM	Shannon Airport	Shanwick Oceanic ACC
127.6500	127.6500	AM	RAF West Drayton	Oceanic Clearance (E of 30°W)
127.7000	127.7000	AM	RAF West Drayton	Air Traffic Control
127.7250	127.7250	AM	Southend Airport	Tower
127.7500	127.7500	AM	RAF Leeming	Approach
127.8500	127.8500	AM	Reims Airport	ACC/UACC
127.8750	127.8750	AM	RAF West Drayton	Air Traffic Control
127.9000	127.9000	AM	Shannon Airport	Shanwick Oceanic ACC
127.9500	127.9500	AM	RAF West Drayton	Air Traffic Control
127.9750	127.9750	AM	Filton (BAe)	Approach
		AM	Warton (BAe)	Boffin Ops
128.0000	128.0000	AM	Dublin Airport	Approach
128.0250	128.0250	AM	London Docklands	Radar/City Radar
128.0500	128.0500	AM	RAF West Drayton	Air Traffic Control
128.1000	128.1000	AM	St Kilda	Tower
		AM	Paris Airport	ACC/UACC
128.1250	128.1250	AM	RAF West Drayton	Air Traffic Control
128.1500	128.1500	AM	Exeter Airport	Approach
128.2000	128.2000	AM	Brussels Airport	ACC

Base	Mobile	Mode	Location	User and Notes
128.2500	128.2500	AM	RAF West Drayton	London Military
128.3000	128.3000	AM	Aberdeen/Dyce Airport	Radar
		AM	Netheravon	Army Tower
128.3500	128.3500	AM	Amsterdam Schipol	Dutch Military
		AM	Newcastle Airport	Army Tower
128.4000	128.4000	AM	RAF West Drayton	Air Traffic Control/TMA
128.4250	128.4250	AM	RAF West Drayton	Air Traffic Control
128.4500	128.4500	AM	Brussels Airport	ACC
128.4750		AM	Gatwick	ATIS
128.5000	128.5000	AM	Caen	Tower
		AM	Prestwick Airport	Scottish Air Traffic Control
128.5500	128.5500	AM	Clonbullogue Aerodrome	Tower
		AM	Clonbullogue	Air-Ground
128.5875		AM	RAF West Drayton	London VOLMET South
128.6500	128.6500	AM	Alderney Airport	Approach
		AM	Guernsey Airport	Approach
128.6750	128.6750	AM	West Malling	Tower
		AM	Manchester	Pennine Radar
128.7000	128.7000	AM	RAF West Drayton	London Military
128.7500	128.7500	AM	Luton Airport	Approach
128.7750	128.7750	AM	RAF Manston	Tower
128.8000	128.8000	AM	Brussels Airport	ACC
128.8500	128.8500	AM	Southampton Airport	Approach
		AM	Teesside Airport	Radar
		AM	Nationwide	Eastern Airlines Packet Channel
128.9000	128.9000	AM	RAF Lakenheath	MATZ
128.9500	128.9500	AM	Southend Airport	Approach
128.9750	128.9750	AM	Edinburgh Airport	Radar
129.0000	129.0000	AM	Alderney Airport	Air-Ground
		AM	Brest	ACC/UACC
		AM	Nationwide	Hang Gliders & Ballons
		AM	Paris Airport	UIR Control
		AM	Whitchurch	Tilstock Radio
129.0250	129.0250	AM	Nationwide	Air France Company Chan
		AM	Gatwick	Radar Standby
129.0500	129.0500	AM	RAF Lakenheath	Approach/Departure Control
		AM	RAF Mildenhall	Departure Control
129.0750	129.0750	AM	RAF West Drayton	ATC
129.1000	129.1000	AM	RAF West Drayton	Air Traffic Control
		AM	Walney Island	Lakes Gliding Club
129.1250	129.1250	AM	RAF Linton-on-Ouse	Approach
		AM	RAF Marham	Talkdown
		AM	RAF Northolt	Radar
129.1750	129.1750	AM	Dublin	ACC
129.2000	129.2000	AM	RAF West Drayton	Air Traffic Control
		AM	Nationwide	American Airlines Packet
129.2250	129.2250	AM	Weston-super-Mare	Approach
		AM	Wroughton	PFA Circuit

Base	Mobile	Mode	Location	User and Notes
		AM	Prestwick	ATC
129.2500	129.2500	AM	RAF Fairford	Tower (Airshows Only)
129.3000	129.3000	AM	Amsterdam Schipol	ACC
129.3500	129.3500	AM	Paris Airport	ACC/UACC
129.3750	129.3750	AM	RAF West Drayton	ATC
129.4000	129.4000	AM	Biggin Hill	Approach
129.4250	129.4250	AM	RAF West Drayton	ATC
129.4500	129.4500	AM	Kent	Kent Radar
129.4750	129.4750	AM	Copenhagen	Copenhagen Information
129.5000	129.5000	AM	Brest	UACC
		AM	Nationwide	Delta Airlines Packet Channel
129.5500	129.5500	AM	Luton Airport	Approach
129.6000	129.6000	AM	RAF West Drayton	Air Traffic Control
		AM	Nationwide	Delta Airlines Packet Channel
129.6250	129.6250	AM	Nationwide	TWA Packet Frequency
129.6500	129.6500	AM	Brussels Airport	ACC
129.7000	129.7000	AM	Alderney	Trinity Lightship Heliport
		AM	Baldonnel Airport	Radar
		AM	Blackbushe Aerodrome	A.T.S.
		AM	Casquets	Trinity Lightship Heliport
		AM	English Channel	Bishops Rock Trinity Lightship
		AM	English Channel	Casquets Trinity Lightship
		AM	English Channel	Flatholm Trinity Lightship
		AM	English Channel	Hanois Trinity Lightship
		AM	English Channel	Inner Dowsing Trinity L.ship
		AM	English Channel	Longships Trinity Lightship
		AM	English Channel	Lundy South Trinity Lightship
		AM	English Channel	Round Island Trinity Lightship
		AM	English Channel	Royal Sovereign Trinity L.ship
		AM	English Channel	Skerries Trinity Lightship
		AM	English Channel	Skokholm Trinity Lightship
		AM	English Channel	Smalls Trinity Lightship
		AM	English Channel	South Bishop Trinity Lightship
		AM	English Channel	St Anns Head Trinity Lightship
		AM	Glasgow Airport	Northwest
		AM	Jersey	Aviation Beauport Ops
		AM	North Sea	Amoco Arbroath Field
		AM	North Sea	Amoco Montrose Field
		AM	Nationwide	Britannia Ops
		AM	Southend	Express Flight
		AM	London Heathrow	Mam Aviation
		AM	Prestwick	Ogden Aviation
		AM	IAC Baldonnel	Military Radar
129.7250	129.7250	AM	Conington Aerodrome	Tower
		AM	Warton (BAe)	Boffin Ops
129.7500	129.7500	AM	Filton (BAe)	Rolls Royce Ops
		AM	Gleneagles	Gleneagles Helicopters
		AM	North Sea	Elf Aquataine Norge Frigg

Base	Mobile	Mode	Location	User and Notes
		AM	North Sea	Kewanee Nordsee Field
		AM	North Sea	Total/Elf Frigg Field
		AM	Nationwide	Manx Ops
		AM	Nationwide	Loganair Ops
		AM	Norwich Airport	Air UK Ops
		AM	Stansted Airport	Servisair Ops
		AM	Nationwide	Air Express Ops
		AM	Nationwide	BMA Ops
		AM	Nationwide	Bourn Air Ops
		AM	Nationwide	Brymon Airways
129.8000	129.8000	AM	Bourn Aerodrome	Tower
		AM	Breighton Aerodrome	Tower
		AM	Carrickfin	Tower
		AM	Donegal Aerodrome	Tower
		AM	Popham Aerodrome	Popham Radio
		AM	Truro Aerodrome	Tower
129.8250	129.8250	AM	Cromer (Northrepps)	Tower
		AM	Insch Airfield	Tower
		AM	Lodge Farm	Air-Ground
		AM	Redlands	Redlands Radio
		AM	Nationwide	Microlight Common
129.8500	129.8500	AM	Chester Garrison	Army Helicopter Tower
		AM	Charles De Gaulle	Air France Ops
		AM	Hawarden Aerodrome	Radar
		AM	Waterford	Air-Ground
129.8750	129.8750	AM	Enstone Aerodrome	Tower
		AM	Hethersett Aerodrome	Hethersett Radio
		AM	North Sea	Amethyst Field
		AM	North Sea	BP Cleeton Field
		AM	North Sea	BP Ravenspurn Field
		AM	North Sea	BP West Sole Field
		AM	North Sea	British Gas Rough Field
129.9000	129.9000	AM	Brunton Aerodrome	Tower
		AM	High Easter Aerodrome	AFIS
		AM	Langar Airfield	Tower
		AM	Lasham Aerodrome	Tower
		AM	North Sea	Phillips Ekofisk Field
		AM	North Sea	Phillips Emden Field
		AM	Old Sarum Aerodrome	Tower
		AM	Strathallan Aerodrome	Air-to-Ground
		AM	Nationwide	Air Ambulance
		AM	Nationwide	Hang Gliding
		AM	Nationwide	Hot Air Ballooning
		AM	Nationwide	RAF Formation Air-Air
		NFM	Nationwide	RAC Network Q Medivac Helo
		AM	Pocklington	Glider Air-Ground
129.9500	129.9500	AM	North Sea	Cormorant Deck
		AM	North Sea	North Cormorant

Base	Mobile	Mode	Location	User and Notes
		AM	North Sea	Shell/Esso Tern Field
		AM	North Sea	Shell/Esso Dunlin Field
		AM	North Sea	Viking Oil Field
		AM	Sumburgh Airport	Helicopter Information
		AM	Shetland Basin	Viking Approach
129.9750	123.0000	AM	North Sea	Helicopter Common
		AM	Nationwide	Gliding
		AM	North Weald Aerodrome	Gliders
		AM	Tibenham	Tibenham Radio
		AM	Wattisham Army Airfield	Air-Ground
		AM	Sealand	Glider Control
		AM	Swansea Airport	ATC Glider Training
130.0000	130.0000	AM	Bedford (MoD Airfield)	Approach
		AM	Boscombe Down (MoD)	Tower
130.0250	130.0250	AM	Southend	British World Ops
		AM	Biggin Hill	Srikair
		AM	Nationwide	Dollar Air Metro
		AM	London	Capital Radio Flying Eye Ops
		AM	Woodford	BAe Ops
130.0500	130.0500	AM	Sandy	Tower
		AM	Aberdeen/Dyce Airport	Ground Staff
		AM	Farnborough	Radar
		AM	West Freugh (MoD)	Approach
		AM	Woodford	Radar
130.0750	130.0750	AM	Gatwick	Servisair Ops
		AM	London Heathrow	Air Malta Ops
		AM	RAF Brize Norton	Brize Ops
130.1000	130.1000	AM	Long Marston Aerodrome	Tower
		AM	Netheravon	Tower
		AM	Pocklington Aerodrome	Tower
		AM	Rufforth Aerodrome	Tower
		AM	Strubby Aerodrome	Strubby Base
		AM	Tibenham	Tibenham Radio (Gliders)
		AM	Nationwide	Gliders
130.1250	130.1250	AM	Nationwide	Glider Training
130.1500	130.1500	AM	Bitteswell Aerodrome	Approach
		AM	Deptford Aerodrome	Approach
		AM	Netheravon	Salisbury Plain Tower
		AM	RAF Upavon	Tower
		AM	London Heathrow	Emirates Ops
130.1625	130.1625	NFM	Space	Mir
130.1750	130.1750	AM	Blackbushe	Air Lynton Ops
		AM	Cambridge Airport	Magnet Air
		AM	Cambridge	Suckling Ops
		AM	London Heathrow	Ambassador Ops
		AM	London Heathrow	Corporate Jet Ops
		AM	London Heathrow	Gama Ops
		AM	Blackpool	Janes Ops

Base	Mobile	Mode	Location	User and Notes
		AM	Blackpool	Lynton Ops
		AM	North Weald Aerodrome	Aceair Company Channel
		AM	Exeter Airport	Handling
		AM	Manchester	Ryan Air Ops
		AM	Luton	Magec Ops
		AM	Exeter	Markair Ops
		AM	Liverpool Airport	Royal Mail Ops
		AM	Liverpool Airport	Emerald Ops
130.2000	130.2000	AM	North Sea	Alwyn Field
		AM	North Sea	Chevron Ninian Field
		AM	RAF Chivenor	Approach
		AM	RAF Cottesmore	Approach
		AM	RAF Wittering	Approach
130.2500	130.2500	AM	RAF Abingdon	Tower
		AM	East Midlands	Donington Aviation
		AM	Henstridge	Tower
		AM	Nationwide	American Airlines Packet
130.3000	130.3000	AM	Sturgate Aerodrome	Tower
130.3250	130.3250	AM	Paris	Leadair Ops
130.3500	130.3500	AM	RAF Northolt	Talkdown
		AM	Unst Aerodrome	Tower
130.3750	130.3750	AM	Blackbushe Aerodrome	Air Hanson
		AM	Bognor Regis Aerodrome	Company Channel
		AM	Farnborough	Executive Ops
		AM	Manchester	FLS Engineering Ops
130.4000	130.4000	AM	Edinburgh Airport	Approach
		AM	Rufforth Aerodrome	Tower
		AM	Thirsk Aerodrome	Thirsk radio
		AM	Nationwide	Gliders Channel
		AM	Punchestown	Air-Ground
130.4250	130.4250	AM	Badminton Aerodrome	Tower
		AM	Halton Aerodrome	Tower
		AM	Sandtoft Aerodrome	Tower
		AM	Nationwide	SAR Incident
130.4500	130.4500	AM	Glenrothes	Tower
		AM	Paris	EuroAir Ops
		AM	Skegness Aerodrome	Tower
		AM	Thruxton Aerodrome	Tower
		AM	Wellesbourne Mountford	Tower
130.4750	130.4750	AM	Gamston Aerodrome	Tower
130.5000	130.5000	AM	Nationwide	Aquilla Air-to-Air
		AM	Castleforbes Aerodrome	Tower
130.5500	130.5500	AM	Andrewsfield Aerodrome	Tower
		AM	Brough Aerodrome	Tower/Approach
		AM	Brussels	Abelag Ops
		AM	Holme-next-the-Sea	Approach
		AM	North Sea	Amoco Vauxhall Field
		AM	North Sea	Phillips Albuskjell Field

Base	Mobile	Mode	Location	User and Notes
		AM	North Sea	Phillips Cod Field
		AM	North Sea	Phillips Edda Field
		AM	North Sea	Phillips Ekofisk Field
		AM	North Sea	Phillips Eldfisk Field
		AM	North Sea	Phillips Tor Field
130.5750	130.5750	AM	Stansted Airport	Universal Air Handling
		AM	London Heathrow	Shell Ops
		AM	Gatwick	Interflight Ops
130.6000	130.6000	AM	Aberdeen/Dyce Airport	Servisair
		AM	Aberdeen/Dyce Airport	Air UK
		AM	Belfast/Aldergrove	Servisair
		AM	Birmingham Airport	Servisair
		AM	Blackpool Airport	Servisair
		AM	Bournemouth Airport	Channel Express
		AM	Bristol Airport	Servisair
		AM	Cardiff Airport	Servisair
		AM	Gatwick	British Caledonian
		AM	Guernsey	Servisair
		AM	Jersey	Servisair
		AM	London Heathrow	Fields Aviation Ops
		AM	London Heathrow	Huntair
		AM	RAF Manston	KIA Ops
		AM	Manchester	Servisair
		AM	Nationwide	Brymon Airways Ops
		AM	Nationwide	Delta Airlines Ops
		AM	Nationwide	Servisair
		AM	Newcastle	Servisair
		AM	Stansted	Air UK Leisure Ops
		AM	Edinburgh Airport	Servisair
130.6250	130.6250	AM	Aberdeen/Dyce Airport	Granite Ops
		AM	Bristol Airport	Clifton Ops
		AM	East Midlands Airport	Donington Aviation Ops
		AM	Ronaldsway	Island Aviation
		AM	Horsham Aerodrome	Tower
		AM	Southend Airport	British Air Ferries Ops
130.6500	130.6500	AM	Barra	Tower
		AM	Bournemouth Airport	Services
		AM	Foulsham Aerodrome	Tower
		AM	Gatwick	American Airlines
		AM	Gatwick	China Airlines
		AM	Gatwick	Dan Air Ops
		AM	Gatwick	Euro Air Ops
		AM	Gatwick	Handling
		AM	Gatwick	Korean Airlines
		AM	Gatwick	Northwest Orient
		AM	Kyle of Lochalsh	RN Heliport
		AM	Glasgow	Loganair Ops
		AM	Glasgow	Maersk Ops

Base	Mobile	Mode	Location	User and Notes
		AM	Manchester	Handling
		AM	Manchester	Northern Executive
		AM	Manchester	LTU Ops
		AM	Manchester	Aer Lingus Ops
		AM	Skye	Tower
		AM	Jersey	Company Ops
130.6750	130.6750	AM	RAF Marham	Tower
130.7000	130.7000	AM	Bedford (MoD Airfield)	Approach
		AM	Cleeton Aerodrome	Tower
		AM	Connaught Airport	Tower
		AM	Land's End Airport	Tower
		AM	Wroughton	Tower
130.7250	130.7250	AM	North Sea	Total/Elf Frigg/Fergus Field
		AM	West Freugh (MoD)	Radar
130.7500	130.7500	AM	Belfast Harbour	Tower
		AM	Boscombe Down (MoD)	Talkdown
		AM	Cambridge Airport	Radar
		AM	Manchester	Aer Lingus Ops
		AM	Sydenham Aerodrome	Tower
		AM	Woodford	Approach
130.7750	130.7750	AM	Braintree Airfield	Tower
130.8000	130.8000	AM	English Channel	Fisheries Protection
		AM	Hatfield Aerodrome	Tower
		AM	Hucknall Aerodrome	Tower
		AM	North Sea	Amoco NW Hutton
		AM	North Sea	Conoco Hutton
		AM	Warton (MoD)	Tower
		AM	Yeovil Aerodrome	Approach
130.8250	130.8250	AM	Farnborough	Talkdown
130.8500	130.8500	AM	Brawdy	Approach
		AM	Filton	Approach
		AM	Gransden	Tower
		AM	Borough	Approach
		AM	Belfast Harbour	Approach
		AM	Little Gransden	Tower
		AM	Sydenham Aerodrome	Approach
130.8750	130.8750	AM	West Malling Aerodrome	Tower
130.9250	130.9250	AM	RAF West Drayton	London TMA
130.9500		AM	Shannon Airport	ATIS
131.0000	131.0000	AM	Southampton Airport	Approach
131.0500	131.0500	AM	RAF West Drayton	London UIR ATC
131.0750	131.0750	AM	Gatwick	Servisair
131.1000	131.1000	AM	Brussels Airport	ACC
		AM	Nationwide	British Airways Packet
131.1250	131.1250	AM	RAF West Drayton	Air Traffic Control
		AM	Manchester	ATC
		AM	Manchester	ATC
131.1500	131.1500	AM	Shannon Airport	ACC

Base	Mobile	Mode	Location	User and Notes
131.1750	131.1750	AM	Brest	UACC
131.2000	131.2000	AM	RAF West Drayton	Air Traffic Control
131.2500	131.2500	AM	Paris Airport	ACC/UACC
131.3000	131.3000	AM	Lydd Airport	Tower
		AM	Prestwick Airport	Scottish Air Traffic Control
131.3250	131.3250	AM	Birmingham Airport	Approach
131.3750	131.3750	AM	Glasgow Airport	Air Canada
131.4000	131.4000	AM	London Heathrow	Bangladesh Biman
		AM	London Heathrow	CSA
		AM	London Heathrow	Kenya Airways
		AM	London Heathrow	Trans Mediterranean
		AM	London Heathrow	Zambian Airlines
131.4250	131.4250	AM	Amsterdam	KLM Commuter Ops
		AM	London Heathrow	Saudia Ops
		AM	Birmingham	Allied
		AM	Birmingham	Ogden Aviation
		AM	London Gatwick	Ogden Aviation Ops
		AM	London Gatwick	Air New Zealand Ops
		AM	London Gatwick	Virgin Ops
		AM	London Gatwick	Virgin Ops
		AM	Dublin	British Midlands Ops
		AM	London Heathrow	British Midlands Ops
		AM	Manchester	Cathay Pacific Ops
		AM	London Heathrow	Royal Jordanian Ops
131.4500	131.4500	AM	Brussels	Speedbird Ops
		AM	Amsterdam	Martinair Ops
		AM	Amsterdam	Philips Ops
		AM	London Heathrow	Air Canada Ops
		AM	London Heathrow	Air Malta Ops
		AM	London Heathrow	Alitalia Ops
		AM	London Heathrow	BWIA Ops
		AM	London Heathrow	Cathay Pacific Ops
		AM	London Heathrow	KLM Ops
		AM	London Heathrow	Pakistan International Ops
		AM	London Heathrow	Aer Lingus Ops
		AM	London Heathrow	Thai Airways Ops
		AM	Prestwick Airport	Air Canada Ops
		AM	Shannon	Servisair
131.4750	131.4750	AM	Brussels	Servisair
		AM	Dublin	Translift Ops
		AM	Gatwick	British Airways Maintenance
		AM	Gatwick	Caledonian Ops
		AM	London Heathrow	Sabena
		AM	London Heathrow	GB Airways Ops
		AM	London Heathrow	Maersk Ops
		AM	London Heathrow	All Nippon Ops
		AM	London Heathrow	Speedbird Control North
		AM	London Heathrow	TAT Ops

Base	Mobile	Mode	Location	User and Notes
		AM	Nationwide	Canadian Armed Forces
131.5000	131.5000	AM	Cork Airport	Aer Lingus Ops
		AM	Dublin Airport	Aer Lingus
		AM	London Heathrow	Air France Ops
		AM	London Heathrow	British Airways Ops
		AM	London Heathrow	Kuwait Airways Ops
131.5250	131.5250	AM	Luton Airport	Ryan Air
		AM	Luton Airport	Monarch Airlines
		AM	Luton Airport	London European Airways
		AM	Manchester	American Ops
131.5500	131.5500	AM	Amsterdam	Ground Services
		AM	Dublin	Ryanair Ops
		AM	London Heathrow	Ryanair Ops
		AM	London Heathrow	Luxair Ops
		AM	London Heathrow	British Airways Parking
		AM	London Heathrow	Springbok Ops
		AM	Dinard	Aurigny Air Services
131.5750	131.5750	AM	Belfast/Aldergrove	British Midlands
		AM	Birmingham Airport	TEA Operations
		AM	East Midlands Airport	British Midlands
		AM	East Midlands Airport	Excalibur Ops
		AM	Guernsey	British Midlands Ops
		AM	Jersey	British Midlands Jersey Ops
		AM	London Heathrow	El Al
		AM	London Heathrow	Iran Air Ops
		AM	Plymouth	Brymon
		AM	Birmingham	Loganair
		AM	London Heathrow	Manx Ops
		AM	London Heathrow	Channel Express Ops
		AM	Edinburgh Airport	British Midland
131.6000	131.6000	AM	London Heathrow	Air Lines Ops
		AM	London Heathrow	TWA Ops
		AM	London Heathrow	Fields Ops
		AM	East Midlands	UPS Ops
		AM	London Gatwick	TWA Ops
		AM	Amsterdam	TWA Ops
		AM	Brussels	TWA Ops
		AM	Paris Charles De Gaulle	TWA Ops
		AM	Gatwick Airport	City Flyer Ops
131.6250	131.6250	AM	Gatwick	British Caledonian
		AM	Gatwick	Canadian Pacific Ops
		AM	London Gatwick	British Airways
		AM	London Heathrow	Royal Jordanian Ops
		AM	London Heathrow	Sabena
		AM	Portishead	Aero Radio Telephones
		AM	Shannon	Aerofolt Ops
131.6500	131.6500	AM	Amsterdam Schipol	KLM Ops
		AM	London Heathrow	Air Malta Ops

Base	Mobile	Mode	Location	User and Notes
		AM	London Heathrow	Dan Air Ops
		AM	London Heathrow	Japan Airlines Ops
		AM	London Heathrow	KLM Ops Terminal 4
131.6750	131.6750	AM	Luton Airport	Britannia Airways
131.7000	131.7000	AM	Gatwick	Jetset Ops
		AM	London Heathrow	Crossair Ops
		AM	London Heathrow	Delta Ops
		AM	London Heathrow	KLM
		AM	London Heathrow	Sabena
		AM	London Heathrow	SAS Ops
		AM	London Heathrow	Swissair Ops
		AM	Manchester	Swissair Ops
		AM	Manchester	SAS Ops
		AM	London Heathrow	Air 2000 Ops
		AM	Birmingham	Air 2000 Ops
		AM	Glasgow	Air 2000 Ops
		AM	Manchester	Air 2000 Ops
131.7250	131.7250	AM	Nationwide	ACARS Frequency
131.7500	131.7500	AM	Frankfurt	Lufthansa Ops
		AM	London Heathrow	Lufthansa Ops
		AM	London Heathrow	Aer Lingus Ops
		AM	London Heathrow	Air UK
		AM	London Heathrow	Kenya Airways
		AM	London Heathrow	TAP Air Portugal
		AM	Manchester	Aer Lingus Ops
		AM	London Gatwick	Continental
131.7750	131.7750	AM	Amsterdam	Martinair Maintenance
		AM	Amsterdam	Air Holland
		AM	London Heathrow	Aeroflot
		AM	London Heathrow	British Airways Ops
		AM	London Heathrow	CSA
		AM	London Heathrow	Icelandair
		AM	London Heathrow	JAT
		AM	London Heathrow	Korean Air Ops
		AM	London Heathrow	LOT
		AM	London Heathrow	Malev
		AM	London Heathrow	Olympic
		AM	London Heathrow	Sabena
		AM	Birmingham Airport	Air Foyle
		AM	Luton Airport	Air Foyle
		AM	Luton Airport	Britannia Airways Maintenance
		AM	Paris Charles De Gaulle	British Airways
		AM	Stansted	Air Foyle
131.8000	131.8000	AM	London Heathrow	British Airways
		AM	Nationwide	Fisheries Protection
		AM	Amsterdam	Ogden Aviation Ops
		AM	Edinburgh Airport	British Airways
131.8250	131.8250	AM	Amsterdam	KLM Maintenance

Base	Mobile	Mode	Location	User and Notes
		AM	London Heathrow	Federal Express Ops
		AM	London Heathrow	Gibair Ops
		AM	Dublin	Park Aviation
		AM	London Heathrow	Cathay Pacific Ops
		AM	Jersey	Company Ops
131.8500	131.8500	AM	Aberdeen/Dyce Airport	British Airways Ops
		AM	Amsterdam	Singapore Airlines Ops
		AM	Belfast/Aldergrove	British Airways Ops
		AM	Benbecula Airport	British Airways Ops
		AM	Birmingham Airport	British Airways Ops
		AM	Birmingham Airport	Birmingham Executive
		AM	Cork Airport	Aer Lingus Company Chan.
		AM	Inverness Airport	British Airways Ops
		AM	Jersey	British Airways Jersey Ops
		AM	London Heathrow	Malaysian Airlines
		AM	London Heathrow	Zambian Airlines
		AM	London Heathrow	United Ops
		AM	London Heathrow	Emirates Ops
		AM	Manchester	British Airways Ops
		AM	Nationwide	British Airways Ops
131.8750	131.8750	AM	London Heathrow	Quantas Ops
		AM	Manchester	Euro Manx Ops
131.9000	131.9000	AM	Prestwick	Eastern Airlines Ops
		AM	London Heathrow	British Airways Speedbird Ops
		AM	London Heathrow	South African Airlines
		AM	London Heathrow	TAT Ops
		AM	London Heathrow	Conair Ops
		AM	Gatwick	Air 2000
131.9250	131.9250	AM	London Heathrow	American Ops
		AM	London Heathrow	Lufthansa
		AM	London Heathrow	American Airlines Maintenance
		AM	Birmingham	Lufthansa
		AM	Manchester	Lufthansa
		AM	London Heathrow	Air India Ops
		AM	Gatwick	American Airlines
131.9500	131.9500	AM	Nationwide	AAC Eagles Air to Air Secondary
		AM	Brussels Airport	Sabena Ops
		AM	Dublin	Aer Turas Ops
		AM	Manchester	Federal Express
		AM	London Heathrow	Federal Express
		AM	London Heathrow	El Al
		AM	London Heathrow	MEA Ops
		AM	London Heathrow	Iberia Airlines Ops
		AM	London Heathrow	Nigerian Airlines Ops
		AM	London Heathrow	Olympic Airways Ops
		AM	London Heathrow	Singapore Airlines Ops
		AM	London Heathrow	Viva Ops
		AM	Nationwide	Air France Company Channel

Base	Mobile	Mode	Location	User and Notes
131.9750	131.9750	AM	Glasgow	British Airways
		AM	Glasgow Airport	British Airways Ops
		AM	London Heathrow	El Al
		AM	London Heathrow	United Ops
		AM	London Heathrow	Nigerian Airlines Ops
132.0000	132.0000	AM	Paris Airport	ACC/UACC
132.0500	132.0500	AM	Brest	UACC
		AM	London Heathrow	Departure/TMA
132.0750		AM	Edinburgh Airport	ATIS
132.1000	132.1000	AM	Paris Airport	ACC/UACC
132.1250	132.1250	AM	Brest	UACC
132.1500	132.1500	AM	Shannon Airport	ACC
132.2000	132.2000	AM	Prestwick	Scottish Control
		AM	Reykjavik	Reykjavik ATC
		AM	Maastricht	UAC
		AM	RAF West Drayton	Air Traffic Control
132.3250	132.3250	AM	Full Sutton	Flying Club
132.3500	132.3500	AM	Amsterdam Schipol	Dutch Military
		AM	Filton (BAe)	Filton Director
132.3750	132.3750	AM	Paris Airport	ACC/UACC
132.4000	132.4000	AM	Bristol Airport	Approach
		AM	Shoreham	ATIS
132.4500	132.4500	AM	RAF West Drayton	Air Traffic Control
132.5000	132.5000	AM	Reims Airport	ACC/UACC
132.5250	132.5250	AM	Amsterdam Schipol	Dutch Military
132.5500	132.5500	AM	Luton	Tower
132.6000	132.6000	AM	RAF West Drayton	London UIR ATC
132.6250	132.6250	AM	Reims Airport	ACC/UACC
132.6500	132.6500	AM	RNAS Lee on Solent	Solent Rescue
		AM	Kent	Kent Air Ambulance
		AM	London Heathrow	Medivac
		AM	RAF Northolt	Queen's Flight Ops
		AM	Oxford	Churchill Hospital
		AM	Nationwide	Royal Flights
132.7000	132.7000	AM	London Docklands	Approach/Thames Radar
132.8000	132.8000	AM	RAF West Drayton	Air Traffic Control
132.8250	132.8250	AM	Paris Airport	ACC/UACC
132.8500	132.8500	AM	Maastricht	UAC
132.9000	132.9000	AM	West Malling	Tower
		AM	Epsom	Racecourse Tower
		AM	Wroughton	PFA Arrivals
		AM	Manchester	Pennine Radar
132.9500	132.9500	AM	RAF West Drayton	Air Traffic Control
133.0000	133.0000	AM	Brest	ACC/UACC
133.0500	133.0500	AM	Manchester Airport	Manchester Air Traffic Control
133.0750		AM	London Heathrow	ATIS
133.1000	133.1000	AM	Amsterdam Schipol	ACC
133.1750	133.1750	AM	RAF West Drayton	Air Traffic Control

Base	Mobile	Mode	Location	User and Notes
133.2000	133.2000	AM	Prestwick	Scottish Information
133.2500	133.2500	AM	Maastricht	UAC
133.3000	133.3000	AM	RAF West Drayton	London Military
133.3500	133.3500	AM	Maastricht	UAC
133.4000	133.4000	AM	Manchester Airport	Manchester Air Traffic Control
133.4500	133.4500	AM	RAF West Drayton	London Control (Clacton)
133.4750	133.4750	AM	Brest	UACC
133.5000	133.5000	AM	Paris Airport	ACC/UACC
133.5250	133.5250	AM	RAF West Drayton	London Air Traffic Control
133.5500	133.5500	AM	Plymouth Airport	Approach
133.5750	133.5750	AM	Reims	Control
133.6000	133.6000	AM	RAF West Drayton	Air Traffic Control
133.6500	133.6500	AM	Weston on the Green	Weston Radio
		AM	Wroughton	Tower
133.6750	133.6750	AM	Prestwick Airport	Scottish UIR ATC
133.7000	133.7000	AM	RAF West Drayton	Air Traffic Control
133.7500	133.7500	AM	RAF Brize Norton	Approach
133.8000		AM	RAF West Drayton	Oceanic Track Broadcasts
		AM	Shannon Airport	N Altantic Track Broadcasts
133.8250	133.8250	AM	Reims Airport	ACC/UACC
133.8500	133.8500	AM	Bristol	Tower
		AM	Bristol Airport	Tower
		AM	Maastricht	UAC
133.9000	133.9000	AM	RAF West Drayton	London Military
133.9250	133.9250	AM	Paris Airport	ACC/UACC
133.9500	133.9500	AM	Maastricht	UAC
133.9750		AM	London Heathrow	ATIS
134.0500	134.0500	AM	RAF Wyton	Approach
		AM	RNAS Culdrose	Approach
134.1000	134.1000	AM	RAF Buchan	Highland Radar
134.1250	134.1250	AM	RAF West Drayton	Air Traffic Control
134.1500	134.1500	AM	RAF Northolt	Tower/Approach/Dir
		AM	Shetland	Radar
134.1750	134.1750	AM	RAF West Drayton	Air Traffic Control
134.2000	134.2000	AM	Brest	ACC
134.2250	134.2250	AM	Gatwick	Aproach/Radar/ Tower
134.2500	134.2500	AM	RAF West Drayton	London UIR ATC
134.2750	134.2750	AM	Shannon	ACC
134.3000	134.3000	AM	Prestwick Airport	Scottish Military
		AM	RAF Abingdon	Centralised Approach Cont.
		AM	RAF Benson	Centralised Approach Control
		AM	RAF Brize Norton	Brize Radar
		AM	RAF Buchan	Highland Radar
		AM	RAF Fairford	Centralised Approach Control
		AM	RAF Greenham Common	Centralised Approach Control
		AM	RAF Kemble	Radar
		AM	RAF Lyneham	Centralised Approach Cont.
134.3500	134.3500	AM	Farnborough	Approach

Base	Mobile	Mode	Location	User and Notes
		AM	RAF Valley	Approach
134.3750	134.3750	AM	Maastricht	UAC
134.4000	134.4000	AM	Reims Airport	ACC/UACC
134.4250	134.4250	AM	RAF West Drayton	Air Traffic Control
134.4500	134.4500	AM	London Heathrow	London Zone
		AM	RAF West Drayton	London Control (Hurn)
134.4750	134.4750	AM	Prestwick Airport	Scottish Military
134.5000	134.5000	AM	Filton (BAe)	Filton Ops
134.6000	134.6000	AM	Beccles	Heliport Air/Gnd
		AM	Bacton	Air/Gnd
		AM	Beccles Heliport	Tower
134.6250	134.6250	AM	Shannon	ATC
134.6500	134.6500	AM	Nationwide	RAF Flight Checker
134.6750	134.6750	AM	Copenhagen	Copenhagen ATC
134.7000	134.7000	AM	RAF Brize Norton	Brize Radar
		AM	RAF West Drayton	London FIR Information
134.7500	134.7500	AM	RAF West Drayton	UIR ATC
134.7750	134.7750	AM	Prestwick Airport	Scottish Air Traffic Control
134.8000	134.8000	AM	Belfast Harbour	Radar
		AM	Biggin Hill	Tower
134.8250	134.8250	AM	Brest	UACC
134.8500	134.8500	AM	Prestwick Airport	Scottish Air Traffic Control
		AM	Duxford Aerodrome	Air Display Channel
134.8750	134.8750	AM	Brest	UACC
134.9000	134.9000	AM	RAF West Drayton	Air Traffic Control
134.9750	134.9750	AM	London Heathrow	Approach
		AM	Nationwide	CAA Tests Flight
135.0000	135.0000	AM	Nationwide	CAA Tests Flight
135.0500	135.0500	AM	RAF West Drayton	Air Traffic Control
135.0750	135.1250	AM	Heathrow	Approach
		AM	Heathrow	Approach
135.1500	135.1500	AM	Maastricht	UAC
		AM	RAF West Drayton	London Military ICF
135.1750	135.1750	AM	Dunsfold	Approach
		AM	Aberdeen	Aberdeen Radar
135.2000	135.2000	AM	RAF Wattisham	Approach MATZ
135.2250	135.2250	AM	Shannon	ATC
135.2500	135.2500	AM	RAF West Drayton	London Air Traffic Control
135.2750	135.2750	AM	RAF West Drayton	London Military ICF
135.3000	135.3000	AM	Paris Airport	ACC/UACC
135.3250	135.3250	AM	RAF West Drayton	London Air Traffic Control
135.3750	135.3750	AM	RAF West Drayton	London VOLMET Main
135.4250	135.4250	AM	RAF West Drayton	London Air Traffic Control
135.4500	135.4500	AM	Maastricht	UAC
135.4750	135.4750	AM	Nationwide	CAA Tests Flight
135.5000	135.5000	AM	Reims Airport	ACC/UACC
		AM	Prestwick	Shanwick Clearance
135.5250	135.5250	AM	RAF West Drayton	Air Traffic Control

Base	Mobile	Mode	Location	User and Notes
		AM	Shannon Airport	Shanwick Oceanic ACC
135.5750	135.5750	AM	Gatwick	Radar Standby
		AM	RAF West Drayton	London TMA
135.6000	135.6000	AM	Shannon Airport	ACC
135.6500	135.6500	AM	Brest	UACC
135.6750	135.6750	AM	Prestwick Airport	Scottish Air Traffic Control
135.7000	135.7000	AM	RNAS Lee-on-Solent	Tower
135.7500	135.7500	AM	Farnborough	Air Show Approach
		AM	Nationwide	CAA Tests Flight
135.8000	135.8000	AM	Paris Airport	ACC/UACC
135.8500	135.8500	AM	Prestwick Airport	Scottish UIR ATC
135.9000	135.9000	AM	Paris Airport	ACC/UACC
135.9500	135.9500	AM	Blackpool Airport	Approach
135.9750	135.9750	AM	Maastricht	UACC
		NFM	RAF Fairford	Silver Eagles Display Team
		AM	Nationwide	Army Air-Air
		AM	Liverpool Airport	Mail Flights (Air-Air)
		AM	Nationwide	Ryanair (Air-Air)

136.0000 - 136.9750 MHz NATIONAL & INTERNATIONAL AIR TRAFFIC CONTROL CENTRES 25 kHz

Base	Mobile	Mode	Location	User and Notes
136.0500		NFM	Nongeostationary	Canada Isis 1
136.0750	136.0750	AM	Paris	ACC
136.0800		NFM	Nongeostationary	Canada Isis 2
136.1000		NFM	Nongeostationary	NASA Explorer 15
136.1100		NFM	Nongeostationary	NASA Explorer 35
136.1110		NFM	Nongeostationary	NASA Explorer 18
136.1120		NFM	Nongeostationary	Japan MOS-1
		NFM	Nongeostationary	France/US Ayame 2
136.1250		NFM	Nongeostationary	NASA Explorer 28
136.1410		NFM	Nongeostationary	NASA Explorer 34
136.1420		NFM	Nongeostationary	NASA Explorer 21
136.1450		NFM	Nongeostationary	NASA Explorer Series
136.1590		NFM	Nongeostationary	Japan Ohsumi 1
136.1600		NFM	Nongeostationary	ESRO Aurorae
136.1700		NFM	Nongeostationary	US Echo 2
		NFM	Nongeostationary	NASA Explorer 42
136.1710		NFM	Nongeostationary	NASA Explorer 22
136.1750	136.1750	NFM	RAF Fairford	Chilean Air Force Display Team
136.2000		NFM	Nongeostationary	US Injun SR3
		NFM	Nongeostationary	US Cameo 1
		NFM	Nongeostationary	US Nimbus 2
136.2000	136.2000	AM	RAF West Drayton	Air Traffic Control
136.2200		NFM	Nongeostationary	US OAO 1
136.2300		NFM	Nongeostationary	US ESSA 1
		NFM	Nongeostationary	US SERT 2
136.2310		NFM	Nongeostationary	US Tiros 9
136.2330		NFM	Nongeostationary	US Tiros 8

Base	Mobile	Mode	Location	User and Notes	
136.2340		NFM	Nongeostationary	US	Tiros 7
136.2500		NFM	Nongeostationary	France	Castor
136.2600		NFM	Nongeostationary	NASA	OV5-3
		NFM	Nongeostationary	US	ERS 20
136.2730		NFM	Nongeostationary	NASA	Explorer Series
136.2750		NFM	Nongeostationary	NASA	Explorer 26
136.2750	136.2750	AM	RAF West Drayton	Air Traffic Control	
136.2900		NFM	Nongeostationary	NASA	Hawkeye
136.2900		NFM	Nongeostationary	NASA	Explorer 40
136.2930		NFM	Nongeostationary	NASA	Explorer 25
136.3000		NFM	Nongeostationary	NASA	SMS 1
136.3190		NFM	Nongeostationary	USAF	GGSE 1
136.3200		NFM	Nongeostationary	USAF	Ferret
136.3200		NFM	Nongeostationary	USAF	Ferret
136.3200		NFM	Nongeostationary	NASA	GEOS 3
136.3482		NFM	Nongeostationary	Australia	WRESAT 1
136.3500		NFM	Nongeostationary	France	EOLE 1
		NFM	Nongeostationary	France	FR 1
		NFM	Nongeostationary	USAF	SR 11B
136.3800		NFM	Nongeostationary	US	ERS 27
136.4000	136.4000	AM	Brest	ATC	
136.4100		NFM	Nongeostationary	ITSO	Intelsat
		NFM	Nongeostationary	Canada	Isis 1
136.4150		NFM	Nongeostationary	USAF	ERS 6
136.4300		NFM	Nongeostationary	India	Bhaskara
136.4400		NFM	Nongeostationary	USAF	ERS 15
136.4500	136.4500	AM	Brest	UACC	
136.4680		NFM	Nongeostationary	NASA	SYNCOM 2
136.5000		NFM	Nongeostationary	NASA	ATS Series
		NFM	Nongeostationary	NASA	Injun
		NFM	Nongeostationary	NASA	SR 3
		NFM	Nongeostationary	US	NOAA 10
136.5100		NFM	Nongeostationary	NASA	OVS 9
136.5210		NFM	Nongeostationary	US	SOLRAD 11B
136.5300		NFM	Nongeostationary	US	OV 5-9
		NFM	Nongeostationary	US	Vela Hotel 8
		NFM	Nongeostationary	US	SOLRAD 11B
136.5500	136.5500	AM	RAF West Drayton	Air Traffic Control	
136.5600		NFM	Nongeostationary	Germany	GRS-A
136.5630		NFM	Nongeostationary	US	RADSAT 43
136.5900		NFM	Nongeostationary	Canada	Alouette 1
		NFM	Nongeostationary	Canada	Isis 1 & 2
136.6000	136.6000	AM	RAF West Drayton	Air Traffic Control	
136.6100		NFM	Nongeostationary	ESA	Arian LO3
		NFM	Nongeostationary	ESA	CAT 1
136.6200		NFM	Nongeostationary	Italy	Sirio 1
		NFM	Nongeostationary	USAF	OV 5
136.6300		NFM	North West	PMR	

Base	Mobile	Mode	Location	User and Notes	
		NFM	Nongeostationary	France	Signe 3
136.6500		NFM	Nongeostationary	USAF	OV 5-5
		NFM	Nongeostationary	US	TRAAC
		NFM	Nongeostationary	US	Transit 5B5
136.6500	136.6500	AM	Manchester	Ringway Handling	
136.6510		NFM	Nongeostationary	USAF	SN-43
136.6780		NFM	Nongeostationary	US	SMS
136.6940		NFM	Nongeostationary	Japan	Shinsei
136.6950		NFM	Nongeostationary	Japan	Jiki'ken
136.7100		NFM	Nongeostationary	US	OSO-4
136.7120		NFM	Nongeostationary	US	OGO-2
136.7130		NFM	Nongeostationary	NASA	OSO-2
		NFM	Nongeostationary	Japan	Tansei
136.7250		NFM	Nongeostationary	Japan	CORSA B
136.7400		NFM	Nongeostationary	France	ERS-A
136.7680		NFM	Nongeostationary	ESA	ERS-17 ORS3
136.7700		NFM	Nongeostationary	US	NOAA 6
		NFM	Nongeostationary	US	NOAA 8
		NFM	Nongeostationary	US	NOAA 9
136.7710		NFM	Nongeostationary	USAF	ERS-13 TRS6
136.8000		AM	Nationwide	Kestrel Ops	
136.8000	136.8000	AM	Manchester Airport	Airtours Ops	
		AM	Manchester Airport	Tourjet Ops	

136.8000 - 136.9750 MHz International Operations & Datalinks 25 kHz

Base	Mobile	Mode	Location	User and Notes	
136.8010		NFM	Nongeostationary	USAF	SOLRAD 7B
136.8040		NFM	Nongeostationary	US	EGRS SECOR
136.8097		NFM	Nongeostationary	Japan	UME 1 & 2
136.8100		NFM	Nongeostationary	Japan	ETS-1 KIKU
136.8250	136.8250	AM	Nationwide	Dutch Ops	
		AM	Dublin	City Jet Ops	
		AM	London City Airport	City Jet Ops	
		AM	Manchester	American Airlines Ops	
136.8300		NFM	Nongeostationary	USAF	EGRS 8
		NFM	Nongeostationary	USAF	ERS 28
136.8400		NFM	Nongeostationary	USAF	TOPO 1
		NFM	Nongeostationary	USAF	EGRS 9
136.8500	136.8500	AM	East Midlands Airport	UPS Ops	
136.8600		NFM	Nongeostationary	USAF	OV5-4
		NFM	Nongeostationary	NASA	RMS
		NFM	Nongeostationary	USAF	Cannonball 2
		NFM	Nongeostationary	NASA	IUE TETR 2
		NFM	Nongeostationary	USA	Landsat 2
		NFM	Nongeostationary	US	ERS 21
136.8700		NFM	Nongeostationary	US	Injun 3
136.8750	136.8750	AM	Nationwide	Monarch Airlines Ops	
		AM	Gatwick	Monarch Airlines Ops	
		AM	Luton	Monarch Airlines Ops	

Base	Mobile	Mode	Location	User and Notes
		AM	Manchester	Monarch Airlines Ops
136.8870		NFM	Nongeostationary	USAF SOLRAD 7A
136.8900		NFM	Nongeostationary	USAF SOLRAD 6
		NFM	Nongeostationary	USAF ERS 9 TRS4
136.8900		NFM	Nongeostationary	NASA Explorer 47
136.8910		NFM	Nongeostationary	USAF ERS 9
136.8920		NFM	Nongeostationary	USAF ERS 5
136.9190		NFM	Nongeostationary	US Tiros 9
136.9200		NFM	Nongeostationary	USAF OSO 8
		NFM	Nongeostationary	USAF SERT 28
136.9500		NFM	Nongeostationary	ESA COS B1
136.9750	136.9750	AM	Nationwide	Sharks Helicopter Displays
		AM	London Heathrow	British Airways SpeedbirdOps
		AM	London Heathrow	South African Airlines
		AM	London Heathrow	TAT Ops
		AM	London Heathrow	Conair Ops
137.0400		NFM	Nongeostationary	USAF Ferret
137.0800		NFM	Nongeostationary	ESA Meteorsat 1/2
137.1100		NFM	Nongeostationary	US ATS 6
137.1400		NFM	Nongeostationary	ERS ECS 2
137.1500		NFM	Nongeostationary	USSR Meteor
137.1700		NFM	Nongeostationary	ERS MARECS A
		NFM	Nongeostationary	France MAROTS
137.1900		NFM	Nongeostationary	US GEOS 3
137.2000		NFM	Nongeostationary	USSR Meteor
		AM	RAF Lakenheath	Dep Con
137.2300		NFM	Nongeostationary	India/USSR Bhaskara 2
		NFM	Nongeostationary	US NOAA 61
137.2600		NFM	Nongeostationary	US OAO-A2
137.3000		NFM	Nongeostationary	USSR Meteor 2-18
		NFM	Nongeostationary	US Meteor 2-17
		NFM	Nongeostationary	USSR Meteor 2-5
		NFM	Nongeostationary	US Meteor 3-2
		NFM	Nongeostationary	US Timation 2
137.3800		NFM	Nongeostationary	USAF OVS 3
137.4000		NFM	Nongeostationary	USAF SMS-2
		NFM	Nongeostationary	USSR Meteor 2-16/17
137.4100		NFM	Nongeostationary	USSR Meteor 3-1
		NFM	Nongeostationary	USAF Explorer 30
137.4200		NFM	Nongeostationary	India Rohini
137.4400		NFM	Nongeostationary	India Aryabhata
		NFM	Nongeostationary	India Bhaskari 3
137.5000		NFM	Nongeostationary	USSR Meteor 3-1
		NFM	Nongeostationary	US NOAA 6
		NFM	Nongeostationary	US NOAA 10
137.5300		NFM	Glossop	Builders' Merchants
137.5600		NFM	Nongeostationary	UK UK 6
137.5700		NFM	Nongeostationary	NASA Explorer Series

Base	Mobile	Mode	Location	User and Notes
137.6200		NFM	Nongeostationary	NASA NOAA 9
		NFM	Nongeostationary	NASA NOAA 11
137.6760		NFM	Nongeostationary	US P76-5
137.7700		NFM	Nongeostationary	US NOAA 9
137.8000		NFM	Nongeostationary	USAF SOLRAD 11
137.8500		NFM	Nongeostationary	USSR Meteor 2-19
		NFM	Nongeostationary	USSR Meteor 2-16
		NFM	Nongeostationary	USSR Meteor 2-15
		NFM	Nongeostationary	USSR Meteor 3-3
		NFM	Nongeostationary	USSR Intercosmos 18
137.8600		NFM	Nongeostationary	US Landsat 2
137.8750		NFM	Newport	Pager
137.8900		NFM	Nongeostationary	US ANS-1
		NFM	Nongeostationary	NASA RMS
137.9500		NFM	Nongeostationary	Canada Isis
		NFM	Nongeostationary	NASA Explorer 45

137.9625 - 138.2125 MHz Nationwide Paging 12.5 kHz

Base	Mobile	Mode	Location	User and Notes
137.9750		NFM	Nationwide	Paging
137.9800		NFM	Nongeostationary	NASA Explorer 50
138.0000		NFM	Nongeostationary	USAF Hilat 1

138.00625 - 140.49375 MHz PMR VHF High Band 12.5 kHz Public Utiliy

Base	Mobile	Mode	Location	User and Notes
138.02500		AM	Kent	Southern Gas
		AM	York	North East Gas
138.03125		NFM	Westerfield	Train Link
138.04375		NFM	English Channel	Train Link
138.06000		NFM	London	Calling Points
138.06875		NFM	Ipswich	Train Link
138.09375	138.09375	NFM	England & Wales	Police Heli-Teli Channel 1
		NFM	Merseyside	Police Air Support Grp (M1)
138.10000	138.1000	NFM	London	Police Helicopter
138.10500	138.1050	NFM	Merseyside	Police Air Support Unit (I99)
		NFM	Gt Manchester	Police Air Support Unit (I99)
		NFM	Great Lippits Hill	Police Heli-Teli Chan 40
138.10625		NFM	West Midlands	Police Helicopter Downlink
		NFM	Gt Manchester	Police Helicopter
138.10625	138.10625	NFM	England & Wales	Police Heli-Teli Channel 2
138.15000		NFM	Nationwide	Vodafone Paging
138.16125		NFM	Windermere	Data Link
138.17500		NFM	Nationwide	Mercury Personal Pagers
138.20000		AM	Gloucester	Gas Board
138.24375		NFM	Brampton	BR Train Link
		NFM	Darsham	BR Train Link
		NFM	Halesworth	BR Train Link
		NFM	Saxmundham	BR Train Link
		NFM	Suffolk	BR Train Link
		NFM	Woodbridge	BR Train Link

Base	Mobile	Mode	Location	User and Notes
		NFM	Ipswich	BR Train Link
		NFM	Lowestoft	BR Train Link
138.25625		NFM	Perth	Data Link
138.29375	138.29375	NFM	England & Wales	Police Heli-Teli Channel 3
		NFM	Cheshire	Police Helicopter
138.3000	138.3000	AM	Nationwide	USAF Air to Air
138.30625	138.30625	NFM	England & Wales	Police Heli-Teli Channel 4
		NFM	Lancashire	Police Helicopter
138.32500		NFM	Nationwide	British Rail RETD
		NFM	Woodbridge	East Suffolk Line RETB
138.33000		NFM	London	BR Train Link
138.33125		NFM	London	BR Train Link
		NFM	Tayside	Data Link
138.33750		NFM	Newmarket	Data Link
138.34375		NFM	Norfolk	BR Data Link
		NFM	Suffolk	BR Data Link
138.35000		NFM	Nationwide	BR Radiophone
138.35625		NFM	Nationwide	BR Radiophone
		NFM	Nationwide	BR Radiophone
138.36550		NFM	Nationwide	BR Radiophone
138.36875		NFM	Nationwide	BR Radiophone
		NFM	Norfolk	Data Link
		NFM	Suffolk	Data Link
138.38750		AM	Halifax	North East Gas
138.39375		AM	Holdengate, Keighley	British Gas North Eastern
		AM	Southowram, Halifax	British Gas North Eastern
138.40000		AM	Bradford	North East Gas
138.40625		AM	Southowram, Halifax	British Gas North Eastern
		AM	Holdengate, Keighley	British Gas North Eastern
138.41250		AM	Keighley	North East Gas
138.41875		AM	Tingley, Leeds	British Gas North Eastern
		AM	Wetherby	British Gas North Eastern
138.43125		AM	Moortop, Horsforth	British Gas North Eastern
138.44000		AM	Swindon	Gas Board
138.44375		AM	Queensbury, Bradford	British Gas North Eastern
138.45625		AM	Wetherby	British Gas North Eastern
		AM	Tingley, Leeds	British Gas North Eastern
		AM	Moortop, Leeds	British Gas North Eastern
138.46250		AM	Skipton	North East Gas
138.46875		AM	Heyshaw, Harrogate	British Gas North Eastern
		AM	Nappa, Keighley	British Gas North Eastern
		AM	Todmorden, Halifax	British Gas North Eastern
		AM	Moortop, Ilkley	British Gas North Eastern
		AM	Brighouse, Halifax	British Gas North Eastern
138.47500		AM	Otley	North East Gas
138.48125		AM	Tingley, Leeds	British Gas North Eastern
		AM	Moortop, Horseforth	British Gas North Eastern
138.50000		AM	Nationwide	Military Test Flights

Base	Mobile	Mode	Location	User and Notes
		NFM	Nationwide	BR Radiophone
138.54375		AM	Essex	Eastern Gas
138.63135		AM	Luton	Gas Ch2
138.70000	138.7000	AM	Nationwide	Search And Rescue
138.75005		NFM	Yorkshire	Mercury Paging
138.75625		AM	Brecon	Welsh Gas
		AM	Suffolk	Gas Board
138.82000		AM	Gt Manchester	Gas Board
138.83125		AM	Brecknock East	Welsh Gas
		AM	Bury St Edmonds	Gas Board
		AM	Luton	Gas Board
138.84000		AM	Falkirk	Scottish Gas
138.84375		AM	Peterborough	Gas Board Ch 1
138.85200		AM	Yorkshire	Gas Board
138.85625		AM	Brecon	Welsh Gas
		AM	Norfolk	Eastern Gas
		AM	Suffolk	Eastern Gas
138.86635		AM	Norwich	Gas Ch 2
138.86875		AM	Norwich	Gas Board
138.88755		NFM	Belfast	Data Link
138.95625		AM	Nationwide	PLC Plant Hire
138.96875	148.46875	NFM	Yorkshire	British Coal Security
138.97500		AM	Glasgow	Hydro Electric
		AM	Nationwide	AAC Eagles Air to Air
138.98000		AM	Edinburgh	British Gas
		AM	Aberdeen	Gas Board
138.98125		AM	Brecon	Welsh Gas
		AM	Peterborough	Gas Board
		AM	Keighly	Gas
		AM	Peterborough	Gas Ch 2
138.99375		AM	Brecknock East	Welsh Gas
		AM	Lincolnshire	Gas Board
		AM	Luton	Gas Board Ch 1
139.0000		AM	Glasgow	Hydro Electric
		NFM	Nationwide	Illegal Bugging Devices
		AM	Hull	Eastern Gas Board
139.00625		AM	Derbyshire	Gas Board
		AM	Ipswich	Gas Board
		AM	Norwich	Gas Board
		AM	Humberside	North East Gas
139.0125		AM	Barrow	Gas Board
		AM	Cumbria	Gas Board
		AM	Oxford	Gas Board
		AM	Truro	Gas Board
139.01875		AM	Oxfordshire	Gas Board
139.03125		AM	Bradford	North East Gas
		AM	Luton	Gas Board
		AM	Peterborough	Gas Board

Base	Mobile	Mode	Location	User and Notes
		AM	Bradford	North East Gas
		AM	Norwich	Gas
		NFM	Lancaster	Gas Board
		NFM	Morecambe	Gas Board
139.03375		AM	Kent	Southern Gas
139.04375		AM	Bradford	North East Gas
139.05600		NFM	Nongeostationary	US ATS 6
139.05626		AM	Bradford	North East Gas
139.06250		AM	Edinburgh	British Gas
		AM	Bradford	Gas Board
139.06875		NFM	Nationwide	Press Construction Ltd
		AM	Suffolk	Gas Board
139.08125		AM	Essex	Essex Gas
		AM	Reading	Gas Board
		AM	Radnor	Welsh Gas Channel 3
139.10000		AM	Oxford	Gas Board
139.10625		AM	Balshall	Gas Board
		AM	Grimsby	Gas Board
		AM	Ipswich	Gas Board
		AM	Kings Heath	Gas Board
139.11575		AM	Kent	Southern Gas
139.11875		AM	Oxford	Gas Board
139.12250		AM	Bath	Gas Board
139.12500	139.12500	AM	Kent	Gas Board
		AM	Nationwide	USAF 496 TFW Air-Air
139.13000		AM	Milton Keynes	British Gas
139.13125		AM	Bath	Gas Board
		AM	Brecon	South Wales Electric
		AM	Milton Keynes	Gas Board
139.13750		AM	East Sussex	Gas Board
		AM	London	Gas Board
139.14000		AM	Truro	Gas Board
139.14375		AM	Kent	Southern Gas
139.15000		AM	Leicester	Gas Board
		AM	Manchester	Gas Board
139.15500		AM	Crewe	Gas Board
139.16250		AM	Surrey	Gas Board
139.16250		AM	Yorkshire	Yorkshire Electric
139.16275		NFM	Essex	North Thames Gas
139.17000	139.1700	AM	Farnborough	Gas Board
		NFM	Scarborough	Gas Board
139.17500		AM	Halifax	Gas Board
139.17625		AM	Essex	Eastern Electric
139.18130		AM	Hull	Gas Board
139.19375		NFM	Essex	North Thames Gas
139.19500		AM	Swindon	Gas Board
		AM	South Yorkshire	Gas Board
		NFM	Lancaster	Gas Board

Base	Mobile	Mode	Location	User and Notes
		NFM	Morecambe	Gas Board
139.20000		AM	Yorkshire	Emergency Gas Call Outs
139.20625		AM	Kent	Southern Gas
139.21000		AM	Greater London	Gas Board
139.24375	147.74375	AM	Nationwide	New Power and Fuel Ch
139.25000		AM	Leeds	Gas Board
139.25625	147.75625	AM	Clacton-on-Sea	Gas Board
		AM	Oxford	Western Gas
		AM	Nationwide	New Power and Fuel Ch 1
		AM	Clacton	Gas Board
139.26250		AM	Yorkshire	Gas Board
139.26575		NFM	Kent	Southern Gas
139.26875	147.76875	AM	West Midlands	Electric Company
		AM	Nationwide	New Power and Fuel Ch 2
139.27500		AM	London	Gas Board
139.28125	147.78125	AM	Kent	Southern Gas
		AM	Nationwide	New Power and Fuel Ch 3
139.28750		AM	London	Gas Board
139.29375	147.79375	AM	Nationwide	New Power and Fuel Ch
		AM	Kent	Southern Gas
139.30625	147.80625	AM	Nationwide	New Power and Fuel Ch 5
		AM	Essex	Eastern Electric
139.31250	147.81250	AM	Staines	North Thames Gas
		AM	Wakefield	Gas Board
139.31875	147.81875	AM	Nationwide	New Power and Fuel Ch 6
		AM	Brecon	South Wales Electric
139.33125	147.83125	AM	Nationwide	New Power and Fuel Ch 7
		AM	Kent	Southern Gas
		AM	Manchester	Gas Board
139.34375	147.84375	AM	Nationwide	New Power and Fuel Ch 8
		AM	Kent	Southern Gas
139.3500		AM	Greater London	Gas Board
139.35625	147.85625	AM	Nationwide	New Power and Fuel Ch 9
		AM	Walton-on-Thames	Southern Gas
139.35875		AM	Walton-on-Thames	Southern Gas
139.36250		AM	Surrey	Gas Board
139.36875	147.86875	AM	Nationwide	New Power and Fuel Ch 10
		AM	Woodbridge	Gas Board
139.38125	147.88125	AM	Nationwide	New Power and Fuel Ch 11
139.39375	147.89375	AM	Nationwide	New Power and Fuel Ch 12
		AM	Norfolk	Eastern Gas
		AM	Suffolk	Gas Board
139.40625	147.90625	AM	Nationwide	New Power and Fuel Ch 13
139.41675	147.91875	AM	Nationwide	New Power and Fuel Ch 14
139.4250		AM	Barrow	Gas Board
		AM	Cumbria	Gas Board
139.43125		AM	Kent	Southern Gas
139.43125	147.93125	AM	Nationwide	New Power and Fuel Ch 15

Base	Mobile	Mode	Location	User and Notes
139.43750		AM	Shipley	Yorkshire Electricity
139.44375	147.94375	AM	Nationwide	New Power and Fuel Ch 16
139.4550		AM	Swindon	Gas Board
139.45625	147.95625	AM	Nationwide	New Power and Fuel Ch 17
139.46875		AM	Oxford	Southern Electric
139.5000		AM	Guernsey	BBC Radio Guernsey O/B
139.51250	148.01250	NFM	Newport	Gas Board
139.51875	148.01875	NFM	Nationwide	Electricity Board Ch J22
		AM	Kent	Southern Electric
139.5250		AM	Cumbria	North West Electricity
		NFM	Shrewsbury	Electricity Board
139.5300		NFM	Manchester	Electricity Board
		NFM	Manchester	Electricity Board
139.53125	148.03125	NFM	West Midlands	Electric Company
		NFM	Nationwide	Electricity Board Ch J23
139.54375	148.04375	NFM	Nationwide	Electricity Board Ch J24
		AM	Windsor	Electric Company
		AM	Highlands	Hydro Electric
139.55000		NFM	Plymouth	Parcel Delivery
		NFM	Leeds	Electricity Board
		AM	Tunbridge Wells	Seeboard Power Care
		AM	Nationwide	CEGB Line Faults
		NFM	Jersey	BBC Radio Jersey
139.55625	148.05625	NFM	Nationwide	Electricity Board Ch J25
		AM	Abingdon	Southern Electric
		NFM	West Sussex	Southern Electric
139.56250	139.5625	AM	Nationwide	Military Test Flights
		NFM	Newmarket	Data Link [Multi-Station]
		NFM	Arnside	Voice Link
		AM	Hampshire	Electricity Board
		AM	Milton Keynes	East Mids Electric
		AM	Hull	Yorkshire Electricity
139.5650		AM	Tunbridge Wells	Seeboard Power Care
139.56875	148.06875	NFM	West Midlands	Electric Company
		NFM	Nationwide	Electricity Board Ch J26
		AM	Perth	Hydro Electric Board
		AM	Argyll	Hydro Electric
139.57000		NFM	North West	PMR
		NFM	Newmarket	Data Link
		NFM	Lancaster	Electricity Board
		NFM	Morecambe	Electricity Board
139.57500		NFM	Cheshire	Electric Board
		AM	Bradford	Electricity Board
		NFM	Jersey	BBC Radio Jersey
139.58000		AM	Cornwall	South West Electricity Board
		NFM	Glenrothes	Electricity Board
139.58125	148.08125	NFM	Nationwide	Electricity Board Ch J27
		NFM	Ipswich	Electricity Board

Base	Mobile	Mode	Location	User and Notes
		AM	Thames Valley	Electric Company
139.58500		NFM	Glenrothes	Electricity Board
139.58750		NFM	Glasgow	Data Link
139.59375	148.09375	NFM	Nationwide	Electricity Board Ch J28
139.60000		NFM	Nationwide	Illegal Bugging Devices
		NFM	Lauder	Data Link
139.60500		NFM	Manchester	Electricity Board
139.60625	148.10625	NFM	Nationwide	Electricity Board Ch J29
139.61250		AM	Morecambe	North West Electricity
139.61375		NFM	Stirling	Data Link
139.61875	148.11875	NFM	Nationwide	Electricity Board Ch J30
139.62375		AM	Stirling	Hydro Electric
139.62500		NFM	Alnwick	Data Link
		AM	Perth	Hydro Electric Board
139.62500	148.12500	NFM	Newport	Electricity Board
139.63000		AM	Rayleigh	Eastern Electricity
139.63125	148.13125	NFM	Nationwide	Electricity Board Ch J31
		NFM	West Midlands	Electric Company
		NFM	West Sussex	Southern Electric
		AM	Thames Valley	Electric Company
		AM	Harold Hill	Eastern Electric
139.63750		AM	Morecambe	North West Electricity
		AM	Newmarket	Eastern Electricity
		AM	Kent	Electricity Board
		AM	Aberdeen	Hydro Electric
		AM	Portsmouth	Southern Electric
139.64375	148.14375	NFM	Nationwide	Electricity Board Ch J32
		NFM	West Midlands	Electric Company
		AM	Cambridge	Electric Company
		NFM	Chesterfield	East Midlands Electricity
		AM	Highlands	Hydro Electric
139.64500		NFM	Manchester	Electricity Board
		NFM	Burnley	Norweb
		NFM	Manchester	Electricity Board
		NFM	North West	PMR
139.65000		NFM	Manchester	Norweb
		AM	Immingham	Yorkshire Electricity
139.65625	148.15625	NFM	Nationwide	Electricity Board Ch J33
		AM	Norwich	Electric Company
		AM	Kent	Southern Electric
139.66875	148.16875	NFM	Nationwide	Electricity Board Ch J34
		NFM	West Sussex	Southern Electric
		AM	Clacton-on-Sea	Eastern Electricity
139.67500		AM	Newmarket	Eastern Electricity
		NFM	Dyfed	SWEB
		AM	Perth	Hydro Electric Board
		AM	Surrey	Electricity Board
139.68000		AM	Aberdeen	Hydro Electric

Base	Mobile	Mode	Location	User and Notes
139.68125	148.18125	NFM	Nationwide	Electricity Board Ch J35
		AM	Norfolk	Eastern Electric
139.68200		AM	Perth	Hydro Electric Board
139.68500		AM	Aberdeen	Hydro Electric
139.68750		AM	East Sussex	Electricity Board
139.69000		NFM	Burnley	Norweb
139.69375	148.19375	NFM	Nationwide	Electricity Board Ch J36
		NFM	West Midlands	Electric Company
		AM	Norwich	Electric Company
		AM	Highlands	Hydro Electric
139.69500		NFM	Glenrothes	Electricity Board
		NFM	Tyne & Wear	Electricity Board
		NFM	North West	PMR
139.7000		AM	Kent	Electricity Board
		NFM	Lothian & Borders	Scottish Power
139.70500		NFM	Bolton	Electric Company
		NFM	Norfolk	Street Lighting
		NFM	North West	PMR
139.70625	148.20625	NFM	Nationwide	Electricity Board Ch J37
		NFM	Ipswich	Electricity Board
		AM	Chelmsford	Electric Company
		AM	Dundee	Hydro Electric
139.71250		AM	Aberdeen	Hydro Electric
		NFM	Glasgow	Scottish Power
139.71625		AM	Perth	Hydro Electric Board
139.71875	148.21875	NFM	Nationwide	Electricity Board Ch J38
		AM	Harlow	Electric Company
139.7200		AM	Swindon	Electricity Board
		AM	Glasgow	Electricity Board
139.72375		AM	Stirling	Hydro Electric
139.72500		AM	Hampshire	Electricity Board
		AM	London	Electricity Board
139.73000		AM	South Yorkshire	Electricity Board
139.73125	148.23125	NFM	Nationwide	Electricity Board Ch J39
		AM	Kings Lynn	Electric Company
		AM	Essex	Eastern Electric
		AM	Andover	SElectric Line Faults
		AM	Highlands	Hydro Electric
139.73750	148.23750	AM	Slough	Southern Electric
		AM	Surrey	Electricity Board
		AM	Portsmouth	Southern Electric
		AM	Leeds	Yorkshire Electricity
139.74375	148.24375	NFM	Nationwide	Electricity Board Ch J40
		AM	West Yorkshire	Electric Company
		AM	Essex	Eastern Electric
		NFM	West Midlands	Electric Company
		NFM	West Sussex	Southern Electric
139.74500		NFM	Glossop	Electric Board

Base	Mobile	Mode	Location	User and Notes
139.75000		AM	Hertfordshire	Electricity Board
139.7550		AM	Rayleigh	Eastern Electricity
139.75625	148.26625	NFM	Nationwide	Electricity Board Ch J41
		AM	Essex	Eastern Electric
139.7625	148.2500	NFM	Cardiff	S Wales Electricity Board
		AM	Edinburgh	Scottish Power
		AM	Perth	Hydro Electric Board
		AM	Shepway	Electric Company
139.76875	148.26875	NFM	Nationwide	Electricity Board Ch J42
		AM	Humberside	Electric Company
		NFM	Lancaster	Electricity Board
		NFM	Morecambe	Electricity Board
139.77500		NFM	Huddersfield	Electricity Board
		NFM	Cardiff	Electricity Board
		AM	Halifax	Yorkshire Electricity
139.7800		NFM	North West	PMR
139.78125	148.28125	NFM	Nationwide	Electricity Board Ch J43
		AM	Reading	Electric Company
		NFM	West Midlands	Electric Company
		NFM	West Sussex	Southern Electric
139.78500		AM	Leicester	Electric Company
139.78750		AM	Aberdeen	Hydro Electric
		AM	Loughborough	Electric Company
		NFM	Manchester	Electric Board
		AM	Keighley	Yorkshire Electricity
139.79000	148.29000	NFM	Peterborough	Electricity Board
139.79375	148.29375	NFM	Nationwide	Electricity Board Ch J44
		AM	Aldershot	Electric Company
		AM	Buckinghamshire	Electric Company
		AM	Montgomery	MANWEB
		AM	Salisbury	Electric Company
		AM	Argyll	Hydro Electric
		NFM	West Midlands	Electric Company
139.79500		NFM	North West	PMR
139.79775		AM	Thames	Eastern Electric
139.80000		NFM	Nationwide	Illegal Bugging Devices
		AM	Ipswich	Eastern Electricity
139.80500		NFM	Glenrothes	Electricity Board
		NFM	Stoke-on-Trent	PMR
139.80625	148.30625	NFM	Nationwide	Electricity Board Ch J45
		NFM	West Midlands	Electric Company
139.81250		AM	Newmarket	Eastern Electricity
		AM	Tunbridge Wells	Electric Company
139.81500	139.81500	NFM	Scarborough	Electricity Board
139.81825	148.31825	NFM	Nationwide	Electricity Board Ch J46
139.81875		AM	Buckinghamshire	Electric Company
139.82000		NFM	Wigan	Electricity Board
		NFM	Manchester	Norweb

Base	Mobile	Mode	Location	User and Notes
139.82500		AM	Swindon	Electricity Board
		NFM	Glasgow	Electricity Board
		NFM	W Yorkshire	Electricity Board
139.83125	148.33125	NFM	Nationwide	Electricity Board Ch J47
		AM	Humberside	Electric Company
139.83625		AM	London	London Electric
139.83750		AM	East Sussex	Electric Company
139.84375	148.34375	NFM	Nationwide	Electricity Board Ch J48
		NFM	Sheffield	Yorkshire Electricity Board
		AM	Bury St Edmunds	Eastern Electricity
		AM	London	Electricity Board
		AM	Surrey	Southern Electric
139.84500		AM	Cornwall	South West Electricity Board
		NFM	Glossop	Electric Board
139.85000		AM	Kent	Electricity Board
		AM	Leicester	Electric Company
		AM	Plymouth	SWEB
		AM	Gwynedd	MANWEB
		NFM	Merseyside	Electricity Board
139.85500		NFM	Maidstone	Maidstone Power Care
		NFM	Newcastle	Electricity Board
139.85625	148.35625	NFM	Nationwide	Electricity Board Ch J49
		NFM	West Sussex	Southern Electric
139.86375		AM	Stirling	Hydro Electric
139.86500		NFM	Manchester	Electricity Board
139.86875	148.36875	NFM	Nationwide	Electricity Board Ch J50
		AM	Perth	Hydro Electric Board
		AM	Kings Lynn	Electric Company
		AM	Argyll	Hydro Electric
		NFM	West Midlands	Electric Company
		NFM	Lancaster	Electricity Board
		NFM	Morecambe	Electricity Board
139.87250	139.87250	AM	Nationwide	USAF Air-Air
139.87500		AM	Bradford	Yorkshire Electricity
139.88125	148.38125	NFM	Nationwide	Electricity Board Ch 51
		AM	Essex	Eastern Electric
139.8825		NFM	Essex	Electricity Board
139.8875		NFM	Lauder	Data Link
139.89375	148.39375	NFM	Nationwide	Electricity Board Ch J52
		AM	West Midlands	Electric Company
139.90125		NFM	Ferrybridge	Data Link
		NFM	Lauder	Data Link
		NFM	Stirling	Data Link
139.90625	148.40625	NFM	Nationwide	Electricity Board Ch J53
139.91875	148.41875	NFM	Nationwide	Electricity Board Ch J54
139.93000	148.43000	NFM	Norfolk	Eastern Electricity
139.93125	148.43125	NFM	Nationwide	Electricity Board Ch J55
		AM	Hertfordshire	Electric Company

Base	Mobile	Mode	Location	User and Notes
		AM	Essex	Eastern Electric
		NFM	West Midlands	Electric Company
139.93750		AM	Glasgow	Hydro Electric
		NFM	Cheshire	Electricity Co. Data Link
139.94375	148.44375	NFM	Nationwide	Electricity Board Ch J56
		AM	West Midlands	Electric Company
		NFM	London	North Thames Gas
		NFM	West Midlands	Electric Company
139.95000		NFM	Manchester	Electric Board
139.95600		AM	Berkshire	Southern Electricity
139.95625	148.45625	NFM	Nationwide	Electricity Board Ch J57
		NFM	Sheffield	Yorkshire Electricity Board
		NFM	Birmingham	Electricity Board
		AM	Henley-on-Thames	Southern Electric
		NFM	West Midlands	Electric Company
139.96875	148.96875	NFM	Nationwide	Electricity Board Ch J58
139.97500		NFM	Newmarket	Data Link
		AM	Sheffield	Yorkshire Electricity
139.98125	148.48125	NFM	Nationwide	Electricity Board Ch J59
		AM	Perth	Hydro Electric Data Link
139.98750		NFM	Swansea	South Wales Electricity
139.99000		NFM	Somerset	British Gas
139.99375	148.49375	NFM	Nationwide	Electricity Board Ch J60
140.00000		NFM	Alnwick	Data Link
		NFM	Nationwide	Illegal Bugging Devices
140.00000	140.00000	AM	Nationwide	USAF Air-Air
140.00625	148.50625	NFM	Nationwide	Electricity Board Ch J61
140.01250		NFM	Cumbria	Data Link
		NFM	Lancashire	Data Link
140.01875	148.51875	NFM	Nationwide	Electricity Board Ch J62
140.02000		NFM	Durham	Data Link
140.02500		NFM	Alnwick	Data Link
140.03125	148.53125	NFM	Nationwide	Electricity Board Ch J63
140.03750		NFM	Leeds	British Gas
140.04375	148.54375	NFM	Nationwide	Electricity Board Ch J64
140.04400		AM	Perth	Data Link
140.05000		NFM	Cumbria	Data Link
		NFM	Dundee	Data Link
		NFM	Lauder	Data Link
		NFM	Lancashire	Data Link
		NFM	Nationwide	Mine Rescue Channel
		NFM	Bradford	British Gas
140.0550		NFM	Lancaster	Red Rose Radio Link
140.05625	148.55625	NFM	Nationwide	Electricity Board Ch J65
		AM	Nationwide	NCB Mine Rescue
		NFM	Braintree	Eastern Gas
140.06250		NFM	Glasgow	Data Link
140.07500		NFM	Newmarket	Data Link

Base	Mobile	Mode	Location	User and Notes
		AM	County Durham	Gas Board
140.08125	148.58125	NFM	West Sussex	British Gas Southern
140.10000		NFM	Haggerston	Data Link
		NFM	W Yorkshire	British Gas
140.10625	148.60625	NFM	Nationwide	British Gas Trunked System
		NFM	West Midlands	Gas Board
		NFM	Ferrybridge	British Gas
140.11250		AM	County Durham	Gas Board
		AM	Selby	North East Gas
		NFM	Cheshire	Gas Board
140.11875	148.61875	NFM	Nationwide	British Gas Trunked System
		NFM	Stirling	Data Link
		NFM	West Midlands	Gas Board
140.12000		NFM	Stockport	PMR
140.12500		NFM	Glasgow	PMR
140.13125	148.63125	NFM	Nationwide	British Gas Trunked System
		NFM	West Midlands	Gas Board
140.13750		AM	Leeds	North East Gas
140.13875		NFM	Stirling	Data Link
140.14375	148.64375	NFM	Nationwide	British Gas Trunked System
		NFM	Nationwide	NCB Ambulance Channel
		NFM	West Midlands	Gas Board
		NFM	Colchester	Eastern Gas
		AM	London	London Electric
140.15000		AM	County Durham	Gas Board
140.15625		AM	West Midlands	Bus Company
		AM	Cleveland	Gas Board
140.16500		NFM	Bradford	British Gas
140.16875	140.10625	AM	Perth	Hydro Electric Board
140.16875	148.66875	NFM	Nationwide	British Gas Trunked System
		NFM	West Midlands	Gas Board
		NFM	West Sussex	British Gas Southern
140.17500		NFM	Glasgow	British Gas
		AM	Bolton	Gas Board
		AM	Manchester	Gas Board
140.18000		NFM	North West	PMR
140.18125		AM	Nationwide	CEGB Line Faults
140.18250		AM	Nationwide	CEGB Line Faults
140.18750		AM	Nationwide	CEGB Line Faults
140.19375		AM	Nationwide	CEGB Line Faults
140.19500		AM	Hull	British Gas
140.19500		NFM	North West	PMR
140.20000		AM	Nationwide	CEGB Line Faults
		NFM	Dundee	Data Link
		NFM	Leeds	British Gas
140.20500		NFM	Portsmouth	Water Board
140.20625		AM	Nationwide	CEGB Line Faults
		NFM	Clacton	Eastern Electric

Base	Mobile	Mode	Location	User and Notes
140.21125	148.71125	NFM	London	Gas Board
140.21250		AM	Portmouth	Southern Gas
		AM	Fareham	Southern Gas
		AM	Gosport	Southern Gas
140.21875		AM	Clacton-on-Sea	CEGB Repairs Depot
		AM	Surrey	Southern Electric
140.22000		AM	Rainham	Seeboard Power Care
		NFM	Glossop	PMR
140.22500		AM	Tayside	Hydro Board
		NFM	Wakefield	British Gas
140.23125		AM	Ipswich	CEGB Repairs Depot
140.23750		AM	Newcastle	Gas Board Repairs
140.24375	148.74375	NFM	Nationwide	British Gas Trunked System
		AM	Bury St Edmonds	CEGB Repairs Depot
		NFM	West Midlands	Gas Board
		AM	Colchester	Eastern Gas
140.25000		NFM	Leeds	British Gas
140.25500		NFM	North West	PMR
140.25625	148.75625	NFM	Nationwide	British Gas Trunked System
		AM	Ipswich	Gas Board Repairs
		NFM	West Midlands	Gas Board
140.26125		NFM	Stirling	Data Link
140.26875	148.76875	NFM	Nationwide	British Gas Trunked System
		NFM	West Midlands	Gas Board
140.27000		NFM	Runcorn	Gas Board
140.28000		NFM	North West	PMR
140.28750		NFM	Manchester	PMR
140.29375	148.79375	NFM	Nationwide	British Gas Trunked System
		NFM	West Sussex	British Gas Southern
		NFM	West Midlands	Gas Board
140.29500		AM	Manchester	Gt Manchester Buses
140.30000		NFM	Glasgow	Gas Board
		NFM	Keighley	British Gas
140.30625	148.80625	NFM	Nationwide	British Gas Trunked System
		NFM	Newcastle	Gas Board
		NFM	West Midlands	Gas Board
140.31250		NFM	Dewsbury	British Gas
140.32125		NFM	London	London Transport
140.32500		NFM	Glasgow	British Gas
		NFM	S London	British Gas
140.33125	148.83125	NFM	West Sussex	British Gas Southern
		NFM	Surrey	Southern Gas
140.33750		AM	Portmouth	Southern Gas
		AM	Fareham	Southern Gas
		AM	Gosport	Southern Gas
140.34500		NFM	Darlington	BT Buses
140.35000		AM	West Midlands	Bus Company
		NFM	Ferrybridge	British Gas

Base	Mobile	Mode	Location	User and Notes
		AM	Plymouth	SWEB
		NFM	Pontefract	British Gas
140.35125		NFM	Surrey	Southern Gas
140.35625	140.10625	AM	Perth	Hydro Electric Board
		NFM	Manchester	PMR
140.36250		AM	Pontefract	North East Gas
140.37500		NFM	Wiltshire	Electricity Board
140.38000		AM	Manchester	Gt Manchester Buses
140.38750		AM	County Durham	Northern Electric
		NFM	Tyne & Wear	Metro Controller
140.39375	148.89375	NFM	Nationwide	British Gas Trunked System
		NFM	West Midlands	Gas Board
140.40000		NFM	North West	Gas Board
140.40000	148.8000	AM	London	Gas Board Croydon
140.40625		AM	Colchester	CEGB Repairs Depot
		AM	South Yorkshire	Greenland Bus Company
140.41250		NFM	Edinburgh	Gas Board
140.41875	148.91875	NFM	Nationwide	British Gas Trunked System
		NFM	West Midlands	Gas Board
		NFM	Surrey	Southern Gas
140.42500		NFM	Lauder	Data Link
140.42500	148.8250	AM	Newcastle	Gas Board
		NFM	Bradford	British Gas
		NFM	Bolton	Council Handhelds
140.43000		NFM	North West	PMR
140.43125	148.93125	NFM	Nationwide	British Gas Trunked System
		NFM	West Midlands	Gas Board
140.43750		AM	Fife	British Gas
140.44000		NFM	Manchester	Electricity Board
		NFM	Manchester	Electricity Board
140.44375		NFM	London	London Transport
140.44500		NFM	Newcastle	Buses
140.45000		AM	Newmarket	Telephone Link
		AM	West Midlands	Bus Company
		AM	Plymouth	SWEB
		NFM	SE London	British Gas
140.45600	148.45000	NFM	Tamworth	Gas Board
140.45625	148.95625	NFM	Nationwide	British Gas Trunked System
		NFM	West Midlands	Gas Board
		NFM	Wolverhampton	Bus Company
		AM	Ipswich	CEGB Engineering
		NFM	Wolverhampton	Buses

140.45625 - 140.99500 MHz ITN Live Talkback, DTI 28 Day Hire, Bus

Base	Mobile	Mode	Location	User and Notes
140.46250		AM	Glasgow	Hydro Electric
140.46875	148.96875	NFM	Nationwide	British Gas Trunked System
		AM	Ipswich	CEGB Repairs Depot
		NFM	Manchester	Gt Manchester Buses

Base	Mobile	Mode	Location	User and Notes
		NFM	West Midlands	Gas Board
140.47500		NFM	Glasgow	British Gas
140.48000	148.88000	NFM	Barrow	Gas Board
140.48125	148.98125	NFM	Nationwide	British Gas Trunked System
		NFM	West Midlands	Gas Board
		NFM	Surrey	Southern Gas
140.48750		NFM	London	London Transport
140.50000		NFM	London	London Transport
140.50625		NFM	London	London Transport
		NFM	Nationwide	National Bus Company
140.52500		NFM	Bradford	City Buses
140.53125		NFM	Manchester	Gt Manchester Buses
140.54375		NFM	Manchester	Gt Manchester Buses
140.58175		AM	London	Electricity Board
140.63125		NFM	Newcastle	City Transport
140.67500		NFM	North London	North Thames Gas
140.70625		NFM	South yorkshire	South Yorkshire Bus Co.
140.71875		NFM	Newcastle	City Transport
140.73750		NFM	London	London Transport
140.74375		NFM	London	London Transport
140.76250		NFM	London	London Transport
		AM	Goole	North East Gas
140.76875		NFM	London	London Transport
140.77500		NFM	Humberside	O/B Studio
140.83000		NFM	Burnley	British Gas
140.83125		NFM	London	London Transport
140.83750		AM	Pontefract	North East Gas
140.84375		NFM	London	London Transport
140.85625		NFM	South Yorkshire	South Yorkshire Bus Co.
140.87500		AM	Hull	British Gas
		NFM	Isle of Man	Manx Electricity Board
140.90500		NFM	Burnley	British Gas
140.90625		NFM	South London	North Thames Gas
140.93125		NFM	Kent	Southern Gas
140.94375		NFM	Nationwide	NCT Bus Channel
		NFM	Bognor Regis	Brighton & Hove Bus Co.
		NFM	Nationwide	LWT Engineering Talkback
		NFM	Brighton	Brighton & Hove Bus Co
140.96875		NFM	Nationwide	DTI Short Term 28 Day Hire
140.99375		NFM	London	LWT TV O/B
		NFM	London	Screen TV O/B
		NFM	London	ITN 6 O'Clock News
140.99500		NFM	London	ITN London Weekend TV
		NFM	Leeds	ITV Studio Maintenance

141.0000 - 141.2000 MHz ILR, BBC AND LOCAL RADIO TALKBACK

Base	Mobile	Mode	Location	User and Notes
141.01250		NFM	Nationwide	ILR Talkback Channel 1
141.01875		NFM	Inverness	Moray Firth Radio O/B

Base	Mobile	Mode	Location	User and Notes
141.02500		NFM	Humberside	Viking Radio Links
		NFM	Nationwide	ILR Common Talkback Ch 5
		NFM	Pittendynie	ILR Talkback
141.03125		NFM	Stoke on Trent	Signal Radio
141.03750		NFM	Nationwide	Ch4 Engineering /News
		NFM	Nationwide	ILR Primary O/B Channel 2
		NFM	Moneydie	ILR Engineering
		NFM	Nationwide	ILR Engineering Ch 4
141.04375	141.04375	NFM	Berkshire	Radio 210
		NFM	Wolverhampton	Beacon Radio O/B
		NFM	Hampshire	Radio 210
141.0500	141.1875	NFM	Andover	Independent Local Radio
		NFM	Basingstoke	Independent Local Radio
		NFM	Bristol	Independent Local Radio
		NFM	Chelmsford	Independent Local Radio
		NFM	Cornwall	Independent Local Radio
		NFM	Hereward	Independent Local Radio
		NFM	Inverness	Independent Local Radio
		NFM	Liverpool	Independent Local Radio
		NFM	Newcastle	Independent Local Radio
		NFM	Oxford	Independent Local Radio
		NFM	Peterborough	Independent Local Radio
		NFM	Reigate	Independent Local Radio
		NFM	Sheffield	Independent Local Radio
		NFM	Wolverhampton	Independent Local Radio
141.0560		NFM	Nongeostationary	US ATS 6
141.05625		NFM	Preston	Red Rose Radio
141.0625	141.1125	NFM	Huddersfield	Independent Local Radio
		NFM	Exeter	Independent Local Radio
		NFM	Gloucester	Independent Local Radio
		NFM	Great Yarmouth	Independent Local Radio
		NFM	Gwynedd	Independent Local Radio
		NFM	Hereford	Independent Local Radio
		NFM	Leicester	Independent Local Radio
		NFM	Maidstone	ILR
		NFM	Reading	Independent Local Radio
		NFM	Shrewsbury	Independent Local Radio
		NFM	Nationwide	2CR Eye in the Sky
141.06875		NFM	Liverpool	Radio City
141.0750		NFM	Manchester	Radio ILR
		NFM	Aberdeen	Independent Local Radio
		NFM	Barnsley	Independent Local Radio
		NFM	Berwick-upon-Tweed	Independent Local Radio
		NFM	Cardiff	Independent Local Radio
		NFM	Coventry	Independent Local Radio
		NFM	Glasgow	Independent Local Radio
		NFM	London	Independent Local Radio
		NFM	Portsmouth	Independent Local Radio

Base	Mobile	Mode	Location	User and Notes
		NFM	Ipswich	Independent Local Radio
		NFM	Stoke on Trent	Independent Local Radio
		NFM	Swindon	Independent Local Radio
141.08125	NFM		Manchester	Piccadilly Radio
141.0875	141.1500	NFM	Bedford	Independent Local Radio
		NFM	Bournemouth	Independent Local Radio
		NFM	Eastbourne	Independent Local Radio
		NFM	Edinburgh	Independent Local Radio
		NFM	Guildford	Independent Local Radio
		NFM	Hereford	Independent Local Radio
		NFM	Humberside	Independent Local Radio
		NFM	Ipswich	Independent Local Radio
		NFM	Manchester	Independent Local Radio
		NFM	Nottingham	Independent Local Radio
		NFM	Plymouth	Independent Local Radio
		NFM	Swansea	Independent Local Radio
		NFM	Trent	ILR
		NFM	Whitehaven	Independent Local Radio
141.1000	141.2000	NFM	Bognor Regis	Independent Local Radio
		NFM	Bradford	Independent Local Radio
		NFM	Bury St Edmunds	Independent Local Radio
		NFM	Derby	Independent Local Radio
		NFM	Dorchester	Independent Local Radio
		NFM	Dumfries	Independent Local Radio
		NFM	Gwent	Independent Local Radio
		NFM	London	Capitol Radio Link
		NFM	London	Independent Local Radio
		NFM	Londonderry	Independent Local Radio
		NFM	Milton Keynes	Independent Local Radio
		NFM	Newport	Independent Local Radio
		NFM	Northampton	Independent Local Radio
		NFM	Stranraer	Independent Local Radio
		NFM	Weymouth	Independent Local Radio
		NFM	Wrexham	Independent Local Radio
141.1250	141.1750	NFM	Aylesbury	Independent Local Radio
		NFM	Birmingham	Independent Local Radio
		NFM	Belfast	ILR
		NFM	Blackpool	ILR
		NFM	Cambridge	Independent Local Radio
		NFM	Canterbury	ILR
		NFM	Dover	ILR
		NFM	Dundee	Independent Local Radio
		NFM	Leeds	Independent Local Radio
		NFM	Middlesborough	Independent Local Radio
		NFM	Newmarket	Independent Local Radio
		NFM	Perth	Independent Local Radio
		NFM	Preston	ILR
		NFM	Southampton	Independent Local Radio

Base	Mobile	Mode	Location	User and Notes
		NFM	Taunton	BBC
		NFM	Yeovil	Independent Local Radio
		NFM	Taunton	BBC
141.13125		NFM	Manchester	BBC GMR
141.13750		NFM	Nationwide	IBA Local Radio Engineers
		NFM	West of England	HTV Clean Feed
141.14375		NFM	Kent	Invicta FM
141.15000		NFM	Nationwide	IBA Local Radio Engineers
		NFM	Trent	ILR Talkback
		NFM	Humberside	Viking Radio O/B
141.15625	469.2625	NFM	London	LBC Radio Flying Eye
141.16250		NFM	Dorset	2CR Studio Talkback
141.16875		NFM	Coventry	Mercia Sound
141.17500		NFM	Wirral	Gas Board
141.18000		NFM	Leicester	Sunrise Radio O/B
141.18125		NFM	London	Independent Radio O/B
141.18750		NFM	Humberside	Viking Radio O/B
141.18750	469.46250	NFM	Cowley	Fox FM Flying Eye Uplink
141.19375		NFM	London	LBC
		NFM	Birmingham	BRMB/Xtra AM
141.19500		NFM	London	Radio Piccadilly Studio Link
		NFM	London	LBC Production
141.20000		NFM	Hampshire	BBC radio solent
141.20500	141.20500	NFM	York	BBC Radio York Talkback
141.20625		NFM	Northamptonshire	BBC Radio Northants
141.20625	224.11875	NFM	Birmingham	BBC Radio West Midlands
141.21875		NFM	London	BBC Radio Car O/B
		NFM	Hereford & Worcester	BBC Radio Worcester
141.22000	141.2200	NFM	Lincoln	BBC Radio Lincs Talkback
141.22500		NFM	North West	PMR
141.23125		NFM	Surrey	BBC Radio Surrey
141.23750		NFM	Taunton	BBC Talkback
141.24300		NFM	Berkshire	BBC Radio Berkshire
141.24375		NFM	Berkshire	BBC Radio Surrey & Berks
		NFM	London	BBC Radio Car O/B
141.24375	224.16875	NFM	Coventry	BBC CWR
141.24375	224.01875	NFM	Channel Islands	ITN
		NFM	Norfolk	ITN
141.24375	224.10625	NFM	Cornwall	ITN
141.25000		NFM	London	ITN Music Link
141.25500		NFM	Stoke on Trent	Radio Stoke Engineering
141.25625		NFM	London	BBC Radio Car O/B
		NFM	West Sussex	BBC Radio Sussex
141.25625	224.10625	NFM	Stoke on Trent	BBC Radio Stoke
141.25630	213.73750	NFM	Sussex	ITN
		NFM	Cambridge	ITN
141.25630	224.09375	NFM	Leeds	ITN
141.25630	224.10625	NFM	Stoke	ITN

Base	Mobile	Mode	Location	User and Notes
		NFM	Wiltshire	ITN
141.25630	224.10875	NFM	Devon	ITN
141.25680	224.16750	NFM	Channel Islands	ITN
141.29000	141.29000	NFM	Hull	BBC Radio Humberside
141.29350	224.15625	NFM	Shropshire	ITN
141.29375		NFM	London	BBC Radio Car O/B
141.29375	224.15625	NFM	Shrewsbury	BBC Radio Shrewsbury
141.29380	224.10875	NFM	Newcastle	ITN
141.29380	224.13125	NFM	Humberside	ITN
141.29750		NFM	York	Radio York O/B
141.30625	224.13125	NFM	Leicester	BBC Radio Leicester
141.30630	213.76250	NFM	Bedfordshire	ITN
141.30630	224.13125	NFM	Leicester	ITN
141.30630	224.11875	NFM	Cleveland	ITN
141.30630	224.14375	NFM	Gloucester	ITN
141.31825		NFM	London	BBC Radio Car O/B
141.32000		NFM	Nationwide	BBC O/B Link
141.35000		NFM	Belfast	Data Link
		NFM	London	ITN Music Links
		NFM	Nationwide	BBC Radio 2 Engineering
141.37500		NFM	Nationwide	BBC O/B Talkback
		NFM	London	BBC1 TV Studio Sound Link
		NFM	London	BBC1 Clean Feed
		NFM	Yorkshire	IBC Talkback
141.37500	224.23350	NFM	Ipswich	Local Radio
141.38750	468.13750	NFM	Manchester	Key 103 O/B
141.41250		NFM	Newmarket	Paging
141.44500		NFM	London	BBC2 TV Studio Sound Link
141.45000		NFM	London	ITN Music Link
141.46250		NFM	London	BBC TV O/B
		NFM	London	BBC1 Link
		NFM	Leicester	BBC1 West Midlands Link
		NFM	Manchester	BBC TV
141.47500		WFM	Southampton	BBC TV South Feed to OB
141.55000		NFM	Nationwide	BBC Radio 2 O/B
141.61875		NFM	Trent	BBC Radio Trent O/B
		NFM	Essex	BBC
		NFM	Surrey	BBC
		NFM	Nottingham	BBC
		NFM	Cornwall	BBC
141.63125		NFM	Norfolk	BBC
		NFM	Chrewsbury	BBC
		NFM	Bedford	BBC
141.64375		NFM	Nationwide	BBC Outside Broadcasts
141.65625		NFM	Brighton	BBC
		NFM	York	BBC
		NFM	Northampton	BBC
141.66825		NFM	Sussex	BBC

Base	Mobile	Mode	Location	User and Notes
141.66875		NFM	Nationwide	BBC Engineering Talkback
		NFM	Lancashire	BBC
		NFM	Herefood	BBC
		NFM	London	Electronic News Gathering
141.67000		NFM	Nationwide	TV News ENG
		NFM	Lancaster	Radio Lancashire
141.67500		NFM	London	Breakfast Time News
141.68125		NFM	Lincolnshire	BBC TV O/B
		NFM	Linconshire	BBC
		NFM	Bedford	BBC
141.69375		NFM	Nationwide	GLR Talkback
		NFM	Bangor	BBC
		NFM	Gloucester	BBC
141.69790		NFM	London	Radio London.
141.70625		NFM	Leicesier	BBC
		NFM	Devon	BBC
141.71350		NFM	Merseyside	BBC
141.71625		NFM	Glasgow	BBC
141.71875		NFM	Solent	BBC
141.71875	150.21875	NFM	Upminster	Electricity
141.72500		NFM	Sheffield	BBC Radio Sheffield O/B
		NFM	Northampton	BBC
		NFM	Sheffield	BBC
141.73125		NFM	Newcastle	BBC
		NFM	West Midlands	BBC
		NFM	Wiltshire	BBC
		NFM	Cambridge	BBC
		NFM	Sheffield	BBC
141.74375		NFM	London	Radio News
		NFM	Nationwide	BBC Radio Cue
141.75500		NFM	Stoke on Trent	Radio Stoke Engineering
141.75625		NFM	Humberside	BBC
		NFM	Stoke-on-trent	BBC
		NFM	Cardiff	BBC
		NFM	Suffolk	BBC
141.76625		NFM	Foyle	BBC
141.76875		NFM	Nationwide	BBC Radio Cue
		NFM	Edinburgh	BBC
		NFM	Crystal palace	BBC Radio News
141.77500		NFM	Nationwide	BBC Radio OB
		NFM	Sheffield	BBC Radio Sheffield O/B
141.78125		NFM	Leeds	BBC
		NFM	Bristol	BBC
		NFM	Derby	BBC
		NFM	Cumbria	BBC
141.78750		NFM	Manchester	Radio Manchester O/B
141.79375		NFM	Cleveland	BBC
		NFM	Cambridge	BBC

Base	Mobile	Mode	Location	User and Notes
		NFM	Kent	BBC
		NFM	Thames Valley	BBC
		NFM	Warwickshire	BBC
		NFM	Manchester	BBC
141.79500		NFM	Manchester	Radio Manchester O/B
141.80000		NFM	Lincolnshire	BBC TV O/B
141.81875		NFM	Nationwide	BBC News ENG
		NFM	Nationwide	BBC ENG
141.82500		NFM	Nationwide	BBC News DB Link
141.83875		NFM	Nationwide	BBC TV O/B's Data
		NFM	Nationwide	BBC O/B Camera Data
141.85750		NFM	Nationwide	BBC Transmitter Group
		NFM	Brookman Park	BBC TX Group
141.86000		NFM	Holme Moss	BBC Maintenance
141.86250		NFM	Crystal Palace	BBC ENG
		NFM	Dorset	2CR Eye-In-The-Sky
141.8750	141.8750	AM	Nationwide	BBC TV O/B's Data
141.8875	141.8875	AM	Nationwide	BBC TV Air-Ground
141.8925	141.8925	AM	Nationwide	BBC TFS Air-Ground
141.9000		NFM	North West	PMR

141.9000 - 142.0000 MHz GOVERNMENT AGENCIES NFM

Base	Mobile	Mode	Location	User and Notes
141.9125		NFM	Nationwide	Army
141.9125		NFM	Swansea	Government Surveillance
141.9375		NFM	Winter Hill-Isle of Man	Mould Link
141.9625		NFM	Nationwide	Army
141.9875		NFM	London	Police Wembley Relay
141.9875		NFM	Swansea	Government Surveillance

142.0000 - 142.9750 MHz MoD, USAF & SOVIET SPACE COMMUNICATIONS

Base	Mobile	Mode	Location	User and Notes
142.0250	142.7250	AM	Nationwide	USAF Air-Air
142.0250	142.0250	AM	Nationwide	MoD Aircraft
142.0500	142.0500	AM	Nationwide	USAF Air-Air
142.0750	142.0750	AM	Nationwide	USAF Air-Air
142.0750	142.0750	AM	RAF Mildenhall	Departures
142.0875		NFM	Strathclyde	Mould
		NFM	North Yorkshire	Army
142.0875	149.0875	NFM	South Wales	Mould
142.1000	142.1000	AM	Nationwide	USAF Air to Air
142.1125	149.1125	NFM	South Wales	Mould
142.1250		NFM	Wembley, London	Police Relay Transmitter
142.1500		NFM	Humberside	USAF
142.1750		NFM	Wembley, London	Police Relay Transmitter
142.2125		NFM	Wembley, London	Police Relay Transmitter
142.2250		AM	RAF Fairford	Tower
142.2500		AM	RAF Manston	Ground
142.2750	142.2750	AM	RAF Mildenhall	Ground
142.2875		NFM	Wembley, London	Police Relay Transmitter

Base	Mobile	Mode	Location	User and Notes
142.2950	142.2950	AM	RAF Coltishall	Approach
		AM	RAF Wittering	Approach
		AM	RAF Wyton	Tower
142.3125		NFM	Wembley, London	Police Relay Transmitter
142.3375		NFM	Humberside	USAF
142.3750	149.3750	NFM	Chepstow	Mould
142.4000		NFM	Space	Soviet Mir Space Station
142.4125		NFM	Nationwide	Mould
142.4125	149.4125	NFM	South Wales	Mould
142.4170		NFM	Space	Soviet Mir/Salyut 7
142.4200		NFM	Space	Soviet Mir Space Station
142.4250		NFM	Gosport	Fort Monkton Camp
		NFM	Sussex	Royal Sigs Excerices
142.4750	142.4750	AM	RAF Lakenheath	Approach
142.4875		NFM	Strathclyde	Mould
142.5000		NFM	London	High Speed Computer Link
		NFM	Brighton	MI5 Encrypted
		NFM	London	MI5 Encrypted
		NFM	Coulport	MoD Police
142.6000		NFM	Space	Soviet Mir Space Station
142.6125	149.8675	NFM	Cranmore	Mould
142.6125	149.6125	NFM	Dorset	Mould HF Links
142.6750		NFM	Nationwide	MoD Paging
142.6750	149.8250	NFM	Nationwide	National MoD Radiopaging
142.7000	142.7000	AM	Nationwide	USAF Air-Air
142.7050		NFM	Nationwide	BBC Radio 1 Roadshow
142.7200	142.7200	AM	Nationwide	USAF Air to Air
142.7250		AM	RAF Brize Norton	101 Sqn Air-Air
142.7250	142.7250	AM	Nationwide	USAF Air to Air
142.7875	149.7875	NFM	Dorset	Mould HF Links
142.7875	149.7125	NFM	Newton/Morgans	Mould
142.8000	142.8000	AM	Nationwide	Backup NATO UFR
142.8250	142.8250	AM	Nationwide	USAF Air to Air
142.8375		NFM	Lochaber	Fire Brigade
142.8500	142.8500	AM	RAF Mildenhall	Command Post
142.8550		AM	Fort William	Hydro Electric
142.8975		NFM	Nationwide	Mould
142.9000	142.9000	AM	RAF Coltishall	Ops
142.9125		NFM	Strathclyde	Mould
142.9125	149.9125	NFM	Leicester	Mould
142.9375	149.9375	NFM	Cornwall	Mould
		NFM	Dorset	Mould
		NFM	Suffolk	Mould
142.9500	142.9500	AM	Nationwide	USAF Air-Air
142.9750	142.8500	AM	RAF Mildenhall	US Navy Duty Air to Gnd

143.0000 - 144.0000 MHz METROPOLITAN AND SW SCOTTISH POLICE MOBILES

Base	Mobile	Mode	Location	User and Notes
143.0000	143.0000	AM	Nationwide	USAF Air-Air

Base	Mobile	Mode	Location	User and Notes
143.0125	143.0125	NFM	Strathclyde	Police
143.0750	143.0750	NFM	Strathclyde	Police
143.1125	143.1125	NFM	Strathclyde	Police
143.1440		NFM	Nongeostationary	Soviet Voice Channel
143.1500	143.1500	NFM	Strathclyde	Police
143.2125	143.2125	NFM	Strathclyde	Police
143.2375	143.2375	NFM	Stockport	Newspaper Photographers
143.3000	143.3000	AM	RAF Sculthorpe	USAF
		NFM	Strathclyde	Police
143.3500	143.3500	AM	RAF Sculthorpe	PAR
143.3500	143.3500	NFM	Strathclyde	Police
143.4250	143.4250	NFM	Strathclyde	Police
143.4500	143.4500	AM	RAF West Drayton	London Military
143.5500	143.5500	NFM	Strathclyde	Police
143.5625	143.5625	NFM	Strathclyde	Police
143.6000	143.6000	AM	Nationwide	USAF Air-Air
143.6125	143.6125	NFM	Strathclyde	Police
143.6250	166.1250	NFM	Nongeostationary	Soviet Voice Channel (Myr)
143.6250	143.6250	NFM	Strathclyde	Police
143.6375	143.6375	NFM	Strathclyde	Police
143.8000	143.8000	AM	Nationwide	USAF Air-Air
143.8250		NFM	Nongeostationary	Soviet Military Coded Ch
143.8875		NFM	Belfast	Data Link
143.9000	143.9000	AM	Nationwide	USAF Air to Air

144.0000 - 146.0000 MHz 2M AMATEUR RADIO

Base	Mobile	Mode	Location	User and Notes
144.0500	144.0500	CW	Nationwide	CW Calling Frequency
144.2600	144.2600	NFM	Nationwide	Raynet
144.3000	144.3000	SSB	Nationwide	SSB Calling Frequency
144.5000	144.5000	NFM	Nationwide	SSTV Calling
144.5000	144.5000	CW	Nongeostationary	OSCAR 5 Telemetry Bcn
144.5500		AM	Manchester	Carrier
144.6000	144.6000	NFM	Nationwide	RTTY Calling
144.6750	144.6750	NFM	Nationwide	Data Calling
144.7000	144.7000	NFM	Nationwide	FAX Calling
144.7250		NFM	North West	Amateur Radio repeater
144.7500	144.7500	NFM	Nationwide	ATV Calling
144.7750	144.7750	NFM	Nationwide	Raynet
144.8000	144.8000	NFM	Nationwide	Raynet
144.8250	144.8250	NFM	Nationwide	Raynet
144.8500		NFM	Leicester	Raynet
144.8875		NFM	North West	Amateur Radio repeater
144.9050		CW	France	Beacon (FX3THF)
144.9125		CW	St Austell	Beacon (GB3MCB)
144.9175		CW	Portlaw	Beacon (EI2WRB)
144.9250		CW	Wrotham	Beacon (GB3VHF)
144.9625		CW	Lerwick	Beacon (GB3LER)
144.9750		CW	Dundee	Beacon (GB3ANG)

Base	Mobile	Mode	Location	User and Notes
144.9830	144.9830	CW	Nongeostationary	OSCAR 1 & 2 Beacon
145.2000	145.2000	NFM	Nationwide	Raynet S08
145.2250	145.2250	NFM	Nationwide	Raynet S09
145.2500	145.2500	NFM	Nationwide	Channel S10
145.2750		NFM	Fort William	Emergency Planning Team
145.2750	145.2750	NFM	Nationwide	Channel S11
145.3000	145.3000	NFM	Nationwide	Channel S12
145.3250		NFM	North West	Amateur Radio repeater
145.3250	144.7250	NFM	Caen	Repeater (FZ2VHB)
145.3250	145.3250	NFM	Nationwide	Channel S13
145.3500	145.3500	NFM	Nationwide	Channel S14
145.3750		NFM	North West	Amateur Radio Repeater
145.3750	145.3750	NFM	Nationwide	Channel S15
145.4000	145.4000	NFM	Nationwide	Channel S16
145.4250	145.4250	NFM	Nationwide	Channel S17
145.4500	145.4500	NFM	Nationwide	Channel S18
145.4750	145.4750	NFM	Nationwide	Channel S19
145.5000	145.5000	NFM	Nationwide	Channel S20
145.5250		NFM	Southampton	GB2RS
145.5250	145.5250	NFM	Nationwide	Channel S21
145.5500	145.5500	NFM	Nationwide	Channel S22
145.5750	145.5750	NFM	Nationwide	Channel S23
145.6000	145.0000	NFM	Charnwood Forest	Amateur Repeater (GB3CF)
		NFM	Nationwide	Channel R0
		NFM	Brighton	Amateur Repeater (GB3SR)
		NFM	Burntisland	Amateur Repeater (GB3FF)
		NFM	Bury	Amateur Repeater (GB3MB)
		NFM	Calbeck	Amateur Repeater (GB3AS)
		NFM	Elgin	Amateur Repeater (GB3SS)
		NFM	Limavady	Amateur Repeater (GB3LY)
		NFM	London	Amateur Repeater (GB3EL)
		NFM	London	Amateur Repeater (GB3EL)
		NFM	Mendip Hills	Amateur Repeater (GB3WR)
		NFM	Mendips	Amateur Repeater (GN3WR)
		NFM	StBrieuc	FZ3VHF
145.6250		NFM	Isle of Man	GD Repeater
145.6250	145.0250	NFM	Nationwide	Channel R1
		NFM	Bournemouth	Amateur Repeater (GB3SC)
		NFM	Dover	Amateur Repeater (GB3KS)
		NFM	London	Amateur Repeater (GB3WL)
		NFM	Malvern	Amateur Repeater (GB3MH)
		NFM	Paisley	Amateur Repeater (GB3PA)
		NFM	Peterhead	Amateur Repeater (GB3NG)
		NFM	Snaefell	Amateur Repeater (GB3GD)
		NFM	St Ives	Amateur Repeater (GB3SI)
		NFM	Wymondham	Amateur Repeater (GB3NB)
		NFM	Isle Of Man	TT & MGP Marshalls
145.6500	145.0500	NFM	Nationwide	Channel R2

Base	Mobile	Mode	Location	User and Notes
		NFM	Birmingham	Amateur Repeater (GB3BX)
		NFM	Duns	Amateur Repeater (GB3SB)
		NFM	Ipswich	Amateur Repeater (GB3PO)
		NFM	Jersey	Amateur Repeater (GB3GJ)
		NFM	Kirkwall	Amateur Repeater (GB3OC)
		NFM	Little Weighton	Amateur Repeater (GB3HS)
		NFM	London	Amateur Repeater (GB3SL)
		NFM	Patna	Amateur Repeater (GB3AY)
		NFM	Stockport	Amateur Repeater (GB3MN)
		NFM	Swindon	Amateur Repeater (GB3WH)
		NFM	Torquay	Amateur Repeater (GB3TR)
145.6750		NFM	Lochgilphead	Amateur Repeater (GB3LG)
145.6750	145.0750	NFM	Nationwide	Channel R3
		NFM	Barnsley	Amateur Repeater (GB3NA)
		NFM	Birmingham	Amateur Repeater (GB3BM)
		NFM	Dorset	Amateur Repeater (GB3DR)
		NFM	Hastings	Amateur Repeater (GB3ES)
		NFM	Lerwick	Amateur Repeater (GB3LU)
		NFM	Ulverston	Amateur Repeater (GB3LD)
		NFM	Perth	Amateur Repeater (GB3PR)
		NFM	Peterborough	Amateur Repeater (GB3PE)
		NFM	Reading	Amateur Repeater (GB3RD)
		NFM	Swansea	Amateur Repeater (GB3SA)
		NFM	France	Amateur Repeater (FZ3VHC)
145.6875	145.0875	NFM	Lille, France	Amateur Repeater (FZ3VHF)
145.7000	145.1000	NFM	Nationwide	Channel R4
		NFM	Appleby	Amateur Repeater (GB3EV)
		NFM	Arfon	Amateur Repeater (GB3AR)
		NFM	Aylesbury	Amateur Repeater (GB3VA)
		NFM	Berwick-upon-Tweed	Amateur Repeater (GB3BT)
		NFM	Brecon	Amateur Repeater (GB3BB)
		NFM	Buxton	Amateur Repeater (GB3HH)
		NFM	Dartmoor	Amateur Repeater (GB3WD)
		NFM	Isle of Mull	Amateur Repeater (GB3HI)
		NFM	Maidstone	Amateur Repeater (GB3KN)
		NFM	Northern France	FZ3THF
145.7250	145.1250	NFM	Nationwide	Channel R5
		NFM	Belfast	Amateur Repeater (GB3NI)
		NFM	Burnhope	Amateur Repeater (GB3TW)
		NFM	Danbury	Amateur Repeater (GB3DA)
		NFM	Fourmarks	Amateur Repeater (GB3SN)
		NFM	Inverness	Amateur Repeater (GB3BI)
		NFM	Lincoln	Amateur Repeater (GB3LM)
		NFM	St Austell	Amateur Repeater (GB3NC)
		NFM	Le Havre	FZ2VHT
145.7500	145.1500	NFM	Nationwide	Channel R6
		NFM	Aviemore	Amateur Repeater (GB3IB)
		NFM	Barkway	Amateur Repeater (GB3WS)

Base	Mobile	Mode	Location	User and Notes
		NFM	Birmingham	Amateur Repeater (GB3AM)
		NFM	Blackhill	Amateur Repeater (GB3CS)
		NFM	Hexham	Amateur Repeater (GB3TY)
		NFM	Horsham	Amateur Repeater (GB3WS)
		NFM	Moel-y-Parc	Amateur Repeater (GB3MP)
		NFM	Mynydd Machen	Amateur Repeater (GB3BC)
145.7750	145.1750	NFM	Nationwide	Channel R7
		NFM	Burnley	Amateur Repeater (GB3RF)
		NFM	Crosshands	Amateur Repeater (GB3WW)
		NFM	Durris	Amateur Repeater (GB3GN)
		NFM	Leamington Spa	Amateur Repeater (GB3WK)
		NFM	London	Amateur Repeater (GB3NL)
		NFM	Newtown	Amateur Repeater (GB3PW)
		NFM	Old Bolingbroke	Amateur Repeater (GB3FR)
		NFM	Portsmouth	Amateur Repeater (GB3PC)
		NFM	Worthing	Amateur Repeater (GB3SR)
		NFM	Dumfries And Galloway	Amateur Repeater (GB3DG)
		NFM	Northern France	Repeater (FZ3VHB)
145.8000		NFM	Nationwide	Raynet
145.8100		CW	Nongeostationary	OSCAR 10 Beacon
145.8175		CW	Nongeostationary	OSCAR 21 Beacon
145.8250		CW	Nongeostationary	OSCAR 9 & 11 Telemetry
145.9500		CW	Nongeostationary	OSCAR Beacons
145.9750		CW	Nongeostationary	OSCAR 7 Telemetry Bcn
145.9870		NFM	Nongeostationary	OSCAR 10 Engineering
145.9875		NFM	Nongeostationary	OSCAR 21 Calling Channel

146.0000 - 148.0000 MHz GOVERNMENT AND POLICE (REPEATERS + 8.0 MHz)

Base	Mobile	Mode	Location	User and Notes
146.0000	154.1000	NFM	Hereford/Worcs	Fire Brigade (YB)
146.0000	154.5750	NFM	North Hampshire	Fire Brigade (ND)
146.0000	154.2250	NFM	Cheshire	Fire Brigade (CF)
146.0000	154.2500	NFM	West Midlands	Fire Brigade (FB)
146.0000	154.3125	NFM	Gloucester	Fire Brigade (OF)
146.0000	154.3750	NFM	South Yorkshire	Fire Brigade (OS)
146.0000	154.4000	NFM	Norfolk	Fire Brigade (VF)
146.0000	154.5000	NFM	Avon/Somerset	Fire Brigade (GC)
146.0000	154.5500	NFM	Oxford	Fire Brigade (HI)
146.0000	154.6000	NFM	Humberside	Fire Brigade (XT)
146.0000	154.6500	NFM	Cheshire	Fire Brigade (CF)
146.0000	154.7250	NFM	Norfolk	Fire Brigade (VF)
146.0000	154.7500	NFM	Kent	Fire Brigade (KA)
146.0000	154.7625	NFM	Hampshire	Fire Brigade (H)
146.0000	154.7750	NFM	North Humberside	Fire Brigade (XT)
146.0000	154.8500	NFM	Norfolk	Fire Brigade (VF)
146.0000	155.2250	NFM	Leamington	Fire Brigade (YS)
146.0100	146.0100	NFM	Netherlands	Disaster Ch 21
146.0125		NFM	Newcastle	Police
146.0125	154.9500	NFM	Thames Valley	Police

Base	Mobile	Mode	Location	User and Notes
		NFM	Gwent	Fire Brigade (WR)
146.0250		AM	West Sussex	Police (M2KB)
		AM	Surrey	Fire Brigade (HF)
		NFM	West Mercia	Police (YK)
		NFM	Tyne & Wear	Fire Brigade (LP)
		NFM	Darlington	Police
146.0250	146.0250	NFM	Dyfed & Powys	Police (WH)
		NFM	North Wales	Police (WA) Channel 2
146.0300	146.0300	NFM	Netherlands	Disaster Ch 22
146.0375		NFM	Gerrards Cross	Police
146.0375	154.8750	NFM	Gwent	Fire Brigade (WP)
		NFM	Thames Valley	Police
146.0500		NFM	Yorkshire	Fire Brigade
		NFM	Essex	Police
		NFM	Newport	Police
146.0500	146.0500	NFM	Netherlands	Disaster Ch 23
146.0625	154.9250	NFM	Thames Valley	Police (HB)
146.0700	146.0700	NFM	Netherlands	Disaster Ch 24
146.0750	154.9625	NFM	South Wales	Police (WS)
		NFM	Warwickshire	Police (YJ)
146.0750	155.1500	NFM	Manchester	Police (CK)
146.0875		NFM	North Wales	Police Channel 4
146.0900	146.0900	NFM	Netherlands	Disaster Ch 25
146.1000		AM	Stockport	Police Mobile
146.1000	146.1000	NFM	Gloucester	Police (QL) Channel 1
146.1000	146.9000	NFM	Suffolk	Police (VL) Channel 1
146.1000	154.7000	NFM	Suffolk	Police (VL) Channel 3
146.1000	154.8625	NFM	Suffolk	Police (VL) Channel 1
146.1000	155.0875	NFM	Manchester	Police (CK)
146.1000	155.8750	NFM	Dorset	Police (OC)
146.1100	146.1100	NFM	Netherlands	Disaster Ch 26
146.1125	155.6375	NFM	Cumbria	Police (CC)
		NFM	Warwickshire	Police (YJ)
146.1250	146.1250	NFM	Wiltshire	Police (QM)
146.1250	154.0125	NFM	Lancashire	Police (BB)
		NFM	North M25	Police (SM)
146.1250	154.8875	NFM	South Wales	Police (WL)
146.1250		NFM	Cardiff	Police (WY)
146.1300	146.1300	NFM	Netherlands	Disaster Ch 27
146.1375		NFM	North Wales	Police Channel 1
146.1375	154.0500	NFM	West Mercia	Police (K)
146.1375	154.1000	NFM	Thames Valley	Police (HB)
146.1500	146.1500	NFM	Loansdean	Police (M2LB)
		NFM	Dyfed & Powys	Police (WH)
146.1500	154.8875	NFM	South Wales	Police (WY)
146.1500	146.1500	NFM	Netherlands	Disaster Ch 28
146.1625	154.0875	NFM	South M25	Police (SM)
146.1700	146.1700	NFM	Netherlands	Disaster Ch 29

Base	Mobile	Mode	Location	User and Notes
146.1750		NFM	West Mercia	Police (YK)
		NFM	Cambridgeshire	Fire Brigade
146.1750	154.0750	NFM	Thames Valley	Fire Brigade (Q)
		NFM	Devon/Cornwall	Fire Brigade (OA)
		NFM	Berkshire	Fire Brigade (G)
		NFM	Lancashire	Police (BD)
146.1750	154.1250	NFM	Wiltshire	Fire Brigade (GM)
		NFM	Cambridgeshire	Fire Brigade (VP)
		NFM	London	Fire Brigade (FN)
		NFM	West Mercia	Police (YK)
		NFM	Staffordshire	Fire Brigade (YG)
146.1750	154.4750	NFM	Wiltshire	Fire Brigade (GM)
		NFM	Kent	Fire Brigade (HO)
		NFM	Staffordshire	Fire Brigade (YG)
146.1750	154.9375	NFM	South Wales	Police (WX)
146.1875		AM	West Sussex	Police (M2KB)
146.1875	154.9000	NFM	Dorset	Police (OC)
146.1900	146.1900	NFM	Netherlands	Disaster Ch 30
		NFM	Netherlands	Trauma Teams Ch 71
146.2000	146.2000	NFM	Jersey	Emergency Services
		NFM	Essex	Police (VB) Channel 2
146.2000	155.8000	NFM	Surrey	Police (HJ)
146.2000	155.8875	NFM	Cumbria	Police (BB)
146.2125		NFM	Essex	Police
146.2125	146.2125	NFM	West Haverford	Police (WL)
146.2125	155.0125	NFM	Manchester	Police (CK)
146.2125	155.4625	NFM	Devon & Cornwall	Police (GB)
146.2250	146.2250	NFM	Staffordshire	Police (YB)
		NFM	Devon & Cornwall	Police (QD)
		NFM	Thames Valley	Police (HU)
146.2250	155.6375	NFM	Surrey	Police (HJ)
146.2300	146.2300	NFM	Netherlands	Disaster Ch 31
146.2375	155.0625	NFM	Manchester	Police (CK)
146.2375	155.3250	NFM	Devon & Cornwall	Police (GB)
146.2500	155.5875	NFM	Cumbria	Police (BB)
146.2500	155.8625	NFM	Surrey	Police (HJ)
146.2625	155.3625	NFM	Devon & Cornwall	Police (DB)
146.2625	155.6500	NFM	Derbyshire	Police (NA)
146.2700	146.2700	NFM	Netherlands	Disaster Ch 33
146.2750		NFM	Lancashire	Police Helicopter
146.2750	154.6750	NFM	London Area	Fire Brigade (FE)
		NFM	Nottinghamshire	Fire Brigade (NZ)
146.2750	154.8375	NFM	Thames Valley	Police (HB)
146.2750	154.9375	NFM	Lancashire	Police (BB)
146.2875	146.2875	NFM	Jersey	Ambulance Ch 3
146.2875	155.5750	NFM	Cheshire	Fire Brigade (CF)
		NFM	Devon & Cornwall	Police
146.2875	155.8375	NFM	Derbyshire	Police (NA)

Base	Mobile	Mode	Location	User and Notes
146.2900	146.2900	NFM	Netherlands	Disaster Ch 34
146.3000	146.3000	NFM	Jersey	Fire Brigade Ch 3
		NFM	Jersey	Ambulance Ch 8
146.3000	155.4625	NFM	Lancshire	Police
146.3000	154.7750	NFM	Thames Valley	Police
146.3100	146.3100	NFM	Netherlands	Trauma Teams Ch 72
146.3125		NFM	Sussex	Police
146.3125	146.3125	NFM	Jersey	Ambulance Ch 4
146.3125	155.2625	NFM	Cheshire	Police
146.3250	154.6250	NFM	West Midlands	Police
146.3250		AM	West Sussex	Police (M2KB)
		NFM	Dyfed	Police (WH)
		NFM	Avon	Police (QP)
146.3300	146.3300	NFM	Netherlands	Disaster Ch 35
146.3375	155.2250	NFM	Sussex	Police
146.3375	155.4875	NFM	Cheshire	Police
146.3500		NFM	Newport	Police
146.3500	146.3500	NFM	Jersey	Fire Brigade Ch 4
		NFM	Jersey	Ambulance Ch 9
		NFM	Gwent	Police (WO/WE)
146.3500	154.4500	NFM	West Midlands	Police
146.3500	154.1750	NFM	London Area	Fire Brigade
146.3625	155.0500	NFM	Sussex	Police
146.3625	155.3875	NFM	Cheshire	Police
146.3625	154.1375	NFM	Cambridge	Police
146.3700	146.3700	NFM	Netherlands	Disaster Ch 36
146.3750	154.7000	NFM	West Midlands	Police
146.3875		AM	West Sussex	Police Mobile
146.3875	155.4250	NFM	Manchester	Police
146.3875	155.1875	NFM	Sussex	Police (KB)
146.3900	146.3900	NFM	Netherlands	Disaster Ch 37
146.4000		NFM	Lincoln	Police
		NFM	Cleveland	Police
146.4000	146.4000	NFM	Northamptonshire	Police (NB) Channel 2
146.4000	155.0875	AM	Hampshire	Police
146.4125		AM	Kent	Fire Brigade (KF)
		NFM	Wetherby	Police Repeater (GS)
		AM	Stockport	Police Mobile
146.4125	155.6125	NFM	Manchester	Police
146.4125	155.2875	NFM	Sussex	Police
146.4250	154.9750	NFM	West Midlands	Police
146.4250	146.4250	NFM	North Wales	Police (WA) Channel 1
146.4300	146.4300	NFM	Netherlands	Disaster Ch 38
146.4375	155.1000	NFM	North Wales	Police
146.4375	155.1125	NFM	Hampshire	Police
146.4500		NFM	Essex	Fire Brigade (VD)
146.4500	146.4500	NFM	Northamptonshire	Police (NB)
146.4500	146.4500	NFM	Devon	Police (QB)

Base	Mobile	Mode	Location	User and Notes
146.4500	155.6375	NFM	Cumbria	Police
146.4500	146.4500	NFM	Netherlands	Trauma Teams Ch 73
146.4500	154.3125	NFM	West Midlands	Police
146.4625	154.4255	NFM	North Wales	Police
146.4625	155.1625	NFM	Hampshire	Police
146.4625	155.5375	NFM	West Midlands	Police
146.4700	146.4700	NFM	Netherlands	Trauma Teams Ch 74
146.4750		AM	West Sussex	Police (M2KB)
		NFM	Lewes	Police
		NFM	Darlington	Police
146.4750	154.2625	NFM	West Midlands	Police
146.4875	154.1000	NFM	North Wales	Police
146.4875	154.9125	NFM	Norfolk	Police
146.4875	155.2625	NFM	Hampshire	Police
146.4900	146.4900	NFM	Netherlands	Disaster Ch 39
146.5000		NFM	Durham	Fire Brigade (M2LF)
146.5000	154.5000	NFM	Jersey	Police
146.5100	146.5100	NFM	Netherlands	Disaster Ch 40
146.5125	154.0250	NFM	West Mercia	Police
146.5250		NFM	Hertfordshire	Police
146.5250	154.5500	NFM	Suffolk	Fire Brigade
146.5300	146.5300	NFM	Netherlands	Disaster Ch 41
146.5375	154.0500	NFM	Derbyshire	Fire Brigade
		NFM	West Mercia	Fire Brigade
		NFM	Yorkshire	Fire Brigade (XK)
146.5500	146.5500	NFM	Loansdean	Fire Brigade (M2LJ)
		NFM	Jersey	Police (M2GS) Ch 5
		NFM	Netherlands	Disaster Ch 42
		AM	Cardiff	Police (WY)
146.5500		AM	South Wales	Police (WJ)
		AM	South Glamorgan	Police (WY)
146.5675	154.1125	NFM	West Mercia	Fire Brigade
146.5700	146.5700	NFM	Netherlands	Trauma Teams Ch 75
		NFM	Suffolk	Police (VL) Channel 1
146.5750	155.1500	NFM	Avon & Somerset	Police
146.5750	155.8125	NFM	Suffolk	Police (154.8625)
146.5750	146.9250	NFM	Suffolk	Police (154.8875, 152.8375)
		NFM	Suffolk	Police (154.8875, 154.2750)
146.5875	154.2000	NFM	Staffordshire	Police
146.5875	155.1000	NFM	Kent	Police
146.6000		AM	Newcastle	Police
146.6000	155.2000	NFM	Hertfordshire	Police
146.6000	155.4750	NFM	Dyfed, Powys	Police
146.6075	154.0250	NFM	Cambridge	Police (VB)
146.6100	146.6100	NFM	Netherlands	Disaster Ch 43
146.6125	154.0250	NFM	East Sussex	Fire Brigade
146.6125	154.5500	NFM	Staffordshire	Police
146.6125	154.9375	NFM	Kent	Police

Base	Mobile	Mode	Location	User and Notes
146.6175	154.9625	NFM	Kent	Police
146.6250	154.6250	NFM	Jersey	Police
146.6250	155.1250	NFM	Hertfordshire	Police
146.6250	155.1625	NFM	Warwickshire	Police
146.6250	155.2750	NFM	Powys	Police
146.6250	155.4125	NFM	Dyfed & Wales	Police
146.6300	146.6300	NFM	Netherlands	Disaster Ch 44
146.6375		AM	Newcastle	Police
146.6450		NFM	Hutton	Police Link
146.6500	155.2375	NFM	Hertfordshire	Police (VH)
146.6500	155.2000	NFM	Dyfed	Police (WH)
146.6500	146.6500	NFM	Netherlands	Disaster Ch 45
146.6625	155.0500	NFM	South Wales	Police (WA)
146.6625	155.1375	NFM	Kent	Police (KA)
146.6700	146.6700	NFM	Netherlands	Disaster Ch 46
146.6750	154.1500	NFM	Gloucester	Police (OL)
146.6750	154.9875	NFM	Norfolk	Police (VK)
146.6875	154.9750	NFM	Hampshire	Police (HK)
146.6900	146.6900	NFM	Netherlands	Disaster Ch 47
146.7000	154.2250	NFM	Staffordshire	Fire Brigade (YG)
		NFM	Gloucester	Fire Brigade (GL)
146.7000	154.8250	NFM	Humberside	Fire Brigade (XT)
146.7100	146.7100	NFM	Netherlands	Disaster Ch 48
146.7125		NFM	Gwynedd	Fire Brigade (WC)
146.7250		NFM	Norfolk	Fire Brigade
146.7250	154.3625	NFM	Gloucester	Fire Brigade (GL)
146.7250	154.8000	NFM	Leicester	Police
		NFM	Sussex	Fire Brigade (KV)
		NFM	Lancashire	Police
146.7300	146.7300	NFM	Netherlands	Disaster Ch 49
146.7375		AM	Hungerford	Police (HU)
146.7375	154.3375	NFM	Thames Valley	Police
		NFM	Haverfordwest	Police (WH)
146.7500	146.7500	NFM	Netherlands	Disaster Ch 50
146.7625	155.0625	NFM	Avon & Somerset	Police
146.7700	146.7700	NFM	Netherlands	Disaster Ch 51
		AM	Newport	Police Helicopter
146.7750	154.9125	NFM	Gwent	Police
		NFM	Kent Motorways	Police (TD)
146.7875	155.0375	NFM	Avon & Somerset	Police
146.7900	146.7900	NFM	Netherlands	Disaster Ch 52
146.8000	154.7875	NFM	Gwent	Police
146.8125	155.0125	NFM	Avon & Somerset	Police
146.8250		AM	West Sussex	Police (M2KB)
		NFM	Lewes	Fire Brigade
146.8250	154.0625	NFM	Merseyside	Police
146.8300	146.8300	NFM	Netherlands	Disaster Ch 53
146.8375	154.9000	NFM	Bedfordshire	Police

Base	Mobile	Mode	Location	User and Notes
		NFM	Merseyside	Police
146.8500	154.9875	NFM	Avon & Somerset	Police
		NFM	Norfolk	Police
146.8500	146.8500	NFM	Netherlands	Disaster Ch 54
146.8625	154.7375	NFM	Bedfordshire	Police
146.8626		NFM	London	MI5 Encrypted
146.8700	146.8700	NFM	Netherlands	Disaster Ch 55
146.8750	154.8125	NFM	Gwent	Police
146.8750		AM	West Hoathly	Police Link (M2KB)
146.8750		NFM	Lewes	Police
146.8875	155.9375	NFM	Thames Valley	Police
146.9000		NFM	Merseyside	Police
146.9000	146.9000	NFM	Loansdean	Police (M2LB)
146.9000	154.8625	NFM	Suffolk	Police (VK)
146.9000	154.9250	NFM	Merseyside	Police (CM)
		NFM	Devon & Cornwall	Police
146.9125		NFM	West Midlands	Police (MA)
146.9125	155.0125	NFM	Wiltshire	Police
146.9250		NFM	Merseyside	Police
146.9250	146.5750	NFM	Suffolk	Police (VL) Channel 1
146.9250	154.8875	NFM	Suffolk	Police (VL)
146.9250	155.1750	NFM	Merseyside	Police
146.9250	155.5125	NFM	Devon & Cornwall	Police
146.9300	146.9300	NFM	Netherlands	Disaster Ch 56
146.9375	155.8500	NFM	Wiltshire	Police
146.9500		AM	West Sussex	Police (M2KB)
		NFM	Lewes	Police
146.9500	155.2250	NFM	Merseyside	Police
146.9500	155.3875	NFM	Devon & Cornwall	Police
146.9500	146.9500	NFM	Netherlands	Disaster Ch 57
146.9625	155.9000	NFM	Wiltshire	Police
146.9750	155.3250	NFM	Merseyside	Police
146.9750	155.3000	NFM	Devon & Cornwall	Police
147.0000	154.5750	NFM	Hampshire	Fire Brigade
147.0000	155.3375	NFM	Hampshire	Fire Brigade
147.0000	155.4000	NFM	Hereford/Worcester	Fire Brigade
147.0000	155.4500	NFM	West Midlands	Fire Brigade
147.0000	155.6000	NFM	Staffordshire	Fire Brigade
147.0125		NFM	London	Diplomatic Protection (Ranger)
147.0125	147.0125	NFM	Crickhowel	Army
		AM	Wiltshire	Fire Brigade
147.0125	155.9250	NFM	Dorset	Police
147.0250	154.7875	NFM	Cambridge	Police
147.0375		NFM	Newcastle	Police
147.0500		AM	Newcastle	Data Link
147.0500	146.5750	NFM	Shropshire	Fire Brigade (YU)
147.0500	147.0500	NFM	Netherlands	Disaster Ch 58
147.0600		AM	West Sussex	Police (M2KB)

Base	Mobile	Mode	Location	User and Notes
147.0625		AM	West Sussex	Police (M2KB)
		NFM	Lewes	Police
		NFM	Northampton	Police
147.0700	147.0700	NFM	Netherlands	Disaster Ch 59
147.0750	154.6125	NFM	Wiltshire	Police
147.0875	155.2125	NFM	Avon & Somerset	Police
147.0900	147.0900	NFM	Netherlands	Disaster Ch 60
147.1000		AM	West Sussex	Police (M2KB)
147.1250		AM	West Sussex	Police (M2KB)
147.1250	147.1250	NFM	London Heathrow	Airport Police (India Hunter)
147.1500		NFM	Barkingside	Police (JB)
147.1700	147.1700	NFM	Netherlands	Disaster Ch 61
147.1900	147.1900	NFM	Netherlands	Disaster Ch 32
147.2000		NFM	London	Diplomatic Protection (Ranger)
147.2125	155.3125	NFM	Brick Lane	Police (HR)
		NFM	Brockley	Police (PK)
		NFM	Harrow Road	Police (DR)
		NFM	Kings Cross	Police (HD)
		NFM	Croydon	Police (ZD)
		NFM	Kenley	Police (ZK) CTCSS Tones
		NFM	Notting Hill	Police (BZ) CTCSS Tones
		NFM	Bethnal Green	Police (HB) Channel 26
147.2250	155.3250	NFM	Barkingside	Police (JB)
		NFM	Beckenham	Police (PB)
		NFM	Brockley	Police (PK)
		NFM	Loughton	Police (JO)
		NFM	Wallington	Police (ZW)
		NFM	Deptford	Police (PP)
		NFM	Epsom	Police (ZP)
		NFM	Fulham	Police (FF)
		NFM	Hendon	Police (HO)
		NFM	Hainault	Police (JT)
		NFM	Leman Street	Police (HD)
		NFM	Lewisham	Police (PL)
		NFM	Stoneleigh	Police (ZS)
		NFM	Sutton	Police (ZT)
		NFM	Wallington	Police (ZW)
		NFM	Waltham Abbey	Police (JA)
		NFM	Woodford Green	Police (JF)
		NFM	Banstead	Police (ZB) Channel 27
147.2375		AM	Stockport	Police Mobile
147.2375	155.3375	NFM	Camberwell	Police (MC)
		NFM	East Dulwich	Police (ME)
		NFM	Hackney	Police (GH)
		NFM	Norbury	Police (ZN)
		NFM	Peckham	Police (MM)
		NFM	Shepherd's Bush	Police (FS)
		NFM	Stoke Newington	Police (GN)

Base	Mobile	Mode	Location	User and Notes
		NFM	Dalston	Police (GA) Channel 28
147.2500	155.3500	NFM	Bushey	Police (SU)
		NFM	City Road	Police (GD)
		NFM	Dalston	Police (GA)
		NFM	Radlett	Police (SE)
		NFM	Rochester Row	Police (AR)
		NFM	Whetstone	Police (ST)
		NFM	Barnet	Police (SA)
		NFM	Hackney	Police (GH)
		NFM	Norbury	Police (ZD) CTCSS Tones
		NFM	North Addington	Police (ZA) CTCSS Tones
		NFM	Potter's Bar	Police (SP)
		NFM	Shenley	Police (SY)
		NFM	South Mimms	Police (SM)
		NFM	South Norwood	Police (ZS) CTCSS Tones
		NFM	Stoneleigh	Police (ZL)
		NFM	Whetstone	Police (ST)
		NFM	Borehamwood	Police (SD) Channel 29
147.2625	155.3625	NFM	Beckenham	Police (PB)
		NFM	Bromley	Police (PR) CTCSS Tones
		NFM	Chigwell	Police (JD)
		NFM	Chingford	Police (JC)
		NFM	Debden	Police (JE)
		NFM	Hampstead	Police (EH)
		NFM	Lewisham	Police (PL)
		NFM	Penge	Police (PG) CTCSS Tones
		NFM	Vine Street	Police (CV)
		NFM	Waltham Abbey	Police (JA)
		NFM	Walthamstow	Police (JW)
		NFM	West End Central	Police (CD)
		NFM	West Hampstead	Police (EW)
		NFM	Waltham Abbey	Police (JA) Channel 30
		NFM	Canterbury	Police
147.2750	155.3750	NFM	Forest Gate	Police (KF)
		NFM	Bow Street	Police (CB)
		NFM	Harold Hill	Police (KA)
		NFM	Bushey	Police (SC)
		NFM	Borenhamwood	Police (SD)
		NFM	Barnet	Police (SA)
		NFM	Lee Road	Police (PE)
		NFM	Radlett	Police (SE)
		NFM	Plaistow	Police (KO)
		NFM	Potters Bar	Police (SP)
		NFM	Shenley	Police (SY)
		NFM	Sydenham	Police (PS) CTCSS Tones
		NFM	West Ham	Police (KW)
		NFM	Whetstone	Police (ST)
		NFM	West End Central	Police (CD)

Base	Mobile	Mode	Location	User and Notes
		NFM	Vine Street	Police (CV) Channel 31
		NFM	Catford	Police (PD) CTCSS Tones
		NFM	Westminster	Police (AP) Channel 32
147.2875	155.3875	NFM	Westcombe Park	Police (RK)
		NFM	Kingsbury	Police (RK)
		NFM	Battersea	Police (WA)
		NFM	Chingford	Police (JC)
		NFM	Earlsfield	Police (WF)
		NFM	Croydon	Police (ZD)
		NFM	Trinity Road	Police (WT)
		NFM	Eltham	Police (RD)
		NFM	Feltham	Police (TF)
		NFM	Greenwich	Police (RG)
		NFM	Harrow Road	Police (DR)
		NFM	Belvedere	Police (RB)
		NFM	Walthamstow	Police (JW)
		NFM	Waltham Abbey	Police (JA)
		NFM	Hounslow	Police (TD)
		NFM	Tooting	Police (WD)
147.3000	155.4000	NFM	Harlesden	Police (QH)
		NFM	Kensington	Police (LK)
		NFM	Kilburn	Police (OK)
		NFM	St Anne's Road	Police (YA)
		NFM	Staines	Police (TG)
		NFM	Sunbury	Police (TY)
		NFM	Teddington	Police (TT)
		NFM	Tottenham	Police (YT)
		NFM	Twickenham	Police (TW)
		NFM	Shepperton	Police (TG)
		NFM	Brixton	Police (LD)
		NFM	Staines	Police (TW)
		NFM	Willesden Green	Police (QL)
		NFM	Wood Green	Police (YD)
		NFM	Edgware	Police (QE)
		NFM	Hampton	Police (TM) Channel 33
147.3125	155.4125	NFM	Chobham	Police (VC)
		NFM	East Molesey	Police (VE)
		NFM	Esher	Police (VH)
		NFM	Gerard Road	Police (AP)
		NFM	Kingsbury	Police (QY)
		NFM	Kingston	Police (VK)
		NFM	New Malden	Police (VN)
		NFM	Plumstead	Police (RP)
		NFM	Shooters Hill	Police (RH)
		NFM	West Hendon	Police (SW)
		NFM	Chelsea	Police (BC)
		NFM	Norfolk	Police (VK)
		NFM	Lewisham	Police (PL)

Base	Mobile	Mode	Location	User and Notes
		NFM	Shooters Hill	Police (RH)
		NFM	Surbiton	Police (VS)
		NFM	Hyde Park	Police (AH)
		NFM	Westcombe Park	Police (QY)
		NFM	Greenwich	Police (RG)
		NFM	Woolwich	Police (RW)
		NFM	Wembley	Police (QD)
		NFM	Thamesmead	Police (RT)
		NFM	Belvedere	Police (RB) Channel 34
147.3250	155.4250	AM	Rainham	Police (KM)
		NFM	Collier Row	Police (KL)
		NFM	Earlsfield	Police (WF)
		NFM	Enfield	Police (YF)
		NFM	Goffs Oak	Police (YG)
		NFM	Harlesden	Police (QH)
		NFM	Harold Hill	Police (KA)
		NFM	Hornchurch	Police (KC)
		NFM	Ponders End	Police (YP)
		NFM	Putney	Police (WP)
		NFM	Romford	Police (KD)
		NFM	Staines	Police (TS)
		NFM	Tooting	Police (WD)
		NFM	Tower Bridge	Police (MT)
		NFM	Upminster	Police (KU)
		NFM	Wandsworth	Police (WW)
		AM	Cheshunt	Police (YC) Channel 35
147.3375	155.4375	NFM	London	Police (GT) Channel 36
147.3500	155.4500	NFM	Biggin Hill	Police (PH)
		NFM	Chiselhurst	Police (PC)
		NFM	Farnborough	Police (PF)
		NFM	Highbury Vale	Police (NV)
		NFM	Holloway	Police (NH)
		NFM	Kensington	Police (BD)
		NFM	Lewisham	Police (PL)
		NFM	Mitcham	Police (VM)
		NFM	Northwood	Police (XN)
		NFM	Notting Hill	Police (BH)
		NFM	Orpington	Police (PN)
		NFM	Ruislip	Police (XB)
		NFM	St Mary Cray	Police (PM)
		NFM	Uxbridge	Police (XU)
		NFM	Wimbledon	Police (VW)
		NFM	Harefield	Police (XF) Channel 37
147.3625	155.4625	NFM	Cavendish	Police (LC)
		NFM	Clapham	Police (LM)
		NFM	Dagenham	Police (KG)
		NFM	Finchley	Police (SF)
		NFM	Golders Green	Police (SG)

Base	Mobile	Mode	Location	User and Notes
		NFM	Leyton	Police (JL)
		NFM	Leytonstone	Police (JS)
		NFM	Barking	Police (KB) Channel 38
147.3750	155.4750	NFM	Arbour Square	Police (HA)
		NFM	Barking	Police (KB)
		NFM	Cannon Row	Police (AD)
		NFM	City Road	Police (GD)
		NFM	East Ham	Police (KE)
		NFM	Harold Hill	Police (KA)
		NFM	Hayes	Police (XY)
		NFM	Hendon	Police (SN)
		NFM	Hyde Park	Police (AH)
		NFM	Mill Hill	Police (SH)
		NFM	Kings Cross	Police (HD)
		NFM	North Woolwich	Police (KN)
		NFM	Plaistow	Police (KO)
		NFM	West Hendon	Police (SG)
		NFM	West Ham	Police (KW)
		NFM	West Drayton	Police (XW)
		NFM	Wellington	Police (AW) Channel 39
147.3875	155.4875	NFM	Belvedere	Police (RB)
		NFM	Brixton	Police (LD)
		NFM	Erith	Police (RE)
		NFM	Gerard Road	Police (AL)
		NFM	Harrow Road	Police (DR)
		NFM	Highgate	Police (YH)
		NFM	Hornsey	Police (NR)
		NFM	Marylebone Lane	Police (PM)
		NFM	Muswell Hill	Police (YM)
		NFM	Paddington Green	Police (DD)
		NFM	Sidcup	Police (RS)
		NFM	St Annes Road	Police (YA)
		NFM	Welling	Police (RL)
		NFM	Wood Green	Police (YD)
		NFM	Bexley Heath	Police (RY) Channel 40
147.4000	155.5000	NFM	Barnes	Police (TN) Channel 41
		NFM	Gipsy Hill	Police (LG)
		NFM	Hampton	Police (TM)
		NFM	Holborn	Police (EO)
		NFM	Richmond	Police (TR)
		NFM	Streatham	Police (LS)
		NFM	Twickenham	Police (TW)
		NFM	Tottenham Court Road	Police (ET)
		NFM	West Ham	Police (TH)
147.4125	155.5125	NFM	Caledonian Road	Police (NC)
		NFM	Chadwell Heath	Police (JH)
		NFM	Chigwell	Police (JD)
		NFM	Ilford	Police (JI)

Base	Mobile	Mode	Location	User and Notes
		NFM	Islington	Police (NI)
		NFM	Kings Cross	Police (ND)
		NFM	Lavender Hill	Police (WL)
		NFM	New Southgate	Police (YN)
		NFM	Nine Elms	Police (WN)
		NFM	Wanstead	Police (JN)
		NFM	Battersea	Police (WA) Channel 42
147.4250	155.5250	NFM	Bow Street	Police (CB)
		NFM	Ealing	Police (XD)
		NFM	Edmonton	Police (YE)
		NFM	Epsom	Police (ZP)
		NFM	Bow Street	Police (CB)
		NFM	Edmonton	Police (YE)
		NFM	Southgate	Police (YS)
		NFM	Stoneleigh	Police (ZL)
		NFM	Wembley	Police (QD)
		NFM	Winchmore Hill	Police (YW)
		NFM	Acton	Police (XA) Channel 43
147.4375	155.5375	NFM	Barkingside	Police (JB)
		NFM	Brick Lane	Police (HR)
		NFM	Chelsea	Police (BC)
		NFM	Greenford	Police (XG)
		NFM	Isle of Dogs	Police (HI)
		NFM	Kings Cross	Police (HD)
		NFM	Limehouse	Police (HH)
		NFM	Loughton	Police (JO)
		NFM	Norwood Green	Police (XW)
		NFM	Poplar	Police (HP)
		NFM	Southall	Police (XS)
		NFM	Waltham Abbey	Police (JA)
		NFM	Bow	Police (HW) Channel 44
147.4500	155.5500	NFM	Chiswick	Police (TC)
		NFM	Paddington	Police (DD)
		NFM	Rotherhithe	Police (MR)
		NFM	Southwark	Police (MD)
		NFM	St Johns Wood	Police (DS)
		NFM	Tower Bridge	Police (MT)
		NFM	Camberwell	Police (MC)
		NFM	Carter Street	Police (MS)
		NFM	Edgware	Police (QE)
		NFM	Hammersmith	Police (FH)
		NFM	Marylebone	Police (DM)
		NFM	Harrow	Police (QA)
		NFM	Harrow Road	Police (DR)
		NFM	Kentish Town	Police (EK)
		NFM	Pinner	Police (QP)
		NFM	Richmond	Police (TR)
		NFM	Wealdstone	Police (QW)

Base	Mobile	Mode	Location	User and Notes
		NFM	Brentwood	Police (TB) Channel 45
147.4625	155.5625	NFM	London	Met Police (GT)
147.4750	155.5750	NFM	Edgeware	Police (QE)
		NFM	Southwark	Police (MD)
		NFM	Camberwell	Police (MC)
		NFM	Westcombe Park	Police (QY)
		NFM	Marylebone	Police (DM)
		NFM	Kentish Town	Police (EK)
		NFM	Wealdstone	Police (QW)
		NFM	Carter Street	Police (MS)
		NFM	Harlesden	Police (QH)
		NFM	Harrow	Police (QA)
		NFM	Tottenham Court Road	Police (ET)
		NFM	Shephards Bush	Police (FH)
		NFM	London	Police (FD) F Div HQ
		NFM	Pinner	Police
		NFM	Albany Street	Police (ED) Channel 47
147.4875	155.5875	NFM	London	TSG Special Events
		NFM	London	Police (GT) Channel 48
147.5000		NFM	Enniskillen	Military Data Link
147.5000	155.6000	NFM	London	Police (GT) Channel 49
147.5125	155.6125	NFM	London	Police Engineers (GT)
		NFM	London	Police (GT) Channel 50
147.5250	155.6250	NFM	Wembley Stadium	Police Events
		NFM	London	Police Engineers (GT)
		NFM	London	Police (GT) Channel 51
147.5375	154.0625	NFM	Chichester	Fire Brigade
147.5375	155.6375	NFM	Streatham	Police (LS)
		NFM	London	Police Engineers (GT)
147.5500	155.6500	NFM	Wembley Stadium	Police Events
		NFM	London	Police Engineers (GT)
		NFM	London	Police (GT) Channel 53
147.5750		NFM	Eastleigh	Fire Brigade
147.5875	155.6875	NFM	Norfolk	Police (VK1)
		NFM	London	Police Inter-County Channel
147.6000		NFM	Hereford & Worcester	Fire Brigade (YB)
147.6000	155.7000	NFM	Nationwide	RCS Channel 57
		NFM	Sussex	RCS
147.6250	155.7250	NFM	West Midlands	Police (YM) Channel 58
		NFM	Nationwide	RCS Channel 59
147.6500		NFM	Lincolnshire	Police (NC) Channel 1
		NFM	West Mercia	Police (YK)
		NFM	Lewes	Police
147.6500	155.7500	AM	West Sussex	Police (M2KB)
		NFM	Nationwide	RCS Surveillance Channel 61
147.6625	147.6625	AM	Lancashire	Police (Car-Car)
		NFM	Bolton	Police Motorcycle Instructors
147.6750		NFM	Eastleigh	Fire Brigade

Base	Mobile	Mode	Location	User and Notes
147.6750	155.7500	NFM	Leman Street	Police (HD)
147.7000	168.7000	NFM	Nationwide	RCS Secure Cougar System
147.7250	168.8000	NFM	Nationwide	RCS Secure Cougar System
147.7750	147.7750	NFM	London	Police (MP)
147.7750	155.8750	NFM	Kensington	Police (BD)
		NFM	Nationwide	RCS Channel 71
147.8000	155.9000	AM	Nationwide	Fire Alert
		NFM	Jersey	Fire Paging
147.8125	147.8125	NFM	Strathclyde	Police
147.8500		NFM	Lincolnshire	Police (NC) Channel 2
147.8500	147.8500	AM	Newcastle	MoD Police
		NFM	Strathclyde	Fire Brigade (GX)
		AM	Wiltshire	Police
147.8500	147.9500	NFM	London	Police Dartford Tunnel
147.8625	147.8625	NFM	London	Police Engineers Channel 78
147.8750	147.8750	AM	London	Police (MP)
		AM	M25	Police Speed Traps
		NFM	Kent	Police (Tour De France)
		NFM	England & Wales	Police Mobiles Channel 21
147.8875		NFM	Kent Motorways	Police (TD)
147.9000		NFM	England	Fire Brigade Pagers
		NFM	Strathclyde	Fire Brigade (GX)
		NFM	Newport	Fire Brigade
147.9125	147.9125	NFM	London	Police (MP)
		NFM	England & Wales	Police Mobiles Channel 22
		NFM	Nationwide	RCS Car-to-Car Channel 82
147.9250	147.9250	NFM	Strathclyde	Fire Brigade (GX)
		NFM	London	Police Engineers Channel 83
147.9375	147.9375	NFM	London	Police (MP)
		NFM	Nationwide	RCS Channel 84
147.9500	147.9500	NFM	London	Police Metropolitan CID
		NFM	Nationwide	RCS Channel 00
147.9750	149.9750	NFM	London	Police Metropolitan CID
		NFM	Nationwide	RCS Channel 00

148.00000 - 148.99875 MHz   NATIONAL POWER COMPANIES

Base	Mobile	Mode	Location	User and Notes
148.0000	139.5688	NFM	Nationwide	Electricity Channel J21
148.0188	139.5188	NFM	Nationwide	Electricity Channel J22
148.0313	139.5113	NFM	Nationwide	Electricity Channel J23
148.0433	139.5439	NFM	Nationwide	Electricity Channel J24
148.0563	139.5563	NFM	Nationwide	Electricity Channel J25
148.0811	139.5813	NFM	Nationwide	Electricity Channel J27
		NFM	Luton	Electricity
		NFM	Nationwide	Electricity Channel J27
148.0938	139.5938	NFM	Nationwide	Electricity Channel J28
148.1063	139.6063	NFM	Nationwide	Electricity Channel J29
148.1188	139.6188	NFM	Nationwide	Electricity Channel J30
148.1313	139.6313	NFM	Nationwide	Electricity Channel J31

Base	Mobile	Mode	Location	User and Notes
148.1438	139.6438	NFM	Nationwide	Electricity Channel J32
		NFM	Cambridge	Electricity
148.1563	139.6563	NFM	Nationwide	Electricity Channel J33
		NFM	Norfolk	Electricity
148.1688	139.6688	NFM	Nationwide	Electricity Channel J34
		NFM	Peterborough	Electricity
		NFM	Clacton	Electricity
148.1813	139.6813	NFM	Nationwide	Electricity Channel J35
		NFM	Suffolk	Electricity
148.1938	139.6938	NFM	Nationwide	Electricity Channel J36
		NFM	Norwich	Electricity
148.2063	139.7063	NFM	Nationwide	Electricity Channel J37
		NFM	Chelmsford	Electricity
		NFM	Clacton	Electricity
		NFM	Ipswich	Electricity
148.2188	139.7188	NFM	Nationwide	Electricity Channel J38
		NFM	Harrow	Electricity
148.2313	139.7313	NFM	Nationwide	Electricity Channel J39
		NFM	Kings Lynn	Electricity
		NFM	Ipswich	Electricity
		NFM	Enfield	Electricity
148.2438	139.7438	NFM	Nationwide	Electricity Channel J40
148.2500		AM	RAF Sculthorpe	Approach
148.2563	139.7563	NFM	Nationwide	Electricity Channel J41
		NFM	Nationwide	Electricity Channel J41
148.2688	139.7688	NFM	Nationwide	Electricity Channel J42
148.2813	139.7813	NFM	Nationwide	Electricity Channel J43
148.2938	139.7938	NFM	Nationwide	Electricity Channel J44
148.2938	139.7938	NFM	Nationwide	Electricity Channel J44
148.29500		NFM	Durham	AA
148.2970		NFM	West Sussex	Police (M2KB)
148.3063	139.8063	NFM	Nationwide	Electricity Channel J45
148.3183	139.8183	NFM	Nationwide	Electricity Channel J46
		NFM	Nationwide	Electricity Channel J46
148.3250		NFM	Bolton	Norweb
148.3313	139.8313	NFM	Nationwide	Electricity Channel J47
148.3438	139.8436	NFM	Nationwide	Electricity Channel J48
		NFM	Nationwide	Electricity Channel J48
148.3563	139.6563	NFM	Nationwide	Electricity Channel J49
148.3688	139.8688	NFM	Nationwide	Electricity Channel J50
		NFM	Nationwide	Electricity Channel J50
148.37000		NFM	Durham	AA
148.3813	139.8813	NFM	Nationwide	Electricity Channel J52
148.3938	139.6938	NFM	Nationwide	Electricity Channel J52
148.4000	148.4000	AM	RAF Sculthorpe	Approach
		AM	RAF Lakenheath	Approach
148.4063	139-9063	NFM	Nationwide	Electricity Channel J53
148.4188	139.9188	NFM	Nationwide	Electricity Channel J54

Base	Mobile	Mode	Location	User and Notes
148.4311	139.9313	NFM	Nationwide	Electricity Channel J55
		NFM	Nationwide	Electricity Channel J55
148.4438	139.9438	NFM	Nationwide	Electricity Channel J56
148.4563	139.9563	NFM	Nationwide	Electricity Channel J57
148.4688	139.9668	NFM	Nationwide	Electricity Channel J58
148.4813	139.9813	NFM	Nationwide	Electricity Channel J59
148.4938	139.9938	NFM	Nationwide	Electricity Channel J60
148.5063	140.0063	NFM	Nationwide	Electricity Channel J61
148.5188	140.0188	NFM	Nationwide	Electricity Channel J62
148.5313	140.0313	NFM	Nationwide	Electricity Channel J63
148.5438	140.0438	NFM	Nationwide	Electricity Channel J64
148.5563	140.0563	NFM	Nationwide	Electricity Channel J65
148.5688	140.0688	NFM	Nationwide	Electricity Channel J66
148.5813	140.0813	NFM	Nationwide	Electricity Channel J67
148.5938	140.0938	NFM	Nationwide	Electricity Channel J68
148.6063	140.1063	NFM	Nationwide	Electricity Channel J69
148.6163	140.1188	NFM	Nationwide	Electricity Channel J70
148.6313	140.1313	NFM	Nationwide	Electricity Channel J71
148.6438	140.1438	NFM	Nationwide	Electricity Channel J72
148.6563	140.1563	NFM	Nationwide	Electricity Channel J73
148.6688	140.1688	NFM	Nationwide	Electricity Channel J74
148.6813	140.1813	NFM	Nationwide	Electricity Channel J75
148.6938	140.1938	NFM	Nationwide	Electricity Channel J76
148.7063	140.2043	NFM	Nationwide	Electricity Channel J77
148.7188	140.2188	NFM	Nationwide	Electricity Channel J78
148.7250		NFM	Jersey	BBC Radio Jersey O/B
148.7313	140.2313	NFM	Nationwide	Electricity Channel J79
148.7438	140.2438	NFM	Nationwide	Electricity Channel J80
148.7563	140.2563	NFM	Nationwide	Electricity Channel J81
148.7625		NFM	Newcastle	Link
148.7688	140.2688	NFM	Nationwide	Electricity Channel J82
148.7813	140.2813	NFM	Nationwide	Electricity Channel J83
148.7938	140.2938	NFM	Nationwide	Electricity Channel J84
148.8063	140.3063	NFM	Nationwide	Electricity Channel J85
148.8188	140.3188	NFM	Nationwide	Electricity Channel J86
148.8200		NFM	Durham	British Gas
148.8250		NFM	England	Fire Brigade Pagers
148.8313	140.3313	NFM	Nationwide	Electricity Channel J87
148.8436	140.3438	NFM	Nationwide	Electricity Channel J88
148.8563	140.3563	NFM	Nationwide	Electricity Channel J89
148.8688	140.3689	NFM	Nationwide	Electricity Channel J90
148.8750		NFM	England & Wales	Fire Brigade Alerters
148.8750		NFM	Humberside	Fire Brigade
148.8813	140.3813	NFM	Nationwide	Electricity Channel J91
148.8938	140.3938	NFM	Nationwide	Electricity Channel J92
148.9063	140.4063	NFM	Nationwide	Electricity Channel J93
148.9188	140.4188	NFM	Nationwide	Electricity Channel J94
148.9313	140.4313	NFM	Nationwide	Electricity Channel J95

Base	Mobile	Mode	Location	User and Notes
148.9438	140.4438	NFM	Nationwide	Electricity Channel J96
148.9500	148.9500	AM	Nationwide	USAF General
148.9563	140.4563	NFM	Nationwide	Electricity Channel J97
148.9688	140.4688	NFM	Nationwide	Electricity Channel J98
148.9813	140.4813	NFM	Nationwide	Electricity Channel J99

149.0000 - 149.9000 MHz Government & MoD Mould Repeaters

Base	Mobile	Mode	Location	User and Notes
149.0000		NFM	Nationwide	MoD Repeaters
149.0125		NFM	South Wales	Mould
149.0125		NFM	Leicester	Mould
149.0375	149.0375	NFM	Aberfield	MoD Police
149.0625		NFM	S Wales	Mould
		NFM	S Wales	Mould
149.0750		NFM	S Wales	Mould
		NFM	Cornwall	Mould
		AM	Nationwide	ATC Channel V5
149.0875	142.4125	NFM	Cornwall	Mould
149.1000	149.1000	AM	Nationwide	USAF Rescue Helicopter
149.1250		NFM	RAF Carewent	Store Security
149.1750		NFM	S Wales	Mould
149.2375		NFM	Nationwide	MoD Establishments
149.2500		NFM	S Wales	Mould
149.2625		NFM	Cornwall	Mould
149.2750		NFM	RAF Spadeadam	Forward Air Controller
		AM	Nationwide	ATC Channel V6
149.2750	149.2750	NFM	Nationwide	RAF Cadets Channel V6
149.2875		NFM	Tayside	Mould
149.3250		NFM	MoD Aberporth	Ops
149.3625		NFM	Nationwide	MoD Establishments
149.3875		NFM	Nationwide	MoD Establishments
		NFM	MoD Aberporth	Ops
149.3875	142.0625	NFM	Shoeburyness	Mould
149.4000		NFM	Nationwide	Army Cadet Corps
		AM	Nationwide	ATC Channel V2
149.4000	149.4000	NFM	Nationwide	RAF ATC Channel V2
		NFM	Caerleon	ATC Ch 1
149.4125		NFM	Nationwide	MoD Establishments
149.4125	142.1125	NFM	S Wales	Mould
149.4175		NFM	S Wales	Mould Ch 4
149.4250		NFM	Nationwide	Sea Cadets
149.4275		NFM	S Wales	Mould
149.4625		NFM	S Wales	Mould
149.5000		NFM	S Wales	Mould
149.5375		NFM	Manchester	Mould
		NFM	Midlands	Mould
149.6250		NFM	Cornwall	Mould
149.6500		NFM	RAF Lakenheath	Radar
		NFM	RAF Midenhall	US Navy

Base	Mobile	Mode	Location	User and Notes
149.6500	149.6500	NFM	Nationwide	USAF Air-Air
149.7000	149.7215	NFM	Leicester	Mould
		NFM	S Wales	Mould
149.7375		NFM	Tayside	Mould
		NFM	Manchester	Mould
		NFM	Brecon Beacons	Mould
149.7375	149.7375	NFM	Edzell	US Navy Edzell Security
		NFM	Caerwent	MOD Ops
149.7625		NFM	Nationwide	MoD Establishments
149.7750	149.7750	NFM	Nationwide	MoD Police Helicopters
		NFM	Nationwide	USAF Air-Air
		NFM	Nationwide	MoD Regional Police Ch 1
149.7750	168.8250	NFM	Nationwide	MoD Police Helicopter
149.8000		NFM	S Wales	Mould
149.8125		NFM	Salisbury Plain	Army
149.8125	149.8375	NFM	S Wales	Mould
149.8250	149.8250	NFM	London	MoD Police
		NFM	Portsmouth	Whale Island MoD Police
149.8450	149.8450	NFM	Portsmouth	Whale Island MoD Police
149.8500		NFM	DRA Farnborough	MoD Police (FP)
149.8500	149.8500	NFM	Nationwide	Common Base Channel
		NFM	Hadleigh	MoD Police
		NFM	Portsmouth Dockyard	MoD Police
		NFM	Colchester	MoD Police
		NFM	Aldershot Barracks	MoD Police
		NFM	Nationwide	MoD Police Channel 3
149.8675		NFM	S Wales	Mould
		NFM	Tayside	Mould
		NFM	S Wales	Mould
149.9000	149.9000	NFM	Nationwide	RAF Air Training Corps Ch 2
		NFM	Caerleon	ATC Ch 2

149.9500 - 150.0500 MHz   SOVIET SATELLITE BEACONS

Base	Mobile	Mode	Location	User and Notes
149.9700		NFM	Space	Polar Bear 8688A
149.9800		NFM	Space	Soviet Cosmos Satellites

150.0500 - 152.0000 MHz   RADIO ASTRONOMY, PAGING AND TELEMETRY BEACONS

Base	Mobile	Mode	Location	User and Notes
150.0500		NFM	MoD, London	Procurement Executive Ch 1
150.0620	156.6900	NFM	Eligum, Holland	Taxi Service
150.0750		NFM	MoD, London	Procurement Executive Ch 2
150.1100		NFM	Nationwide	Oil Slick Markers
150.1850		NFM	Nationwide	Oil Slick Markers
150.3000		NFM	Non-Geostationary Orbit	Russian Cosmos Geodetic
150.5000		NFM	Nationwide	Nissan Racing Team
150.5625		NFM	Enniskillen	Military Data Link
151.0000	151.4000	NFM	Paris, France	GMS Carphones
		NFM	Nice, France	GMS Carphones

Base	Mobile	Mode	Location	User and Notes
		NFM	Lyons, France	GMS Carphones
151.3250		NFM	Nationwide	Army Bomb Squad
151.6000	156.6000	NFM	Gravesend	Pool Control
		NFM	Essex	Colchester Docks
		NFM	London	Pool of london piers
		NFM	London	Tower Bridge Control
151.6750		NFM	Newmarket	Paging
151.7125	151.7125	NFM	Netherlands	Disaster Ch 62
151.7375	151.7375	NFM	Netherlands	Disaster Ch 63
151.7625	151.7625	NFM	Netherlands	Disaster Ch 64
151.7750		NFM	Galway	University Hospital Paging
151.7875	151.7875	NFM	Netherlands	Disaster Ch 65
151.8375	151.8375	NFM	Netherlands	Disaster Ch 66
151.8875	151.8875	NFM	Netherlands	Disaster Ch 67
151.9625	151.9625	NFM	Netherlands	Disaster Ch 68
151.9875	151.9875	NFM	Netherlands	Disaster Ch 69
152.0000 - 152.9875 MHz			**POLICE & FIRE PMR 12.5 kHz**	
152.0000	143.0750	NFM	Leicester	Police (NL) Channel 1
152.0000	143.2625	NFM	London	Police (MP) Channel 11
152.0125	143.1625	AM	Isle of Man	Police (MX) Channel 1
152.0125	143.5625	AM	West Yorkshire	Police (XW) Channel 3
152.0125		NFM	Dumfries And Galloway	Police (AJ)
		NFM	Strathclyde	Police Data Channel
		NFM	Isle Of Man	Police
		AM	W Yorkshire	Police (M2XW) Ch 2
152.0250	143.0250	NFM	Strathclyde	Police Channel 1
152.0250	143.0625	NFM	London	Police (MP) Channel 3
152.0250	143.2625	NFM	Strathclyde	Police Channel 49
152.0375	143.0750	AM	Leicester	Police (NL) Channel 1
152.0375		NFM	Dumfries And Galloway	Police (AJ)
152.0500	143.0250	NFM	Strathclyde	Police
152.0500	143.0500	NFM	Glasgow	Strathclyde Police (AS)
152.0500	143.1125	NFM	London	Police (MP) Channel 5
152.0500	143.5875	AM	West Yorkshire	Police (XW) Channel 5
		NFM	Dumfries And Galloway	Police (AJ)
		NFM	Co. Durham	Police
		AM	W Yorkshire	Police Ch 5
152.0625	143.3125	AM	Scarborough	Police 'D' Division
		AM	North Yorkshire	Police (XN) Channel 2
152.0625		NFM	Mosspaul	Police
152.0750	152.6750	NFM	Ottercops	Police (M2LB)
152.0750	143.4375	NFM	Strathclyde	Police Channel 32
152.0750		NFM	Strathclyde	Police Data Channel
		NFM	Yorkshire	Fire Brigade Control
		NFM	Langholm	Police
152.0875	143.0875	NFM	Berwick	Police
152.0875	143.0750	AM	Northumberland	Police (M2LB) Channel 1

Base	Mobile	Mode	Location	User and Notes
152.0875	152.0875	NFM	Netherlands	Disaster Ch 69
		NFM	Lincolnshire	Police (NC)
152.1000	143.4375	NFM	London	Police (MP)
		NFM	Strathclyde	Police Channel 31
152.1000	143.2625	AM	London	Police (MP) Channel 11
152.1000		NFM	Strathclyde	Police Data Channel
		NFM	Strathclyde	Police Channel 31
152.1250	146.9500	NFM	Beacon Lough	Police (M2LB)
152.1250	143.0250	NFM	Strathclyde	Police Channel 4
152.1250	152.7250	NFM	Quarry House	Police (M2LB)
152.1250	143.2000	NFM	Strathclyde	Police Channel 13
152.1250	143.1250	NFM	Strathclyde	Police Channel 35
152.1250		NFM	Ayr	Police (R)
		NFM	Strathclyde	Police Data Channel
152.1375	143.5125	NFM	Dumfries And Galloway	Police (AJ)
152.1375	143.3125	NFM	London	Police (MP) Channel 13
152.1500	143.3625	AM	North Yorkshire	Police (XN) Channel 4
152.1500	143.2000	NFM	Strathclyde	Police Channel 11
152.1625	143.0625	NFM	Strathclyde	Fire Brigade (GX) Channel 8
152.1625	143.2125	NFM	London	Police (MP) Channel 9
152.1625	143.2875	NFM	Strathclyde	Police Channel 46
152.1625	143.3375	NFM	Strathclyde	Fire Brigade (GX) Ch 28
		NFM	Strathclyde	Fire Brigade Channel 28
152.1625	143.3750	NFM	Strathclyde	Fire Brigade (GX) Channel 5
		NFM	Strathclyde	Fire Brigade Channel 41
152.1625	143.4250	NFM	South Yorkshire	Police (XS) Channel 5
152.1625	143.5250	NFM	Strathclyde	Fire Brigade (GX) Ch 10
152.1625		NFM	Strathclyde	Police Channel 3
		NFM	Scotland	Fire Brigades Channel 28
152.1750	143.1000	AM	Leicester	Police (NL) Channel 3
152.1750	143.2000	NFM	Strathclyde	Police Channel 12
152.1750		NFM	Teeside	Police
152.1875	143.0375	NFM	Strathclyde	Fire Brigade (GX) Ch 2
152.1875	143.0375	NFM	Strathclyde	Fire Brigade Channel 22
152.1875	143.1000	AM	Northumberland	Police (M2LB) Channel 2
		NFM	Dumfries & Galloway	Fire Brigade Channel 15
152.1875	143.1375	NFM	Strathclyde	Fire Brigade (GX) Ch 11
152.1875	143.2875	NFM	Strathclyde	Fire Brigade (GX) Ch 46
152.1875	143.4625	NFM	Strathclyde	Fire Brigade (GX) Ch 7
152.1875		NFM	Dumfries And Galloway	Fire Brigade (Fire Control)
		NFM	Strathclyde	Fire Brigade (GX)
		NFM	Strathclyde	Police
		NFM	Wisham	Fire Brigade
		NFM	Sandwich	Police
		NFM	Brockely	Police
		NFM	Bovington	Police
152.2000	143.5875	NFM	Staffordshire	Police (YF) Channel 1
152.2000	143.2000	NFM	Strathclyde	Police Channel 09

Base	Mobile	Mode	Location	User and Notes
152.2000	143.3625	NFM	London	Police (MP) Channel 15
152.2000	143.2625	NFM	Strathclyde	Police Channel 47
152.2000		NFM	Dumfries And Galloway	Police (AJ)
152.2125	143.4125	NFM	Strathclyde	Police Channel 36
152.2125		NFM	Dumfries And Galloway	Police (AJ)
152.2250	143.2750	NFM	Strathclyde	Police
152.2250	146.1500	NFM	Quarry House	Police (M2LB)
152.2250	143.1375	NFM	London	Police (MP) Channel 6
152.2250	143.2750	NFM	Strathclyde	Police Channel 18
152.2250		NFM	Wigton	Police (W)
152.2375	143.4625	NFM	Strathclyde	Fire Brigade (GX) Ch 2
152.2375	143.6625	NFM	Strathclyde	Fire Brigade (GX) Ch 7
152.2375	143.0375	NFM	Strathclyde	Fire Brigade (GX) Ch 23
152.2375	143.7125	NFM	Strathclyde	Fire Brigade (GX) Ch 35
152.2375		NFM	Strathclyde	Fire Brigade (GX)
		NFM	Strathclyde	Police
		NFM	Nottingham	Police
152.2500	143.2750	NFM	Strathclyde	Police
152.2500	143.2750	NFM	Strathclyde	Police Channel 5
152.2500	143.5125	NFM	Dumfries And Galloway	Police (AJ)
152.2500	143.7125	NFM	Strathclyde	Fire Brigade (GX)
152.2500	143.2750	NFM	Strathclyde	Fire Brigade (GX) Ch 13
152.2625	143.3875	AM	North Yorkshire	Police (XN) Channel 5
152.2625	143.1875	NFM	London	Police (MP) Channel 8
152.2625	143.4125	NFM	Strathclyde	Police Channel 37
152.2625	143.2625	NFM	Strathclyde	Police Channel 45
152.2625		NFM	London	Police Diplomatic Protection
		NFM	Bridge Of Orchy	Police
152.2750	143.4000	NFM	Dumfries And Galloway	Police (AJ)
152.2750	152.6625	NFM	Ottercops	Police (M2LB)
152.2750	143.4500	NFM	Strathclyde	Police Channel 26
152.2750		NFM	Strathclyde	Police Data Channel
152.2875	143.0375	NFM	Strathclyde	Fire Brigade (GX) Ch 56
152.2875	143.1375	NFM	Strathclyde	Fire Brigade (GX) Ch 11
152.2875	143.2875	NFM	Strathclyde	Fire Brigade (GX) Ch 48
152.2875	143.4625	NFM	Strathclyde Fire Brigade	Fire Brigade (GX) Channel 7
152.2875	143.6625	NFM	Strathclyde	Fire Brigade (GX) Channel 9
152.2875	143.7125	NFM	Strathclyde	Fire Brigade (GX) Ch 36
152.2875	143.7250	NFM	Dumfries And Galloway	Fire Brigade Chan16
152.2875		NFM	Strathclyde	Police
152.3000	143.2375	NFM	London	Police (MP) Channel 10
152.3000	143.2000	NFM	Strathclyde	Police Channel 14
152.3125	143.0375	NFM	Strathclyde	Fire Brigade Channel 2
152.3125	143.1000	NFM	Dumfries And Galloway	Fire Brigade (Fire Control)
152.3125	143.1375	NFM	Strathclyde	Fire Brigade (GX) Ch 11
152.3125	143.1500	NFM	Dumfries And Galloway	Fire Brigade (Fire Control)
152.3125	143.1625	AM	Humberside	Police (XH)
152.3125	143.2875	NFM	Strathclyde	Fire Brigade (GX)

Base	Mobile	Mode	Location	User and Notes
		NFM	Strathclyde	Police Channel 44
152.3125	143.4625	NFM	Strathclyde	Fire Brigade (GX)
152.3125		NFM	Strathclyde	Police Channel 27
152.3250	143.1625	NFM	London	Police (MP)
152.3250	143.2750	NFM	Ayr	Police
		NFM	Strathclyde	Police
152.3250	152.8500	NFM	Quarry House	Police (M2LB)
152.3250	152.3250	NFM	London	Met Police Anti Terroist Ch.7
152.3375	143.0375	AM	West Yorkshire	Police (XW) Channel 1
		NFM	Strathclyde	Fire Brigade (GX)
		NFM	Strathclyde	Police Channel 26
152.3375	143.0625	NFM	Strathclyde	Fire Brigade (GX)
152.3375	143.3375	NFM	Strathclyde	Fire Brigade (GX)
		NFM	Strathclyde	Police Channel 30
152.3375	143.3750	NFM	Strathclyde	Fire Brigade (GX)
		NFM	Strathclyde	Police Channel 39
152.3375	143.4625	NFM	Strathclyde	Fire Brigade (GX)
152.3500	143.1250	AM	Leicester	Police (NL) Channel 4
152.3500	143.2000	NFM	Strathclyde	Police Channel 10
152.3500	143.3125	NFM	Strathclyde	Police Channel 50
152.3500	143.3250	NFM	Dumfries And Galloway	Police (AJ)
152.3500	143.6375	NFM	Strathclyde	Police Channel 30
152.3500		AM	Leicestershire	Police Force HQ
152.3625	143.3625	NFM	Strathclyde	Fire Brigade (GX)
		NFM	Strathclyde	Police
152.3625	143.0375	AM	London	Police (MP) Channel 2
152.3750	143.3875	NFM	Strathclyde	Police Channel 19
152.3750	143.4500	NFM	Ayr	Police
		NFM	Strathclyde	Police Channel 27
		NFM	Strathclyde	Police Data Channel
152.3750	146.9000	NFM	Round Meadows	Police (M2LB)
152.3750		NFM	Dumfries And Galloway	Police (AJ)
		NFM	Strathclyde	Police Data Channel
152.3870	152.5100	NFM	Holland	Zieenhuizen Hospitals
152.3875	143.0125	NFM	London	Police (MP) Channel 1
152.3875	143.2375	AM	Cleveland	Police (LZ) Channel 1
152.3875	143.3875	AM	City of London	Police (OJ) Channel 1
		NFM	Strathclyde	Fire Brigade (GX)
152.4000	143.2000	AM	Nottinghamshire	Police (NH) Channel 1
152.4000	143.2750	NFM	Strathclyde	Police Channel 16
152.4125	143.1250	AM	Northumberland	Police (M2LB)
		NFM	Strathclyde	Police
		NFM	Strathclyde	Police Channel 33
152.4125	143.3875	NFM	London	Police (OJ)
		NFM	Strathclyde	Police Data Channel
152.4125	143.4125	AM	City of London	Police (OJ) Channel 2
152.4125		NFM	Strathclyde	Police Data Channel
152.4250	143.2250	AM	Nottinghamshire	Police (NH) Channel 2

Base	Mobile	Mode	Location	User and Notes
152.4250	143.2375	NFM	Isle of Man	Fire Brigade
152.4250	143.2625	NFM	Strathclyde	Police Channel 48
152.4250	143.6500	NFM	Strathclyde	Police Channel 20
152.4250		AM	Manchester	Police
152.4375	143.4125	AM	London	Police (OJ) Channel 2
		NFM	Strathclyde	Police Data Channel
152.4375	143.4500	NFM	Strathclyde	Police Channel 29
152.4375	143.5125	NFM	Dumfries And Galloway	Police (AJ)
152.4375		NFM	Strathclyde	Police Data Channel
152.4500	143.1875	AM	Humberside	Police (XH)
152.4500	143.4500	NFM	Strathclyde	Police Channel 28
		NFM	Strathclyde	Police Data Channel
152.4500	143.5125	NFM	Dumfries And Galloway	Police (AJ)
152.4500		NFM	Ferrybridge	Police
		NFM	Strathclyde	Police Data Channel
152.4625	143.0875	NFM	London	Police (MN)
152.4625	143.2875	NFM	Strathclyde	Fire Brigade (GX)
		NFM	Strathclyde	Police
152.4625	143.3750	NFM	Strathclyde	Police
		NFM	Strathclyde	Police Channel 40
152.4625	143.5250	NFM	Strathclyde	Fire Brigade (GX)
152.4750	143.0625	NFM	Strathclyde	Fire Brigade (GX)
152.4750	143.3375	NFM	Scottish Fire Brigades	Police Channel 29
		NFM	Strathclyde	Fire Brigade (GX)
		NFM	Strathclyde	Police
		NFM	Strathclyde Fire Brigade	Police Channel 3
152.4750	143.7750	NFM	Dumfries & Galloway Fire	Police Channel 17
152.4750		NFM	Coatbridge	Fire Brigade
		NFM	Paisley	Fire Brigade
152.4875	143.2625	AM	Cleveland	Police (LZ)
152.4875	143.6500	NFM	Strathclyde	Police Channel 19
152.4875	143.6375	NFM	Strathclyde	Police Channel 30
152.4875	143.3125	NFM	Strathclyde	Police Channel 51
152.5000	143.2500	AM	Nottinghamshire	Police (NH) Channel 3
152.5000	143.5375	NFM	Strathclyde	Police Channel 23
152.5125	143.0875	AM	West Yorkshire	Police (XW) Channel 3
152.5125	143.3375	NFM	London	Police (MP) Channel 14
152.5125	143.6625	NFM	Strathclyde	Fire Brigade (GX)
152.5125	143.7125	NFM	Scottish Fire Brigades	Police Channel 33
		NFM	Strathclyde	Fire Brigade (GX)
		NFM	Strathclyde	Police
152.5125		AM	Manchester	Police
152.5250	143.0375	NFM	Strathclyde	Fire Brigade (GX)
		NFM	Scottish Fire Brigades	Police Channel 25
		NFM	Strathclyde	Police Channel 25
152.5250	143.4625	NFM	Strathclyde	Fire Brigade (GX)
152.5250		NFM	Lothian And Borders	Police (E) East Lothian
152.5375	143.5375	NFM	Strathclyde	Police Channel 22

Base	Mobile	Mode	Location	User and Notes
152.5500	143.1500	AM	Northumberland	Police (M2LB)
152.5500	143.2875	AM	London	Police (MP) Channel 12
152.5500	143.6625	NFM	Strathclyde	Fire Brigade (GX)
152.5500	143.7125	NFM	Scottish Fire Brigades	Police Channel 37
		NFM	Strathclyde	Fire Brigade (GX)
		NFM	Strathclyde	Police Channel 37
152.5625	143.6500	NFM	Strathclyde	Police Channel 21
152.5750	143.0250	AM	Northamptonshire	Police (NG)
		NFM	Strathclyde	Police (AS) Channel 3
152.5750		NFM	Glasgow	Strathclyde police (AS)
152.5875	143.1125	AM	West Yorkshire	Police (XW) Channel 4
152.5875	143.5375	NFM	Strathclyde	Police Channel 24
152.6000	143.0625	NFM	Strathclyde	Fire Brigade (GX)
152.6000	143.1750	AM	Northumberland	Police (M2LB)
		NFM	Dumfries And Galloway	Fire Brigade (Fire Control)
152.6000	143.2875	NFM	Strathclyde	Police Channel 46
152.6000	143.3375	NFM	Scottish Fire Brigades	Police Channel 31
		NFM	Strathclyde	Fire Brigade (GX)
		NFM	Strathclyde	Police
		NFM	Strathclyde Fire Brigade	Police Channel 3
152.6000	143.3750	NFM	Scottish Fire Brigades	Police Channel 43
		NFM	Strathclyde	Fire Brigade (GX)
		NFM	Strathclyde	Police
152.6000	143.5250	NFM	Strathclyde	Fire Brigade (GX)
152.6125	143.9000	NFM	Strathclyde	Police Channel 42
152.6125		AM	Humberside	Police
152.6250	143.7000	NFM	Strathclyde	Police Channel 38
152.6250	143.2625	NFM	Strathclyde	Police Channel 46
152.6375	143.4325	AM	London	Police (MP) Channel 16
152.6375	143.6625	NFM	Strathclyde	Fire Brigade (GX)
152.6375	143.7125	NFM	Scottish Fire Brigades	Police Channel 32
		NFM	Strathclyde	Fire Brigade (GX)
		NFM	Strathclyde	Police
		NFM	Strathclyde	Police Channel 32
152.6375	152.6375	NFM	Northern Ireland	Fire Brigade Handhelds
152.6500	143.9000	NFM	Strathclyde	Police Channel 41
152.6625	146.5500	NFM	Quarry House	Fire Brigade (M2LJ)
152.6625	143.9000	NFM	Strathclyde	Police Channel 44
152.6750	143.1250	NFM	Strathclyde	Police
		NFM	Strathclyde	Police Data Channel
152.6750		NFM	Strathclyde	Police Data Channel
152.6875	143.5125	NFM	Dumfries And Galloway	Police Lowther Hills (AJ)
		AM	Humberside	Police (XH) Channel 3
152.6875		NFM	Ferrybridge	Police
152.7000	143.7000	NFM	Strathclyde	Police
152.7000	143.0500	AM	Northamptonshire	Police (NG) Channel 2
152.7000		NFM	Dumfries And Galloway	Police (AJ)
152.7125	143.0625	AM	West Yorkshire	Police (XW) Channel 2

Base	Mobile	Mode	Location	User and Notes
152.7125	143.3750	NFM	Strathclyde	Fire Brigade (GX)
		NFM	Strathclyde	Police
		NFM	Strathclyde	Police Channel 42
152.7125	143.5250	NFM	Strathclyde	Fire Brigade (GX)
152.7125	143.7750	NFM	Dumfries And Galloway	Fire Brigade (Fire Control)
152.7250	143.3750	AM	Lincolnshire	Police (NC) Channel 1
152.7500	143.5375	NFM	Strathclyde	Police
		NFM	Strathclyde	Police Channel 25
152.7625	143.3125	NFM	Strathclyde	Police Channel 52
152.7625	143.6375	NFM	Strathclyde	Police Channel 30
152.7625	146.9000	NFM	Quarry House	Police (M2LB)
152.7625		NFM	Arrochar	Police (L)
		NFM	Machrihanish	Police (L)
		NFM	Oban	Police (L)
152.7750	143.4625	AM	Lincolnshire	Police (NC) Channel 2
152.7750	146.9000	NFM	Ottercops	Police (M2LB)
152.7875	143.2750	AM	South Yorkshire	Police (XS) Channel 1
152.7875	143.6625	NFM	Strathclyde	Fire Brigade (GX)
		NFM	Strathclyde Fire Brigade	Police Channel 9
152.7875	143.7125	NFM	Scottish Fire Brigades	Police Channel 38
		NFM	Strathclyde	Fire Brigade (GX)
		NFM	Strathclyde	Police
		NFM	Strathclyde Fire Brigade	Police Channel 4
152.8000	143.0250	NFM	Strathclyde	Police Data Channel
		AM	County Durham	Police (LA) Channel 1
152.8000		AM	Newcastle	Police
		NFM	Girvan	Police (R)
		NFM	Strathclyde	Police Data Channel
152.8125	143.1375	AM	West Yorkshire	Police (XW) Channel 5
152.8125	143.4375	NFM	Strathclyde	Police
		NFM	Strathclyde	Police Channel 30
		NFM	Strathclyde	Police Data Channel
152.8125		NFM	Strathclyde	Police Data Channel
		AM	Manchester	Police
152.8250	143.7000	NFM	Strathclyde	Police Channel 39
152.8250		NFM	Castlebar	Paging
		NFM	Galway	Garda
152.8375	143.0500	AM	Durham	Police (LA) Channel 2
152.8375	143.6625	NFM	Strathclyde	Fire Brigade (GX)
		NFM	Strathclyde	Fire Brigade Channel 9
152.8375	143.7125	NFM	Strathclyde	Police
		NFM	Strathclyde	Fire Brigade (GX) Channel 4
		NFM	Strathclyde	Fire Brigade Channel 34
152.8375	146.5750	NFM	Ipswich	Police (VL)
152.8375		NFM	Ayr	Fire Brigade (D)
		NFM	Co. Durham	Police
152.8500	143.3250	AM	South Yorkshire	Police (XS) Channel 3
152.8750	143.1375	NFM	Strathclyde	Fire Brigade (GX)

Base	Mobile	Mode	Location	User and Notes
		NFM	Strathclyde	Fire Brigade Channel 11
152.8750	143.2875	NFM	Strathclyde	Fire Brigade (GX)
		NFM	Strathclyde	Fire Brigade Channel 45
		NFM	Strathclyde	Police
152.8750	143.7750	NFM	Dumfries & Galloway	Fire Brigade Channel 17
152.8875	143.1875	NFM	Isle of Man	Police (MX) Channel 2
152.8875		NFM	Isle Of Man	Police
		NFM	Co. Durham	Police (LA)
152.9000	143.3000	AM	Doncaster	Police
		AM	South Yorkshire	Police (XS) Channel 2
152.9000	143.9000	NFM	Strathclyde	Police Channel 43
152.9000		NFM	Dumfries And Galloway	Police (K)
		NFM	Dumfries And Galloway	Police Cambret Hill (AJ)
152.9250	146.1500	NFM	Ottercops	Police (M2LB)
152.9250	143.3500	AM	South Yorkshire	Police (XS) Channel 4
152.9250		NFM	Ayr	Police (R)
		NFM	Dumfries And Galloway	Police (AJ)
		NFM	Strathclyde	Police Data Channel
152.9375	146.5500	NFM	Round Meadows	Fire Brigade (M2LJ)
152.9500	143.1375	NFM	Strathclyde	Fire Brigade (GX)
		NFM	Strathclyde	Fire Brigade Channel 11
152.9500	143.2875	AM	North Yorkshire	Police (XN)
		NFM	Strathclyde	Fire Brigade (GX)
		NFM	Strathclyde	Police
		NFM	Strathclyde	Police Channel 47
		NFM	Strathclyde	Fire Brigade Channel 6
152.9500	143.3750	NFM	Strathclyde	Fire Brigade (GX)
		NFM	Strathclyde	Fire Brigade Channel 39
152.9500	143.5250	NFM	Strathclyde	Fire Brigade Channel 10
152.9625	143.2125	AM	Isle of Man	Police (MX) Channel 3
152.9625		NFM	Lincolnshire	Police Channel 2
152.9750	143.3375	AM	North Yorkshire	Police (XN)
		NFM	Ferrybridge	Police (WM)
152.9875	146.5500	NFM	Ottercops	Fire Brigade (M2LJ)
152.9875		NFM	Lincolnshire	Police Channel 1
153.0100	153.6300	NFM	Holland	Auotelefoon Net 1
153.0250 - 153.5000 MHz			NATIONAL PAGING	
153.0500		NFM	Nationwide	National Paging Ch 2
153.0750		NFM	Nationwide	Paging
		NFM	Jersey	Paging
		NFM	Nationwide	National Paging Ch 3
153.1250		NFM	Grimsby	BT Radio Paging
		NFM	Nationwide	National Paging Ch 5
		NFM	Yorkshire	Redifon Paging
153.1500		NFM	Nationwide	Paging
		NFM	Newmarket	Paging
		NFM	Yorkshire	Redifon Paging

Base	Mobile	Mode	Location	User and Notes
		NFM	Nationwide	National Paging Ch 6
153.1750		NFM	Nationwide	BT Pagers
		NFM	Yorkshire	BT Pagers
		NFM	Nationwide	National Paging Ch 7
153.2000		NFM	Nationwide	National Paging Ch 8
		NFM	Nationwide	UK Paging Test & Develop.
153.2250		NFM	Yorkshire	Redifon Paging
		NFM	Nationwide	National Paging Ch 9
		NFM	Lincoln	Paging
153.2375		NFM	Nationwide	Paging
153.2500		NFM	Nationwide	Digital Mobile Comms
		NFM	Nationwide	National Paging Ch 10
153.2750		NFM	Nationwide	Air Call Communications
		NFM	Nationwide	National Paging Ch 11
153.3000		NFM	Galway	University Hospital Paging
		NFM	Nationwide	National Paging Ch 12
153.3250		NFM	Nationwide	Air Call Communications
		NFM	Nationwide	National Paging Ch 13
153.3375		NFM	Nationwide	Paging
153.3450		NFM	Lincoln	Paging
153.3500		NFM	Nationwide	Inter City Pagers
		NFM	Nationwide	National Paging Ch 14
153.3625		NFM	Nationwide	Paging
153.3750		NFM	Nationwide	National Paging Ch 15
		NFM	Jersey	Paging
153.4000		NFM	Nationwide	National Paging Ch 16
		NFM	Nationwide	UKAEA Paging
153.4250		NFM	Tayside	Voice Paging
		NFM	Guernsey	Paging
		NFM	Nationwide	National Paging Ch 17
153.4500		NFM	Guernsey	Life Boat Pagers
		NFM	Nationwide	Paging
		NFM	Nationwide	National Paging Ch 18
153.4625	153.4625	NFM	London	Met Police Surveillance
153.4750		NFM	Nationwide	National Paging Ch 19
		NFM	Cambridge	City Council Paging
153.4750	163.0750	NFM	Tilbury	Sun Tug Operations
153.5000		NFM	Nationwide	National Paging Ch 20

153.5000 - 154.0000 MHz	MoD TACTICAL COMMUNICATIONS 25 kHz NFM SIMPLEX			
153.5375		NFM	S Wales	MoD Paging
153.5875		NFM	Bristol	MoD Link
153.7125		NFM	Nationwide	Red Cross
153.7875	153.7875	NFM	Netherlands	Fire Brigades Ch 01
153.8000		AM	Nationwide	ATC Channel V
153.8250		NFM	Galway	Garda Paging
		NFM	Co Mayo	Paging

Base	Mobile	Mode	Location	User and Notes
		AM	Nationwide	ATC Channel V4
153.8250	153.8250	NFM	Nationwide	RAF Cadets Channel V4
153.8375	153.8375	NFM	Netherlands	Fire Brigades Ch 02
153.9375	153.9375	NFM	Netherlands	Fire Brigades Ch 03
154.0000 - 155.9875 MHz			**POLICE BASE REPEATERS 12.5 KHZ**	
154.0000	146.1000	NFM	Kirkaldy	Police (Encrypted)
154.0000	146.5000	NFM	Jersey	Police (M2GS) Ch 1
154.0125		NFM	Fife	Fire Brigade
		NFM	Preston	Police
154.0125	146.1250	NFM	London	Police M25 North (SM) Ch1
		NFM	Lancashire	Police (BD) Channel 3
154.0125	154.0125	NFM	Londom	Met Police Surveillance
		NFM	Netherlands	Fire Brigades Ch 04
154.0250	146.0250	NFM	Glenrothes	Police
154.0250	146.0500	NFM	Fife	Police Traffic Division (ZT)
154.0250	146.1375	NFM	Inverness	Police (UR)
		NFM	Shropshire	Police (YK)
154.0250	146.5125	AM	West Mercia	Police (YK1)
154.0250	154.0250	NFM	Inverness	Fire Brigade
154.0375		NFM	Newcastle	Police
154.0375	146.9000	NFM	Beacon Lough	Police (M2LB)
154.0500	146.0500	NFM	Fife	Police Traffic Division (ZT)
154.0500	146.5375	NFM	Derbyshire	Fire Brigade (M2ND)
		NFM	Shropshire	Police (YK)
		NFM	West Mercia	Police (YK2)
154.0500		AM	Perry Bar	Motorway Police Ch 1
		NFM	Edinburgh	Police (T)
154.0625	146.2125	NFM	Inverness	Fire Brigade (UF)
154.0625	146.9000	NFM	High Spen	Police (M2LB)
154.0625	147.5375	NFM	Burton Down	Fire Brigade
154.0625		NFM	Dumfermline	Fire Brigade (F)
		NFM	Edinburgh	Fire Brigade (F)
154.0750	146.1375	NFM	Inverness	Police (UR)
154.0750	146.1750	AM	M6/M52/M62	Police
		NFM	Berkshire	Fire Brigade (HD)
		NFM	Devon	Fire Brigade (QA)
		NFM	Lancashire	Police (BD) Channel 4
154.0750	146.8750	NFM	Truleigh Hill	Police
154.0750	154.9750	NFM	Inverness	Fire Brigade
154.0750		NFM	Leven	Police (L)
		AM	Manchester	Traffic Police
154.0875	146.1500	NFM	High Spen	Police (M2LB)
154.0875	146.1625	NFM	London	Police M25 South (SM) Ch.2
154.0850		NFM	Fife	Fire Brigade
154.1000	146.1375	AM	Thames Valley	Police (HB) Channel 2
154.1000	146.4875	NFM	North Wales	Police (WA) Channel 4
154.1000		AM	Oxford	Police

Base	Mobile	Mode	Location	User and Notes
		NFM	Kirkaldy	Police (E) Scambled
154.1125	146.5625	AM	West Mercia	Police (YK3)
154.1125	146.9500	NFM	Truleigh Hill	Police
154.1125		NFM	Dumfermline	Fire Brigade (F)
		NFM	Aberdeen	Fire Control
154.1250	146.0500	NFM	Fife	Police Traffic Division (ZT)
154.1250	146.1375	NFM	Inverness	Police (UR)
		NFM	Cambridge	Fire Brigade (VF)
		NFM	London	Fire Brigade (FN)
		NFM	Staffordshire	Fire Brigade (M2YG)
		NFM	West Mercia	Police (YK) Channel 2
154.1250	147.6500	NFM	Beddingham	Police
154.1250		NFM	Edinburgh	Police (T)
154.1375	146.0500	NFM	Fife	Police (ZT)
154.1375	146.3625	AM	Cambridge	Police (VB) Channel 3
154.1375		NFM	Southampton	Police
154.1500	146.4875	NFM	Lothian And Borders	Police
154.1500	146.5500	NFM	High Spen	Fire Brigade (M2LJ)
154.1500	146.6750	AM	Gloucester	Police (QL) Channel 1
154.1500		AM	Stroud	Police
		NFM	Stirling	Fire Brigade (F)
154.1625	146.1625	NFM	Fife	Police (B)
154.1650	146.5250	NFM	Beacon Lough	Police (M2LB)
154.1750		NFM	Dumfermline	Police (D)
		NFM	Stirling	Fire Brigade (F)
154.1750	146.4750	NFM	West Hoathly	Police
154.1875		NFM	Newmarket	Paging
		NFM	Fife	Police
		NFM	Sussex	Police
154.1875	146.0500	NFM	Fife	Police (ZT)
154.1875	146.1500	NFM	Beacon Lough	Police (M2LB)
154.1875	146.4250	NFM	Lochaber	Police (UR)
		NFM	Rannoch Moor	Police
154.1875	146.8750	NFM	Burton Down	Police
154.1875	154.1875	NFM	Inverness	Fire Brigade
154.2000		NFM	Fife	Police
		AM	Cheshire	Police
		AM	Perry Bar	Motorway Police Ch 2
154.2000	146.5250	NFM	High Spen	Police (M2LB)
154.2000	146.5875	AM	Staffordshire	Police (YF) Channel 1
154.2000	147.6500	NFM	Fairlight	Police
154.2125		NFM	Fife	Fire Brigade
154.2250		AM	Bristol	Police
		NFM	Lanark	Police (ZS)
		NFM	Cheshire	Fire Brigade (CF)
154.2250	146.6500	NFM	Fairlight	Police
154.2250	146.7000	NFM	Staffordshire	Fire Brigade (M2YG)
		AM	Gloucester	Police (QL) Channel 2

Base	Mobile	Mode	Location	User and Notes
154.2375		NFM	Bathgate	Police
		NFM	Lanark	Police (ZS)
		NFM	Lothian And Borders	Police (F And ZH)
		NFM	Edinburgh	Police
154.2375	147.2375	NFM	West Lothian	Police
154.2375	154.2375	NFM	Netherlands	Police Ch 161
154.2500		NFM	Edinburgh	Police 'E' Div HQ
154.2500	146.2500	NFM	Lothian And Borders	Police (ZHE) East/Mid Loth.
154.2625		NFM	Edinburgh	Police (ZH) Special Events
154.2625	146.4750	AM	Birmingham	Police (YM)
154.2625	147.0625	NFM	Truleigh Hill	Police
154.2625	154.2625	NFM	Netherlands	Police Ch 162
154.2750	146.1500	NFM	Round Meadows	Police (M2LB)
154.2750	146.5750	NFM	Ipswich	Police (VL) Channel 1
154.2875		NFM	Edinburgh	Police (ZH) Ch 1
154.2875	154.2875	NFM	Netherlands	Police Ch 163
154.3000		NFM	Edinburgh	Police (ZH) Fettes
		NFM	Edinburgh	Police (ZH) Ch 2
154.3000	146.3000	NFM	Edinburgh	Police
154.3125		NFM	Borders	Police (G And ZH)
		NFM	Galashiels	Police
154.3125	146.4500	AM	Birmingham	Police (YM) Channel 5
154.3250	147.8250	NFM	Peebles	Police
154.3375	147.1750	NFM	Greater Manchester	Police
154.3375	146.7375	NFM	Thames Valley	Police (HB) Channel 1
		NFM	Hungerford	Police (HB) Channel 1
		NFM	Wales	Police (WH) Channel 3
154.3500		NFM	Edinburgh	Police (ZH) Fettes
154.3500	146.3500	NFM	Edinburgh	Police
154.3500	146.4250	NFM	Lochaber	Police (UR)
		NFM	Onich	Police
154.3625	154.3625	NFM	Netherlands	Police Ch 164
154.3675	146.7250	AM	Gloucester	Police (QL) Channel 3
154.3750		NFM	Livingstone	Police
		NFM	Edinburgh	Police Radio Engineers
154.3875		NFM	West Mercia	Police (YK)
		NFM	Edinburgh	Police 'E' Div HQ
154.3875	146.2500	NFM	Lothian And Borders	Police (ZHE)
154.3875	154.3875	NFM	Netherlands	Police Ch 165
154.4000	147.8250	NFM	Meigle Hill	Police
154.4125	146.0875	AM	West Mercia	Police (YK)
		AM	Warwickshire	Police (YJ) Channel 1
154.4125	147.6500	NFM	Truleigh Hill	Police
154.4125	147.8250	NFM	Hardens Hill	Police
154.4125	154.4125	NFM	Netherlands	Police Ch 166
154.4250		NFM	Galashields	Police (D)
		NFM	Peebles	Police
154.4250	146.4625	NFM	North Wales	Police (WA) Channel 3

Base	Mobile	Mode	Location	User and Notes
154.4375		NFM	Edinburgh	Police (T) Traffic Division
		NFM	Edinburgh	Police Traffic (T)
154.4500	146.3500	AM	Birmingham	Police (YM)
154.4500	147.1875	NFM	Perth	Police (W)
		NFM	Pitlochry	Police (WP)
154.4600		NFM	Lochaber	Police
154.4625		AM	Preston	Police BD Hutton HQ
		NFM	Galashiels	Police
		NFM	Edinburgh	Police 'E' Div HQ
154.4625	146.2500	NFM	Lothian And Borders	Police (ZHE) East/Mid Loth.
		NFM	Dalkeith	Police
154.4625	146.4250	NFM	Fort William	Police (UR)
		NFM	Lochaber	Police (UR)
		NFM	Fort William	Police
154.4625	146.4875	NFM	Lothian And Borders	Police
154.4750	146.1750	NFM	Kent	Fire Brigade (HO5)
154.4750	146.6250	NFM	Edinburgh	Fire Brigade (F)
154.4750	146.6000	AM	Dyfed	Police (WH) Ch. 1
154.4875		NFM	Central Scotland	Police
154.4875	146.4875	NFM	Lothian And Borders	Police
154.4875	147.0625	NFM	Beddingham	Police
154.4875	154.4875	NFM	Netherlands	Police Ch 167
154.5000		NFM	Eyemouth	Police
		NFM	Avon	Fire Brigade (QC)
154.5000	146.5000	NFM	Jersey	Police (M2GS) Channel 1
154.5000	147.6500	NFM	West Hoathly	Police
154.5125		NFM	Edinburgh	Police 'E' Div HQ
154.5125	146.2500	NFM	Lothian And Borders	Police (ZHE) East/Mid Loth.
		NFM	Dalkeith	Police
154.5125	146.4250	NFM	Ballachulish	Police
154.5125	146.8750	NFM	Beddingham	Police
154.5250		NFM	Central Scotland	Police Traffic Division (T)
		NFM	West Mercia	Police (YK)
		NFM	Galashiels	Police
154.5250	146.4875	NFM	Lothian And Borders	Police
154.5250	146.8500	NFM	Easter Ross	Police (UR)
154.5250	147.8750	NFM	Fairlight	Police
154.5375	146.5375	NFM	Edinburgh	Fire Brigade (F)
154.5500		AM	Merseyside	Police
154.5500	146.5500	NFM	Channel Islands	Harbour Police
154.5500	146.7125	NFM	Kyle of Lochalsh	Police (UR)
154.5500	147.8250	NFM	Ashkirk	Police
154.5500	146.6125	AM	Staffordshire	Police (YF) Channel 2
154.5500	146.5500	NFM	Jersey	Police (M2GS) Channel 5
		NFM	Jersey	Fire Brigade Channel 5
154.5625	146.4875	NFM	Lothian And Borders	Police
154.5625	146.5250	NFM	Caithness	Police
154.5625	146.8625	NFM	Dingwall	Police (UR)

Base	Mobile	Mode	Location	User and Notes
154.5625	154.5625	NFM	Inverness	Fire Brigade
154.5750		NFM	Belfast	Military Tone Encryption
154.5750	146.6500	NFM	Skye	Fire Brigade (UR)
154.5875		NFM	Belfast	Military Tone Encryption
		NFM	West Mercia	Police (YK)
		NFM	Galashiels	Police
154.5875	146.5250	NFM	Caithness	Police
154.6000		NFM	Belfast	Military Tone Encryption
		NFM	Edinburgh	Police (ZH) Fettes
		NFM	Enniskillen	Royal Ulster Constabulary
		NFM	Essex	Police
		AM	Guernsey Aiport	Fire Services
154.6000	147.2375	NFM	Perth	Police (W)
154.6125		AM	Bristol	Police
		NFM	Lanark	Police (S)
		AM	Melksham	Police
		NFM	Edinburgh	Police
		NFM	Manchester	Police
		NFM	Edinburgh	Police
		NFM	Galashiels	Police
154.6125	147.8250	NFM	Hardens Hill	Police
154.6125	147.0750	AM	Wiltshire	Police (OJ) Channel 4
154.6250		NFM	Central Scotland	Fire Brigade (AYS)
		AM	Perry Bar	Motorway Police Ch 3
154.6250	146.3250	AM	Birmingham	Police (YM) Channel 1
154.6250	146.4750	NFM	Truleigh Hill	Police
154.6250	146.6250	NFM	Edinburgh	Fire Brigade (F)
		NFM	Jersey	Police (M2GS) Ch 2
		NFM	Jersey	Police (M2GS) Channel 2
154.6375		NFM	Aberdeen	Police
154.6375	146.5250	NFM	Caithness	Police
154.6375	146.8625	NFM	Dingwall	Police (UR)
		NFM	Poolewe	Police (UR)
154.6375	146.2875	AM	Kent	Police (KA) Channel 5
154.6375	154.6375	NFM	Inverness	Fire Brigade
154.6500		NFM	Edinburgh	Fire Brigade (F)
154.6500	146.1125	AM	West Mercia	Police (YK)
		NFM	East	Fire Brigade
154.6500	146.6500	NFM	Skye	Fire Brigade
154.6500	146.9500	NFM	West Hoathly	Police
154.6500	146.1125	NFM	Warwickshire	Police (YJ) Channel 2
		NFM	Jersey	Ambulance Service Ch.1
154.6625	146.6625	NFM	Perth	Fire Brigade (Fire Control)
154.6625	146.8750	NFM	West Hoathly	Police
154.6625	154.6625	NFM	Netherlands	Police Ch 168
154.6750	146.2750	NFM	Nottinghamshire	Fire Brigade (M2NZ)
154.6875	146.6500	NFM	Skye	Fire Brigade
154.6875	146.8750	NFM	Caithness	Fire Brigade (UF)

Base	Mobile	Mode	Location	User and Notes
154.6875	154.6875	NFM	Northern Ireland	Fire Brigade Handhelds Ch 3
154.7000	146.3750	AM	Birmingham	Police (YM)
154.7000	146.8000	NFM	Sutherland	Police (UR)
154.7000	146.9500	NFM	Burton Down	Police
154.7000	147.8250	NFM	Dunion Hill	Police
154.7000	146.1000	NFM	Suffolk	Police (VL) Channel 3
154.7125	146.5250	NFM	Caithness	Police
154.7125	146.7125	NFM	Kyle of Lochalsh	Police (UR)
154.7125	146.9625	NFM	Perth	Police (W)
154.7250		NFM	Castlebar	Garda
154.7250	146.7125	NFM	Kyle of Lochalsh	Police Applecross (UR)
154.7250	146.7250	NFM	Norfolk	Fire Brigade (VF)
154.7375	146.8625	AM	Bedfordshire	Police (M2VA) Channel 2
154.7500	146.1375	NFM	Inverness	Police (UR)
154.7500	147.0625	NFM	West Hoathly	Police
154.7500	146.2250	NFM	Jersey	Ambulance Service Ch2
154.7625	146.8000	NFM	Sutherland	Police (UR)
154.7625	147.2375	NFM	Perth	Police (W)
154.7750		AM	Berkshire	Police (Motoway Patrols)
154.7750	146.3000	AM	Thames Valley	Police (HB) Channel 8
154.7875		AM	Newmarket	Police
		NFM	Aberdeen	Fire Brigade (Fire Control)
		NFM	Lanark	Police (ZS)
154.7875	146.8625	NFM	Dingwall	Police (UR)
		NFM	Ullapool	Police (UR)
154.7875	146.9500	NFM	Perth	Fire Brigade (Fire Control)
154.7875	146.0250	AM	Cambridge	Police (VB) Channel 1
154.7875	146.8000	AM	Gwent	Police (WE) Channel 2
154.7875	154.7875	NFM	Inverness	Fire Brigade
154.8000		NFM	Bournemouth	Police
154.8000	146.8000	NFM	Sutherland	Police (UR)
154.8000	146.7250	NFM	Leicestershire	Police (NL) Channel 1
154.8000	146.1875	AM	Dorset	Police (QC) Channel 3
154.8000	146.7250	AM	Lancashire	Police (BD) Channel 5
154.8125		NFM	North Wales	Police Channel 1
154.8125	146.8000	NFM	Helmsdale	Police (UR)
		NFM	Sutherland	Police (UR)
154.8125	146.8750	AM	Gwent	Police (WN) Channel 3
154.8250	146.7000	AM	Cheshire	Police (BA)
		NFM	Hull	Fire Brigade (XT)
154.8250	146.6875	AM	Cambridge	Police (VB) Channel 2
154.8375	146.2750	AM	Thames Valley	Police (HB) Channel 4
154.8375	146.8500	NFM	Easter Ross	Police (UR)
154.8375	146.9625	NFM	Perth	Police (W)
154.8375	154.8375	NFM	Netherlands	Police Ch 169
154.8375		NFM	Bicester	Police (SD)
154.8500		AM	Lakenheath	Police
154.8500	146.8500	NFM	Easter Ross	Police (UR)

Base	Mobile	Mode	Location	User and Notes
154.8500	147.0625	NFM	Burton Down	Police
154.8625		AM	Bristol	Police
		NFM	Ipswich	Police (VL)
		AM	Swansea, Severn Bridge	Police (BQ)
		AM	Newmarket	Police
		AM	Cheshire	Traffic Police
		AM	Haverfordwest	Police (WH)
154.8625	146.1250	AM	Brecon	Police (WL)
154.8625	146.8250	AM	Merseyside	Police (CH) Channel 1
154.8625	146.8625	NFM	Dingwall	Police (UR)
		NFM	Inverness	Fire Brigade
154.8625	146.9000	AM	Suffolk	Police (VL) Channel 1
154.8750	146.6625	NFM	Perth	Fire Brigade (Fire Control)
154.8750	146.0375	AM	Thames Valley	Police (HB) Channel 6
154.8875		NFM	Sussex	Police
		NFM	Isle Of Man	Police
154.8875	146.1500	AM	Brecon	Police (WL)
		NFM	South Wales	Police (WY) Channel 2
154.8875	146.4750	NFM	Burton Down	Police
154.8875	146.7125	NFM	Kyle of Lochalsh	Police (UR)
154.8875	146.9250	AM	Newmarket	Police (VL) Channel 2
154.8875	146.9250	AM	Suffolk	Police (VL)
		NFM	Ipswich	Police (VL) Channel 2
		NFM	Suffolk	Police (VL) Channel 2
154.8875	147.2375	NFM	Perth	Police (W)
154.9000		NFM	Merseyside	Police (A)
154.9000	146.8375	AM	Bedfordshire	Police (M2VA) Channel 1
154.9000	146.8500	AM	Merseyside	Police (CH) Channel 2
154.9125		NFM	Lochaber	Fire Brigade
154.9125	147.0500	NFM	Blairgowrie	Police (WB)
		NFM	Perth	Police (W)
154.9125	146.7750	AM	Gwent	Police (WO) Channel 1
154.9125	146.4875	AM	Norfolk	Police (VK) Channel 1
154.9250		NFM	Grampian	Police
154.9250	146.9000	AM	Merseyside	Police (CH) Channel 3
154.9250	146.0625	AM	Thames Valley	Police (HB) Channel 5
154.9375	146.1750	AM	Brecon	Police (WL)
		NFM	South Wales	Police (WX) Channel 4
154.9375	146.2750	AM	Oxford	Police
		NFM	Lancashire	Police (BD) Channel 2
154.9375	146.6125	AM	Kent	Police (KA) Channel 2
154.9375	146.9375	NFM	Perth	Fire Brigade (Fire Control)
154.9500		AM	Thames Valley	Police (Motorway HQ)
		AM	Hampshire	Police (Motorway Patrols)
		NFM	Aberdeen	Fire Brigade (Fire Control)
154.9500	146.8500	AM	Birkenhead	Police (M53)
154.9500	146.0125	AM	Thames Valley	Police (HB) Channel 7
154.9625	146.0750	NFM	Brecon	Police (WL)

Base	Mobile	Mode	Location	User and Notes
154.9625	146.6375	AM	Kent	Police (KA)
		NFM	Kent Motorways	Police (TD)
154.9625	146.9625	NFM	Perth	Police (W)
154.9625	146.0750	NFM	South Wales	Police (WS) Channel 3
154.9750	147.0500	NFM	Aberdeen	Fire Brigade (Fire Control)
		NFM	Blairgowrie	Police (WB)
		NFM	Perth	Police (W)
154.9750	146.4250	AM	Birmingham	Police (YM) Channel 4
154.9750	146.6875	AM	Hampshire	Police (HC) Channel 5
154.9875		NFM	Grampian	Police
154.9875	146.6750	AM	Norfolk	Police (VK)
154.9875	146.8500	AM	Avon	Police (M2QP) Channel 3
		AM	Somerset	Police (QP) Channel 3
155.0000	146.3125	AM	West Sussex	Police (M2KB1) Ctrl & Traffic
155.0000	147.0000	NFM	Jersey	Police (M2GS) Ch 4
		NFM	Jersey	Ambulance Ch 5
		NFM	Jersey	Civil Defence
155.0000	154.1125	AM	Sussex	Police (M2KB) Ch 1
155.0000	154.7000	AM	Sussex	Police (M2KB) Ch 1
155.0125		NFM	Chorlton-cum-Hardy	Police
155.0125	146.2125	AM	Manchester	Police (CK) Channel 1
155.0125	147.5625	NFM	Grampian	Police (UBE)
155.0125	146.8125	AM	Avon	Police (M2QP) Channel 7
		AM	Somerset	Police (QP) Channel 7
155.0250		AM	Newmarket	Police
		NFM	Hereford & Worcester	Fire Brigade (YB)
155.0250	147.0250	NFM	Dundee	Police (ZS)
155.0250	147.1375	AM	Manchester	Police (Traffic)
155.0250	146.2125	AM	Essex	Police (VG) Channel 1
155.0375	147.0625	NFM	Perth	Fire Brigade (Fire Control)
155.0375	147.1875	NFM	Enniskillen	Fire Brigade
155.0375	146.7875	AM	Avon	Police (M2QP) Channel 6
		AM	Somerset	Police (QP) Channel 6
155.0500	146.3625	AM	Llandudno	Police
155.0500	147.0500	NFM	Blairgowrie	Police (WB)
		NFM	Perth	Police (W)
155.0500	146.6625	AM	Powys	Police (WA) Channel 1
155.0500	146.3625	AM	West Sussex	Police (M2KB) Channel 3
155.0500	154.0750	AM	Sussex	Police (M2KB) Ch 3
155.0500	154.1875	AM	Sussex	Police (M2KB) Ch 3
155.0625		AM	Bristol	Police
		AM	Salisbury	Police
		NFM	Manchester	Police
		AM	Merseyside	Police
155.0625	147.0625	NFM	Perth	Fire Brigade (Fire Control)
155.0625	147.2375	AM	Manchester	Police (CK) Channel 4
155.0625	146.7625	AM	Avon	Police (M2QP) Channel 5
		AM	Somerset	Police (QP) Channel 5

Base	Mobile	Mode	Location	User and Notes
155.0750		NFM	Aberdeen	Fire Brigade (Fire Control)
		AM	Bristol	Police
155.0750	147.1875	AM	Essex	Police (VG) Channel 2
		AM	Manchester	Police Traffic (CK) Ch5
155.0870	155.2300	AM	Holland	Public Transport
155.0875		NFM	Holyhead	Police
		AM	Manchester	Police
155.0875	146.1000	AM	Hampshire	Police (HC) Channel 1
		AM	Manchester	Police Channel 5 (CK)
155.1000		NFM	North Wales	Police
		NFM	St Andrews	Police
		NFM	Leuchars	Police
155.1000	146.4375	AM	Anglesey	Police (WA)
		AM	Powys	Police (WA) Channel 2
		NFM	Wrexham	Police (WA)
155.1000	146.5875	AM	Kent	Police (KA) Channel 1
		AM	Southport	Police
155.1000	147.1875	AM	Colwyn Bay	Police HQ
		NFM	Perth	Police (W)
		NFM	Pitlochry	Police (WP)
155.1125		NFM	Hampshire	Police
155.1125	147.0625	NFM	County Down	Fire Brigade
155.1125	146.4375	AM	Hampshire	Police (HC) Channel 2
155.1250	147.4875	NFM	Lothian And Borders	Fire Brigade (ZF)
		NFM	Crumhaugh Hill	Fire Brigade
155.1250	146.6250	AM	Hertfordshire	Police (VH) Channel 2
155.1375	147.0875	NFM	County Armagh	Fire Brigade
155.1375	147.1375	NFM	Perth	Fire Brigade (Fire Control)
155.1375	146.6625	AM	Kent	Police (KA) Channel 4
155.1500		AM	Bristol	Police
155.1500	147.2250	NFM	Perth	Police (W)
155.1500	146.5750	AM	Avon	Police (M2QP) Channel 4
		AM	Somerset	Police (QP) Channel 4
155.1500	146.0750	AM	Manchester	Police (CK) Channel 6
155.1625		NFM	Newmarket	Police
		NFM	Blairgowrie	Police (WB)
		NFM	North Wales	Police Repeater Channel 2
155.1625	147.1125	NFM	County Tyrone	Fire Brigade
155.1625	146.4625	AM	Hampshire	Police (HC) Channel 4
155.1625	147.6125	AM	Warwickshire	Police (YJ) Channel 3
155.1750		AM	Newmarket	Police
		AM	Merseyside	Police
		NFM	Merseyside	Police (E)
155.1750	147.4875	NFM	Lothian And Borders	Fire Brigade (ZF)
155.1750	146.1625	AM	Essex	Police (VG) Channel 3
155.1750	146.9250	AM	Merseyside	Police (CH) Channel 4
155.1875		NFM	North Wales	Police
		NFM	Kent	Police

Base	Mobile	Mode	Location	User and Notes
155.1875	146.3875	AM	Essex	Police (VG)
		AM	Manchester	Police (Traffic)
		AM	West Sussex	Police (M2KB) Channel 4
155.1875	147.1875	NFM	Perth	Police (W)
155.1875	147.4875	NFM	Lothian And Borders	Fire Brigade (ZF)
155.1875	154.4125	AM	Sussex	Police (M2KB) Ch 4
155.2000	146.6000	AM	Manchester	Police
		AM	Hertfordshire	Police (VH) Channel 1
155.2000	146.6500	NFM	Skye	Fire Brigade
155.2000	147.0625	NFM	Perth	Fire Brigade (Fire Control)
155.2000	146.6500	NFM	Dyfed	Police (WH) Channel 2
155.2125		AM	Bristol	Police
		AM	Manchester	Police
155.2125	147.2250	NFM	Perth	Police (W)
155.2125	146.5000	AM	Avon	Police (M2QP) Channel 1
		AM	Somerset	Police (QP) Channel 1
155.2250		AM	Merseyside	Police
155.2250	146.3375	AM	West Sussex	Police (M2KB2) Ctrl & Traffic
155.2250	146.9500	AM	Merseyside	Police (CH) Channel 5
155.2250	147.2250	NFM	Perth	Police (W)
155.2250	154.6250	AM	Sussex	Police (M2KB) Ch 2
155.2250	154.8875	AM	Sussex	Police (M2KB) Ch 2
155.2375	147.0375	NFM	Londonderry	Fire Brigade
155.2375	147.2375	NFM	Perth	Police (W)
155.2375	146.6500	AM	Hertfordshire	Police (VH) Channel 3
155.2500		AM	Bristol	Police
		AM	Cheltenham	Police (QL)
		AM	Gloucester	Police (QL)
		NFM	Glasgow	Fire Brigade (ZF)
		NFM	Newmarket	Police
155.2500	146.2750	AM	Lancashire	Police (BD)
155.2500	146.5250	AM	Manchester	Police
		AM	Somerset	Police (QP)
155.2500	147.4875	NFM	Lothian And Borders	Fire Brigade (ZF)
155.2500	146.5250	AM	Avon	Police (M2QP) Channel 2
155.2500	147.1500	NFM	London	Police (GT) Channel 51
155.2625		NFM	Fife	Police
		NFM	Hampshire	Police
		AM	Manchester	Traffic Police
155.2625	146.4875	AM	Hampshire	Police (HC) Channel 3
155.2625	146.3125	AM	Cheshire	Police (BA 03) Channel 2
155.2750	146.9000	AM	Cornwall	Police (QB) Channel 2
		AM	Devon	Police (QB) Channel 2
155.2750	146.6250	AM	Powys	Police (WH) Channel 4
155.2875		NFM	Grampian	Police (UBG)
		NFM	Aberdeen	Police
155.2875	147.2250	NFM	Perth	Police (W)
155.2875	146.4125	AM	West Sussex	Police (M2KB) Channel 5

Base	Mobile	Mode	Location	User and Notes
155.2875	154.2625	AM	Sussex	Police (M2KB) Ch 5
155.2875	154.8500	AM	Sussex	Police (M2KB) Ch 5
155.3000		NFM	Banchory	Police (UBK)
		NFM	Braemar	Police (UBH)
155.3000	147.1375	NFM	Londonderry	Fire Brigade (North)
155.3000	147.2000	NFM	London	Diplomatic Prot(Ranger)
155.3000	146.9750	AM	Cornwall	Police (QB) Channel 7
		AM	Devon	Police (QB) Channel 7
155.3125	147.2375	NFM	Perth	Police (W)
155.3250		NFM	Merseyside	Police
		NFM	Merseyside	Police (D)
155.3250	146.2375	AM	Cornwall	Police (QB) Channel 4
		AM	Devon	Police (QB) Channel 4
155.3250	146.9750	AM	Merseyside	Police (CH) Channel 6
155.3375	147.1875	NFM	Perth	Police (W)
		NFM	Pitlochry	Police (WP)
		NFM	Perth	Police (W)
155.3500	147.5625	NFM	Grampian	Police (UBE)
155.3625	146.2625	AM	Cornwall	Police (QB) Channel 5
		AM	Devon	Police (QB) Channel 5
155.3750		NFM	Grampian	Police (UBG)
155.3750	147.1625	NFM	Londonderry	Fire Brigade (South)
155.3875	146.3625	AM	West Cheshire	Police (BA 01) Channel 1
155.3875	146.9500	AM	Cornwall	Police (QB) Channel 6
		AM	Devon	Police (QB) Channel 6
155.4000		NFM	Edinburgh	Fire Brigade (F)
		NFM	Perth	Fire Brigade (Fire Control)
155.4125		NFM	Hampshire	Police
155.4125	147.0375	NFM	Highlands And Islands	Fire Brigade
		NFM	Lochaber	Fire Brigade (UF)
		NFM	Ballachulish	Fire
155.4125	146.6250	AM	Dyfed	Police (WH) Channel 2
155.4250		NFM	Aberdeen	Police
		AM	Manchester	Police
		AM	Cheshire	Police Ch 3
155.4250	147.2375	NFM	Perth	Police (W)
155.4250	147.5750	NFM	Northern Ireland	Royal Ulster Constabulary
155.4250	146.3875	AM	Manchester	Police (CK) Channel 2
155.4375		NFM	Perth	Fire Brigade (Fire Control)
155.4375	146.6000	AM	Dyfed	Police (WH)
155.4500	146.4500	NFM	Jersey	Airport Fire Service Ch1
155.4500	147.5625	NFM	Grampian	Police (UBE)
155.4625	146.2125	AM	Cornwall	Police (QB) Channel 1
		AM	Devon	Police (QB) Channel 1
155.4625	146.3000	NFM	Lancashire	Police (BD) Channel 1
155.4625	147.5625	NFM	Grampian	Police (UBE)
155.4750	147.4500	NFM	Northern Ireland	Royal Ulster Constabulary
155.4750	147.5625	NFM	Grampian	Police (UBE)

Base	Mobile	Mode	Location	User and Notes
155.4750	146.6000	NFM	Dyfed & Powys	Police (WH) Channel 1
155.4750	146.1250	NFM	West Mercia	Police (YK) Channel 2
155.4875		AM	Cheshire	Police
155.4875	147.4875	NFM	Lothian And Borders	Fire Brigade (ZF)
155.4875	146.3375	AM	East Cheshire	Police (BA 02) Channel 3
155.5000		NFM	Grampian	Police
		NFM	Shrewsbury	Police
155.5000	146.6500	AM	Dyfed	Police (WH)
155.5000	147.5625	NFM	Grampian	Police (UBE)
155.5125		NFM	Belfast	RUC Voice Encryption
155.5125	147.4875	NFM	Peebles	Fire Brigade
155.5125	146.9250	AM	Cornwall	Police (QB) Channel 3
		AM	Devon	Police (QB) Channel 3
155.5250	147.7000	NFM	Northern Ireland	Royal Ulster Constabulary
155.5375		NFM	Grampian	Police
		NFM	Aberdeen	Police
155.5375	146.4625	AM	Powys	Police (WA)
		NFM	West Midlands	Police (YH) Channel 6
155.5375	147.5625	NFM	Grampian	Police (UBE)
155.5500		NFM	Aberdeen	Police
155.5500	147.5500	NFM	Northern Ireland	Royal Ulster Constabulary
155.5625		NFM	Belfast	Royal Ulster Constabulary
		NFM	London	Police Tactical Support Grp
		NFM	Perth	Police (W)
		NFM	Edinburgh	Police (ZS)
		NFM	Galashiels	Fire Brigade
155.5625	147.0125	NFM	Belfast	Fire Brigade
155.5625	147.4875	NFM	Lothian And Borders	Fire Brigade (ZF)
155.5750		NFM	Grampian	Police (UBG)
		NFM	Perth	Police (W)
155.5750	147.5250	NFM	Northern Ireland	Royal Ulster Constabulary
155.5750	146.2875	AM	Cornwall	Police (QB) Channel 8
		AM	Devon	Police (QB) Channel 8
155.5875		NFM	Grampian	Police
		NFM	Aberdeen	Police
		NFM	Preston	Police
155.5875	146.2500	AM	Cumbria	Police (BB3) M6 Motorway
155.5875	155.5875	NFM	London	Police Brixton
155.6000		NFM	London	Police Helicopter
		AM	Derbyshire	Police (NA)
155.6000	147.7500	NFM	Northern Ireland	Royal Ulster Constabulary
155.6125	147.0375	NFM	Highlands And Islands	Fire Brigade
		NFM	Lochaber	Fire Brigade (UF)
155.6125	147.4875	NFM	Lothian And Borders	Fire Brigade (ZF)
		NFM	Hartside Hill	Fire Brigade
155.6125	146.4125	AM	Manchester	Police (CK) Channel 3
155.6250		NFM	Aberdeen	Police
		NFM	North Wales	Police

Base	Mobile	Mode	Location	User and Notes
155.6250	146.4125	AM	Powys	Police (WA)
		AM	Colwyn Bay	Police (WA) Traffic
155.6250	146.4875	AM	Powys	Police (WA)
		AM	Colwyn Bay	Police (WA) Traffic
155.6250	147.6250	NFM	Grampian	Police (UB)
155.6250	147.7750	NFM	Northern Ireland	Royal Ulster Constabulary
155.6375	147.9375	NFM	Jersey	Fire Brigade Ch 1
155.6375	146.4500	AM	Cumbria	Police (BB) Channel 2
155.6500	146.2625	AM	Derbyshire	Police (NA) Channel 1
155.6500	147.9000	NFM	Northern Ireland	Royal Ulster Constabulary
155.6625	146.2000	AM	Cumbria	Police (BB)
155.6625	147.8875	NFM	Northern Ireland	Royal Ulster Constabulary
155.6625	147.9500	AM	Guernsey	Fire Brigade Ch 1
155.6750	147.8750	NFM	Northern Ireland	Royal Ulster Constabulary
155.6750	147.9625	NFM	Jersey	Fire Brigade Ch 2
155.7000		NFM	Jersey	Police CID Encrypted
		NFM	Jersey	Police Drug Squad
		NFM	Nationwide	Police RCS Ch 02
155.7000	155.7000	AM	Manchester	Police
		NFM	London	Police RCS Handheld (CS)
		NFM	Wiltshire	Police CID
		NFM	Jersey	Police (M2GS) Ch 6
155.7250		AM	Manchester	Police Surveillance Squad
		NFM	Nationwide	Police RCS Ch 03
155.7250	155.7250	NFM	London	Police RCS Handheld (CS)
155.7375		NFM	Grampian	Fire Brigade (Fire Control)
155.7375	147.0375	NFM	Highlands And Islands	Fire Brigade
155.7500		NFM	Nationwide	Police RCS Ch 01
155.7500	155.7500	AM	Manchester	Police
		AM	Chester	Police
		NFM	Jersey	Police Drug Squad
		NFM	London	Police RCS Handheld (CS)
155.7750	147.9500	NFM	Northern Ireland	Royal Ulster Constabulary
155.7750	155.7750	NFM	London	Police RCS Handheld (CS)
155.7875		NFM	Grampian	Fire Brigade (Fire Control)
		NFM	Northern Ireland	Security Forces
155.7875	147.9375	NFM	Northern Ireland	Royal Ulster Constabulary
155.8000		NFM	Belfast	Royal Ulster Constabulary (U)
		NFM	Grampian	Police (UBG)
		NFM	Bangor	Royal Ulster Constabulary
		NFM	Larne	Royal Ulster Constabulary
		AM	Durham	Police
		NFM	Aberdeen	Police
155.8000	146.2000	AM	Surrey	Police (HJ) Channel 1
155.8000	147.7625	AM	Guernsey	Police (QY) Ch 1
155.8000	147.9250	NFM	Northern Ireland	Royal Ulster Constabulary
155.8125		AM	Gloucester	Police (QL)
		NFM	Grampian	Police

Base	Mobile	Mode	Location	User and Notes
		NFM	North Wales	Police
155.8125	146.5750	NFM	Ipswich	Police
155.8125	146.9125	AM	Wiltshire	Police (QJ) Channel 1
155.8125	146.5750	NFM	Suffolk	Police (VL) Channel 3
155.8250		NFM	Belfast	Royal Ulster Constabulary
		NFM	Larne	Royal Ulster Constabulary
155.8250	147.4000	NFM	Northern Ireland	Royal Ulster Constabulary
155.8250	147.9750	AM	Guernsey	Fire Brigade Ch 2
155.8375	146.2250	AM	Surrey	Police (HJ) Channel 2
155.8375	146.2875	AM	Derbyshire	Police (NA) Channel 2
155.8500		AM	Bristol	Police
		AM	Swindon	Police
155.8500	147.4250	NFM	Northern Ireland	Royal Ulster Constabulary
155.8500	146.9375	AM	Wiltshire	Police (QJ) Channel 2
155.8625		NFM	Merseyside	Police
155.8625	146.2500	AM	Surrey	Police (HJ) Channel 3
155.8625	147.7500	NFM	Jersey	Police (M2GS) Ch 3
155.8750		NFM	Belfast	Royal Ulster Constabulary
		NFM	Dumfermline	Fire Brigade (F)
		AM	Wlnforth	Police
155.8750	146.1000	AM	Dorset	Police (QC) Channel 1
155.8750	147.8500	NFM	Northern Ireland	Royal Ulster Constabulary
155.8875	146.2000	AM	Cumbria	Police (BB1) South Lakes
155.9000		AM	Bristol	Police
		AM	Swindon	Police
		NFM	Belfast	Royal Ulster Constabulary
		NFM	Norfolk	Police
155.9000	147.4750	NFM	Northern Ireland	Royal Ulster Constabulary
155.9000	147.8500	AM	Guernsey	Police (QY) Ch 2
155.9000	146.9625	AM	Wiltshire	Police (QJ) Channel 3
155.9125		NFM	Newport	Police
155.9250		NFM	Belfast	Royal Ulster Constabulary
155.9250	147.6250	NFM	Northern Ireland	Royal Ulster Constabulary
155.9250	147.0125	AM	Dorset	Police (QC) Channel 2
155.9375		AM	Slough	Police
		NFM	Bournemouth	Police
155.9375	147.9625	NFM	Northern Ireland	Royal Ulster Constabulary
155.9375	146.8875	AM	Thames Valley	Police (HB) Channel 3
155.9500		NFM	Belfast	Royal Ulster Constabulary
		NFM	Larne	Royal Ulster Constabulary
155.9500	147.9750	NFM	Northern Ireland	Royal Ulster Constabulary
155.9625		NFM	Newmarket	Police
		NFM	Essex	Police
155.9625	147.9875	AM	Essex	Police (VG) Ch 4
155.9625	146.2375	AM	Essex	Police (VG) Channel 4
155.9625	147.9875	NFM	Jersey	Police Speed Traps
		NFM	Jersey	Police (M2GS) Ch 6
		NFM	Jersey	Ambulances Ch 6

Base	Mobile	Mode	Location	User and Notes
		NFM	Jersey	Fire Brigade Ch 8
155.9625	155.9625	NFM	Jersey	All Services Ch 7
155.9750	147.6750	NFM	Northern Ireland	Royal Ulster Constabulary
		AM	Devon	Police (QB) Channel 7

156.0000 - 162.5000 MHz   MARITIME BAND 25 KHZ (SHIP TX/SHORE TX)

Base	Mobile	Mode	Location	User and Notes
156.0000	156.0000	NFM	Nationwide	Channel 0 Coastguard/ Lifeboat Primary Airborne Rescue Coordination
		NFM	Aberdeen	Aberdeen Coastguard
		NFM	Brixham	Brixham Coastguard
		NFM	Crail	Crail Coastguard
		NFM	Solent	Solent Coastguard
		NFM	Falmouth	Falmouth Coastguard
		NFM	Great Yarmouth	Lifeboat
		NFM	Redcar	Redcar Coastguard
		NFM	Swansea	Lifeboat Coordination
156.0250	160.6250	NFM	Nationwide	Channel 60
		NFM	Islay	Working Channel
		NFM	Start Point	Working Channel
156.0500	160.6500	NFM	Nationwide	Channel 01 Port Ops
156.0750	160.6750	NFM	Nationwide	Channel 61
		NFM	Anglesey	Working Channel
		NFM	Scillies	Working Channel
156.1000	160.7000	NFM	Nationwide	Channel 02
		NFM	St Malo	Working Channel
		NFM	Thames	Working Channel
156.1250	160.7250	NFM	Nationwide	Channel 62
		NFM	Forth	Working Channel
		NFM	Thames Navigation	Working Channel
		NFM	Orfordness	Working Channel
		NFM	Pendennis	Working Channel
		NFM	St Peter Port	Working Channel
156.1500	160.7500	NFM	Nationwide	Channel 03
		NFM	Bacton	Working Channel
		NFM	Cardigan Bay	Working Channel
		NFM	Port En Bessin	Working Channel
		NFM	Pembroke	Pembroke Ferry
156.1750	160.7750	NFM	Nationwide	Channel 63
		NFM	Bacton	Working Channel
		NFM	Hastings	Working Channel
156.2000	160.7000	NFM	Nationwide	Channel 04
		NFM	Grimsby	Working Channel
		NFM	Morecambe Bay	Working Channel
		NFM	Niton	Working Channel
156.2250	160.7250	NFM	Nationwide	Channel 64
		NFM	Bacton	Working Channel
		NFM	Lands End	Working Channel

Base	Mobile	Mode	Location	User and Notes
		NFM	Niton	Working Channel
		NFM	Rouen	Working Channel
156.2500	160.7500	NFM	Nationwide	Channel 05
		NFM	Birkenhead	Alfred Docks
		NFM	Liverpool	Gladstone Docks
		NFM	Ilfracombe	Working Channel
		NFM	Lewis	Working Channel
		NFM	North Foreland	Working Channel
		NFM	Weymouth Bay	Working Channel
156.2750	160.7750	NFM	Nationwide	Channel 65
		NFM	North Foreland	Working Channel
		NFM	Start Point	Working Channel
156.3000	156.3000	NFM	Nationwide	Channel 06
		NFM	Milford Haven	Patrol & Pilot Launch
		NFM	Barrow	Port Ops
		NFM	Nationwide	Comms Primary. Used By Coastguard Vessels During SAR Situation.
		NFM	Nationwide	Intership
156.3250	160.9250	NFM	Nationwide	Channel 66
		NFM	North Foreland	Working Channel
		NFM	Pendennis	Working Channel
156.3500	160.9500	NFM	Nationwide	Channel 07
		NFM	Manchester Canal	Eastham Locks
		NFM	Liverpool	In Bound Ships
		NFM	River Severn	Weather Reports
		NFM	Oban	Harbour
		NFM	Bacton	Working Channel
		NFM	Hastings	Working Channel
		NFM	Ilfracombe	Working Channel
156.3750	156.3750	NFM	Nationwide	Channel 67
		NFM	Nationwide	Coastguard Secondary
		NFM	Swansea	Weather & Coastguard
		NFM	Solent	Solent Coastguard
		NFM	Milford Haven	Patrol & Pilot Launch
		NFM	Solent	Coastguard
		NFM	Edinburgh	Marine Weather
		NFM	Bantry	Working Channel
		NFM	Bawdsey	Working Channel
		NFM	Belmullet	Working Channel
		NFM	Cork	Working Channel
		NFM	Glen Head	Working Channel
		NFM	Hull	Saltend Jetty
		NFM	Jersey	Working Channel
		NFM	Guernsey	Working Channel
		NFM	Malin Head	Working Channel
		NFM	Minehead	Working Channel
		NFM	Rosslare	Working Channel

Base	Mobile	Mode	Location	User and Notes
		NFM	Shannon	Working Channel
		NFM	Valentia	Working Channel
		NFM	Walton-on-the-Naze	Coastguard
156.4000	156.4000	NFM	Nationwide	Channel 08
		NFM	Milford Haven	Patrol & Pilot Launch
		NFM	Manchester Canal	Inbound Tugs
		NFM	Barrow	Port Ops
		NFM	Lancaster	Port of Glasson Dock
		NFM	Liverpool	In Bound Ships
156.4250	156.4250	NFM	Nationwide	Channel 68
		NFM	Port of Heysham	Fishers Shipping
		NFM	Brightlingsea	Harbour Master
		NFM	Ouistreham Marina	Working Channel
156.4500	156.4500	NFM	Nationwide	Channel 09
		NFM	Brest	Working Channel
		NFM	Cherbourg	Working Channel
		NFM	Felixstowe	Pilot Arrangements
		NFM	French Marinas	Working Channel
		NFM	Granville	Working Channel
		NFM	Harwich	Pilot
		NFM	Hull	King George V Docks
		NFM	Kent	Medway Control
		NFM	Liverpool	Mersey Radio (2)
		NFM	Manchester Canal	Alfred Docks
		NFM	Milford Haven	Milford Haven Docks
		NFM	Perth	Harbour Working Channel
		NFM	Solent	Pilot Office &
156.4750	156.4750	NFM	Nationwide	Channel 69
		NFM	Nationwide	Intership
		NFM	Nationwide	HM Customs
		NFM	Lancaster	Port of Glasson Dock
		NFM	Dover	Dover Coastguard
156.5000	156.5000	NFM	Nationwide	Channel 10 Pollution
		NFM	Manchester Canal	Outbound Tugs
		NFM	Barrow	Port Ops
		NFM	Liverpool	Mersey Ship to Tugs
		NFM	Liverpool	Out Bound Ships
156.5250	156.5250	NFM	Nationwide	Channel 70
		NFM	Nationwide	Digital Selective Calling
156.5500	156.5500	NFM	Nationwide	Channel 11 Port Ops
		NFM	Milford Haven	Patrol & Pilot Launch
		NFM	Cherbourg	Traffic
		NFM	Fleetwood	Fish Quay
		NFM	Liverpool	Pilot
		NFM	Portsmouth	Queens Harbour Master
		NFM	Spurn Point	Pilot's Channel
156.5750	156.5750	NFM	Nationwide	Channel 71 Port Ops
		NFM	Manchester Canal	Weather Navigation

Base	Mobile	Mode	Location	User and Notes
		NFM	Harwich	Harbour
		NFM	RNAS Portland	Royal Navy
156.6000	156.6000	NFM	Nationwide	Channel 12
		NFM	Liverpool	Mersey Radio (1)
		NFM	Milford Haven	Patrol & Pilot Launch
		NFM	Milford Haven	Milford Haven Docks
		NFM	Barrow In Furness	Harbour
		NFM	Fleetwood	Port Ops
		NFM	Isle of Man	Douglas Harbour Control
		NFM	Southampton	VTS
		NFM	Padstow	Working Channel
		NFM	Braye	Port
		NFM	Ardrossan	Harbour Control
		NFM	Humber	Vessel Traffic System
		NFM	Portsmouth	Royal Navy Marine Traffic
		NFM	Solent	Vessel Traffic System
		NFM	Granville	Port
		NFM	Langstone Har	Port
		NFM	St Malo	Port
		NFM	St Peter Port	Working Channel
156.6250	156.6250	NFM	Nationwide	Intership Comms
156.6500	156.6500	NFM	Nationwide	Port Ops
		NFM	Gravesend	Shipping Channel
156.6750	156.6750	NFM	Nationwide	Channel 73 Coastguard
		NFM	Nationwide	Mountain Rescue Ch 73
		NFM	Nationwide	Intership
156.7000	156.7000	NFM	Nationwide	Channel 14
		NFM	Ramsgate	Ramsgate Port Cntrl (Romeo)
		NFM	Milford Haven	Patrol & Pilot Launch
		NFM	Milford Haven	Elf & Gulf Oil Terminals
		NFM	Milford Haven	Texaco Oil Terminal
		NFM	Milford Haven	Milford Haven Docks
		NFM	Manchester Canal	Eastham Control
		NFM	Heysham	Port Ops
		NFM	Glensanda	Super Quarry
		NFM	Manchester	Ship Canal
		NFM	Eastham	Manchester Ship Canal
		NFM	Liverpool	Out Bound Ships
		NFM	Teeside	Tees Harbour Radio
		NFM	Chichester	Port
		NFM	Harwich	Port
		NFM	Humber	Pilot
		NFM	Shoreham	Port
		NFM	St Helier	Port & Marina
		NFM	Ayr	Harbour Control
		NFM	Poole	Harbour Contol
		NFM	Woolwich	Thames Pilot
156.7250	156.7250	NFM	Nationwide	Channel 74

Base	Mobile	Mode	Location	User and Notes
		NFM	Cullercoats	Harbour
		NFM	Lochaber	Caledonian Canal
		NFM	Kent	Medway Radio
		NFM	Nationwide	Ports, Lock
		NFM	Aldernay	Working Channel
		NFM	Gloucester	Docks
		NFM	Gorey	Working Channel
156.7500	156.7500	NFM	Nationwide	Channel 15 Port Ops
		NFM	Nationwide	On-board Handhelds
156.7625	156.7625	NFM	Nationwide	Channel 75 Guard Band
156.8000	156.8000	NFM	Nationwide	Channel 16
				Distress & Calling
		NFM	Milford Haven	Patrol & Pilot Launch
		NFM	Milford Haven	Elf & Gulf Oil Terminals
		NFM	Milford Haven	Texaco Oil Terminal
		NFM	Milford Haven	Milford Haven Docks
		NFM	Swansea	Coastguard
		NFM	Crail	HM Coastguard
156.8125	156.8125	NFM	Nationwide	Channel 76 Guard Band
156.8250	156.8250	NFM	Nationwide	Direct Printing Telegraphy
156.8500	156.8500	NFM	Nationwide	Channel 17 Port Ops
		NFM	Nationwide	On-board Handhelds
		NFM	English Channel	BCIF
156.8750	156.8750	NFM	Nationwide	Channel 77 Intership
		NFM	Swansea Docks	Swansea-Cork Ferry
156.9000	156.9000	NFM	Nationwide	Channel 18 Port Ops
		NFM	Milford Haven	Elf & Gulf Oil Terminals
		NFM	Manchester Canal	Barton Docks
		NFM	Port En Bessin	Marina Chan
156.9250	161.5250	NFM	Nationwide	Channel 78
		NFM	St Peter Port	Working Channel
156.9500	161.5500	NFM	Nationwide	Channel 19 Port Ops
		NFM	Tranmere	Shell Oil Terminal
156.9750	161.5750	NFM	Nationwide	Channel 79 Port Ops
157.0000	161.6000	NFM	Nationwide	Channel 20 Port Ops
		NFM	Manchester Canal	Stanlow Docks
		NFM	Stanlow	Shell Refinery
		NFM	Liverpool	Garston Docks
157.0250	157.0250	NFM	Milford Haven	Marine & Yacht Station
157.0250	161.6250	NFM	Nationwide	Channel 80
		NFM	Brighton	Marina Ops
		NFM	Dover	Coastguard
		NFM	Hull	Hull Marina
157.0500	161.6500	NFM	Nationwide	Channel 21
		NFM	Milford Haven	Texaco Oil Terminal
		NFM	Manchester Canal	Langton Docks
		NFM	Liverpool	Langton Docks
157.0750	161.6750	NFM	Nationwide	Channel 81

Base	Mobile	Mode	Location	User and Notes
		NFM	Anglesay	Working Channel
		NFM	Niton	Working Channel
157.1000	161.7000	NFM	Nationwide	Channel 22 Port Ops
		NFM	Kent	Medway Radio
157.1250	161.7250	NFM	Nationwide	Channel 82
		NFM	Jersey	Working Channel
		NFM	Morecambe Bay	Working Channel
		NFM	Orfordness	Working Channel
157.1500	161.7500	NFM	Nationwide	Channel 23
		NFM	Bantry	Working Channel
		NFM	Le Havre	Working Channel
		NFM	Malin Head	Working Channel
		NFM	Nationwide	Shore TX Also
		NFM	Rosslare	Working Channel
157.1750	161.7750	NFM	Nationwide	Channel 83
		NFM	Belmullet	Working Channel
		NFM	Dublin	Working Channel
		NFM	Minehead	Working Channel
		NFM	Plougasnou	Working Channel
		NFM	Thames	Working Channel
157.2000	161.8000	NFM	Nationwide	Channel 24
		NFM	Celtic	Working Channel
		NFM	Collafirth	Working Channel
		NFM	Forth	Working Channel
		NFM	Glen Head	Working Channel
		NFM	Humber	Working Channel
		NFM	Ouessant	Working Channel
		NFM	Shannon	Working Channel
		NFM	Skye	Working Channel
		NFM	Valentia	Working Channel
157.2250	161.8250	NFM	Nationwide	Channel 84
		NFM	Cromarty	Working Channel
		NFM	Paimpol	Working Channel
157.2500	161.8500	NFM	Nationwide	Channel 25
		NFM	Portishead	Severn Radio
		NFM	Minehead	Severn Radio
		NFM	Buchan	Working Channel
		NFM	Islay	Working Channel
		NFM	Jersey	Working Channel
		NFM	Whitby	Working Channel
157.2750	161.8750	NFM	Nationwide	Channel 85
		NFM	Bantry	Working Channel
		NFM	Humber	Working Channel
		NFM	Lands End	Working Channel
		NFM	Malin End	Working Channel
		NFM	Niton	Working Channel
157.3000	161.9000	NFM	Nationwide	Channel 26
		NFM	Illfracombe	Severn Radio

Base	Mobile	Mode	Location	User and Notes
		NFM	Anglesey	Working Channel
		NFM	Brest	Working Channel
		NFM	Clyde	Working Channel
		NFM	Cork	Working Channel
		NFM	Cullercoats	Working Channel
		NFM	Hebrides	Working Channel
		NFM	Humber	Working Channel
		NFM	North Foreland	Working Channel
		NFM	Orkney	Working Channel
		NFM	Start Point	Working Channel
		NFM	Stonehaven	Working Channel
157.3250	161.9250	NFM	Nationwide	Channel 86 Link Calls
157.3500	161.9500	NFM	Nationwide	Channel 27
		NFM	Cherbourg	Working Channel
		NFM	Grimsby	Working Channel
		NFM	Lands End	Working Channel
		NFM	Portpatrick	Working Channel
		NFM	Shetland	Working Channel
157.3750	161.9750	NFM	Nationwide	Channel 87
		NFM	Buchan	Working Channel
		NFM	Niton	Working Channel
157.4000	162.0000	NFM	Nationwide	Channel 28
		NFM	Anglesey	Working Channel
		NFM	Brest	Working Channel
		NFM	Cromarty	Working Channel
		NFM	Niton	Working Channel
		NFM	Shannon	Working Channel
		NFM	Valentia	Working Channel
		NFM	Whitby	Working Channel
157.4250	162.0250	NFM	Nationwide	Channel 88 Lighthouse Ch
		NFM	Anvil Point	Lighthouse
		NFM	Calais Main	Lighthouse
		NFM	Lands End	Working Channel
		NFM	North Foreland	Lighthouse
		NFM	Pillar Rock Pt	Lighthouse
157.4500		NFM	Nationwide	Channel 29
		NFM	Torpoint Ferry	Operations
157.4500	157.4500	NFM	Jersey	Local Fishing Boats
		NFM	Plymouth	Torpoint Ferries
157.4500	162.0500	NFM	Channel Island	BIFerries Channel 29
157.4750	162.0750	NFM	Nationwide	Channel 89
157.5000	162.1000	NFM	Swansea Docks	Trinity Lighthouse Crews
		NFM	English Channel	Herm Seaway Channel 30
157.5250	162.1250	NFM	Nationwide	Patrol Boats Channel 90
157.5500	162.1500	NFM	Sark	Working Channel 31
		NFM	Nationwide	RNLI Private Channel
		NFM	Nationwide	Fisheries Protection Ch 31
157.5750	162.1750	NFM	Nationwide	Channel 91

Base	Mobile	Mode	Location	User and Notes
157.6000	162.2000	NFM	Nationwide	Channel 32
157.6250	162.2250	NFM	Nationwide	Channel 92
157.6500	162.2500	NFM	English Channel	Hovercraft Channel 33
		NFM	English Channel	Fishermens Cooperative
157.6750	162.2750	NFM	Greencastle	Fishermens Cooperative
		NFM	Nationwide	Channel 93
157.6875		NFM	Fleetwood	PMR
157.7000	162.3000	NFM	English Channel	Herm Channel 34
		NFM	Nationwide	RNLI Private Channel
157.7250	157.7250	NFM	Jersey	Local Fishing Boats
157.7250	162.3250	NFM	Nationwide	Channel 94
157.7500	157.7500	NFM	Jersey	Local Fishing Boats
157.7500	162.3500	NFM	Dover	Hovercraft Channel 35
157.7750	162.3750	NFM	Nationwide	Channel 95
157.7875		NFM	Thames	Pilot to Tug
157.8000	162.4000	NFM	Nationwide	Channel 36
		NFM	Scilly Isles	St Mary's Boatmans Assoc.
		NFM	Brighton	Marina Security Channel 36
157.8250	162.4250	NFM	Nationwide	Channel 96
157.8500	157.8500	NFM	Milford Haven	Marine & Yacht Station
		NFM	Plymouth	Queen Anne's Battery
		NFM	Brighton	Mariner
		NFM	Hartlepool	Yacht Marina
157.8500	157.8500	NFM	Nationwide	Marinas Channel M1
		NFM	Jersey	St Catherines Yacht Club
157.8750	162.4750	NFM	Nationwide	Channel 97
157.9000	162.5000	NFM	Isle of Man	Steam Packet Ferries
		NFM	English Channel	British Ferries Channel 38
		NFM	Guernsey	Sealink Channel 38
157.9250	162.5250	NFM	Nationwide	Channel 98
157.9500	162.5500	NFM	Nationwide	Channel 39
157.9750	157.9750	NFM	Montrose Docks	Cam Shipping
157.9750	162.5750	NFM	Nationwide	Channel 99
158.0000	162.6000	NFM	Nationwide	Channel 40
158.0250	162.6250	NFM	Nationwide	Channel 100
158.0500	158.0500	NFM	Jersey	Local Fishing Boats
158.0500	162.6500	NFM	English Channel	Battricks Channel 41
158.0750	162.6750	NFM	Nationwide	Channel 101
158.1000	158.1000	NFM	Jersey	Local Fishing Boats
158.1000	162.7000	NFM	Nationwide	Channel 42
158.1250	162.7250	NFM	Nationwide	Channel 102
158.1500	162.7500	NFM	Nationwide	Channel 43
158.1750	162.7750	NFM	Nationwide	Channel 103
158.2000	162.8000	NFM	Moray Firth	Beatrice A/B Platform Ch 44
158.2125	158.2125	NFM	Nationwide	Channel 104
		NFM	Jersey	Marine FAX
158.2250	158.2250	NFM	Nationwide	Marine FAX Channel 104B
158.2500	158.2500	NFM	Jersey	Local Fishing Boats

Base	Mobile	Mode	Location	User and Notes
158.2500	162.8500	NFM	Moray Firth	Beatrice A/B Platform Ch 45
158.2750	162.8750	NFM	Nationwide	Channel 105
158.3000	158.3000	NFM	Jersey	Local Fishing Boats
158.3000	162.9000	NFM	Moray Firth	Beatrice A/B Platform Ch 46
158.3125	162.9125	NFM	Nationwide	Channel 106
158.3500	162.9250	NFM	Moray Firth	Beatrice A/B Platform Ch 47
158.3750	162.9750	NFM	Nationwide	Channel 107
158.4000	163.0000	NFM	Aberdeen Dockside	Channel 48
158.4250	163.0250	NFM	Nationwide	Coast Guards
		NFM	English Channel	Condor Hydrofoils
		NFM	Nationwide	Channel 108
158.4500	163.0500	NFM	Jersey	Channel Isl Yacht Services
		NFM	Bowness	Lake Windermere Steamers
		NFM	Isle Of Rhum	Scottish National Heritage
		NFM	Nigg Bay	Oil Tanker Ldg Channel 49
		NFM	Moray Firth	Beatrice A/B Platform Ch 49
158.4750	163.0750	NFM	Jersey	Ag & Fisheries
		NFM	Aberdeen	Shipping Info Channel 109
158.5000	163.1000	NFM	Solent	Solent Sea Rescue Org.
		NFM	English Channel	Emeraude Line Channel 50
		NFM	Nationwide	Private Shipping Ch 50
		NFM	Nigg Bay	Oil Tanker Ldg Channel 50
158.5125	159.9125	NFM	Nationwide	British Telecom Radiophone
158.5250 - 160.54375 MHz			**PMR AND DATA 12.5 KHZ NFM**	
158.5375	163.0375	NFM	Nationwide	Channel 1
158.5500	163.0500	NFM	Nationwide	Private Shipping Ch 51
158.6000	163.1000	NFM	Nationwide	Private Shipping Ch 52
158.6375	163.1375	NFM	Nationwide	Channel 2
158.6500	158.6500	NFM	Nationwide	Mountain Rescue
		NFM	Scotland	National Mountain Rescue
		NFM	Fort William	Police Rescue Services
		NFM	Nationwide	RAF Mountain Rescue
		NFM	Scotland	Mountain Rescue
		NFM	Nationwide	Private Shipping Ch 53
158.7000	163.3000	NFM	Nationwide	Private Shipping Ch 54
158.7375	163.2375	NFM	Nationwide	Channel 3
158.7500	163.3500	NFM	Nationwide	Private Shipping Ch 55
158.8375	163.3375	NFM	Nationwide	Channel 4
158.8500	163.3500	NFM	Nationwide	British Telecom
158.9375	163.4375	NFM	Nationwide	Channel 5
159.0000	159.0000	NFM	Nationwide	Shipping Rescue
159.0125	159.0125	NFM	Tamworth	Alfred McAlpine Construct.
159.0375	163.5375	NFM	Nationwide	Channel 6
159.1375	163.6375	NFM	Nationwide	Channel 7
159.1875		NFM	Jersey	Surveyors
159.2375	163.7375	NFM	Nationwide	Channel 8
159.2625		NFM	Carlisle	PMR

Base	Mobile	Mode	Location	User and Notes
159.3375	163.8375	NFM	Nationwide	Channel 9
159.4000	163.9000	NFM	Nationwide	Short Term Hire
159.4250	163.9250	NFM	Nationwide	Short Term Hire
159.4375	163.9375	NFM	Nationwide	Channel 10
159.4500	163.9500	NFM	Swansea	Jinks Taxis
159.4875	159.4875	NFM	Nationwide	RAC Network Q Rally
		NFM	Nationwide	Short Term Hire
159.4875	163.9875	NFM	Kent	Tour De France
159.5000	164.0000	NFM	Carlisle	B+Q
		NFM	Nationwide	Short Term Hire
		NFM	Nationwide	New PMR Allocation
159.5375	164.0375	NFM	Nationwide	Channel 11
159.5875	164.0875	NFM	Nationwide	New PMR Allocation
		NFM	Kent(Tour De France)	Marshalls & Security
		NFM	Nationwide	Short Term Hire
159.6250	164.1250	NFM	Nationwide	New PMR Allocation
		NFM	Kent	Tour De France Ch 4 TV
		NFM	Nationwide	Short Term Hire
159.6375	164.1375	NFM	Nationwide	Channel 12
159.6875	164.1875	NFM	Nationwide	New PMR Allocation
		NFM	Kent	Tour De France Start/Finish
		NFM	Nationwide	Short Term Hire
159.7375	164.2375	NFM	Nationwide	Channel 13
159.8375	164.3375	NFM	Nationwide	Channel 14
159.8750	164.3750	NFM	Space	Myr
160.0625	164.5625	NFM	Bolton	Doctors Service
160.1250	164.6250	NFM	Space	Soviet Mir Space Station
		NFM	Kent	Tour De France (Italian)
160.1500	160.1500	NFM	Blackpool	Doctors Messages

160.54375 - 160.6000 MHz   LOCAL AUTHORITY EMERGENCY ALARMS

Base	Mobile	Mode	Location	User and Notes
160.5500		NFM	Nationwide	OAP Alarm System
160.5625		NFM	Nationwide	OAP Alarm System
160.5750		NFM	Nationwide	OAP Alarm System

160.6000 - 160.9750 MHz   INTERNATIONAL MARITIME SHORE TRANSMIT

Base	Mobile	Mode	Location	User and Notes
160.6000	160.6000	NFM	Nationwide	HM Coastguard Auxiliary
		NFM	Nationwide	Coastguard Channel 99
		NFM	Aberdeen	Aberdeen Coastguard
		NFM	Brixham	Brixham Coastguard
		NFM	Crail	Crail Coastguard
		NFM	Falmouth	Falmouth Coastguard
		NFM	Great Yarmouth	Lifeboat
		NFM	Redcar	Redcar Coastguard
160.6250		NFM	Port of Heysham	British Gas
160.8500	156.2500	NFM	Liverpool	Gladstone Dock Ops
		NFM	Liverpool	Alfred Dock Ops
160.9000		NFM	London	LWT Ch 1

Base	Mobile	Mode	Location	User and Notes
160.9500	156.3500	NFM	Eastham	Manchester Ship Canal
		NFM	North Foreland	Working Channel
160.9700		NFM	Lincoln	PMR

160.9750 - 161.4750 MHz   Paging Acknowledgement Channels & International Maritime Service Business Marine Allocation 25 kHz NFM Simplex

Base	Mobile	Mode	Location	User and Notes
161.0000	31.7250	NFM	Nationwide	Hospital Paging
161.0125		NFM	Windsor Castle	PSA
161.0250	31.7500	NFM	Nationwide	Hospital Paging
161.0375	459.3750	NFM	Ipswich	B.H.S Paging
161.0500		NFM	London	LWTV Park Royal Ch 2
161.0500	31.7750	NFM	Nationwide	Hospital Paging
161.0750	459.4375	NFM	Swansea City	Royal Mail
161.0850	164.5100	NFM	Newcastle-under-Lyme	Homebase Paging
161.1300		NFM	Manchester	Norweb
161.1500		NFM	Port of Heysham	British Gas
		NFM	Nationwide	Paging Returns
161.2000	161.2000	NFM	Bacton	Philips Petroleum
161.2050		NFM	Manchester	Norweb
161.2300		NFM	Northampton	Electricity Repairs
161.2450		NFM	Manchester	Norweb
		NFM	Preston	Electric Board Meters
161.2750		NFM	Nationwide	Small Boats Alarms
161.3000	161.3000	NFM	English Channel	British Ch. Island Ferries
		NFM	Swansea Docks	AB Ports
		NFM	Felixstowe	Alexandra Towing Tugs
		NFM	Cardiff	Haulage Firm
		NFM	Nationwide	On-Board Handhelds
161.3250		NFM	Newmarket	Turners of Soham Ltd
161.3450		NFM	Northampton	Company Radio
161.3500	161.3500	NFM	Europort	Townsend Thorenson
		NFM	Fleetwood	Pandora Loading
		NFM	Manchester	Norweb
		NFM	Jersey	BCIF 'Pride of Portsmouth'
		NFM	English Channel	BCIF 'Pride of Portsmouth'
		NFM	Nationwide	On-Board Handhelds
161.3875	161.3875	NFM	Croydon	ITV Thames TV Ch 2
161.4250	161.4250	NFM	Marina & Yachts	Channel M2
		NFM	Jersey	Marina
		NFM	Jersey	Local Fishing Boats
161.4450	161.4450	NFM	Machynlleth	Marina
161.4500	161.4500	NFM	Croydon	ITV Thames TV Ch 3
		NFM	London	LWT Park Royal
		NFM	Northampton	Works Radio
		NFM	Zeebrugge	Townsend Thorenson
		NFM	Nationwide	On-Board Handhelds
161.4700		NFM	Manchester	Norweb

Base	Mobile	Mode	Location	User and Notes
161.4750 - 162.0500 MHz			**INTERNATIONAL MARITIME SHORE TRANSMIT**	
161.5000	156.9000	NFM	Liverpool	Mersey Radio Radar
161.5250		NFM	Hartlepool	Security Firm
161.5500		NFM	Blyth	Harbour
161.5500	156.9500	NFM	Liverpool	Merset Radio Radar
161.5800		NFM	Lancashire	Preston Gas Servicers
161.6000	157.0000	NFM	Garston	Garston Dock Ops
161.6500	157.0500	NFM	Liverpool	Langton Dock Ops
161.6550		NFM	Lincoln	PMR
161.6750		NFM	Nationwide	Marinas & Yachts Ch M2
		NFM	Port of Heysham	British Gas
161.6800		NFM	Lancashire	Leyland Gas Servicers
161.7000	157.1000	NFM	Liverpool	Mersey Radio Radar
161.7550		NFM	Northampton	Works Radio
161.7625		NFM	South Shields	Buses
161.8000		NFM	Edinburgh	International Marine
161.8250		NFM	Manchester	Council
161.8450		NFM	Wallsend	Buses
161.8875		NFM	Brighton	British Gas
161.9000		NFM	Aberystwyth	Hospital Paging
162.0000		NFM	Nationwide	Various Satellites
		NFM	Co Durham	PMR
162.0500 - 163.03125 MHz			**PRIVATE MARINE ALLOCATION 25 kHz NFM SIMPLEX**	
162.0500	157.4500	NFM	Jersey	BCIF Ch 29
162.0750	157.4750	NFM	London	Target Couriers
		NFM	London	Contract Dustcarts
		NFM	Nationwide	Motorola UK Channel 1
		NFM	Teeside	Harbour Pilot
162.0875	157.4875	NFM	Walsall	All-Points Couriers
		NFM	London	Target Couriers
162.1000	157.5000	NFM	Staffordshire	PMR
		NFM	Jersey	Herm Seaway Ch 30
162.1375	157.5375	NFM	Brighton	British Gas
		NFM	Nationwide	RAC Network Q Rally-Subaru
162.1500	157.5500	NFM	Isle of Sark	Shipping Ch 31
162.1750	157.5750	NFM	Driffield	J.R. Hood
		NFM	London	Securicor Trunks
		NFM	Nationwide	Motorola UK Channel 2
162.2000	157.6000	NFM	Merry Hill	Drinks Machines Co.
		NFM	London	Target Couriers
		NFM	Nationwide	Motorola UK Channel 3
162.2250	157.6250	NFM	Lincoln	Taxi Service
		NFM	Bristol	Security Co
		NFM	Nationwide	Motorola UK Channel 4
162.2450		NFM	Machynlleth	Gas Board
162.2500	157.6500	NFM	Jersey	Fishermans Co-op Ch 33

Base	Mobile	Mode	Location	User and Notes
162.2750	157.6750	NFM	Blackpool	Builders
		NFM	Manchester	Delivery Company
162.3000	157.7000	NFM	Jersey	Shipping Co. Ch 34
		NFM	Felixstowe	Shipping Co. Ch 34
162.3250	157.7250	NFM	Boston	Fossitt & Thorne Tyres Ltd
		NFM	London	Contract Bus
		NFM	London	Securicor Trunks
		NFM	London	Buses
		NFM	Nationwide	Motorola UK Channel 5
		NFM	Felixstowe	Shipping Co. Ch 94
162.3500	157.7500	NFM	Bournemouth	Off-shore Drilling Ch 35
162.3625	157.7625	NFM	Nationwide	Motorola UK Channel 6
162.3750	157.7750	NFM	Swindon	Skip Company
		NFM	London	Securicor Trunks
		NFM	Nationwide	Motorola UK Channel 7
162.4000	157.8000	NFM	Space	NOAA Satellite
		NFM	Hull	Humber Tugs
		AM	Wigan	Toyota Emergency Repairs
162.4250	157.8250	NFM	Space	NOAA Satellite
		NFM	Staffordshire	PMR
		NFM	Blackpool	Hospital Cleaners
		NFM	Liverpool	Enegineers
		NFM	N London	Taxis
		NFM	Nationwide	Motorola UK Channel 8
162.4500		NFM	Nationwide	Differential GPS
162.4750	157.8750	NFM	Space	NOAA Satellite
		NFM	Manchester	Delivery Company
		NFM	Bristol	Contractor
		NFM	London	Securicor Trunks
		NFM	London	Buses
		NFM	Nationwide	Motorola UK Channel 9
162.5000	157.9000	NFM	Isle of Man	Steam Packet Ferries
		NFM	Newhaven	Sealink Ch 38
		NFM	Dieppe	Ferry Co. Ch 38
		NFM	Guernsey	Sealink
		NFM	Harwich	Pilots
162.5375	157.9375	NFM	Nationwide	Network Q Rally - Toyota
162.5500	157.9500	NFM	Space	NOAA Satellite
		NFM	Nationwide	Townsend Thoreson Ch 39
162.5750	157.9750	NFM	Nationwide	Motorola UK Channel 10
162.6250		NFM	Lincoln	PMR
162.6800		NFM	Manchester	Piccadilly Radio
162.7000	158.1000	NFM	Bristol	Dock Tugs Ch 42
162.8500	162.850	NFM	Liverpool	Ship Ops
162.8750		NFM	Manchester	Building Firm
		NFM	Manchester	Delivery Company
162.9250	158.3250	NFM	London (Wembley)	Bus Hoppas
		NFM	Manchester	Delivery Company

Base	Mobile	Mode	Location	User and Notes
		NFM	Boston	Fossitt & Thorne Tyres Ltd
		NFM	London	Securicor Trunks
		NFM	London	Buses
162.9375	158.3375	NFM	Bristol	Coast Guard
162.9750	158.3750	NFM	Lincoln	PMR
		NFM	Oldham	Service Engineers
		NFM	Boston	Fossitt & Thorne Tyres Ltd
163.0000		NFM	Southampton	MediCall Ch 1
163.0250		NFM	Isle of Man	Calf of Man Telephone Link
		NFM	Nationwide	Differential GPS

163.03125 - 165.0000 MHz   PMR BAND

Base	Mobile	Mode	Location	User and Notes
163.0500	158.5500	NFM	Peterborough	CBS Repeater
		NFM	Gosport	Buses
		NFM	Fareham	Buses
		NFM	Hampshire	Bus Company
		NFM	Peterborough	Hector
		NFM	Jersey	Trunked PMR
		NFM	Jersey	Securicor
		NFM	Jersey	Gorey Cabs
		NFM	Jersey	Besco
		NFM	Jersey	Dynarod
		NFM	Jersey	Amal-grow
		NFM	Jersey	CTV
163.0625	158.5625	NFM	Peterborough	Various Users
		NFM	Cardiff	PMR
163.0750	158.5750	NFM	Brighton	Construction Company
		NFM	Manchester	Bus Inspectors
163.0875	158.5875	NFM	Nationwide	Road Construct. Engineers
163.1125	158.6125	NFM	Dublin	District Police Surveillance
163.1375	158.6375	NFM	Dublin	District Police Surveillance
163.1500	158.6500	NFM	Swansea City	Warden Patrols
163.1625	158.6625	NFM	Dublin	District Police Surveillance
163.2000	158.7000	NFM	Jersey	Trunked PMR
		NFM	Jersey	Securicor
		NFM	Jersey	Besco
		NFM	Jersey	Dynarod
		NFM	Jersey	Amal-grow
		NFM	Jersey	CTV
		NFM	Jersey	Gorey Cabs
		NFM	Peterborough	CBS Repeater
		NFM	Preston	Lowe's Plant Hire
		NFM	Edinburgh	PMR
		NFM	Bangor	DSS
		NFM	Peterborough	Various Users
163.2125	158.7125	NFM	Peterborough	CBS Repeater
		NFM	London	Doctors & Medics
		NFM	West Perthshire	Electricians

Base	Mobile	Mode	Location	User and Notes
		NFM	North Tayside	Heating Engineers
		NFM	Peterborough	Various Users
163.2250	158.7250	NFM	Peterborough	CBS Repeater
		NFM	Newmarket	PMR
		NFM	Oldham	Emergency Doctor
		NFM	Peterborough	Community Repeater
		NFM	Handcross	Comrep
163.3000	158.7000	NFM	Fleetwood	Golf Club
		NFM	W Yorkshire	Haulage Firm
		NFM	Lea Valley	Hoddesdon & Herts Buses
		NFM	Nationwide	Contactor
163.3250	158.8250	NFM	London	Islington Refuse
163.3500	158.8500	NFM	Cornwall	Repeater
		NFM	Fremont Point, Jersey	Trunked PMR
		NFM	Jersey	Gorey Cabs
		NFM	Jersey	Securicor
		NFM	Jersey	Besco
		NFM	Jersey	Dynarod
		NFM	Jersey	Amal-grow
		NFM	Jersey	CTV
		NFM	Peterborough	CBS Repeater
		NFM	Co Durham	Waste Disposal
		NFM	Plymouth	Granada TV
		NFM	Newton Abbot	Amtrack
		NFM	Oakhampton	Target Express
		NFM	Devon	Associated Leisure
		NFM	Peterborough	Octane
163.3625	158.8625	NFM	Peterborough	CBS Repeater
		NFM	Cleveland	Private Message
		NFM	Newmarket	PMR
		NFM	Newcastle	Security Firm
		NFM	Peterborough	Various Users
163.3750		NFM	Preston	Taxis
163.3750	158.8750	NFM	Nationwide	Contactor
163.4375	158.9375	NFM	Aberdeen	Message Handling
		NFM	Nationwide	New PMR Allocation
163.5125	159.1250	NFM	M6	Motorway Maintenance
		NFM	Nationwide	Contactor
163.5250	159.0250	NFM	Nationwide	New PMR Allocation
		NFM	Edinburgh	PMR
		NFM	Aberdeen	PMR
163.6000	159.1000	NFM	Tyneside	UK Security
163.6125	159.1125	NFM	M25	Engineers
163.6875	159.1875	NFM	London	Community Repeater
163.7250	159.2250	NFM	Nationwide	New PMR Allocation
		NFM	Aberdeen	PMR
163.9000	159.4000	NFM	Peterborough	Viscount Buses
		NFM	Grimsby	Murphy Construction

Base	Mobile	Mode	Location	User and Notes
		NFM	Nationwide	RAC Network Q Rally
		NFM	Nationwide	New PMR Allocation
		NFM	Kent (Tour De France)	Race Direction
		NFM	London	Notting Hill Carnival
		NFM	Nationwide	Short Term Hire
163.9125	159.4125	NFM	Jersey	Island Cabs
163.9250	159.4250	NFM	Nationwide	New PMR Allocation
		NFM	Kent (Tour De France)	Radio Tour & Press
		NFM	Nationwide	Short Term Hire
163.9625	159.4625	NFM	Peterborough	CBS Repeater
		NFM	Fleetwood	Pharmacy Agency
		NFM	Nationwide	New PMR Allocation
		NFM	Aberdeen	PMR
163.9750	159.4750	NFM	Peterborough	Various Users
163.9800	163.9800	AM	Bedford	Repeater
163.9875	159.4875	NFM	Nationwide	New PMR Allocation
		NFM	Nationwide	Short Term Hire
164.0000	159.5000	NFM	Oxford St., London	Splaza Centre Security
		NFM	Nationwide	New PMR Allocation
		NFM	Jersey	Motor Tarffic Dept Ch3
		NFM	London, Oxford St.	Plaza Shopping Centre
		NFM	Nationwide	Short Term Hire
164.0125	164.0125	NFM	Guernsey	Aurigny Airlines
164.0250	159.5250	NFM	Dublin	District Police (E)
164.0375	159.5375	NFM	Jersey	Aurigny Airlines Handhelds
		NFM	Dublin	District Police (N)
164.0500	159.5500	NFM	Oxford St., London	HMV Shop Security
		NFM	Newmarket	Security
		NFM	Edinburgh	Sheriff Court Security
		NFM	Nationwide	National Scout Association
		NFM	Jersey	Euro. Golf Championships
		NFM	Northampton	Golf Club
		NFM	Dublin	District Police (R)
		NFM	City of London	Bus Co.
		NFM	Nationwide	St John's Ambulance Ch 4
		NFM	Nationwide	Short Term Hire
164.0625	159.5625	NFM	Jersey	Euro. Golf Championships
		NFM	Nationwide	National Scout Association
		NFM	Dublin	District Police (K)
		NFM	Morecambe	Sea Scout
		NFM	Jersey	Tilbury Douglas
		NFM	Nationwide	St John's Ambulances Ch 3
164.0750	159.5750	NFM	Dublin	District Police (C)
164.0875	159.5875	NFM	Nationwide	RAC Network Q Rally
		NFM	Nationwide	New PMR Allocation
		NFM	Kent	Tour De France TV Cameras
		NFM	Dublin	District Police (L)
		NFM	Glasgow	Taxis

Base	Mobile	Mode	Location	User and Notes
		NFM	Nationwide	Short Term Hire
164.1000	159.6000	NFM	Dublin	District Police (W)
164.1000	170.1700	NFM	Finland	City Police
164.1125	159.6125	NFM	Dublin	District Police (J)
164.1250	159.6250	NFM	Humberside Airport	Security
		NFM	Nationwide	New PMR Allocation
		NFM	Kent (Tour De France)	Ashford Borough Council
		NFM	Southampton	Taxis
		NFM	Dublin	District Police (F)
		NFM	Nationwide	Short Term Hire
164.1375	159.6375	NFM	Edinburgh	Data Link
		NFM	Dublin	District Police (A)
		NFM	Jersey	Jersey Telecom Cable Laying
164.1625	159.6625	NFM	Dublin	District Police (H)
164.1750	159.6750	NFM	Dublin	District Police (M)
164.1875	159.6875	NFM	Nationwide	RAC Network Q Rally-Toyota
		NFM	Nationwide	New PMR Allocation
		NFM	Nationwide	Short Term Hire
164.2000	159.7000	NFM	Dublin	District Police (D)
		NFM	Nationwide	Paging Speech Return
164.2125	159.7125	NFM	Dublin	District Police (G)
164.2250	159.7250	NFM	Nationwide	Pacnet Data
		NFM	Galway	Community Repeater
		NFM	Dublin	District Police (P)
164.2375	159.7375	NFM	Nationwide	Pacnet Data
		NFM	Tayside	Data Link
164.2500	159.7500	NFM	Glasgow	Data Link
164.2625	159.7625	NFM	Tayside	Data Link
		NFM	Newcastle	Data Link
164.2750	159.7750	NFM	Nationwide	Pacnet Data
164.2875	159.7875	NFM	Nationwide	Pacnet Data
164.3000	159.8000	NFM	Glasgow	Data Link
		NFM	Blackburn	DMC Private Hire
		NFM	Newport	Community Repeater
164.3125	159.8125	NFM	Nationwide	Pacnet Data
164.3250	159.8250	NFM	Nationwide	Pacnet Data
		NFM	Tayside	Data Link
		NFM	Newcastle	Data Link
164.3375	159.8375	NFM	Glasgow	Data Link
164.3500	159.8500	NFM	Tayside	Data Link
164.3625	159.8625	NFM	Nationwide	Pacnet Data
		NFM	Glasgow	Data Link
164.3750	159.8750	NFM	Nationwide	Pacnet Data
		NFM	Newmarket	Security
		NFM	Blackburn	Chippy's Private Hire
164.3875	159.8875	NFM	West Perthshire	Data Link
		NFM	Nationwide	Airport Duty Officer Ch2
		NFM	Newport	Community Repeater

Base	Mobile	Mode	Location	User and Notes
164.4000	159.9000	NFM	Manchester	Service Engineers
		NFM	Blackburn	C&M Private Hire
		NFM	Nationwide	BT Selcal to Mobiles
164.4375	159.9375	NFM	Peterborough	CBS Repeater
		NFM	Nationwide	Mobile Phone Link
		NFM	Peterborough	Various Users
164.4450	159.9450	NFM	London	Vehicle Recovery
		AM	Bedfordshire	Repeater
164.4500	159.9500	NFM	Peterborough	CBS Repeater
		NFM	Cleveland	Security Firm
		NFM	Newmarket	Taxis
		NFM	Haverfordwest	Coin Machines
		NFM	Pembrokeshire	Riverlea Tractors
		NFM	Dyfed	Riverlea Tractors
		NFM	Peterborough	Ranger
		NFM	Peterborough	Beeline
		NFM	Cleveland	Community Security
164.4625	159.9625	NFM	Glasgow	Community Repeater
		NFM	Newmarket	PMR
		NFM	Penrith	County Taxis
		NFM	Southampton	Aircall
		NFM	Horsham	Comrep
		NFM	Gloucester	Security Firm
		NFM	Peterborough	Various Users
		AM	Luton	PMR
164.4750	159.9750	NFM	Peterborough	CBS Repeater
		NFM	Nationwide	Aircall Ch 10
		NFM	Brighton	Aircall (Doctors)
		NFM	Peterborough	Optic
164.4875	159.9875	NFM	Manchester	PMR
		NFM	Crewe	Recovery Vehicles
		NFM	Bishop Stortford	Taxis
		NFM	Southampton	Taxis
		NFM	Poole	Repeater
164.5000	160.0000	NFM	Bolton	Transport Service
		NFM	Warrington	Garden Centre
		NFM	Southampion	Skip Hire Co
164.5125	160.0125	NFM	Portsmouth	Nynex
		NFM	Nationwide	Aircall
		NFM	Newport	Parcel Company
		NFM	Cardiff	PMR
		NFM	Peterborough	Various Users
		NFM	Newcastle-under-Lyme	PMR
164.5250	160.0250	NFM	Glasgow	PMR
		NFM	Kent	Taxis
164.5375	160.0375	NFM	Galway	Community Repeater
		NFM	East Durham	Doctors On Call
		NFM	West Midlands	All Waist

Base	Mobile	Mode	Location	User and Notes
164.5500	160.0500	NFM	Hull	Dynarod Ltd
		AM	Grimsby	Aircall
		NFM	Cardiff	Emergency Doctors
		NFM	Co Durham	Alarm Engineers
		NFM	Blackburn	CRM Private Hire
		NFM	Peterborough	Castor
		NFM	Nationwide	Aircall
		NFM	Hull	East Yorks Buses
		NFM	Nationwide	Aircall Ch 5
164.5625	160.0625	NFM	Yorkshire	Air Call Medics
		NFM	Peterborough	CBS Repeater
		NFM	S Yorkshire	Deputising Service
		NFM	Edinburgh	Doctors Service
		NFM	Bournemouth	Emergency Services
		NFM	Southampton	MediCall Ch 2
		NFM	Nationwide	Aircall
		NFM	South Yorkshire	Aircall Medical
		NFM	Sheffield	Aircall (Doctors)
		NFM	Peterborough	Various Users
		NFM	Edinburgh	Aircall Doctors
		NFM	Tyne & Wear	Doctors On Call
164.5750	160.0750	NFM	Nationwide	Aircall
		NFM	Peterborough	Various Users
164.5875	160.0875	NFM	Hull	Emergency Doctors
		NFM	London	Minicab Firm Croydon
		NFM	Sheffield	Community Repeater
		NFM	Peterborough	CBS Repeater
		NFM	Manchester	Emergency Doctors
		NFM	Bury	Emergency Doctor
164.6000	160.1000	NFM	Poole	Repeater
		NFM	Cardiff	PMR
		NFM	Sheffield	Community Repeater
		NFM	Nationwide	Aircall
164.6125	160.1125	NFM	Bournemouth	Council Road Gangs
		NFM	Poole	Repeater
		NFM	Nationwide	Aircall Ch 2
164.6250	160.1250	NFM	Hampshire	Aircall
		NFM	Peterborough	CBS Repeater
		NFM	Nationwide	Aircall
		NFM	Plymouth	Emergency Doctors Service
		NFM	Poole	Repeater
		NFM	Nationwide	Aircall Ch 5
		NFM	London	Medic Pager
		NFM	Peterborough	Tango
		NFM	Bournemouth	St John's
		NFM	Parkstone	Aristoview
164.6375	160.1375	NFM	Wolverhampton	Doctors Service
		NFM	Tyne & Wear	Taxis

Base	Mobile	Mode	Location	User and Notes
		NFM	Southampton	Taxis
		NFM	Portsmouth	MediCall Ch 1
		NFM	Newport	Paramedic Doctors Service
		NFM	S Glasgow	Doctors Service
		NFM	Swansea City	Doctors on Call
164.6500	160.1500	NFM	Glasgow	Strathclyde Medicall
		NFM	Wakefield	Doctor's DepService
		NFM	Cardiff	Emergency Doctors
		NFM	Birmingham	Doctors Service
		NFM	Nationwide	Doctors Common
		NFM	London	Parcel Deliveries
		NFM	Poole	Paramedics
		NFM	Bournemouth	Medicare
		NFM	Sheffield	Medicare
		NFM	N Glasgow	Doctors Service
164.6625	160.1625	NFM	Newmarket	PMR
		NFM	Poole	Repeater
164.6750	160.1750	NFM	Severn Bridge	Toll Booths
164.6875	160.1875	NFM	County Durham	Doctor's Medicall
164.7000	160.2000	NFM	West Midlands	Burglar Alarms
		NFM	Nationwide	Teleacoustic
164.7125	160.2125	NFM	London	Medical & Rescue Services
		NFM	Gloucester	Repeater
		NFM	Peterborough	Various Users
164.7250	160.2250	NFM	Peterborough	CBS Repeater
		NFM	Gravesend	Doctors
		NFM	Crewe	Taxis
		NFM	Poole	Repeater
		NFM	London	Bermondsey Council
		NFM	Newmarket	Trunked PMR
		NFM	London	Security Company
		NFM	Peterborough	Spark
164.7375	160.2375	NFM	Cleveland	Doctors On Call
		NFM	Nationwide	Lodge Radio Service
164.7500	160.2500	NFM	London	St John's Ambulance
		NFM	Ely	Taxis
		NFM	Wrexham	Haulage Contractor
		NFM	Southern England	Saxon Security
		NFM	Netherlands	Fire Pagers Ch F1
164.7625	160.2625	NFM	Newmarket	Transport Firm
		NFM	Portsmouth	Taxi
		NFM	Kent	Eurotunnel
		NFM	Peterborough	Various Users
164.7700	164.7700	NFM	Netherlands	Fire Pagers Ch F2
164.7750	160.2750	NFM	Newmarket	Trunked PMR
		NFM	London	Medicall South London
		NFM	Lothian And Borders	Lothian Regional Council
		NFM	West Perthshire	Delivery Company

Base	Mobile	Mode	Location	User and Notes
		AM	Leeds	Taxis
164.7875	160.2875	NFM	Blackpool	Haulage Contractors
		NFM	Nationwide	Teleacoustic
		NFM	Morecambe	PMR
		NFM	Bournemouth	Council Lighting
164.8000	160.3000	NFM	Bodmin	Vet Services
		NFM	Nationwide	Teleacoustic
		NFM	Bournemouth	Aircall Radio
		NFM	Norfolk	Red Star Parcels
		AM	Bedford	PMR
164.8125	160.0125	NFM	Newmarket	PMR
		NFM	Poole	Repeater
		NFM	Bristol	Taxis
		NFM	Bath	Strode Sound CBS
		NFM	Poole	Repeater
164.8250	160.3250	NFM	Central London	Motor Rescue Service
		NFM	Poole	Repeater
		NFM	London	St Mary's Hospital Ambul.
		NFM	Peterborough	Various Users
		NFM	London	Auto Breakdown Service
164.8375	160.3375	NFM	Newmarket	PMR
		NFM	Poole	Repeater
		NFM	Bournemouth	Express Carriers
		NFM	Peterborough	Various Users
164.8500	160.3500	NFM	Wadesbridge	Builder's Merchants
		NFM	Nationwide	Message Handling
		NFM	Colwyn Bay	BR Station
164.8625	160.3625	NFM	Manchester	Plant Firm
		NFM	Manchester	Bouncey Castle Hire
		NFM	South West Wales	DSS Fraud Teams
164.8750	160.3750	NFM	Poole	Repeater
		NFM	Northen Ireland	NCF Milk Tankers
		NFM	Norfolk	Alpha Drains
		NFM	Nationwide	Mobile Phone Link
		NFM	Sussex Coast	Coastway Hospital Radio
164.8875	160.3875	AM	Bedfordshire	Vehicle Recovery
		NFM	Newcastle	Data Link
		NFM	Nationwide	Mobile Phone Link Ch 2B
		NFM	London	Security Company
164.9000	160.4000	NFM	Lincoln	Gas Suppliers
		NFM	Manchester	Delivery Company
		NFM	Wirral	Data Link
		NFM	Cheshire	Tyre Services
		AM	Bedfordshire	Repeater
164.9125	160.4125	NFM	Bournemouth	Taxi Hire Co.
		NFM	Ipswich	Garage
		NFM	Newport	Central Heating Company
164.9250	160.4250	NFM	Kent	Tour De France (French)

Base	Mobile	Mode	Location	User and Notes
		NFM	Peterborough	CBS Repeater
		NFM	Peterborough	Anglo
		NFM	Norfolk	ANC Parcels
		NFM	Suffolk	Morlings TV Rentals
		NFM	Brighton	RCS Comrep Ch 8
164.9375	160.4375	NFM	Bristol	Security Co
		NFM	Poole	Repeater
		NFM	Bristol	Co-Channel Electric
164.9500	160.4500	NFM	Glasgow	Taxi
		NFM	Grangetown	Private Message
		NFM	London	Ambulance Service
		NFM	Gloucester	Group 4 Static Guards
164.9625	160.4625	NFM	Jersey	Links CBS 4
164.9750	160.4750	NFM	Merseyside	Surveyors
164.9875	160.4875	NFM	Kent	Tour De France (French)
165.0000	160.5000	NFM	Peterborough	CBS Repeater
		AM	Bedfordshire	Repeater
		NFM	Newmarket	Medical
		NFM	Ipswich	Paging
		NFM	Felixstowe	Paging
		NFM	Peterborough	Various Users
		NFM	Bath	Bath University Research
		NFM	Poole	Taxi
		NFM	Sweden	Business Comms
		NFM	New Malden	North West Cars

165.0125 - 168.2250 MHz   VHF HIGH BAND PMR BASE/REPEATERS (MOBILE SPLIT + 4.8 MHz) AMBULANCE SERVICES (ENGLAND & WALES)

Base	Mobile	Mode	Location	User and Notes
165.0125	169.8125	NFM	Aberdeen	Northern Garage
		NFM	Bath	Bath University Research
		NFM	Blackburn	City Private Hire
		NFM	Cornwall	Repeater
		NFM	Dorking	RCS Comrep Ch 3
		NFM	Kent	Doctors On Call
		NFM	London	ODRATS Ch5
		NFM	Manchester	Plant Firm
		NFM	Manchester	Security
		NFM	Morecambe	Security Vans
165.0250	169.8250	NFM	Burnley	Delivery Service
		NFM	Dover	Castle Comms
		NFM	Blackpool	First Aid Council Post
		NFM	Cardiff	Commercial Rigging
		NFM	Bath	Bath University Research
		NFM	Bristol	City Link Parcel Express
		NFM	Guernsey	Repeater
		NFM	Morecambe	PMR
		NFM	North Yorkshire	Doctor Service

Base	Mobile	Mode	Location	User and Notes
		NFM	Guernsey	Links CBS 3
165.0375	169.8375	NFM	London	National Aircall Radio
		NFM	Tyne & Wear	British Gas
		NFM	Cardiff	PMR
		NFM	Nottingham	Taxis
		NFM	Preston	Farm Suppliers
		NFM	Jersey	Eurocar Hire
		NFM	Poole	Repeater
		NFM	Newcastle	Site Delivery
		NFM	City of Westminster	Cleansing Dept.
		NFM	Newport	Community Repeater
165.0500	169.8500	NFM	Birmingham	Ambulance Service
		NFM	Peterborough	Osbourne Plumbing
		NFM	Bournemouth	Critax Taxis
		NFM	Blackburn	B&B Private Hire
		NFM	Cheetham	Ekko Private Hire
		NFM	Manchester	Taxi
		NFM	Bathgate	Taxi
		NFM	Dumfries	Taxis
		NFM	Guernsey	Circuit Skips
		NFM	Hull	Taxis
		NFM	Jersey	SGB Scaffolding Erectors
		NFM	Newtown	Newtown Taxis
		NFM	Plymouth	AA Taxis
		NFM	Swindon	Inta-Car Taxis
165.0625	169.8625	NFM	Aberdeen	ANC
		NFM	Bristol	Auto Glass
		NFM	Carlisle	Biffa
		NFM	Crewe	Garage
		NFM	Cromer	Tylers Waste Management
		NFM	Essex	Warrior Skips
		NFM	Guernsey	Links Community Repeater 1
		NFM	Indian Queens	Interlink Parcels
		NFM	Ipswich	Keiths Co
		NFM	Perth	King Contractors (King Base)
		NFM	Perth	Council Investigators
		NFM	Pocklington	Town Travel Taxis
		NFM	Poole	Repeater
		NFM	Rillington	H Atkinson Slaughter House
		NFM	Scarborough	TWDB
		NFM	Suffolk	Garage Supplies
165.0750	169.8750	NFM	Dover Castle	Security/Council Works Dept
		NFM	Newport	R.E.
		NFM	Suffolk	May Gurney & Co
		NFM	Fife	Fife Regional Council
		NFM	M1	Associated Asphalt
		NFM	Nationwide	Road Engineers
		NFM	Norfolk	May Gurney

Base	Mobile	Mode	Location	User and Notes
		NFM	Perth	Community Repeater
		NFM	London	Central Government
165.0875	169.8875	NFM	Portsmouth	Bus Service
		NFM	Blackpool	C Cabs
		NFM	Liverpool	Local Authority Security
		NFM	Chestwood	Chestwood Mushrooms
		NFM	Hatfield	Tarmac Construction
		NFM	London	Minicab Firm Penge
		NFM	Plymouth	University Security
		NFM	Ipswich	Motorways Recovery M5
		NFM	RAF Brize Norton	Base Special
		NFM	Jersey	Securicor
		NFM	Jersey	Normans Ltd Ch 1
165.1000	169.9000	NFM	Peterborough	EMap
		NFM	Edinburgh	Taxis
		NFM	Wickford	Taxis
		NFM	Carlisle	Abbey Skip Hire
		NFM	Bournemouth	Wade's Taxis
		NFM	St Austell	Davis Automatics
		NFM	Seaforth	Dale's Taxis
		NFM	Newcastle	Taxis
		NFM	Hazelgrove	Lynx Private Hire
		NFM	Stockport	Taxi
		NFM	Leigh	Swift Next Day
		NFM	Gt Manchester	Swift Next Day
		NFM	Little Downham	Mott Farmers
		NFM	Havant	Taxis
		NFM	Blackpool	C Cabs
		NFM	Clacton	Clacton Taxis
		NFM	Fordham	D. Jenkins TV
		NFM	Gorleston-on-Sea	Ace Day & Night Taxis
		NFM	Guernsey	Transfer Taxis
		NFM	Kings Lynn	Geoff's Taxis
		NFM	London, Acton	Minicab Firm
		NFM	London, Croydon	Minicab Firm
		NFM	Woodbridge	TV Repairs
		NFM	Glasgow	Drumchaple Taxis
		NFM	Manchester	Bishop's security Company
		NFM	Saxmundham	Fishwick Vets
		NFM	Poole	Rapid Lads
		NFM	Fordham	D Jenkins TV
		NFM	London	SEB Scaffold
		NFM	Korleston	Ace Day And Night
		NFM	Kings Lynn	Geoffs Taxis
		NFM	Saxmundham	Fishwich
		AM	Glasgow	Taxi
		NFM	Bristol	Durston Plant
		NFM	Peterborough	Evening Telegraph

Base	Mobile	Mode	Location	User and Notes
		NFM	Lincoln	City Taxis
		NFM	Stoke-on-Trent	Taxis
		NFM	Montrose	Taxis
165.1125	169.9125	NFM	Walton-on-Thames	Vending Machine Company
		NFM	Manchester	PMR
		NFM	Carlisle	Borders Cabs
		NFM	Dyfed	J Lawrence Tractors
		NFM	Pembrokeshire	J Lawrence Tractors
		NFM	Swansea	Abba Taxis
		AM	Barrow	Taxis
		NFM	Cambridge	Inter-City Cabs
		NFM	Dymchurch	Dymchurch Light Railway
		NFM	Guernsey	Fuel Supplies
		NFM	Jersey	Domino Cars
		NFM	London	Minicab Firm North London
		NFM	Sandy	Ariston Group Service
		NFM	Bournemouth	Brown Motors
		NFM	Glasgow	Taxi
		NFM	Jersey	Beeline Taxis Ch1
165.1250	169.9250	NFM	Cosham	Taxis
		NFM	Failsworth	Embassy Cars
		NFM	Oldham	Embassy Cars
		NFM	Portsmouth	Taxis
		NFM	Slough	Topcars
		AM	Aberdeen	Amtrak
		AM	Glasgow	Taxi
		NFM	Burnley	Taxis
		NFM	Edinburgh	Taxi
		NFM	Guernsey	CBichard Vehicle Recovery
		NFM	Hadleigh	Wilsons Corn & Milling
		NFM	Huntingdon	Mercury Bluebird Taxis
		NFM	Immingham	Taxis
		NFM	Jersey	Farm
		NFM	London	Minicab Firm Croydon
		NFM	Perth	Taxi
		NFM	Sudbury	Wilsons Corn & Milling Co
		NFM	Sudbury	Woods Taxis
		NFM	Waltham	Ariston Group Service
		NFM	Weymouth	Taxi Co
165.1375	169.9375	NFM	Aberystwyth	County Council Highways
		NFM	Isle of Man	Electric Suppliers
		NFM	Hull	Reckitts Security
		NFM	Guernsey	Stan Brouard Ltd
		NFM	London	Lambeth Council
		NFM	London	Redbridge Council
		NFM	London	MI5 Encrypted
		NFM	London	Royal Parks Police
		NFM	Manchester	Motorway Maintenance

Base	Mobile	Mode	Location	User and Notes
		NFM	Poole	Repeater
		NFM	RAF Cardingdon	MoD
		NFM	Swaffham	Reed & Mikik Ltd
165.1500	169.9500	NFM	Anglesey	Council Bin men
		NFM	Brighton	Group 4
		NFM	Jersey	R.G. Romeril Plant Hire
		NFM	Guernsey	Norman Piette
		NFM	Telford	Wrekin District Council
		NFM	Grimsby	Doctors Night Call Service
		NFM	Glasgow	Taxi
		NFM	Nationwide	Group Four Security Ch1
165.1625	169.9625	NFM	Wakefield	The Riding Centre
		NFM	Hull	Reckitts Security
		NFM	Guernsey	Vehicle Recovery Service
		NFM	Ipswich	Spotcheck Security
		NFM	Nottingham	Nottingham University
		NFM	Perth Royal Infirmary	Security & Maintenance
		NFM	Bournemouth	Beach Patrol
		NFM	Bedfordshire	Repeater
165.1750	169.9750	NFM	Cleveland	Group 4 Security
		NFM	Nationwide	Group 4 Security Ch 2
		NFM	Bristol	Group 4 Security
165.1875	169.9875	NFM	Aberdeen	Security
		NFM	Ayr	Butlins Mat
		NFM	Hull	Security Firm
		NFM	Norfolk	Pritchard Security
		NFM	Perth	Taxi
		NFM	Bournemouth	Securitas Security
		NFM	Manchester	Man. City FC Stewards
165.2000	168.4000	NFM	France	DGT
165.2000	170.0000	NFM	Peterborough	CBS Repeater
		NFM	Newmarket	Cambridge Cable
		NFM	Isle of Man	Electricians
		NFM	Edinburgh	Taxi
		NFM	Aberdeen	Aberdeen Vets
		NFM	Cheshire	Alternative Taxis
		NFM	Norwich	Esso Heating
		NFM	Poole	Repeater
		NFM	Guernsey	States Works
165.2125	170.0125	NFM	Hull	Security Co
		NFM	Milton Keynes	Milton Keynes Taxis
		NFM	Edinburgh	Scottish & Newcastle Brew.
		NFM	Grafton	Grosvenor Estates
		NFM	Cambridge	Grafton Centre
		NFM	Bolton	College Security
		NFM	Hull	Security Firm
		NFM	Ipswich	Dock Security
		NFM	London	US Embassy Secret Service

Base	Mobile	Mode	Location	User and Notes
		NFM	Nationwide	British Coal Security
		NFM	Sheffield	Group 4 Security
165.2250	170.0250	NFM	Southampton	Taxis
		NFM	Tamworth	Taxis
		NFM	Leicester	LCL Cable Comms
		NFM	Heathrow	Interlink
		NFM	Blackburn	Arcade Private Hire
		NFM	Langley	Station Minicabs
		NFM	Jersey	Flying Dragon Cabs
		NFM	London	Minicab Firm Woodford
		NFM	Slough	Minicab Firm
		NFM	Portishead	Esso Fuels Docks
		NFM	Frome	Blue Taxis
		NFM	Weymouth	Dorset Alarms
165.2375	170.0375	NFM	Wales	Black And White Taxis
		NFM	Yorkshire	Norweb
		NFM	Glossop	Thameside Council
		NFM	Plymouth	Taxis
		NFM	Carlisle	Taxis
		NFM	Anglesey	Benji's Taxis
		NFM	Poole	Repeater
		NFM	Cardiff	Cardiff Taxis
		NFM	Crewe	Taxi
		NFM	Guernsey	Access Skips
		NFM	Leighton Buzzard	Choake Billington
		NFM	London	Minicab Firm Ealing
		NFM	Torpoint	Taxis
		NFM	Glasgow	Taxi
		AM	Barrow	Taxis
		NFM	Cardiff	Amber Taxis Ch 2
165.2500	170.0500	NFM	Lancing	Taxis
		NFM	Southend	Taxis
		NFM	Milton Keynes	Ace Cars
		NFM	Slough	Compass Cars
		NFM	Elvington	Warter Estate Farms
		NFM	Manchester	Taxi
		AM	Aberdeen	Lucas
		NFM	March	Middle Level Commissioner
		NFM	Slough	Minicab Firm
		NFM	Airdrie	Monkland Independant Taxis
		NFM	Glasgow	Taxi
		NFM	Montrose	Radio TV Company
		NFM	Guernsey	Island Taxis
165.2625	170.0625	NFM	Dudley	TV Repairs
		NFM	Walsall	GB Engineering
		NFM	Southampton	Ravenscroft Motors
		NFM	Preston	Council Dog Warden
		NFM	Cheltenham	Bus Engineers

Base	Mobile	Mode	Location	User and Notes
		NFM	Jersey	CSL Repeater
		NFM	Lancashire	Barkley Council
		NFM	Poole	Repeater
		NFM	Snaefell, Isle of Man	Repeater
		NFM	Sheffield	Crystal Peaks SC Security
		NFM	Ipswich	Security
		NFM	Reading	Centurian Security
		NFM	Southampton	B&K Security
		AM	Bedfordshire	Parcels Service
		AM	Buckinghamshire	Parcels Service
165.2750	170.0750	NFM	Portsmouth	Taxis
		AM	Exeter	City Minibus Co.
		AM	Glasgow	Taxi
		NFM	Bath	Orange Grove Taxis
		NFM	Benfleet	Wheel's Taxis
		NFM	Brierley Hill	Lady Cabs
		NFM	Guernsey	H.F. Gaudion
		NFM	Halstead	Gosling Bros
		NFM	Ipswich	Comm Repeater
		NFM	Kingston	Minicab Firm
		NFM	London	Minicab Firm Holloway
		NFM	Manchester	Taxi
		NFM	Mansfield	Ace Taxis
		NFM	Montrose	Taxis
		NFM	Newport	Show Taxis
		NFM	Perth	Data
		NFM	Poole	Repeater
		NFM	Portsmouth	Taxis
		NFM	Shire Oaks	Shire Oaks Colliery Security
		NFM	Swindon	Swindon Taxis
		NFM	Swinton	Lynch Private Hire
165.2875	170.0875	NFM	Spalding	Baytree Nurseries
		NFM	Chestercord	Park Research.
		NFM	Cleveland	Boro Taxis
		NFM	Colchester	Taxis
		NFM	Cumbria	South Lakes District Council
		NFM	Downham Market	Lindsay Smith
		NFM	Falkirk	Taxi
		NFM	Ferndown	Taxis
		NFM	Jersey	Polar Car Hire
		NFM	Lincoln	Imp Taxis
		NFM	London	Minicab Firm Bechenham
		NFM	London	Minicab Firm Bromley
		NFM	Macclesfield	Silvertown Taxis
		NFM	Montrose	Taxis
		NFM	New Quay	New Quay Taxis
		NFM	Rochdale	Streamline Taxis
		NFM	Woolwich	Taxis

Base	Mobile	Mode	Location	User and Notes
165.3000	170.1000	NFM	Edinburgh	Taxis
		NFM	Colwyn Bay	Taxis
		NFM	Nationwide	Community Repeater
		NFM	Oxfordshire	Security Firm
		NFM	East Dereham	Dereham Taxis
		NFM	Guernsey	Links Community Repeater 2
165.3125	170.1125	NFM	Peterborough	Euro Cabs
		AM	Cleethorpes	Taxis
		NFM	Christchurch	Taxis
		NFM	Ely	Garrett
		NFM	Glasgow	Taxi
		NFM	Glossop	Padtax Taxis
		NFM	Jersey	Harbour Dept
		NFM	Launceston	Roscar Electronics
		NFM	Leigh	Avacab
		NFM	London	Minicab Firm Putney
		NFM	Manchester	Taxi
		NFM	Merseyside	Taxis
		NFM	Morecambe	Taxis
		NFM	Northampton	Taxis
		NFM	Nottingham	Taxis
		NFM	Plymouth	Council Security
		NFM	Southampton	Taxis
		NFM	Stansted	Aircars
		NFM	Swindon	Ace Taxis
		NFM	Taunton	Alpha/Apex Taxis
165.3250	170.1250	NFM	Southampton	Taxis
		NFM	Lincoln	Council
		NFM	Peterborough	CBS Repeater
		NFM	Bristol	Paramedics
		NFM	London	Diplomatic Transport
		NFM	Plymouth	City Security (Papa Control)
		NFM	Poole	Repeater
		NFM	Stirling	PMR
		NFM	Humberside	Haulage Co
		NFM	London	Diplomatic Transport
		NFM	Edinburgh	Taxis
165.3375	170.1375	NFM	Clacton	Bernies Taxis
		NFM	Southampton	Taxis
		NFM	Calne	Taxis
		NFM	Winchester	Taxis
		NFM	Carlisle	Auto Recoveries
		NFM	East London	Traffic Wardens
		NFM	Wrexham	Atax Taxis
		NFM	Eccles	Minicars Ltd
		NFM	Manchester	Taxi
		NFM	Clacton-on-Sea	Bernies Taxis
		NFM	Kings Lynn	Simons

Base	Mobile	Mode	Location	User and Notes
		NFM	Letchwood	John's Taxis
		NFM	London	Minicab Firm Campden
		NFM	Stirling	PMR
		NFM	Stowmarket	ICI Paint Depot
		NFM	Lytham	Lytham Taxis
		AM	Cleethorpes	Taxis
		NFM	Glasgow	Clydeside Taxi
		NFM	Swindon	Taxis
		NFM	Cleethropes	AA Car Taxis
		NFM	Stoke On Trent	Z Carz Taxis
165.3500	170.1500	NFM	Luton	Victor Taxis
		NFM	Bury	Star Taxis
		NFM	Manchester	Taxi
		NFM	Dumfries	Diamond Taxis
		NFM	Bury	Taxis
		NFM	London	Minicab Firm Lewisham
		NFM	Nottingham	Doctors Service
		NFM	Glasgow	Taxi
		NFM	Guernsey	PMR
		NFM	Bath	Twerton Taxis
		NFM	Peterborough	ABC Taxis
		NFM	Lincoln	Security
		NFM	Great Melton	Downham Farm Services
165.3625	170.1625	NFM	Matlock	Haulage Company
		NFM	Gosport	Taxis
		NFM	Southampton	Security
		NFM	Greenham	Council
		NFM	Isle of Wight	Plant Hire
		NFM	Bournemouth	CBS Lynx Carriers
		NFM	Derby	Community Repeater
		NFM	Poole	Repeater
		NFM	StMonans	Bass Rock Oil CoLtd.
		NFM	Dundee	Car Hire Service
		NFM	Edinburgh	Community Repeater
		NFM	Leicester	Taxi
		NFM	Liverpool	Taxis
		NFM	Perth	Community Repeater
		NFM	Kent	Thanet Bus Company
		NFM	Oxfordshire	Security Firm
		NFM	Plymouth	Devro Security
165.3750	170.1750	NFM	Ramsbottom	Snobs Private Hire
		NFM	Reading	Checkers Cars
		NFM	Cambridge	Able Cars
		NFM	Dumfries	Bee Hive Taxis
		NFM	Harlow	Regency Cars
		NFM	London	Minicab Firm Nine Elms
		NFM	London	US Embassy Secret Service
		NFM	Plymouth	Olympic Taxis

Base	Mobile	Mode	Location	User and Notes
		NFM	Warrington	Warrington Borough County
		NFM	Glasgow	Taxi
		NFM	Bath	Rainbow Taxis
		NFM	Bath	Rainbow Taxis
		NFM	Chelmsford	Taxis
165.3875	170.1875	NFM	Portsmouth	Taxis
		NFM	Cambridge	Alf Bucks
		NFM	Carlisle	Taxis
		NFM	Clacton-on-Sea	Apollo Taxis
		NFM	Cumbria	Repeater South Lakes
		NFM	Fakenham	Selective Fertilisers
		NFM	Glasgow	Taxi
		NFM	Grampian	Farm Workers
		NFM	Jersey	F Brown Recovery
		NFM	Louth	Community Repeater
		NFM	Luton Airport	Lep Transport
		NFM	Morecambe	Joe's Taxis
		NFM	Motherwell	United Taxis
		NFM	Newport	Red Dragon Taxis Ch 1
		NFM	Peterlee	Yellow Cabs
		NFM	Retford	Malcolm's Taxis
		NFM	Soham	Tompsett
		NFM	Tayside	Farm Workers
165.4000	170.2000	NFM	Peterborough	CBS Repeater
		NFM	Aberdeen	Oil Fabricators
		NFM	Bedford	Community Repeater
		NFM	Cambourne	Vending Firm
		NFM	Cornwall	Houpers Haulage
		NFM	Cumbria	Repeater South Lakes
		NFM	East Durham	Private Message
		NFM	Ipswich	Repeater
		NFM	Lancashire	Andersons Pumps
		NFM	London	IBA Maintenance
		NFM	London Underground	Baker Street
		NFM	London Underground	Balham
		NFM	London Underground	Clapham Common
		NFM	London Underground	Clapham North
		NFM	London Underground	Clapham South
		NFM	London Underground	Monument
		NFM	London Underground	Oxford Circus
		NFM	London Underground	Spare Channel
		NFM	London Underground	Tooting Bec
		NFM	London Underground	Tooting Broadway
		NFM	London (Neasden)	London Underground
		NFM	Milton Keynes	Repeater
		NFM	Morecambe	Delivery Service
		NFM	Nottingham	Taxis
		NFM	Worthing	Transport Co.

Base	Mobile	Mode	Location	User and Notes
165.4125	170.2125	NFM	Leeds	Motor Factors
		NFM	Brighton	Dyke Golf Club
		NFM	Bristol	Avon Alpha Control
		NFM	Cornwall	Kay Base
		NFM	Fife	Fife Regional Council
		NFM	London Underground	Bakerloo
		NFM	London Underground	District
		NFM	London Underground	Northern
		NFM	Newcastle	Plumbers
		NFM	Perth	King Contractors
		NFM	Plymouth	Ranger Base
		NFM	Shrewsbury	Flower Show Officals
165.4250	170.2250	NFM	Calne	Taxis
		NFM	Plymouth	Associated Leisure
		NFM	Chatteris	WBarnes
		NFM	Falkirk	Bruce Taxis
		NFM	Hitchin	DER Television
		NFM	Hull	Taxis
		NFM	Plymouth	Night Watch Security
		AM	Cleethorpes	Beavers Cars
		NFM	Pontypridd	Regal Taxis
		NFM	Wakefield	Taxls
165.4375	170.2375	NFM	Carlisle	H & E Trotter
		NFM	Truro	Pellows Waste
		NFM	Manchester	Taxis
		NFM	Haverfordwest	Taxis
		NFM	Humberside	Cash register Co
		NFM	Birmingham	Castle Security
		NFM	East Anglia	Eastern Counties Farmers
		NFM	Carnforth	Council Roads Department
		NFM	London Underground	East London
		NFM	Mansfield	Doctors Service
		NFM	Nationwide	Community Repeater
		NFM	Hull	Refrige Co
		NFM	West Midlands	Castle Security
		NFM	Peterborough	City Aerials Ltd
		NFM	Bristol	Taxis
165.4500	170.2500	NFM	Milton Keynes	Municipal Cleaning Services
		NFM	Southampton	PMR
		NFM	Edinburgh	Central Taxis
		NFM	London	Minicab Firm Greenford
		NFM	Nationwide	Community Repeater
		NFM	Nationwide	IBA Maintenance
		NFM	Poole	Repeater
		NFM	Newport	Alfa Taxis
		NFM	Frome	Taxis
165.4625	170.2625	NFM	Worthing	Nynex Cable Comms
		AM	Belfast	Water Board

Base	Mobile	Mode	Location	User and Notes
		AM	Sussex	Nynex Cable Comms
		NFM	Ipswich	Polar Base Freezers
		NFM	London Underground	Central
		NFM	London Underground	Jubilee
		NFM	London Underground	Victoria
		NFM	Nationwide	Community Repeater
		NFM	Poole	Repeater
		NFM	Ipswich	Freezer Co
		NFM	Gloucester	Repeater
		NFM	Tayside	Vets
		NFM	Grampian	Vets
		NFM	Bristol	Community Repeater
165.4750	170.2750	NFM	Scunthorpe	Courier Service
		NFM	Peterborough	CBS Repeater
		NFM	Southampton	MediCall Ch 3
		NFM	Jersey	Honorary Police
		NFM	Norfolk	Carphones
		NFM	Plymouth	Red Lightning Dispatch
		NFM	Poole	Repeater
		NFM	Suffolk	Carphones
		NFM	Newport	Community Repeater
		NFM	Fort Regent, Jersey	Honorary Police Ch 1
165.4875	170.2875	NFM	Birmingham	Taxis
		NFM	Milton Keynes	Quicker Cars
		NFM	Carlisle	Taxis
		NFM	Ashton-under-Lyne	Stamford Private Hire
		NFM	Oldham	Delta Cars
		NFM	Manchester	Taxi
		NFM	London	ODRATS
		NFM	Little Hulton	Radio Cars Ltd Taxis
		NFM	Barry	Flat Holm Maintenance
		NFM	Montrose	Taxis
165.5000	170.3000	NFM	Holyhead	Taxis
		NFM	Gorton	Beue Vue Cars
		NFM	Paisley	Taxis
		NFM	Cambridge	DER Television
		NFM	Letchwood	GFolly Builders
		NFM	Plymouth	Tower Cabs
		AM	Cleethorpes	Fon-a-Car
		NFM	Bournemouth	Token Amusements Ltd
		NFM	Dover	P&O Ferries Bus System
		AM	Glasgow	Taxi
165.5125	170.3125	NFM	Aberystwyth	Aber Cars
		NFM	Aberdeen	Taxi
		NFM	Bishop Stortford	Taxis
		NFM	Bolton	Halliwell Taxis
		NFM	Cambridge	Browns Taxis
		NFM	Gatwick	Airport Parking

Base	Mobile	Mode	Location	User and Notes
		NFM	Gloucester	TV Repairs
		NFM	Jersey	States
		NFM	Liverpool	Taxi
		NFM	Manchester	Taxi
		NFM	Poole	Repeater
		NFM	Stockport	Taxi
		NFM	Swansea	Lakes Taxis
		NFM	Worthing	Taxis
		NFM	Wrexham	Club Taxis
165.5250	170.3250	NFM	Peterborough	Moore TV Rental
		NFM	Bristol	Community Repeater
		NFM	Central London	Courier
		NFM	Dudley	Merry Hill Security
		NFM	London	Embassy Cars
		NFM	Manchester	Taxi
		NFM	Morecambe	PMR
		NFM	Peterborough	DER Television
		NFM	Reading	1st Yellow Cars
		NFM	Urmston	Phoenix Taxis
		NFM	Wiltshire	TV Repairs
165.5375	170.3375	NFM	Wolverhampton	Skip Hire
		NFM	Oxford	Community Repeater
		NFM	Scunthorpe	British Steel Emergency
		NFM	Abingdon	Eagle Security Co
		NFM	Heathfield	Comrep
		NFM	North Yorkshire	Doctor Service
165.5500	170.3500	NFM	Southampton	Taxis
		NFM	Edinburgh	Qeo Couriers
		NFM	Blackburn	Intack Private Hire
		NFM	Edinburgh	Tarmac Roadstone
		NFM	Nationwide	Community Repeater
		NFM	Plymouth	Military Security (RM)
		NFM	London	Dry Cleaning Company
		NFM	London Campden	Council Traffic Wardens
165.5625	170.3625	NFM	Norwich	Blueline Taxis
		NFM	Yorks	Water Board
		NFM	Tyne & Wear	Healthcall Service
		NFM	Swindon	Games Machines
		NFM	Wirral	Brombourgh Cabs
		NFM	Poole	Fernside Recovery
		NFM	Edinburgh	Trinity Roofing
		NFM	Edinburgh	Castle Security
		NFM	Nationwide	Community Repeater
		NFM	Poole	Repeater
		NFM	Edinburgh	Carpet Fitting Co.
		NFM	Suffolk	East Counties Farmers Ch2
		NFM	Brighton	Security Company
		NFM	Glasgow	Taxi

Base	Mobile	Mode	Location	User and Notes
		NFM	Gloucester	Monarch Security
		NFM	Cheltenham	Bus Inspectors
		NFM	Bristol	Community Repeater
		NFM	Gloucester	Fruit Mach. Engineers Ch 1
		NFM	East	East Counties Farmers Ch2
		NFM	Portsmouth	Bus Co
165.5750	170.3750	AM	Manchester	New United Taxis
		NFM	Edinburgh	Eden Aerial Riggers
		NFM	Accrington	D-Line Cars
		NFM	Cambridge	HRobinson
		NFM	Felixstowe	Taxis
		NFM	Haverhill	Jennings Transport
		NFM	Kings Lynn	DER Television
		NFM	Woodbridge	KTuckwell Engineers
		AM	Grimsby	Taxis
		NFM	Newport	Star Taxis
		NFM	Montrose	Farm Workers
165.5875	170.3875	NFM	Blackburn	A&B Private Hire
		NFM	Stockport	Taxis
		NFM	Swinton	Radio Cars Ltd
		NFM	Manchester	Taxi
		NFM	Macclesfield	Taxi
		NFM	Hull	Rediffusion TV Rental
		NFM	Harpenden	DER Television
		NFM	Luton	DER Television
		NFM	Hewhaven	Taxis
165.6000	170.4000	NFM	Stockport	Taxi
		NFM	Aldridge	Alpha Taxis
		NFM	Bury	Taxis
		NFM	Cornwall	English China Clay
		NFM	Glasgow	Taxi
		NFM	Glossop	Shadow Taxis
		NFM	London	Carreras Rothams Displays
		NFM	Manchester	Taxi
		NFM	Paddington	Z Car hire
		NFM	Paisley	Taxis
		NFM	Strathclyde	British Transport Police (D)
		NFM	Swansea Docks	Train Signal Box
165.6125	170.4125	NFM	Scunthorpe	Steel Works Maintenance
		NFM	Castleton	Castleton Cars
		NFM	Dunstable	Hunter Taxis
		NFM	Grimsby	Council Maintenance
		NFM	Jersey Airport	Airport Duty Officer Ch1
		NFM	Kirkham	Taxis
		NFM	Lakenheath	Base Taxis
		NFM	Linlithgow	Taxi
		NFM	Perth	Council Plumbers
		NFM	Sheffield	Indoor Market Security

Base	Mobile	Mode	Location	User and Notes
		NFM	St Austell	ECC Pits
		NFM	Stanstead	Taxis
165.6250	170.4250	NFM	Manchester	PMR
		NFM	Co. Durham	Haulage Coal Wagons
		NFM	Plymouth	Taxis
		NFM	Glasgow	Taxis
		NFM	Southampton	Buses
		NFM	Oxford	Royal Taxis
		NFM	Leicester	City Buses
		NFM	Bolton	Tonge Moor Private Hire
		NFM	Nationwide	Transport Police Channel 3
		NFM	London	Transport Police
		NFM	Brighton	Transport Police
		NFM	Plymouth	Central Taxis
		AM	Bristol	Bond Delivery
		NFM	East Dereham	Acab Taxis
165.6375	170.4375	NFM	Swansea	BT Police
		NFM	Newport	BT Police
		NFM	Birmingham	BR Transport Police
		NFM	Chester	BR Transport Police
		NFM	Crewe	BR Transport Police
		NFM	Liverpool	Transport Police
		NFM	London	BR Transport Police (Victoria)
		NFM	Manchester	Transport Police
		NFM	Nationwide	Transport Police Channel 2
		NFM	Glasgow	Taxi
		NFM	Avon	British Transport Police
165.6500	170.4500	NFM	Glasgow	Railway Workmen
		NFM	London	Transport Police
		NFM	Brighton	British Transport Police
		NFM	London Underground	Transport Police
		NFM	Lothian And Borders	British Transport Police (DA)
		NFM	Nationwide	British Transport Police Ch 1
165.6625	170.4625	NFM	Llandudno	Taxi Service
		NFM	Consett	Taxis
		NFM	Amlwch	Taxis
		NFM	Rochdale	Strand Private Hire
		NFM	Macclesfield	Macc Radio Cars
		NFM	Manchester	Taxi
		NFM	Cornwall	English China Clay
		NFM	Jersey	Public Services
		NFM	Bristol	City Line Buses
		NFM	Jersey	Public Works
		AM	Scarborough	Laker Taxis
		NFM	London	Auto Car Repair
165.6750	170.4750	NFM	Reading	ABC Cars
		NFM	Manchester	Taxi
		NFM	St Annes	West Star Taxis

Base	Mobile	Mode	Location	User and Notes
		AM	Scarborough	Laker Taxis
		NFM	Glasgow	PMR
		NFM	Bolton	Taxis
		NFM	Sheffield	Taxis
		NFM	Stanwell	TNT Carriers
		NFM	Dunstable	E.JAllan
		NFM	Hull	British Rail
		NFM	Scunthorpe	British Steel Transport
		AM	Ipswich	Crown Taxi
165.6875	170.4875	NFM	Lincoln	Amusement Mach. Mainten.
		NFM	Peterborough	Bell Fruit Machines
		NFM	Cheshire	Fruit Machine Servicing
		NFM	Edinburgh	Bell Fruit Machines
		NFM	Ipswich	Bell Fruit Machines
		NFM	London	Bell Fruit Machines
165.7000	170.5000	NFM	Portsmouth	Aqua Taxis
		AM	Christchurch	Critax Taxis
		NFM	Brighton	Taxis
		NFM	Brighton	Taxis
		NFM	Chatteris	Catwood Potatoes
		NFM	Glasgow	Taxis
		NFM	Guernsey	T & D Services
		NFM	Hamilton	Cadzow Cars
		NFM	Humberside	Transport Co
		NFM	Ipswich	Clarke Demolition
		NFM	Ipswich	Thompson & Morgan
		NFM	Jersey	T & D Services
		NFM	Kings Lynn	Ambassador Taxis
		NFM	Saffron Walden	Crusader Cars
		NFM	Shaw	Motown Private Hire
		NFM	Southampton	Taxis
165.7125	170.5125	NFM	Edinburgh	Taxis
		NFM	Tamworth	Acorn Taxis
		NFM	Basildon	Taxis
		NFM	Crewe	Taxis
		NFM	Folkestone	Folkestone City Buses
		NFM	Ipswich	E.HRoberts
		NFM	Newcastle	Castle Cars
		NFM	Aldershot	Taxi Co
		NFM	Headham	Gower Ltd
		NFM	Cambridge	Four Four Taxis
		NFM	Ipswich	E H Roberts
		NFM	Bristol	Blue Iris Coaches
		NFM	Bognor Regis	Taxis
		NFM	Edinburgh	Taxis
165.7250	165.7250	NFM	Luton	PMR
		NFM	Truro	Hospital Services
		NFM	Ayr	Railway Workmen

Base	Mobile	Mode	Location	User and Notes
		NFM	Blackburn	Manhattan Private Hire
		NFM	Hatfield	Tarmac Construction
		NFM	Bolton	MacArthur Private Hire
		NFM	Hockwold Cum Wilton	Bob's Taxis
		NFM	Woodbridge	Notcutt Nurseries
		NFM	Scunthorpe	British Steel Trains
		NFM	Hockwold	Bobs Taxis
		NFM	Nationwide	Tarmac Construction Co
		NFM	Ipswich	DER
		NFM	Bournemouth	Southern Dispatch Couriers
		NFM	Woodbridge	Notgutt Nurseries
165.7375	170.5375	NFM	Widnes	Taxis
		NFM	East Durham	PMR
		NFM	Bury	Royal Taxis
		NFM	Belfast	TNT Carriers
		NFM	Danbury	Amey Roadstones
		NFM	Sudbury	Amey Roadstones
		NFM	Swindon	Tramps Taxis
		NFM	Stockton-on-Tees	Taxi Service
165.7500	170.5500	NFM	Machynlleth	Hendre Quarry
		NFM	Bournemouth	Dustvans
		NFM	Cambridge	Cambus
		NFM	Carlisle	Council Highways
		NFM	Dundee	Taxi
		NFM	East	Norfolks Coach Company
		NFM	Hove	Council
		NFM	Luton	Luton Borough Council
		NFM	Newark	Taxis
		NFM	Norfolk	Bus Company
		NFM	Norwich	ECOC
		NFM	Perth	Taxi
		NFM	Peterborough	Viscount Travel
		NFM	Reading	Council
		NFM	Stoke-on-Trent	Council
		NFM	Swindon	Town Council
		NFM	Wiltshire	Thamesdown Council
165.7625	170.5625	NFM	Brierley Hill	Council
		AM	London	Southall Council
		NFM	Aberdeen	Waste Masters
		NFM	Bedfordshire	District Council
		NFM	Bolton	District Council
		NFM	Bournemouth	Yellow Buses
		NFM	Bournemouth	Public Transport Ch 1
		NFM	Cunninghame	SRC Local Council Services
		NFM	Dundee	City Council Dog Catcher
		NFM	Edinburgh	Lothian Regional Council
		NFM	Ipswich	Housing Board
		NFM	St Saviour Parish, Jersey	Honorary Police Ch 5

Base	Mobile	Mode	Location	User and Notes
		NFM	Llanelli	Council
		NFM	Luton	Contractor
		NFM	Newcastle	PMR
		NFM	Norfolk	Norfolk County Council
		NFM	North West	PMR
		NFM	Poole	Repeater
		NFM	Preston	District Council
165.7750	170.5750	NFM	Havant	Council
		AM	London	Croydon Council
		NFM	Cwmbran	Cwmbran Plumbing Plc
		NFM	Dudley	Council
		NFM	Glasgow	Strathkelvin District Council
		NFM	Hayling Island	Council
		NFM	Huntingdon	County Council
		NFM	Ipswich	Brough Transport
		NFM	Jersey	States of Jersey Repeater
		NFM	North Yorkshire	Doctor Service
		NFM	Norwich	Norwich City Council
		NFM	Portsmouth	City Council
		NFM	Somerset	County Council
		NFM	Southend	Council Civil Patrol
		NFM	Southend on Sea	District Council
		NFM	Stoke-on-Trent	Council Parks Dept.
		NFM	Wiltshire	Wilts County Council
		NFM	Wycombe	Council Ducks
165.7875	170.5875	NFM	Peterborough	Betta Cars
		NFM	Stoke-on-Trent	Skip Hire
		NFM	Fawley	Power Station
		NFM	Carlisle	County Contracting North
		NFM	Boston	OLGA
		NFM	London	US Embassy Secret Service
		NFM	Manchester	Motorway Maintenance
		NFM	Poole	Repeater
		NFM	Suffolk	Mid Suffolk District Council
		NFM	Swindon	Thamesdown Council
		NFM	Hyndburn	Accrington Bus Control
		NFM	Peterborough	Betta Cabs
		NFM	Bournemouth	Council
		NFM	Suffolk	Council
		NFM	Peterborough	Betta Cars Amalgamated
165.8000	170.6000	NFM	Dudley	Five Star Taxis
		NFM	Brighton	Streamline Taxis
		NFM	Bristol	RSPCA
		NFM	Dundee	Taxis
		NFM	Felixstowe	Peewit Caravans
		NFM	Jersey	Normans Channel 2
		NFM	Kent	Tour De France (French)
		NFM	London	Taxis

The UK Scanning Directory

Base	Mobile	Mode	Location	User and Notes
		NFM	Luton	C.JPrivate Hire
		NFM	Sheffield	Taxis
		NFM	Swansea	Hooper Taxis
165.8100	165.8100	NFM	Belgium	Fire & Ambulance
165.8125	170.6125	NFM	Preston	Cabtax Taxis
		NFM	St Austell	Taxis
		NFM	Cambridge	Panther Cars
		NFM	London	ODRATS
		NFM	Cleethorpes	Bob's Cars
		NFM	Bath	Abbey Taxis Ch 2
		NFM	Preston	Taxis
165.8250	170.6250	NFM	Glasgow	Taxi Company
		NFM	Dudley	Midland Taxis
		NFM	Bath	Abbey Taxis
		NFM	Bolton	ABA Private Hire
		NFM	North West	PMR
		NFM	Ipswich	Wilding & Smith
		NFM	March	Worral Potatoes
		NFM	Oxford	ABC Taxis
		NFM	Bath	AA Taxis
		NFM	Bath	Abbey Taxis Ch 1
		NFM	Ipswich	Wilding & Smith Aggregate
		NFM	March	Worrall Potatoes
165.8300	165.8300	NFM	Belgium	Fire & Ambulance
165.8375	170.6375	NFM	Peterborough	Ace Taxis
		NFM	Plymouth	Taxis
		NFM	Oldham	Limeline Private Hire
		NFM	Macclesfield	Taxi
		NFM	Ely	A.ELee Farms
		NFM	Cardiff	Transport Firm
		NFM	London	ODRATS
		NFM	St. Osyth	Tudor Taxis
		NFM	Glasgow	Taxi
		NFM	Peterborough	Hereward Ace Taxis
		NFM	Caistor	Hurdiss Quarries
165.8500	165.8500	NFM	Belgium	Fire & Ambulance
165.8500	170.6500	NFM	Plymouth	Estate Security
		AM	Jersey	Tantivy Coaches
		NFM	Bristol	RSPCA
		NFM	Carlisle	Carlisle Drivers
		NFM	Carlisle	Taxis
		NFM	Falkirk	Blue Star Taxis (Star)
		NFM	Gt. Manchester	Avacabs
		NFM	Haddenham	A.F. Buck
		NFM	Leigh	Avacabs
		NFM	Liverpool	City Cars
		NFM	London	ODRATS
		NFM	Three Holes	Hallsworth Framing Co.

Base	Mobile	Mode	Location	User and Notes
165.8625	170.6625	NFM	Leeds	Courier Service
		NFM	North West	PMR
		NFM	Hythe	Hythe Ferry And Pier
		NFM	Cambridge	Securicor
		NFM	Cardiff	PMR
		NFM	Jersey	Pony Express Delivery
		NFM	Nationwide	Securicor Channel 6
165.8700	165.8700	NFM	Belgium	Fire & Ambulance
165.8750	170.6750	NFM	Birmingham	Black Cabs
		NFM	Birmingham	Gas Contractors
		NFM	Fleetwood	Nightwatchmen
		NFM	Edinburgh	Pony Express Couriers
		NFM	Guernsey	Securicor
		NFM	Space	Myr Space Station
		NFM	Avon	Community Repeater
		NFM	Nationwide	Securicor Channel 2
165.8875	170.6875	NFM	Horwich	Duval Security
		NFM	Preston	Builders
		NFM	Bournemouth	Council Tarmac Gang
		NFM	Nationwide	Securicor Channel 3
165.8900	165.8900	NFM	Belgium	Fire & Ambulance
165.9000	170.7000	NFM	Sheffield	Amusement Mach. Mainten.
		NFM	Rochdale	Norden Cars
		NFM	West Drayton	LHR Express Cars
		NFM	Wantage	Robert's Taxis
		NFM	Ipswich	Taxis
		NFM	Dartford	Abba Dart Taxis
		NFM	Swansea	Lloyds Taxis
		NFM	Atherton	Atherton Cab Co.
		NFM	Leigh	Atherton Cab Co.
		NFM	Gt. Manchester	Atherton Cab Co.
		AM	Swindon	Viking Taxis
		NFM	Dundee	Taxi
		NFM	Hitchin	Duggan's Taxis
		NFM	London	US Embassy Secret Service
		NFM	Airdrie	Twin Cabs
165.9100	165.9100	NFM	Belgium	Fire & Ambulance
165.9125	170.7125	NFM	Walsall	MFI Deliveries
		NFM	Jersey	A1 Double Glazing
		NFM	Devizes	Community Repeater
		NFM	Nationwide	Securicor Channel 7
165.9250	170.7250	NFM	Portsmouth	Aqua Cabs
		NFM	Cleveleys	Taxis
		NFM	Portsmouth	Taxis
		NFM	Carlisle	PMR
		NFM	Middleton	Middleton Radio Cars
		NFM	Manchester	Taxi
		NFM	Aberdeen	Oil Industry

Base	Mobile	Mode	Location	User and Notes
		NFM	Jersey	Hire Cars
		NFM	Nationwide	Community Repeater
		NFM	Poole	Data Repeater
		NFM	Sheffield	Valley Taxis
		NFM	Stockton-on-Tees	Taxi Service
		NFM	Cirencester	Gerry's Cars
		NFM	Brighton	Car Mechanics Ch 1
		NFM	Cleveland	6767 Taxis
165.9300	165.9300	NFM	Belgium	Fire & Ambulance
165.9375	170.7375	NFM	Newcastle	Central Heating Co.
		AM	Portsmouth	American News
		NFM	Liverpool	Gas Fitters
		NFM	North West	PMR
		NFM	Swansea	Thorn Homeserve
		NFM	Nationwide	Securicor Channel 8
165.9500	170.7500	NFM	March	SMorton Ltd
		NFM	Northampton	Taxis
		NFM	Norwich	Taxis
		NFM	Belgium	Fire & Ambulance
		NFM	Cumbria	South Lakes Bin Men
		NFM	Jersey	Collas & Le Sueur
		NFM	London	Minicab Firm Southall
		NFM	March	Guy Morton
		NFM	Norfolk	Norfolk Farm Produce
		AM	Grimsby	Fletchers Taxis
		NFM	Dundee	Taxis
		NFM	Brighton	Car Mechanics Ch 2
165.9625	170.7625	NFM	Birmingham	Gas Contractors
		NFM	Newcastle	PMR
		NFM	Bournemouth	Driving School
		NFM	Bournemouth	Council Parks Division
		NFM	Bournemouth	Garage Repairs
		NFM	Liverpool	Taxi
		NFM	Jersey	PMR
		NFM	Isle of Wight	Landscaping Service
		NFM	Nationwide	Securicor Channel 4
165.9700	165.9700	NFM	Belgium	Fire & Ambulance
165.9750	170.7750	NFM	Bristol	Video Company
		NFM	Brighton	Securicor
		NFM	Haverfordwest	Securicor
		NFM	St Annes	Night Security
		NFM	Nationwide	Securicor Chan 1 Emerg.
165.9875	170.7875	NFM	North West	PMR
		NFM	Jersey	Securicor
		NFM	Nationwide	Securicor Channel 5
165.9900	165.9900	NFM	Belgium	Fire & Ambulance
166.0000	170.8000	NFM	Hull	Taxis
		NFM	Chelmsford	Farmers Supplies

Base	Mobile	Mode	Location	User and Notes
		NFM	Prestatyn	Robert's Taxis
		NFM	Stevenage	Parker Cars
		NFM	West Drayton	Station Cars
		NFM	Swansea	Taxi Shop
		NFM	Space	Soviet Satellite (Myr)
		AM	Sheffield	Ace Taxis
		NFM	Guernsey	Vaudins Taxi
		NFM	Linlithgow	Taxi
		NFM	Martham	Fleggmart
		NFM	Perth	Taxis
		NFM	Tollerton	Gadd's Farm
		NFM	Torpoint	Taxis
		NFM	Winton	M&G Electronics
		NFM	Glasgow	Taxi
166.0100	166.0100	NFM	Belgium	Fire & Ambulance
166.0125	170.8125	NFM	Aberdeen	Taxi
		NFM	Peterborough	On Site Tyres
		NFM	Hamilton	Taxi Owners Association
		NFM	Kings Lynn	Baconpac Co
		NFM	Peterborough	On-Site-Tyres
		NFM	Glasgow	Taxi
		NFM	Cardiff	Roath Taxis
166.0250	170.8250	NFM	Newcastle	Taxis
		NFM	Oldham	Taxis
		NFM	Manchester	Taxi
		NFM	Peterborough	Hotpoint
		NFM	Hillingdon	Civic Centre Security
		AM	Aberdeen	Oil Industry
		NFM	Bolton	Taxis
		NFM	Cornwall	English China Clay
		NFM	Kennyhill	J.A Butcher
		NFM	Peterborough	Hotpoint
		NFM	Wooddridge	Council Vans
166.0300	166.0300	NFM	Belgium	Fire & Ambulance
166.0375	170.8375	AM	Grimsby	Taxis
		NFM	Peterborough	A2B Taxis
		NFM	E London	Taxis
		NFM	Redruth	Amtrack Deliveries
		NFM	Macclesfield	Atax
		AM	Aberdeen	Taxi
		NFM	Cromer	Biffa Ltd
		NFM	Jersey	Pentagon Ltd
		NFM	Motherwell	Forgewood Security
		NFM	London	Biffa Waste Disposal
		NFM	Newport	A1 Ship Hire
166.0500	166.0500	NFM	Belgium	Fire & Ambulance
166.0500	170.8500	NFM	Bowness	Lake Windermere Rangers
		NFM	Liverpool	Bruno Security

Base	Mobile	Mode	Location	User and Notes
		NFM	Hawick	Roxburgh Taxis
		NFM	Chelmsford	Borough Council
		NFM	Walsall	Environmental Health
		NFM	Southampton	Council Engineering
		NFM	Cardiff	Council
		NFM	Lancashire	Road Repairs
		AM	Belfast	Water Board
		NFM	Preston	Council
		NFM	Doncaster	Council Manual Workers
		NFM	Jersey	PMR
		NFM	Newcastle	PMR
		NFM	Oxford	Oxford City Council
		NFM	Suffolk	Suffolk Coastal Council
		NFM	Motherwell	District Council
		NFM	London	Hillingdon Council
		NFM	Suffolk Coastal	Council
		NFM	Wokinghan	Council
		NFM	Doncaster	Metro Borough Council
		NFM	Suffolk	Coastal District Council
		NFM	Gloucester	County Council
		NFM	Powys	Ambulance
166.0625	170.8625	AM	Brent	Council
		NFM	Colchester	Council
		NFM	Manchester	City Council
		NFM	Slough	Borough Council
		NFM	Blackburn	Silverline Private Hire
		NFM	Slough	Council
		NFM	Newbury	Council
		NFM	Eakering	BP Depot
		NFM	Colchester	Borough Council
		NFM	Dundee	City Council Workshop
		NFM	Tonbridge	Borough Council
		AM	Cleethorpes	Coaches (Peter Sheffield)
		NFM	Cleethorpes	Borough Council
		NFM	Hertfordshire	County Council
		NFM	Slough	Council
		NFM	Luton	Repeater
166.0700	166.0700	NFM	Belgium	Fire & Ambulance
166.0750	170.8750	NFM	Luton	Repeater
		NFM	Manchester	Dog Warden
		NFM	Stoke-on-Trent	PMR
		NFM	Chelmsford	Dustcart
		NFM	Cleveland	Gritters
		NFM	Carlisle	County Contracting East
		NFM	Manchester	Trafford Council
		NFM	Southampton	MediCall Ch 4
		NFM	Edinburgh	Lothian Regional Council
		NFM	Hertfordshire	District Council

Base	Mobile	Mode	Location	User and Notes
		NFM	Ipswich	Borough Council (Parks)
		NFM	Jersey	Elizabeth Castle
		NFM	Jersey	Public Services
		NFM	Nationwide	Securicor
		NFM	Public	works guernsey
		NFM	London, Harringay	Council Floods Control
		NFM	Ipswich	Council parks Dept Anglla
166.0875	170.8875	NFM	Surrey	Surrey Council (callsign zulu)
		NFM	Fleetwood	Wyre Council
		NFM	Fleetwood	Lifeguards
		NFM	Poulton	Council
		NFM	Southampton	City Buses
		NFM	Oldham	Council Rubbish Men
		NFM	Wirral	Education Security
		NFM	Berkshire	Council Ch 1
		NFM	Bristol	Ambulance Service
		NFM	Bolton	District Council
		NFM	Edinburgh	Lothian Regional Council
		NFM	Essex	Havering Council
		NFM	Tayside	Council Leisure & Recreation
		NFM	Tayside	Council Roads Depart.
		NFM	Wirral	Education Security
		NFM	Cleethorpes	G.C Transport
		NFM	Grimsby	G.C Transport
		NFM	London	Westminster Council
		NFM	Grimsby	Stagecoach Buses
166.0900	166.0900	NFM	Belgium	Fire & Ambulance
166.1000	170.9000	NFM	Sandwell	Medicall
		NFM	Avon	Ambulance
		NFM	Bristol	Ambulance Service
		NFM	Chester	Ambulance Service
		NFM	Jersey	Turner/Bluebird Cabs
		NFM	Merseyside	Ambulance Service
		NFM	Norfolk	Ambulance Service
		NFM	North Yorkshire	Ambulance Service
		NFM	Northumberland	Ambulance Service
		NFM	Nottinghamshire	Ambulance Service
		NFM	Oxfordshire	Ambulance Service
		NFM	Tyne And Wear	Ambulance Service
166.1100	166.1100	NFM	Belgium	Fire & Ambulance
166.1125	170.9125	AM	Grimsby	Town Council
		NFM	Wakefield	District Council.
		NFM	Newcastle	Council
		NFM	Newmarket	British Legion Security
		NFM	Isle of Man	Local Government
		NFM	Doncaster	Council Metro Clean
		NFM	Nationwide	Community Repeater
		NFM	Newcastle	PMR

Base	Mobile	Mode	Location	User and Notes
		NFM	Poole	Repeater
		NFM	Grimsby	Road Maintainence
		NFM	London	Camden Council
		NFM	London	Tower Hamlets Council
166.1250	170.9250	NFM	Peterborough	Holland Farms
		NFM	Carlisle	County Contracting West
		NFM	Bexley Heath	Council
		NFM	London	Taxis
		NFM	Swansea City	Roads Department
		NFM	Hounslow	Traffic Wardens
		NFM	Scarborough	Council
		NFM	Aylesbury	District Council
		NFM	Space	Soviet Mir Telemetry
		NFM	Doncaster	Council Emergency Callout
		NFM	London	Bexley Council
		NFM	Aylesbury	Vale Council
		NFM	Buckinghamshire	Council
		NFM	Newport	Neighbourhood Watch
		NFM	Barrow	PMR
		NFM	Poole	Repeater
166.1300	166.1300	NFM	Belgium	Fire & Ambulance
166.1375	170.9375	NFM	Newmarket	McCourts Ch 9
		NFM	Merseyside	Ambulance Service
		NFM	Basildon	District Council
		NFM	Hertfordshire	District Council
		NFM	London	Harrow Council
		NFM	Oxford	Bus Company
		NFM	Sheffield	Brown Construction
		NFM	Brent	Council
		NFM	Surrey	Council
		NFM	Isle of wight	water Board
		NFM	Oxford	Motor Service Inspectors
		NFM	Hertfordshire	Council
		NFM	Basildon	Council
		NFM	Glasgow	Taxi
		NFM	Newport	Refuse Skip Control
166.1500	166.1500	NFM	Belgium	Fire & Ambulance
166.1500	170.9500	NFM	Bromley	Bromley Park Police
		NFM	Doncaster	City Council
		NFM	Fleetwood	PMR
		NFM	Workington	PMR
		NFM	Brighton	Council
		NFM	Wirral	Council Housing
		NFM	Llandudno	Flood Planning
		NFM	Berkshire	Council Ch 2
		NFM	Windsor	Council
		NFM	Brighton	Brough Council
		NFM	Aberdeen	Dee Van Hire

Base	Mobile	Mode	Location	User and Notes
		NFM	Doncaster	Council Office Workers
		NFM	Liverpool	City Council
		NFM	Nationwide	Community Repeater
		NFM	Poole	Repeater
		NFM	Wirral	Council Security
		NFM	London	Bromley Council
		NFM	London	Enfield Council
		NFM	London	Epping Forest Council
		NFM	London	Southwark Council
		NFM	Bromley	Council
		NFM	Brighton	Local Authority
		NFM	Newport	Council Ch 1
166.1625	170.9625	NFM	Bracknell	District Council
		NFM	North West	PMR
		NFM	Sheffield	Parks Security
		NFM	Salford	District Council
		NFM	Stirling	PMR
		AM	London	Hammersmith Council
		NFM	Forest Heath	Council
		NFM	Winboune	Council
166.1700	166.1700	NFM	Belgium	Fire & Ambulance
166.1750	170.9750	NFM	Manchester	PMR
		NFM	Nottinghamshire	Ambulance Service
		NFM	Burnley	Council Inspectors
		NFM	Manchester	City Council
		AM	Belfast	NI Railways
		NFM	Macclesfield	Taxi
		NFM	Manchester	Taxi
		NFM	Vale of White Horse	District Council
		NFM	Thanet	District Council
		NFM	Cambridge	District Council
		NFM	Central Scotland	Stirling Council
		NFM	Grays	District Council
		NFM	Ipswich	Jewsons Builders Merchants
		NFM	Kings Lynn	District Council
		NFM	London	Thames Ditton Council
		NFM	Newcastle	Council Housing Repairs
		NFM	Norfolk	District Council
		NFM	Christchurch	Council
		NFM	St Albans	Council Maintenance
		NFM	Welwyn Garden City	District Council
		NFM	Grimsby	Council
		NFM	London	Lewisham Council
		NFM	Ipswich	Jewsons Builders
		NFM	West Norfolk	Council
		NFM	Kings Lynn	West Norfolk Council
		NFM	Abingdon	Council
		NFM	Welwyn & Hatfield	Council

Base	Mobile	Mode	Location	User and Notes
		NFM	Cambridge	Council
		NFM	Brighton	Local Authority
		NFM	Newport	Council Dustbins
		NFM	Lanark	Council Repairs
		NFM	Burnley	Burnley Borough Council
		NFM	Harrow	Council
		NFM	Lancaster	Council
		NFM	Morecambe	Council
		NFM	Viewpark	Council Repairs
166.1875	170.9875	NFM	Hull	City Council
		NFM	West Midlands	Environmental Health
		NFM	Dudley	Ambulance Service
		NFM	Carlisle	City Council
		NFM	Ealing Cduncil	london
		NFM	Aberdeen	Council Roads Department
		NFM	Folkestone	District Council
		NFM	Hull	Council Cleansing Dept.
		NFM	Ipswich	Doctor's Call Outs
		NFM	London	Ealing Borough Council
		NFM	Manchester	Water Board
		NFM	Poole	Repeater
		NFM	Tandridge	Council
		NFM	Spelthorth	Council
		NFM	Nottingham	County Council
		NFM	Tedford	Council
		NFM	Ipswich	Doctors on Call
166.1900	166.1900	NFM	Belgium	Fire & Ambulance
166.2000	168.3000	NFM	France	TEC
166.2000	171.0000	NFM	Wakefield	Hospital Services
		NFM	Dudley	Ambulance Service
		NFM	Dyfed	West Wales Ambulance
		NFM	Nationwide	Manpower Services
		NFM	Cheshire	Ambulance Service
		NFM	Cleveland	Ambulance Service
		NFM	Dyfed	Ambulance Service
		NFM	Hampshire	Ambulance Service
		NFM	Lancashire	Ambulance Service
		NFM	Lincolnshire	Ambulance Service
		NFM	London	Ambulance (Orange)
		NFM	Mid Glamorgan	Ambulance Service
		NFM	Merseyside	Ambulance Service
		NFM	Perth	Community Data Repeater
		NFM	Warrington	Ambulance Service
		NFM	West Midlands	Ambulance Service
		NFM	West Yorkshire	Ambulance Service
		NFM	Chichester	St Richards Hospital
166.2100	166.2100	NFM	Belgium	Fire & Ambulance
166.2125	170.0125	NFM	Newport	Gwent Council Decorators

Base	Mobile	Mode	Location	User and Notes
		NFM	London	US Embassy Secret Service
		NFM	Manchester	District Council
		NFM	Swindon	Cooper's Metals
		NFM	Hampshire	Council
		NFM	Essex	Council
		NFM	Chiltern	Council Amersham Ducks
		NFM	Greenwich	Council
		NFM	Woking	Council
		NFM	Glasgow	Taxi
		NFM	Cardiff	Bunnon
		NFM	Crawley	Crawley BC
		NFM	Castle Point	Borough Council
		NFM	Norfolk	ICL
166.2250	171.0250	NFM	Nottingham	Taxis
		NFM	Preston	Refuse Collectors
		NFM	Preston	Council Maintenance
		NFM	Reigate & Banstead	Council
		NFM	Jersey	Gas Board
		AM	Plymouth	City Bus Company
		NFM	Bridgnorth	Bridgnorth District Council
		NFM	Aberdeen	Fish Market
		NFM	Ashford	District Council
		NFM	Jersey	Gas Board
		NFM	Kilmarnock	Parks Department
		NFM	Livingstone	West Lothian District Council
		NFM	Nationwide	Local Authorities
		NFM	London	Kensington Council
		AM	London	Newham Council
		NFM	Guildford	Council
		NFM	Lewisham	Council
		NFM	Newham	Council
		NFM	Ashford	Council
		NFM	Eastlelgh	Council
		NFM	Cambridge	Council
		NFM	Gwent	Blaena Gwent Council
		NFM	Lincoln	Local Authority
166.2300	166.2300	NFM	Belgium	Fire & Ambulance
166.2375	171.0375	NFM	Ashton	Ambulance
		NFM	Manchester	Thameside Council
		NFM	Chichester	Council
		NFM	Aberdeen	TV Repairs
		NFM	Bathgate	Streamline Taxis (Streamline)
		NFM	Nationwide	Community Repeater
		NFM	Cwnbran	Council
		NFM	Norfolk	Haller's Skip Hire
166.2500	166.2500	NFM	Luton	Contractor
166.2500	171.0500	NFM	Elmbridge	Council
		NFM	Hull	City parks

Base	Mobile	Mode	Location	User and Notes
		NFM	Tyneside	Tyne Tunnel
		NFM	Chandlers Ford	Taxis
		NFM	Hertfordshire	District Council
		NFM	Belgium	Fire & Ambulance
		NFM	Humberside	Beverly Council
		NFM	Harlow	Council
		NFM	Basingstoke	Council.
		NFM	Lambeth	Council
		NFM	Dundee	Electrical Repairs
		NFM	Manchester	House Calls
		NFM	Poole	Repeater
		NFM	Hull	Parks Dept
		NFM	Brighton	Brighton Council
		NFM	Jersey	Tantivy Holiday Coaches
		NFM	Trowbridge	Builders
		NFM	Bury St Edmunds	Bury Council
		NFM	Kingston	Council
166.2625	171.0625	NFM	Dundee	Data Link
		NFM	Essex	Council Ch2
		NFM	Bolton	Dog Warden
		NFM	Braintree	Borough Council
		NFM	Preston	Preston Buses
		NFM	London	Bus & Coach Co.
		NFM	Nuneaton & Bedworth	Council
		NFM	Edinburgh	Citadel Couriers (City)
		NFM	Rochford	Council
		NFM	Richmond	Council
		NFM	Chesterfield	Bus Company
		NFM	Braintree	Council
		NFM	Thetford	Broadland Council
166.2700	166.2700	NFM	Belgium	Fire & Ambulance
166.2750	171.0750	NFM	Grangemouth	Central Taxis (Central)
		NFM	Lancashire	Ambulance Service
		NFM	Lincolnshire	Ambulance Service
		NFM	London	Ambulance (Orange) S West
		NFM	Somerset	Ambulance Service
		NFM	Sussex	Ambulance Service
		NFM	West Midlands	Ambulance Service
		NFM	South Cumbria	Ambulance Service
166.2875	171.0875	NFM	Belfast	NI Ambulance Service
		NFM	Buckinghamshire	Ambulance Service
		NFM	Cornwall	Ambulance Service
		NFM	Kent	Ambulance Service
		NFM	Manchester	Ambulance Service
		NFM	Nottinghamshire	Ambulance Service
		NFM	Northumberland	Ambulance Service
		NFM	Tyne And Wear	Ambulance Service
		AM	Withenshaw	Paramedics

Base	Mobile	Mode	Location	User and Notes
166.2900	166.2900	NFM	Belgium	Fire & Ambulance
166.3000	171.1000	NFM	Carlisle	Ambulance Service
		NFM	Cumbria	Ambulance Service
		NFM	Dorset	Ambulance Service
		NFM	Grimsby	Ambulance Service
		NFM	Hull	Ambulance Service
		NFM	Humberside	Ambulance Service
		NFM	Leicestershire	Ambulance Service
		NFM	London	Ambulance (Gold) N East
		NFM	Manchester	Ambulance Service
		NFM	South Glamorgan	Ambulance Service
		NFM	West Yorkshire	Ambulance Service
		NFM	Grimsby	Ambulance
		NFM	Pontypridd	Doctors Service
166.3100	166.3100	NFM	Belgium	Fire & Ambulance
166.3125	171.1125	NFM	Cambridge	MAGPAS
		NFM	Belfast	NI Ambulance Service
		AM	Plymouth	Devon Ambulance Service
		NFM	Cambridgeshire	Ambulance Service
		NFM	Derbyshire	Ambulance Service
		NFM	Gwynedd	Ambulance Service
		NFM	London	Ambulance (Red) East
		NFM	Dyfed	Doctor's Radio
		NFM	Powys	Ambulance Service
		NFM	Salop	Ambulance Service Ch 3
166.3250	171.1250	NFM	Lincoln	PMR
		NFM	Rhymney Valley	Ambulance Service
		NFM	Belfast	NI Ambulance Service
		NFM	Hull	Ambulance Service
		NFM	Humberside	Ambulance Service
		NFM	Lincolnshire	Ambulance Service
		NFM	Mid Glamorgan	Ambulance Service
		NFM	London	Ambulance (Orange) S West
		NFM	Merseyside	Ambulance Service
166.3300	166.3300	NFM	Belgium	Fire & Ambulance
166.3375	171.1375	NFM	Portsmouth	Health Service
		NFM	Belfast	NI Ambulance Service
		NFM	North West	PMR
		NFM	Dundee	City Council Data Link
		NFM	Kent	Ambulance Service
		NFM	Merseyside	Ambulance Service
		NFM	North Yorkshire	Ambulance Service
		NFM	Suffolk	Ambulance Service
		NFM	Hertfordshire	Ambulance Service
		NFM	Somerset	Ambulance Service
		NFM	Bedfordshire	Ambulance Service
166.3500	166.3500	NFM	Belgium	Fire & Ambulance
166.3500	171.1500	NFM	Sheffield	Health Centre

Base	Mobile	Mode	Location	User and Notes
		NFM	Manchester	Satellite Installers
		NFM	Swansea	Ambulance Service
		NFM	Peterborough	MAGPAS
		NFM	Whittlesey	Luxicabs
		NFM	Cleveland	Ambulance Service
		NFM	Cambridgeshire	Ambulance Service
		NFM	Cumbria	Ambulance Service
		NFM	London	Ambulance (Red) East
		NFM	West Glamorgan	Ambulance Service
		NFM	West Midlands	Ambulance Service
166.3625	171.1625	NFM	Channel Tunnel	Maintenance
		NFM	Cheshire	Ambulance Service
		NFM	Crewe	Ambulance
		NFM	Dyfed	Ambulance Service
		NFM	Essex	Ambulance Service
		NFM	Gloucester	Ambulance Service
		NFM	Hampshire	Ambulance Service
		NFM	Lincolnshire	Ambulance Service
		NFM	Liverpool	Ambulance Service
		NFM	Mid	GP Service (MAGPAS)
		NFM	Pembroke	Ambulance Service
166.3700	166.3700	NFM	Belgium	Disaster Channel 1
166.3750	171.1350	NFM	Fleetwood	Medicall
		NFM	Isle of Wight	Ambulance Service
		NFM	Cumbria	Ambulance Service
		NFM	Derbyshire	Ambulance Service
		NFM	Dundee	Taxi
		NFM	Hereford & Worcester	Ambulance Service
		NFM	London South East	Ambulance (Green)
		NFM	Sussex	Ambulance Service
		NFM	Stockport	Ambulance Service
		NFM	Whittlesey	Jenner Health Centre
166.3875	171.1875	NFM	Berkshire	Ambulance Service
		NFM	Kent	Ambulance Service
		NFM	Lancashire	Ambulance Service
		NFM	North Yorkshire	Ambulance Service
		NFM	Staffordshire	Ambulance Service
		NFM	Staffordshire	North Staffordshire Infirmary
		NFM	West Yorkshire	Ambulance Service
		NFM	Cambridgeshire	Ambulance Service
		NFM	Peterborough	Ambulance Service
166.3900	166.3900	NFM	Belgium	Fire & Ambulance
166.4000	171.2000	NFM	Blackburn	Euro Private Hire
		NFM	Belfast	NI Ambulance Service
		NFM	Derbyshire	Ambulance Service
		NFM	Blackburn	Ambulance Service
		NFM	East Sussex	Ambulance Service
		NFM	Gwent	Ambulance Service

Base	Mobile	Mode	Location	User and Notes
		NFM	Hull	Ambulance Service
		NFM	Humberside	Ambulance Service
		NFM	London	US Embassy Secret Service
		NFM	Lincolnshire	Ambulance Service
		NFM	Northumberland	Ambulance Service
		NFM	Tyne And Wear	Ambulance Service (Red)
		NFM	West Yorkshire	Ambulance Service
166.4100	166.4100	NFM	Belgium	Fire & Ambulance
166.4125	171.2125	NFM	Lincoln	Ambulance Service
		NFM	Rhyl	Dee's Taxis
		NFM	Dyfed	Ambulance Service
		NFM	Dyfed	Doctor's Radio
		NFM	Leicestershire	Ambulance Service
		NFM	Nottinghamshire	Ambulance Service
		NFM	Shropshire	Ambulance EMS
		NFM	Swindon	Ambulance Service
		NFM	West Yorkshire	Ambulance Service
		NFM	Wiltshire	Ambulance Service
		NFM	London	Ambulance (Red) S Ch 3.
166.4250	171.2250	NFM	Birmingham	Emergency Doctor Service
		NFM	W Yorkshire	Deputising Service
		NFM	West Midlands	Doctors on Call
		NFM	Liverpool	Emergency Doctors
		AM	Stoke on Trent	Emergency Doctor
		NFM	Bradford	Doctors On Call
		NFM	Kilmarnock	Johnnie Walker Distillery
		NFM	London	Ambulance (Gold) N East
		NFM	Shropshire	Ambulance Service
		NFM	Norfolk	Emergency Doctor Service
		NFM	Norfolk	Community Nurses
		NFM	Kings Lynn	Dr Ewlett
		NFM	Cambridge	Dr Lankester
		NFM	Glasgow	Taxi
		NFM	Birmingham	Locums Service
		NFM	Norfolk	Doctors On Call
		NFM	Salop	Midwives Ch 4
166.4300	166.4300	NFM	Belgium	Fire & Ambulance
166.4375	171.2375	NFM	Devon	Air Ambulance
		NFM	London	Air Ambulance
		NFM	Manchester Airport	Ambulances
		NFM	Bedfordshire	Ambulance Emergency
		NFM	Berkshire	Ambulance Emergency
		NFM	Buckinghamshire	Ambulance Emergency
		NFM	Cambridgeshire	Ambulance Emergency
		NFM	Cheshire	Ambulance Emergency
		NFM	Cleveland	Ambulance Emergency
		NFM	East Sussex	Ambulance Emergency
		NFM	Essex	Ambulance Emergency

Base	Mobile	Mode	Location	User and Notes
		NFM	Hampshire	Ambulance Emergency
		NFM	Humberside	Ambulance Emergency
		NFM	Leicestershire	Ambulance Emergency
		NFM	Lincolnshire	Ambulance Emergency
		NFM	London	Ambulance Emergency
		NFM	Merseyside	Ambulance Emergency
		NFM	Norfolk	Ambulance Emergency
		NFM	North Yorkshire	Ambulance Emergency
		NFM	Northamptonshire	Ambulance Emergency
		NFM	Suffolk	Ambulance Emergency
		NFM	Surrey	Ambulance Emergency
		NFM	Tyne And Wear	Ambulance Emergency
		NFM	West Midlands	Ambulance Emergency
		NFM	West Sussex	Ambulance Emergency
		NFM	West Yorkshire	Ambulance Emergency
		NFM	Nationwide	Emergency Ambulance
166.4400	166.4400	NFM	Belgium	Disaster Channel 2
166.4500	166.4500	NFM	Belgium	Fire & Ambulance
166.4500	171.2500	NFM	W Yorkshire	Lexicon Deputising Service
		NFM	London	Ambulance (Blue) N West
		NFM	Manchester	Ambulance Service
		NFM	Blackburn	Blackburn Health Authority
		NFM	Poole	East Dorset Health Authority
		NFM	Derby	District Nurses
		NFM	Wisbeach	Clarkson Health Centre
		NFM	Wantage	Doctors
		NFM	Bristol	Roman Taxis
		NFM	St Ouen, Jersey	Honorary Police Ch 2
		NFM	Bradford	Doctor Dep Service
166.4625	171.2625	NFM	Bedfordshire	Ambulance Service
		NFM	Cheltenham	Metro Buses
		NFM	Clwyd	Ambulance Service
		NFM	Coventry	Ambulance Service
		NFM	East Sussex	Ambulance Service
		NFM	London	US Embassy Secret Service
		NFM	North Yorkshire	Ambulance Service
		NFM	Swindon	Metro Buses
		NFM	West Midlands	Ambulance Service
		NFM	West Yorkshire	Ambulance Service
		NFM	Rhyl (Clwyd)	Emergency Ambulances
166.4700	166.4700	NFM	Belgium	Fire & Ambulance
166.4750	171.2750	NFM	Gwynedd	Ambulance Service
		NFM	Hampshire	Ambulance Service
		NFM	Hereford & Worcester	Ambulance Service
		NFM	London	Ambulance (Blue) N West
		NFM	Merseyside	Ambulance Service
		NFM	North Yorkshire	Ambulance Service
		NFM	Scarborough	Ambulance Service

Base	Mobile	Mode	Location	User and Notes
		NFM	Jersey	Honorary Police Channel 4
166.4875	171.2875	NFM	Blackburn	Ambulance Service
		NFM	Dorset	Ambulance Service
		NFM	Essex	Ambulance Service
		NFM	Jersey	Honorary Police
		NFM	London	US Embassy Secret Service
		NFM	Northumberland	Ambulance Service
		NFM	Manchester	Ambulance Service
		NFM	Oxfordshire	Ambulance Service
		NFM	South Yorkshire	Ambulance Service
		NFM	Tyne And Wear	Ambulance Service
		NFM	Jersey	Honorary Police Ch 3
166.4900	166.4900	NFM	Belgium	Fire & Ambulance
166.5000	171.3000	AM	Bury	Medical
		NFM	Cambridgeshire	Ambulance Service
		NFM	Avon	Ambulance Service
		NFM	Cornwall	Ambulance Service
		NFM	London	Ambulance (Gold) N East
		NFM	Manchester	Ambulance Service
		NFM	North Yorkshire	Ambulance Service
		NFM	Northumberland	Ambulance Service
		NFM	Staffordshire	Ambulance Service
		NFM	West Midlands	Ambulance Service
		NFM	Warwickshire	Ambulance Service
166.5100	166.5100	NFM	Belgium	Fire & Ambulance
166.5125	171.3125	NFM	County Durham	Ambulance Service (DC)
		NFM	Oldham	Ambulance Service
		AM	Cambridge	Ambulance
		AM	Northumberland	Ambulance
		NFM	Lancashire	Ambulance Service
		NFM	London	US Embassy Secret Service
		NFM	Manchester	Ambulance Service
		NFM	Shropshire	Ambulance PTS
		NFM	Surrey	Ambulance Service
		NFM	Warwickshire	Ambulance Service
		NFM	Peterborough	Ambulance Service
166.5250	171.3250	NFM	Hull	Ambulance Service
		NFM	East Ridding	Ambulance Service
		NFM	Humberside	Ambulance Service
		NFM	Ipswich	Ambulance Service
		NFM	Lancashire	Ambulance Service
		NFM	London	Ambulance (Red) South
		NFM	Mid Glamorgan	Ambulance Service
		NFM	North Yorkshire	Ambulance Service
		NFM	Suffolk	Ambulance Service
		NFM	Warwickshire	Ambulance Service
		NFM	West Sussex	Ambulance Service
166.5300	166.5300	NFM	Belgium	Fire & Ambulance

Base	Mobile	Mode	Location	User and Notes
166.5375	171.3375	NFM	Leeds	Doctor DepService
		NFM	Leicestershire	Ambulance Service
		NFM	Blackburn	Ambulance Service
		NFM	North Yorkshire	Ambulance Service
		NFM	Surrey	Ambulance Service
		NFM	West Yorkshire	Ambulance Service
166.5500	166.5500	NFM	Belgium	Fire & Ambulance
166.5500	171.3500	NFM	Portsmouth	Ambulance Service
		NFM	Devon	Patient Ambulance Service
		NFM	Doncaster	Doctors On Call
		NFM	Essex	Ambulance Service
		NFM	Hampshire	Ambulance Service
		NFM	Hull	Ambulance Service
		NFM	Lancashire	Ambulance Service
		NFM	Northamptonshire	Ambulance Service
		NFM	Sheffield	Ambulance Emergency
		NFM	South Yorkshire	Ambulance Service
		NFM	West Yorkshire	Ambulance Service
		NFM	West Midlands	Ambulance Service
		NFM	Cirencester	Hospital Doctors
		NFM	Cardiff	TNT Deliveries Ch 3
166.5625	171.3625	NFM	Barnsley	Hospitial services
		NFM	Bournemouth	Hospital Minibus
		NFM	Buckinghamshire	Ambulance Service
		NFM	Clwyd	Ambulance Service
		NFM	Devon	Ambulance Service
		NFM	Dundee	National Carriers
		NFM	Hereford & Worcester	Ambulance Service
		NFM	Norfolk	Ambulance Service
		NFM	Perth	Ready Mixed Concrete
		NFM	Sheffield	Ambulance Out-Patients
		NFM	South Yorkshire	Ambulance Service
		NFM	West Sussex	Ambulance Service
		NFM	Mold (Clwyd)	Ambulance Service
166.5700	166.5700	NFM	Belgium	Fire & Ambulance
166.5750	171.3750	NFM	Abram	Medical Centre
		NFM	Gwent	Ambulance Service
		NFM	Gwynedd	Ambulance Service
		NFM	Leeds	Ambulance Service
		NFM	Bolton	Doctors On Call
		NFM	Hereford & Worcester	Ambulance Service
		NFM	Inner London	Ambulance (White)
		NFM	Hampshire	Ambulance Service
		NFM	Humberside	Ambulance Service
		NFM	Merseyshire	Ambulance Service
		NFM	Northumberland	Ambulance Service
		NFM	Northamptonshire	Ambulance Service
		NFM	West Glamorgan	Ambulance Service

Base	Mobile	Mode	Location	User and Notes
		NFM	North Yorkshire	Ambulance Service
166.5875	171.3875	NFM	Scunthorpe	Taxi
		NFM	Holywell	Tower Taxis
		AM	Sefton	Ambulance
		NFM	Aberdeen	Surveyors
		NFM	Durham	Ambulance Service
		NFM	Hampshire	Ambulance Service
		NFM	Hertfordshire	Ambulance Service
		NFM	Merseyside	Ambulance Service
		NFM	South Yorkshire	Ambulance Service
		NFM	Staffordshire	Ambulance Service
		NFM	South Glamorgan	Ambulance Service
		NFM	St Helens	Ambulance Service
166.5900	166.5900	NFM	Belgium	Fire & Ambulance
166.6000	171.4000	NFM	Preston	Electricians
		NFM	Peterborough	Dr. Gray
		AM	Saffron Walden	Accident Group
		AM	Swaffham	Dr. Pilkington
		NFM	Colchester	NEEDES
		NFM	Northumberland	Ambulance Service
		NFM	Ipswich	Doctor's Surgery
		NFM	Manchester	Ambulance Service
		NFM	Stirling	PMR
		NFM	Tyne And Wear	Ambulance Service
		NFM	West Midlands	Ambulance Service
		AM	England & Wales	Doctors Special Services
166.6100	166.6100	NFM	Belgium	Fire & Ambulance
166.6125	171.4125	NFM	Havant	Dixies Taxis
		NFM	Berkshire	Ambulance Service
		NFM	Hertfordshire	Ambulance
		NFM	Hull	Ambulance Service
		NFM	Humberside	Ambulance Service
		NFM	North Yorkshire	Ambulance Service
		NFM	West Perthshire	Electricians
		NFM	Oxfordshire	Ambulance Service
		NFM	Staffordshire	Ambulance Service
		NFM	Wiltshire	Ambulance Service
		NFM	Barking	Council
166.6250	171.4250	NFM	Eltham	Taxis
		NFM	Hampshire	Streamline Cabs
		NFM	Bournemouth	Breakdown Recovery
		NFM	Cambridge	Cambridge Growers
		AM	Aberdeen	Retail Park
		AM	Nationwide	Ambulance-to-Hospital Link
		NFM	Bolton	Cobra Taxis
		NFM	Cambridge	Todd
		NFM	Poole	Repeater
		NFM	Lytham	Whitesides Taxis

Base	Mobile	Mode	Location	User and Notes
		NFM	Bristol	Red Taxis
		NFM	Bath	Francis Plant Hire
		NFM	Cardiff	City Taxis
		NFM	Dundee	Taxis
166.6300	166.6300	NFM	Belgium	Fire & Ambulance
166.6375	171.4375	NFM	Oldham	Taxis
		NFM	Lancing	Access Cars
		NFM	Carlisle	PMR
		NFM	London	Taxis
		NFM	Drayton	Draytax Taxis
		NFM	Manchester	Taxi
		NFM	Nationwide	Rediffusion
		NFM	Isle of Wight	Grange Taxis
		NFM	Aberdeen	Radio Specialists
		NFM	Nationwide	Rediffussion Comms
		NFM	Bolton	Taxis
		NFM	Collyhurst	Taxis
		NFM	Royston	Farmers Fertilisers
		NFM	Whittlesey	S & S Tractors
		NFM	Woodbridge	Greenwell Farms
166.6500	166.6500	NFM	Belgium	Fire & Ambulance
166.6500	171.4500	NFM	Hampshire	Wessex Plant Hire
		NFM	Central London	Taxis
		NFM	Flixton	Beaumont's Private Hire
		NFM	Belfast	Ferguson Flowers
		NFM	Bedfordshire	Bedfordshire Growers
		NFM	Bury	Byford Taxis
		NFM	Huntingdon	R. O'Connell
		NFM	Ipswich	Taxi Association
		NFM	London	ODRATS
		NFM	Glasgow	Taxi
		NFM	Cardiff	ICL Computers
166.6625	171.4625	NFM	Manchester	Taxi
		NFM	Sussex	Tarmac Contractors
		NFM	London	Scorpio Cars
		AM	Swinton	Skytax
		NFM	Manchester	Taxi
		NFM	Grimsby	Peter Sheffield Buses
		NFM	Baldock	Butts Taxis
		NFM	Bury	British Sugar
		NFM	Barkway	British Sugar
		NFM	Cantley	British Sugar
		NFM	Dullingham	P.BTaylor
		NFM	Perth	Tay Taxis
		NFM	Sudbury	A Line Taxis
		NFM	Bristol	Aerial Riggers
		NFM	Nationwide	ICL Channel 1
166.6700	166.6700	NFM	Belgium	Fire & Ambulance

Base	Mobile	Mode	Location	User and Notes
166.6750	171.4750	NFM	Ipswich	Taxis
		NFM	Ealing	Taxis
		NFM	Southhall	Taxis
		NFM	North London	Taxis
		NFM	Hull	Security Co
		NFM	Glasgow	Taxi Company
		NFM	Hounslow	Minicab Co
		NFM	Southampton	ATS Taxis
		NFM	Lancaster	District Nurse
		NFM	Morecambe	District Nurse
		NFM	Northampton	Taxis
		NFM	Hampshire	Ace Taxis
		NFM	Mostyn	Dave's Taxis
		NFM	Radcliffe	Harvey's Taxis
		NFM	Elvington	Rolawn Turf Suppliers
		NFM	Winbourne	Skiphire
		NFM	Alconbury	Steve's Taxis
		NFM	Bolton	Best Way Taxis
		NFM	Alderney	Alderney Taxis
		NFM	Radcliffe	Taxis
		NFM	London, Wimbledon	Minicab Firm
		NFM	Southampton	A2B Taxis
		NFM	Glasgow	Taxi
		AM	West Midlands	Cashmore's Steel
		NFM	Nationwide	ICL Channel 2
		NFM	Alconbury	Steve's Taxi
166.6875	171.4875	NFM	Portsmouth	CTE Television
		NFM	Berinsfield	Star Cars
		NFM	Northampton	Taxis
		NFM	Buxton	Crane & Son
		NFM	Bury St Edmonds	British Sugar
		NFM	Chatteris	Whitworth Produce
		NFM	Guernsey	AC Heating
		NFM	Guernsey	Cobo Building
		NFM	Ipswich	Ransomes
		NFM	Kings Lynn	British Sugar
		NFM	Norfolk	Crane & Son
		NFM	Peterborough	Co-Op TV Services
		NFM	Swindon	Starlight Taxis
		NFM	East Kilbride	Kelvin Kabs
		NFM	Glasgow	Taxi
		NFM	Newport	Town Taxis
166.6900	166.6900	NFM	Belgium	Fire & Ambulance
166.7000	171.5000	NFM	Sheffield	Taxis
		NFM	Southampton	RMS Motors
		NFM	Northampton	Taxis
		NFM	Hampshire	Haverson Electronics
		NFM	Hull	Parks Department

Base	Mobile	Mode	Location	User and Notes
		NFM	Guernsey	Central Transfers
		NFM	London	US Embassy Secret Service
		NFM	Methwold	Darby Bros Farms
		NFM	Norwich	Bestway Taxis
		NFM	Cirencester	Radio Cars
		NFM	Montrose	Taxis
		NFM	Bestway	Taxis
166.7100	166.7100	NFM	Belgium	Fire & Ambulance
166.7125	171.5125	NFM	Havant	Jacks Taxis
		NFM	Canvey Island	Taxis
		NFM	Southampton	Taxis
		NFM	Edinburgh	Festival Cars
		NFM	Abingdon	Grayston Plant Hire
		NFM	Morecambe	Taxis
		NFM	Edinburgh	Taxi (C)
		NFM	Wispington	British Sugar
		AM	Grimsby	Taxis
		NFM	Abingdon	JMB Plant Hire
		NFM	Norwich	Knight Benjamin
166.7250	171.5250	NFM	Lowestoft	Birds Eye
		NFM	Alderney	Alderney Emergency Service
		NFM	Sharnbrook	Unilever
		NFM	Gt. Yarmouth	Birds Eye Vans
166.7300	166.7300	NFM	Belgium	Fire & Ambulance
166.7375	171.5375	NFM	Pitsea	Taxis
		NFM	Essex	Taxis
		NFM	Rochdale	Globe Taxis
		NFM	Manchester	Taxi
		NFM	Bolton	Cross Private Hire
		NFM	Norwich	Knight Benjamin
		NFM	Poulton	Poulton Cabs
		NFM	London	National Radio Cars
		NFM	Nationwide	ICL Channel 3
		AM	Colchester	Rainbow Taxis
		NFM	Grampian	Transport
166.7500	166.7500	NFM	Belgium	Fire & Ambulance
166.7500	171.5500	NFM	Portsmouth	Ambulance Service
		NFM	Nationwide	DSS Dole Fraud Teams
		NFM	Banchory	Taxi
		NFM	Crewe	Ambulance
		NFM	Lancaster	Council
		NFM	Morecambe	Council
		NFM	Stirling	PMR
		NFM	Surrey	Ambulance Service
		NFM	Co Durham	Emergency Doctors Service
166.7625	171.5625	NFM	Bournemouth	Traffic Wardens
		NFM	Castle Donington	Race Control
		NFM	Irvine	Shopping Centre Security

Base	Mobile	Mode	Location	User and Notes
		NFM	Poole	Guardforce Security
		NFM	Swindon	Oasis Leisure Centre
		NFM	Ipswich	Taxis
		NFM	Rother Valley	Sports Centre
		NFM	Nationwide	DSS Dole Fraud Teams
		NFM	Finchley	Medics
166.7700	166.7700	NFM	Belgium	Fire & Ambulance
166.7750	171.5750	NFM	Birmingham	Doctors Service
		NFM	Cardiff	Health Service
		NFM	Manchester	Taxi
		NFM	Abingdon	Abingdon Hospital
		NFM	Bedfordshire	Midwives
		NFM	Dover	Council
		NFM	Hampshire	Health Service
		NFM	Lancaster	District Nurse
		NFM	Morecambe	District Nurse
		NFM	Warwickshire	Ambulance Service
		NFM	Nationwide	DSS Dole Fraud Teams
		NFM	Ipswich	Midwives
		AM	Burnley	Doctors Call Out
166.7875	171.5875	NFM	Lincoln	PMR
		NFM	Hampshire	Council
		NFM	Bournemouth	Castle Recovery
		NFM	Edinburgh	Diamond Security
		NFM	Grimsby	Mariner Gas
		NFM	Lancaster	District Nurse
		NFM	Morecambe	District Nurse
		AM	Aberdeen	Oil Servicing
		NFM	Cornwall	Vetco Base
		NFM	Nationwide	Community Repeater
		NFM	Plymouth	Co-Op Store Detectives
		NFM	City of London	Shamrock Demolitions
		NFM	Ipswich	Taxis
		NFM	Linconshire	Comunity Repeater
		NFM	Grimsby	Lincs Vending
		NFM	Caterham Hill	RCS Comrep Ch 5
166.7900		NFM	Belgium	Fire & Ambulance
166.8000	171.6000	NFM	Glossop	District Nurses
		NFM	Poole	General Hospital
		NFM	Gloucester	Ambulance Service Ch2
		NFM	Mansfield	Kings Mill Hospital
		NFM	Manchester	Hospital Porters
		NFM	Nationwide	Community Repeater
166.8100	166.8100	NFM	Belgium	Fire & Ambulance
166.8125	171.6125	NFM	Doncaster	Health Centre
		NFM	Yorkshire	Medic Service
		NFM	Stoke-on-Trent	Doctors Service
		NFM	Sussex	Brighton Council

Base	Mobile	Mode	Location	User and Notes
		NFM	Isle of Man	Ambulance Service
		NFM	Llanelli	Doctors on Call
		NFM	North Lancashire	Doctors On Call
		NFM	Northampton	Emergency Doctors
		NFM	Haverfordwest	E Williams Transport
		NFM	Essex	Havering Council
		NFM	Hertfordshire	Doctors Channel
		NFM	Swindon	Ambulance Service
		NFM	Upwell	Health Centre
		NFM	Berkshire	Common Doctors Freq.
		NFM	Oxfordshire	Common Doctors Freq.
		NFM	Welwyn & Hatfield	Accident Services
		NFM	Chapmanslade	Barters Farm
		NFM	Nationwide	Doctors Ch 1
166.8250	171.6250	NFM	Burnley	Council Security Patrols
		NFM	Bournemouth	Emergency Services
		NFM	Swansea City	Ambulance Service
		NFM	Ipswich	Wilding & Smith
		NFM	Clare	Dr Carter
		NFM	Jersey	Yellow Cabs
		NFM	Kent	Ambulance Service
		AM	Thanet	Ambulance
		NFM	Nationwide	DSS Dole Fraud Teams
		NFM	London, Islington	Flood Control
166.8300	166.8300	NFM	Belgium	Fire & Ambulance
166.8375	171.6375	NFM	Emsworth	John's Cabs
		NFM	Hockley	Doctors
		NFM	Amlwch	Renovate Services
		NFM	Hampshire	District Nurse
		NFM	Kent	Health Service
		NFM	Castle Donington	Medic Control
		NFM	Dorset	Health Service
		NFM	Peterborough	Doctors Service
		NFM	S Essex	Mobile Doctors Ch 1
166.8500	166.8500	NFM	Belgium	Fire & Ambulance
166.8500	171.6500	NFM	Cambridgeshire	Emergency Doctors Service
		NFM	Bristol	Washing Machine Engineers
		NFM	Cambridgeshire	Community Nurses
		NFM	Dundee	Christian Salvensen
		NFM	East Sussex	Doctors On Call
		NFM	Edinburgh	Taxi
		NFM	Haverfordwest	Gillmans Quarry
		NFM	Medway	Doctors on Call
		NFM	Kent	Health Service
		NFM	North Humberside	Transport
		NFM	Poole	Taxi
		NFM	Tower Hill	Doctors
166.8575	166.8575	AM	Luton	PMR

Base	Mobile	Mode	Location	User and Notes
166.8625	171.6625	NFM	Yorkshire	Wimpey Homes
		AM	Wigan	Highways Department
		NFM	Swindon	Swindon Bus Co.
		AM	Aberdeen	Rig Servicing
		NFM	Crewe	City Council
		NFM	Edinburgh	Community Repeater
		NFM	Swindon	Thamesdown Buses
		NFM	Hillingdon	Emergency Radio System
		NFM	Jersey	Pioneer Coaches
166.8700	166.8700	NFM	Belgium	Disaster Protection
166.8735	171.6375	NFM	Portsmouth	MediCall Ch 2
		NFM	St Helens	Emergency Doctors
166.8750	171.6750	NFM	Peterborough	CBS Repeater
		NFM	Fleetwood	PMR
		NFM	Gateshead	Security
		NFM	Carlisle	PMR
		NFM	Rhymney Valley	Hotpoint Service Engineers
		NFM	Amlwch	Doctors
		NFM	North West	PMR
		NFM	Preston	Dynarod
		NFM	Grimsby	GY Buses
		NFM	Manchester	Porter's Dairies
		NFM	Aberdeen	Community Repeater
		NFM	Ayr	Carriers
		NFM	Poole	Taxi
		NFM	Oxford	Rascal
		NFM	Dundee	Doctors
		NFM	Freethorpe	Aitchison Bros
		NFM	Norfolk	Auto Windscreens
166.8875	171.6875	NFM	Fleetwood	Works Department
		NFM	Gateshead	Taxis
		NFM	Hampshire	PDSA
		NFM	Blackpool	Council Transport
		NFM	Birmingham	Taxis
		NFM	Benson	A Cabs
		NFM	Lancaster	Council
		NFM	Morecambe	Council
		NFM	Nationwide	Community Repeater
		NFM	Bolton	Express Taxis
		NFM	Poole	Repeater
		NFM	Dorset	Nightguard Security
		NFM	Belgium	Disaster Protection
166.9000	171.7000	NFM	Worthing	Nynex Cable
		NFM	Cannock	Mr Sparks Garage
		NFM	Oldham	Council
		NFM	Aberdeen	Aberdeen Vets
		NFM	Colchester	A.E Arnold
		NFM	Ely	Vets

Base	Mobile	Mode	Location	User and Notes
		NFM	Brighton	Nynex Cablecomms
		NFM	Gloucester	Community Repeater
		NFM	Cardiff	TNT Deliveries Ch 2
166.9100	166.9100	NFM	Belgium	Disaster Protection
166.9125	171.7125	NFM	Nottingham	Taxis
		NFM	Newark	Taxis
		NFM	Maidenhead	Taxis
		NFM	Edinburgh	Scottish & Newcastle Security
		NFM	Durham	TNT Carriers
		NFM	Bolton	Zodiac Taxis
		NFM	Ipswich	British Sugar
		NFM	Peterborough	British Sugar
		NFM	Stretham	N Rose Builders
		NFM	Guernsey	States Electricity
		NFM	Nationwide	TNT Transport
166.9250	171.7250	AM	Oldham	Roller's Private Hire
		NFM	Central Manchester	Lion Private Hire
		NFM	Finchley	Taxis
		NFM	Enfield	Taxis
		NFM	Peterborough	3 Star Taxis
		NFM	Slough	Viking Radio Cars
		NFM	Edinburgh	Community Repeater
		NFM	Guernsey	States Electricity
		NFM	Oldham	Taxis
		NFM	Littleport	J.H Martin
		NFM	Lowestoft	Birds Eye
		NFM	Frome	Taxis
		NFM	Bootle	Taxis
		NFM	Peterborough	3 Star Ambassador
		NFM	Gt Yarmouth	Birds Eye Vans
166.9300	166.9300	NFM	Belgium	Disaster Protection
166.9375	171.7375	NFM	Portsmouth	Harbour Security
		NFM	Aberdeen	Retail Park Security
		NFM	Greenhan County	Council
		NFM	Hindley	Anrich Vets
166.9500	166.9500	NFM	Belgium	Disaster Protection
166.9500	171.7500	NFM	Sheffield	Vending Machine Company
		NFM	Nationwide	BBC Repeater Channel
		NFM	Nationwide	BBC TV O/B Crews
		NFM	East Dereham	Taxis
166.9625	171.7625	NFM	Winchester	Taxis
		NFM	Salford	Taxis
		NFM	London	Taxis
		NFM	Whitefield	Blueline Private Hire
		NFM	Manchester	Taxi
		NFM	Hull	Taxis
		NFM	Prestwich	Taxis
		NFM	Glasgow	Taxi

Base	Mobile	Mode	Location	User and Notes
		NFM	Belgium	Disaster Protection
166.9750	171.7750	NFM	Glasgow	PMR
		NFM	Barnsley	Taxis
		NFM	Peterborough	Associated Adams Taxis
		NFM	Portsmouth	Taxis
		AM	Southampton	Taxis
		NFM	Manchester	Taxi
		NFM	Oxford	001 Cars
		NFM	Dyfed	Crane Hire
		NFM	Edinburgh	Community Repeater
		NFM	Guernsey	Channel TV Rent-a-Set
		NFM	Harwich	Daves Taxis
		NFM	Poole	Knight
		NFM	Portsmouth	Taxis
		NFM	Peterborough	Associated Adams Taxis
		NFM	Haverfordwest	Crane Hire
		NFM	Oxford	001 Cars
166.9875	171.7875	NFM	Portsmouth	Channel Satellites
		NFM	Littleport	Sallis Bros
		NFM	Poole	Council
		NFM	Luton	Silverline Taxis
		NFM	Littlefort	Ballis Bros Ltd
		NFM	Fleetwood	Wyre Borough Council
		NFM	Dunstable	Jim & Jocks Taxis
		NFM	Newmarket	E.FSaltmarsh
		NFM	Felixstowe	Road Haulage Co
		NFM	City of Westminster	Porter Evictions
		NFM	Glasgow	Taxi
		NFM	Belgium	Disaster Protection
		NFM	Cambridgeshire	Haulage Co.
167.0000	163.0000	NFM	Sweden, Stockholm	Gothenburcreft
167.0000	168.0000	NFM	Norway	Mobile Phones
167.0000	171.8000	NFM	Bedfordshire	Vet Service
		NFM	Hampshire	Dickson Bros.
		NFM	Leicester	Taxis
		NFM	Ellerker	F.S& E.MWood Haulage
		NFM	Nationwide	Community Repeater
		NFM	Humberside	RSPCA
		AM	London	BBC/ITN News Room
167.0125	167.0125	NFM	Belgium	Disaster Protection
167.0125	171.8125	NFM	Wales	Council Contractors
		NFM	Binbrook	Nickersons Farmers
		NFM	Newmarket	Suffolk Housing
		NFM	Northampton	Taxis
		NFM	Essex	Telecom Repeater
		NFM	Cardiff	Security
		NFM	Cardiff	Council
		NFM	Swindon	Swindon Bus Company

Base	Mobile	Mode	Location	User and Notes
		AM	Humberside	Birds-Eye Foods
		NFM	Ipswich	Yellow Taxis
		NFM	Burnley	General Hospital Security
167.0250	171.8250	NFM	Whitley Bay	Taxis
		NFM	Leicester	Taxis
		NFM	Benfleet	Vehicle Recovery Co.
		NFM	Whiston	Britannia Taxis
		NFM	Poulton	Poulton Cabs
		NFM	East Dereham	Fransham Farm Co.
		NFM	Ely	Stopps Taxis
		NFM	Hull	Taxis
		NFM	London	US Embassy Secret Service
		NFM	London	Kerri Cars
		NFM	Bolton	Lyma Taxis
		NFM	Glasgow	Taxi
167.0375	167.0375	NFM	Belgium	Disaster Protection
167.0375	171.8375	NFM	Glasgow	Securiguard
		NFM	Isle of Man	Manx Transport Services
		NFM	North West	PMR
		NFM	Lowestoft	Birds Eye
		NFM	Hull	East Yorkshire Motor Services
		NFM	Leicester	Security
		NFM	London	Burns Security
		NFM	Lothian And Borders	Police (ZH) West Lothian
		NFM	Lowestoft	Birds Eye
		NFM	Hull	Birds Eye Pea Vining
		NFM	Wiltshire	Longleat House
		NFM	Newport	Hales TV Repairs
		NFM	Norfolk	Council Car Parks
167.0500	167.0500	NFM	Belgium	Disaster Protection
167.0500	171.8500	NFM	Nottingham	TV Repairs
		NFM	Nationwide	Community Repeater
		AM	Southampton	TVS
167.0625	171.8625	NFM	Newark	Taxis
		NFM	Chelmsford	Car Recovery
		NFM	Abbeywood	Taxis
		NFM	SE London	Taxis
		NFM	Sharnbrook	Associated Asphalt
		AM	Humberside	Haulage Co
		NFM	Salford	Pub Warning & Security
		AM	Bolton	Private Hire
167.0700	167.0700	NFM	Belgium	Disaster Protection
167.0750	171.8750	NFM	Peterborough	CBS Repeater
		NFM	Lincoln	PMR
		NFM	Cleveland	Peter Taxis
		NFM	Chorley	Taxis
		NFM	Forrest Hill	Taxis
		NFM	Guernsey	Bob Froome

Base	Mobile	Mode	Location	User and Notes
		NFM	North Walsham	Norfolk Cannaries
		NFM	Humberside	Haulage Co
		NFM	Motherwell	Redline Cabs (red)
		NFM	Glasgow	Taxi
167.0875	171.8875	NFM	Birmingham	Taxi Company
		NFM	Bristol	Ambulance Service
		NFM	Portsmouth	Council
		NFM	Walsall	Metro Taxis
		NFM	SW London	Taxis
		NFM	Swansea City	County Hall Ops
		NFM	Great Yarmouth	Botton Bros.
		NFM	Torpoint	Taxis
		NFM	Perth	Taxi
		NFM	Poole	Repeater
		NFM	South Humberside	Ross Foods
		NFM	Cwmbran	Aerial Riggers
		NFM	Somerset	Council Ops
167.0900	167.0900	NFM	Belgium	Disaster Protection
167.1000	171.9000	NFM	Hemel Hempsted	Minicab Co
		NFM	Hampshire	Council
		NFM	Carlisle	Cavrays Security
		NFM	Eltham	Taxis
		NFM	Manchester	Taxis
		NFM	Guernsey	Bluebird Taxis
		NFM	Brandon	F Hiam Farms
		NFM	Cambridge	Ace Taxis
		NFM	Hempstead	R.DHaylock
		NFM	Perth	Taxi
		NFM	Thorley	M.S. Smith
		NFM	Stockton-on-Tees	Taxi Service
		NFM	Glasgow	Taxi
		NFM	Cardiff	Capital Taxis
		NFM	Cambridge	Taxis
167.1100	167.1100	NFM	Belgium	Ambulance - Hospital
167.1125	171.9125	NFM	Glasgow	Taxi Company
		NFM	Farnham	Minicab Co
		NFM	South London	National Rescue
		NFM	Great Yarmouth	J & H Bunn
		NFM	Guernsey	Community Repeater
		NFM	Manchester	Taxis
		NFM	Hull	Birds Eye
		NFM	Glasgow	Taxi
		NFM	Bristol	Peters Taxis
		NFM	Swansea	Taxis
		NFM	Rotherham	Crown Taxis
167.1250	171.9250	NFM	Folkstone	Taxis
		NFM	Cardiff	Repair Company
		NFM	Scunthorpe	Transport Firm

Base	Mobile	Mode	Location	User and Notes
		NFM	Hemel Hempsted	Minicab Co
		NFM	Dudley	Skip Hire
		NFM	Liverpool	Taxis
		NFM	Portsmouth	Dog Catcher
		NFM	Burnley	Bus Station Taxi Rank
		NFM	Milton Keynes	Pursell Taxis
		NFM	North West	PMR
		NFM	Swansea	Brynamman Taxis
		NFM	Edinburgh	Taxi
		NFM	Kings Lynn	Watlington Plant
		NFM	March	Ross-Produce
		NFM	Avon	CableTel Ch 2
		NFM	Gwent	CableTel Ch 2
167.1375	171.9375	NFM	Edinburgh	Eagle Couriers
		NFM	Scunthorpe	Taxis
		NFM	Leicester	Taxis
		NFM	Lancashire	Bulkers Commercial Refuse
		NFM	Preston	South Ribble School Bus
		NFM	Blackburn	Golden Line Private Hire
		NFM	Oxford	Streamline Taxis
		NFM	Edinburgh	Community Repeater
		NFM	Kings Lynn	Wheelers TV
		NFM	Jersey	Skips
167.1500	171.9500	NFM	Aberystwyth	University Security
		NFM	Oldham	Startex Cabs
		NFM	West Midlands	ABS Taxis
		NFM	Portsmouth	Repeater
		NFM	Oldham	Taxis
		NFM	Lancashire	South Ribble Refuse
		NFM	Carlisle	Radio Taxis
		NFM	Bury	Bury Taxi Rank Ltd
		NFM	Manchester	Taxi
		AM	Aberdeen	Taxi
		NFM	Guernsey	Ronez
		NFM	Crewe	Taxi
		NFM	St. Neots	T & R Taxis
		NFM	Worlington	Tuckwell
		NFM	Downham Market	THurlow
		NFM	Norwich	taxis
167.1625	171.9625	NFM	Wigan	Cable TV Engineers
		NFM	Central London	Couriers
		NFM	Wrexham	Prostigo Taxis
		NFM	Ipswich	Taxis
		NFM	Keswick	Ambulance
		NFM	Norfolk	ICL
		NFM	Sheffield	City Taxis
		NFM	Swindon	Starlight Taxis
		NFM	Newport	Newport Taxis

Base	Mobile	Mode	Location	User and Notes
167.1750	171.9750	NFM	Portsmouth	PMR
		NFM	Hampshire	Short Term PMR Hire
		NFM	Sidcup	Taxis
		NFM	E London	Couriers
		NFM	Bexley Heath	Taxis
		NFM	Rochdale	Tiger Cars
		NFM	Manchester	Taxi
		NFM	Guernsey	RJLe Huray
		AM	Glasgow	PMR
		NFM	Norfolk	ICL
		NFM	Cheshire	Choice Taxis
		NFM	Rochdale	Taxis
		NFM	Glasgow	Taxi
167.1875	171.9875	NFM	Manchester	Taxi
		NFM	Immingham	Oaklands Taxis
		NFM	Brownhills	Bee-Jays Taxis
		NFM	Milton Keynes	Raffles Taxis
		NFM	Manchester	Midway Taxis
		NFM	Middleton	Swan Cars
		NFM	Macclesfield	Taxi
		NFM	Lancaster	Council Roads Dept
		NFM	Bolton	North West Cars
		NFM	Swindon	Handy Gas Shop
		NFM	Scarborough	Taxis
		NFM	Glasgow	Mac Cars
167.2000	172.0000	NFM	Peterborough	Burghley Steeplechase
		NFM	Barrow	Mobile Community Watch
		NFM	Fleetwood	Taxis
		NFM	Nottinghamshire	Ambulance Service
		NFM	Leicester	Taxis
		NFM	Dunstable	Glider Taxis
		NFM	Hull	Stagecoach Bus Co.
		NFM	Edinburgh	Burtons Security
		NFM	Nationwide	PMR Short Term Hire
		NFM	Lancaster	Security Service
		NFM	Morecambe	Security Service
		NFM	Jersey	Hire Cars
		NFM	Midland	Hutchings
		NFM	Le-Mans	Halya Sport Team
		NFM	Thetford	Abbey Taxis
167.2125	172.0125	NFM	Chelmsford	A1 Demolition
		NFM	Chelmsford	Crest Dairies
		NFM	Newmarket	McCourts
		NFM	Oldham	Home James Taxis
		NFM	Rayleigh	Taxis
		NFM	Edinburgh Airport	Stock Control
		NFM	Belfast	CityCabs
		NFM	Manchester	Taxi

Base	Mobile	Mode	Location	User and Notes
		NFM	Cumbernauld	Yellow Star Taxis (Yellow)
		NFM	Hull	Taxis
		NFM	Jersey	Immigration Department
		NFM	Manchester	Taxis
		NFM	Newcastle	Silver Cars
		NFM	Norfolk	ICL
		NFM	Glasgow	Taxi
		NFM	Manchester	Taxi
167.2250	172.0250	NFM	Thetford	Chisps Taxis
		NFM	Downham Market	B.W Mack
		NFM	Mendips	Business Post
		NFM	Holbeach	Plant Hire
		NFM	Hull	Taxis
		NFM	Jersey	Waverley Coaches
		NFM	Royston	Meltax
		NFM	Worksop	Bee Line Taxis
		NFM	Humberside	Haulage Co
		NFM	Stockton-on-tees	Taxi Service
167.2375	172.0375	NFM	Hampshire	Vets
		NFM	Ashton	Taxis
		NFM	Dartford	Black Cabs
		NFM	Chadderton	Chadderton Cars
		NFM	Oxford	Black Cabs
		NFM	Aberdeen	Taxi
		NFM	Guernsey	Total Oil
		NFM	Haverhill	Chequer Cabs
		NFM	Huntingdon	Pete's Taxis
		NFM	Oxford	G.TTaxis
		NFM	Glasgow	Taxi
		NFM	Norfolk	ICL
		NFM	Felixstowe	BW Mack
167.2500	172.0500	NFM	Brighton	GB2SMR
		NFM	Whiston	Diamond Taxis Ltd
		NFM	Slough	Interpoint Taxis
		NFM	Elvington	Garrowby Estate Farms
		NFM	Swansea	Fishwicks Taxis
		NFM	Aberdeen	Taxi
		NFM	Bolton	Pal Cars Taxis
		NFM	Guernsey	Guernsey Post Office
		NFM	Hull	Goldstar Taxis
		NFM	Newtown	Taxis
		NFM	Plymouth	Armada Taxis
		NFM	Powys	Thomas Jones (Vet)
167.2625	172.0250	NFM	West Midlands	Fruit Machine Repairs
		NFM	Portsmouth	Blue Light Cabs
		NFM	Milton Keynes	Embassy Cars
		NFM	Reading	1st City Cars
		NFM	Haverhill	Havtaxi

Base	Mobile	Mode	Location	User and Notes
		NFM	Guernsey	Guernseybus
		NFM	Stevenage	Freewheelers
		NFM	Blackpool	J Cabs
167.2750	172.0750	NFM	Portsmouth	Taxis
		NFM	Sutton	Darby Plant
		NFM	Huntingdon	HRaby & Sons
		NFM	GtStokely	HRaby & Sons
		NFM	Aberdeen	Office Security
		NFM	Alloa	Taxi
		NFM	Bolton	Red Rose Taxis
		NFM	Brighton	Southern Taxis
		NFM	Hockwold Cum Wilton	JDenney Taxis
		NFM	Hull	Taxis
		NFM	Jersey	States Motor Traffic Dept.
		NFM	Southend on Sea	Associated Radio Cars
		NFM	Weymouth	Taxi Co
		NFM	Nationwide	TNT Transport
167.2875	172.0875	NFM	Peterborough	CBS Repeater
		NFM	Hampshire	Taxis
		NFM	Glasgow	Taxis
		NFM	Leicester	Taxis
		NFM	Eastleigh	Taxis
		NFM	S London	Taxis
		NFM	Haverfordwest	Rocky's Taxis
		NFM	W London	Couriers
		NFM	Wrexham	Ace Taxis
		NFM	Abingdon	Autotaxis
		NFM	Chesterfield	Central Taxis
		NFM	Cardiff	Taxis
		AM	Plymouth	Chequars Cabs
		NFM	Falkirk	Police
		NFM	Norfolk	ICL
		NFM	Glasgow	Taxi
		NFM	Montrose	Taxis
		NFM	Burnley	AK Taxis
		NFM	East Dereham	Breckland Taxis
167.3000	172.1000	NFM	Brighton	Amateur Radio
		NFM	Swindon	Taxis
		NFM	Amwlch	Taxis
		NFM	Luton	Black Cabs
		NFM	Blackburn	Super Line Private Hire
		NFM	Kings Lynn	R.DCarter
		NFM	Norfolk	ICL
		NFM	Oxford	Radiotaxis
167.3125	172.1125	NFM	Newark	Taxis
		NFM	Southampton	Taxis
		NFM	Aberdeen	Office Security
		NFM	Jethou Island	PMR

Base	Mobile	Mode	Location	User and Notes
		NFM	Nationwide	Community Repeater
		NFM	Glasgow	Taxi
167.3250	172.1250	NFM	Central London	Taxis/Couriers
		NFM	Dartford	Taxis
		NFM	Manchester	Taxi
		NFM	Manchester	Astley Van Hire
		NFM	Astley	Astley Van Hire
		NFM	Swansea	A And M Taxis
		NFM	Bedford	Bedfordia Farms
		NFM	Chatteris	Graves & Graves
		NFM	Stirling	Police
		NFM	Glasgow	Taxi
		AM	Shoreham	Shoreham Airport Taxis
		NFM	Ipswich	Robin Hood Taxis
167.3375	172.1375	NFM	Stretford	New Moon Private Hire
		NFM	Heywood	Eagle Cars
		NFM	Cardiff	Taxis
		NFM	Biggleswade	Whitbread Farms
		NFM	Glasgow	Taxi
167.3500	170.1500	NFM	Manchester	Taxi
		NFM	Eccles	Taxi
		NFM	Salford	Taxi
		NFM	Fareham	Taxis
		NFM	Hampshire	Wayne Haverson
		NFM	Tamworth	Taxis
		NFM	Fareham	Taxis
		NFM	Preston	Taxis
		NFM	Whiston	Diamond Taxis Ltd
		NFM	Stockport	Taxis
		NFM	Burnham	Burnham Radio Cabs
		NFM	Rochdale	Central Taxis
		NFM	Cornwall	English China Clay
		AM	Aberdeen	Taxi
		NFM	Fordham	Allen Newport
		NFM	Hull	Taxis
		NFM	Jersey	Regal Construction
		NFM	Whittlesey	Luxicabs
		NFM	Blackpool	RWalker & Co
		NFM	Stoke-on-Trent	Taxis
167.3625	172.1625	NFM	Plymouth	Taxis
		NFM	Bolton	Murtax Taxis
		NFM	Hull	Taxis
		NFM	Soham	Greens of Soham
		NFM	Guernsey	Community Repeater 2
		NFM	E London	Taxis
167.3750	172.1750	NFM	Chippenham	Taxis
		NFM	Southampton	Taxis
		AM	Manchester	Taxifone Taxis

Base	Mobile	Mode	Location	User and Notes
		NFM	Wrexham	Regal Taxis
		NFM	Aberdeen	Tyre Service
		NFM	Nationwide	Comet Television
		NFM	Poole	Repeater
		NFM	Winchester	Council
167.3875	172.1875	NFM	Glasgow	Taxis
		NFM	Manchester	PMR
		NFM	Salford	Swan Private Hire
		NFM	Manchester	Taxi
		NFM	Aberdeen	Taxi
		NFM	Cardiff	Plumbing Company
		NFM	Hull	Taxis
		NFM	Norfolk	ICL
		NFM	Kettering	KLM Taxis
		NFM	Glasgow	Taxi
		NFM	Pontypool	Red Dragon Taxis
		NFM	Devizes	Devizes Taxis
		NFM	Newport	CableTel Ch 1
167.4000	172.2000	NFM	Hampshire	Cascade Cars
		NFM	Leicester	Taxis
		NFM	Oldham	Bluebird Private Hire
		NFM	Manchester	Taxi
		NFM	Colchester	Paxmans Diesels
		NFM	Leigh on Sea	Kelly's Radio
		NFM	Norfolk	Associated Leisure
		NFM	Perth	Taxi
167.4125	172.2125	NFM	Newark	Taxis
		NFM	Leicester	Taxis
		NFM	Bury	Harvey's Taxis
		NFM	Manchester	Taxi
		NFM	Aberdeen	Estate Security
		NFM	Norfolk	ICL
		NFM	Oxford	City Taxis
		NFM	Stoke on Trent	Haulage Company
		NFM	Grimsby	M.D. Cars
		NFM	Glasgow	Taxi
		NFM	Portsmouth	Taxis
167.4250	172.2250	NFM	Bloxwich	Abba Taxis
		NFM	Plymouth	Cotton's Taxis
		NFM	Nottingham	Taxis
		NFM	Aberdeen	Taxi
		NFM	Downham Market	B.WMack
		NFM	Huntingdon	RBrading
		NFM	Larbert	Plough Taxis
		NFM	Norwich	J.BGreen
		NFM	Sheffield	Tram Works Construction
		NFM	Glasgow	Taxi Company
		NFM	Jersey	Jersey States Repeater

Base	Mobile	Mode	Location	User and Notes
		NFM	Jersey	Lucas Bros. Farm Shop
		NFM	Jersey	Ransom Garden Centre
		NFM	Jersey	States Electronics Dept.
		NFM	Jersey	HMP La Moye
167.4375	172.2375	NFM	Cleveland	City Taxis
		NFM	North West	Taxi
		NFM	Norwich	CWace
		NFM	Steeple Bumpstead	Shore Hall Estates
		NFM	Cleveland	Taxis
		NFM	Glasgow	Taxi
		NFM	Newport	French's TV Repairs
		NFM	Montrose	Taxis
		NFM	Airdrie	Taxis
		NFM	Tywyn North Wales	Taxi
167.4500	172.2500	NFM	Musselborough	Taxis
		NFM	Southsea	Pier Security
		NFM	Manchester	White Line Taxis
		NFM	Edinburgh	Taxis
		NFM	Abingdon	Newtop Taxis
		NFM	Knebworth	Vendustrial Ltd
		NFM	Newmarket	Chilcotts Taxis
		NFM	Norfolk	ICL
		NFM	Sheffield	Alpha Taxis
		NFM	Edinburgh	Taxis
167.4625	172.2625	NFM	Oldham	Security
		NFM	Southampton	Taxis
		NFM	Aberdeen	Crane Hire
		NFM	Bristol	Works Dispatch
		NFM	Liverpool	Waterfront Security
		NFM	Lowestoft	Birds Eye
		NFM	Cardiff	PMR
		NFM	Manchester	District Council
		NFM	Nationwide	TNT Offices
		NFM	Nationwide	Tesco Supermarkets
		NFM	Gt. Yarmouth	Birds Eye Vans
		NFM	Peterborough	Tesco
		NFM	Warminster	Taxis
		NFM	Newport	TNT Deliveries Ch 1
		NFM	E London	Taxis/Couriers
167.4750	172.2750	NFM	Liverpool	Car Breakdown Recovery
		NFM	Ancoats	Chariots
		NFM	Poole	Repeater
		NFM	London	National Radio Cars
167.4875	172.2875	NFM	Portsmouth	Council
		NFM	Glasgow	Forge Shop. Mall Security
		NFM	Ryton	A1 Taxis
		NFM	Leicester	Taxis
		NFM	Edinburgh	Taxis

Base	Mobile	Mode	Location	User and Notes
		NFM	Aberdeen	Taxi
		NFM	Glasgow	Taxi
		NFM	Snaefell, Isle of Man	Repeater
		NFM	Newport	Red Base Taxis
		NFM	Grampian	Transport
167.5000	172.3000	NFM	Brighton	John Jug Ltd
		NFM	Blackpool	Streamline Taxis
		NFM	Rochford	Taxis
		NFM	Charminster	Bee Cabs
		NFM	Hemingbrough	AIS Brown Butlin Chemicals
		NFM	Aberdeen	Farm
		NFM	Barway	Shropshire Produce
		NFM	Shipham	William Moorfoot
		NFM	Swindon	Link Taxis
167.5125	172.3125	NFM	Worthing	Nynex Cable
		NFM	Blackley	Avenue Cars
		NFM	Manchester	Taxi
		NFM	Norfolk	ICL
		NFM	Jersey	HM Customs & Excise Ch 5
167.5250	172.3250	NFM	Nottingham	Taxis
		NFM	Cambridge	Able Taxis
		NFM	Salford	Taxis
		NFM	Letchworth	Mick's Taxis
		NFM	Edinburgh	Phone Line Banking
		NFM	Huntingdon	A.E. Abraham
		NFM	Norwich	Five Star Taxis
		NFM	Fort Regent, Jersey	Leisure Complex Ch3
167.5375	172.3375	NFM	Walsall Wood	Barons Taxis
		NFM	Hampshire	Cookie Boy Motors
		NFM	Bury	Peel Cars
		NFM	Aberdeen	Farm
		NFM	Cornwall	English China Clay
167.5500	172.3500	NFM	Portsmouth	City Wide Taxis
		NFM	Grimsby	Evening Telegraph
		NFM	Portsmouth	Taxis
		NFM	London	Taxis
		NFM	Salford	Briffin Cars
		NFM	Colchester	Abbeygate Taxis
		NFM	Newcastle	Forceful Debt Collectors
		NFM	Jersey	Fort Regent Leisure Centre
		NFM	Grimsby	Telegraph Newspaper
		NFM	Weymouth	Taxi Co
		NFM	Bradford-on-Avon	Taxis
167.5500	167.5500	NFM	Netherlands	Ambulance Service Ch 06
167.5625	172.3625	NFM	Worthing	Taxis
		AM	Nottingham	Taxis
		NFM	Isle of Wight	Taxis
		NFM	Gillingham	Taxis

Base	Mobile	Mode	Location	User and Notes
		NFM	Blackburn	Super B Private Hire
		NFM	Salford	Dolphin Cars
		NFM	Aberdeen	Estate
		NFM	Grangemouth	Taxi Owners Association
		NFM	Guernsey	Sunshine Cabs
		NFM	Cheshire	Station Cars
		NFM	March	G.ETribe
		NFM	Nottingham	Toton Plant Hire
		NFM	Plymouth	Key Cab Taxis
		NFM	Glasgow	Taxi
167.5700	167.5700	NFM	Netherlands	Ambulance Service Ch 08
167.5750	172.3750	NFM	Peterborough	CBS Repeater
		NFM	Worthing	Taxis
		NFM	Erith	Taxis
		NFM	Southampton	Taxis
		NFM	London	Courier
		NFM	Essex	Taxis
		NFM	Dumfries	Taxis
		NFM	Salford	Taxis
		NFM	March	David Johnson Farms
167.5875	172.3875	NFM	Leicester	Taxis
		NFM	Swinton	Swintax
		NFM	Elvington	Inturf
		NFM	Bedford	Riverside Taxis
		NFM	Sheffield	RSPCA
		NFM	Glasgow	Taxi
		NFM	Wakefield	Bell
167.5900	167.5900	NFM	Netherlands	Ambulance Service Ch 09
167.6000	172.4000	NFM	Manchester	Taxi
		NFM	Telford	Car Repairs
		NFM	Salford	Central Private Hire
		NFM	Manchester	Taxi
		NFM	Cumbernauld	Central Cab Co.
		NFM	Ipswich	Peter Green
		NFM	Glasgow	Taxi
		NFM	East Dereham	Venture Taxis
167.6100	167.6100	NFM	Netherlands	Ambulance Service Ch 05
167.6125	172.4125	NFM	Fleetwood	PMR
		NFM	London	Taxis
		NFM	London	Taxis
		NFM	Stevenage	Amber Cars
		NFM	Grimsby	Skip Co
		NFM	Bedford	Windshield Enterprise
		NFM	Blantyre	Mac Cars
		NFM	Glasgow	Taxi
167.6250	172.4250	NFM	Isle of Wight	Newport Council
		NFM	Walton	Taxis
		NFM	Blackburn	Blackburn's Taxi Ranks

Base	Mobile	Mode	Location	User and Notes
		NFM	Aberdeen	Deeside Shop Fitters
		NFM	Barway	Shropshire Produce
		NFM	Ipswich	Surveyors
		NFM	Lothian And Borders	East Lothian District Council
		NFM	Perth	Tayside Shopper Fitters
		NFM	Rochford	Andrews Taxis
		NFM	Shropshire	Shropshire Produce
		NFM	Glasgow	Taxi
		NFM	Shropshire	Barkway Ely
167.6300	167.6300	NFM	Netherlands	Ambulance Service Ch 02
167.6375	172.4375	NFM	Nottingham	Taxis
		NFM	Lees	Cartax
		NFM	Manchester	Taxi
		NFM	Suffolk	Rumbelows Television
		NFM	Glasgow	Taxi
		NFM	Trowbridge	Ace's Taxis
		NFM	Breckland	Council House Repairs
167.6500	167.6500	NFM	Netherlands	Ambulance Service Ch 01
167.6500	172.4500	NFM	Glasgow	Taxi Company
		NFM	Southampton	Randals Taxis
		NFM	Wirral	Eastham Cabs
		NFM	Preston	VIP Cabs
		NFM	Welwyn	Target Cars
		NFM	Wickford	Carter & Ward
		NFM	Glasgow	Mosque
		NFM	Humberside	Mechanics
		NFM	Aldershot	Taxi Co
		NFM	Bristol	Hemmings Waste
167.6625	172.4625	NFM	Widnes	Taxis
		NFM	Colchester	Smythe Motors
		NFM	Leicester	Taxi
		NFM	Glasgow	Taxi
167.6700	167.6700	NFM	Netherlands	Ambulance Service Ch 07
167.6750	172.4750	NFM	Scunthorpe	British Steel
		NFM	Portsmouth	Taxis
		NFM	Rochdale	Cozy Cars
		NFM	Guernsey	Central Cabs
		NFM	Guernsey	RG Falla
		NFM	Larbert	Taxi
		NFM	Perth	Tayside Regional Council
		NFM	Scunthorpe	Builders
		AM	Ipswich	Taxis
		NFM	Stevenage	Rowleys Taxis
		NFM	Pontypool	Real Gwent Taxis
167.6875	172.4875	NFM	Medway	Taxis
		NFM	Sale	Trafford Private Hire
		NFM	Cardiff	Taxis
		NFM	Aberdeen	Slatters

Base	Mobile	Mode	Location	User and Notes
		NFM	Nationwide	Community Repeater
		NFM	Dunstable	Threeways Taxis
		NFM	Trowbridge	Taxis
167.6900	167.6900	NFM	Netherlands	Ambulance Service Ch 03
167.7000	172.5000	NFM	Peterborough	Bell CableMedia
		NFM	Southampton	Taxis
		NFM	Manchester	Taxis
		NFM	Ancoats	Town Cars
		NFM	Hull	Willingham's Recovery
		AM	Aberdeen	Security
		NFM	Littleport	HThompson
		NFM	Sheffield	Taxis
		NFM	Peterborough	Cable television
		NFM	Newmarket	Thompson Farms
		NFM	London Finchley	Tally Ho Cars
		NFM	London	Olympic Cars
		NFM	Ramsgate	Kent Medical Services
		NFM	Glasgow	East Kilbride Taxis
		NFM	Portsmouth	Taxis
		NFM	Peterborough	Cablevision
167.7100	167.7100	NFM	Netherlands	Ambulance Service Ch 04
167.7125	172.5125	NFM	Heathrow	Heathrow Luxury Cars
		NFM	Chester	Doctors
		NFM	Prestwich	Magnum Private Hire
		NFM	Cambridge	Jakubowski Builders
		NFM	Prestwich	Taxis
		NFM	Attlebridge	Hales Containers
167.7250	172.5250	NFM	Stourbridge	Taxis
		NFM	Hampshire	Tesco
		NFM	Leicester	Taxis
		NFM	Stockport	Taxis
		NFM	Kilburn	Taxis
		NFM	Reading	ABC Taxis
		NFM	Stockport	Taxi
		NFM	Lowestoft	Birds Eye
		NFM	Notingham	Co-Op TV Service
		NFM	Poole	Repeater
		NFM	Barton	Booth transport
		NFM	Gt. Yarmouth	Birds Eye
		NFM	Tyneside	Unemployment Agency
		NFM	Lowestoft	Birds Eye
167.7300	167.7300	NFM	Netherlands	Ambulance Service Ch 12
167.7375	172.5375	NFM	Bournemouth	Council Electricians
		NFM	Hull	Taxis
		NFM	Manchester	Veterinary Surgeon
167.7500	167.7500	NFM	Netherlands	Fire Brigades Ch 11
167.7500	172.5500	NFM	Wirral	New Brighton Cabs
		NFM	Hull	Taxis

Base	Mobile	Mode	Location	User and Notes
		NFM	Lowestoft	Oulton Radio Taxis
		NFM	Nottingham	Yellow Cabs
		NFM	Dundee	Taxis
		NFM	West Midlands	Wheelchair Cabs
167.7625	172.5625	NFM	Walsall	Taxi
		NFM	Southampton	Hospital Transport
		NFM	Birmingham	Taxis
		NFM	Dunstable	Cannon Cars
		NFM	Bolton	Bank St Taxis
		NFM	Cumbernauld	Cita Taxis (Cita)
		NFM	Bolton	Manor Taxis
		NFM	Nationwide	Community Repeater
		NFM	Glasgow	Taxi
167.7700	167.7700	NFM	Netherlands	Fire Brigades Ch 13
167.7750	172.5750	NFM	Taplow	Burnham Couriers
		AM	Boston	Star Taxis
		NFM	Manchester	Taxi
		NFM	Hull	Taxis
		NFM	Welwyn Garden City	Industrial Services
		NFM	Woburn	Speedwell Farms
		NFM	Norwich	Cablevision
167.7875	172.5875	NFM	lincoln	taxi service
		NFM	Manchester	Taxi
		NFM	Peterborough	ABBA Taxis
		NFM	Eccles	New Lyle Cars
		NFM	Newcastle	Metro Centre Maintenance
		NFM	Rochdale	Town Cars
		NFM	Manchester	Taxi
		NFM	St Andrews	Jay Taxis
		NFM	Basildon	Ace Taxi Group
		NFM	Edinburgh	Falcon Delivery
		NFM	Jersey	Jersey States Housing Dept.
		NFM	Saddleworth	Taxis
167.7900	167.7900	NFM	Netherlands	Fire Brigades Ch 12
167.8000	172.6000	NFM	Nottingham	Amusement Mach. Mainten.
		NFM	Portsmouth	Coop TV Service
		NFM	Manchester	Cresta Cars
		NFM	Wirral	50-50 Cabs
		NFM	Blackburn	Lancs Private Hire
		NFM	Oldham	Britannia Cars
		NFM	Manchester	Taxi
		NFM	Glasgow	Taxi
		AM	Aberdeen	Security
		NFM	Cambridge	United Taxis
		NFM	Dovercourt	Starling Taxis
		AM	Grimsby	Revels Taxis
		NFM	Weymouth	Taxi Co
		NFM	Glasgow	Taxi

Base	Mobile	Mode	Location	User and Notes
		NFM	Burnley	Taxis
167.8100	167.8100	NFM	Netherlands	Fire Brigades Ch 14
167.8125	172.6125	NFM	Glasgow	Taxis
		NFM	Manchester	Kings Private Hire
		NFM	Levenshulme	Kings Private Hire
		NFM	Alloa	Taxi
		NFM	Bedford	M.W. Ward
		NFM	Westmount, Jersey	CSL Repeater
		NFM	Westmount, Jersey	De La Haye Plant Ltd
		NFM	Westmount, Jersey	Keith Prowse Tours
		NFM	Westmount, Jersey	MacLead & Allan
		NFM	Westmount, Jersey	Fuel Supplies Ltd
		NFM	Westmount, Jersey	Ronez Ltd
		NFM	Watlington	Watlington Plant Hire
		NFM	Bath	Abbey Taxis
		NFM	Bootle	Taxis
167.8250	172.6250	NFM	Edinburgh	Taxis
		NFM	Grangemouth	Tartan Line Radio Cabs
		NFM	Bolton	Tele Taxis
		NFM	Ipswich	Robin Hood Taxis
		NFM	Bristol	Downend Taxis
167.8300	167.8300	NFM	Netherlands	Fire Brigades Ch 16
167.8375	172.6375	NFM	Rochdale	Milnrow Cars
		NFM	Manchester	Taxi
		NFM	Nationwide	Community Repeater
		NFM	Polesworth	Polesworth Cabs
167.8500	172.6500	NFM	Bexley Heath	Taxis
		NFM	Cambridge	Clearaway
		NFM	Nottinghamshire	Clumber Park
		NFM	Cleveleys	Ace Cabs
		AM	Blackpool	Ace Cabs
		AM	Ipswich	Taxis
		NFM	Cardiff	Amber Taxis
167.8500	167.8500	NFM	Netherlands	Ambulance Service Ch 10
167.8625	172.6625	NFM	Ormskirk	Taxis
		NFM	Worthing	Taxis
		NFM	Leicester	Taxis
		NFM	Milton Keynes	City Bus Ltd
		NFM	Swansea	E And G Taxis
		NFM	Manchester	Taxi
		NFM	Nationwide	Community Repeater
		NFM	Middleton	Star Taxis
		NFM	Sheffield	Mercury Taxis
		NFM	Wiltshire	Bus Inspectors & Mechanics
167.8700	167.8700	NFM	Netherlands	Fire Brigades Ch 15
167.8750	172.6750	NFM	Plymouth	Taxis
		AM	Sheffield	DB Taxis
		NFM	Birmingham	Triad Removals

Base	Mobile	Mode	Location	User and Notes
		NFM	Nationwide	Community Repeater
		NFM	Scunthorpe	Taxi
167.8875	172.6875	NFM	Oldham	Radio Cars
		NFM	Liverpool	Taxis
		NFM	Eastleigh	Taxis
		NFM	Liverpool	Dock Taxis
		NFM	Atherton	J&K Taxis
		NFM	Glasgow	Taxi Company
		NFM	Nationwide	Community Repeater
		NFM	Cheshire	Whites Taxis
		NFM	Chelmsford	Trade Comms
		AM	Ipswich	Taxis
167.8900	167.8900	NFM	Netherlands	Ambulance Service Ch 13
167.9000	172.7000	NFM	Prescot	All Black Cabs Ltd
		NFM	Northampton	Taxis
		NFM	Winton	Taxis
		NFM	Heywood	Heywood Cars
		NFM	Welwyn Garden City	Garden City Taxis
		NFM	Jersey	HM Customs & Excise Ch 1
167.9100	167.9100	NFM	Netherlands	Ambulance Service Ch 11
167.9125	172.7125	NFM	Newport	Dragon Taxis
		NFM	Wrexham	Cresta Taxis
		NFM	North West	PMR
		NFM	Royston	B & B Taxis
		NFM	Woodbridge	Normans Transport
		AM	Ipswich	Taxis
		NFM	Grain	Geoffrey Clark
		NFM	Sheffield	Blue Star Security
		NFM	Bradford	Turbin Take Away
		NFM	London	Skip Hire
		NFM	Newport	Dragon Taxis Ch 1
167.9250	172.7250	NFM	Leeds	Taxis
		NFM	Stevenage	Sierra Taxis
		NFM	Radcliffe	United Private Hire
		NFM	Chelmsford	Ace Mini Cabs
		NFM	Newmarket	Sound City Cars
		NFM	Ashford	Freightline Parcels
		NFM	Hertsfordshire	Martini Cars
		NFM	London	Bus Company
		NFM	Cheltenham	Taxis
167.9300	167.9300	NFM	Netherlands	Fire Brigades Ch 03
167.9375	172.7375	NFM	Hemel Hempsted	Minicab Co
		NFM	Taunton	Ace Taxis
		NFM	Oldham	Red Cars
		NFM	Bracknell	Bracknell Radio Cars
		NFM	Manchester	Taxi
		NFM	Cumbernauld	Taxi
		NFM	Luton	Harvey Plant Hire

Base	Mobile	Mode	Location	User and Notes
		NFM	Coatbridge	Town Taxis
		NFM	Glasgow	Taxi
		NFM	Tamworth	Taxi Firm
167.9500	167.9500	NFM	Netherlands	Fire Brigades Ch 04
167.9500	172.7500	NFM	Rochdale	Kings Private Hire
		NFM	Jersey	Clarendon Cabs
		NFM	Nationwide	Search And Rescue
		NFM	Glasgow	Taxis
		NFM	Ipswich	Taxis
167.9625	172.7625	NFM	Peterborough	Clover Cars
		NFM	Brighton	Taxis
		NFM	Birkenhead	Robo's Taxis
		NFM	Pocklington	Central Taxis
		NFM	Jersey	Falles Hire Cars
		NFM	Peterborough	Horrells Dairies
		NFM	Bootle	Taxis
167.9700	167.9700	NFM	Netherlands	Fire Brigades Ch 01
167.9750	172.7750	NFM	Lincoln	Taxi Service
		NFM	Peterborough	Crown Taxis
		NFM	Edinburgh	Taxis
		NFM	Liverpool	Taxis
		NFM	Portsmouth	Taxis
		NFM	Royton	Royton Private Hire
		NFM	Ipswich	Hawk's Taxis
		NFM	March	Coy & Manchett
		NFM	Glasgow	Croft Radio Cars
		NFM	Ipswich	Tarmac Roadstones Ltd
		NFM	London	Taxis
167.9875	172.7875	NFM	Sussex	Brighton Marina Security
		NFM	Leicester	Taxis
		NFM	Swansea Docks	Crane Crews
		NFM	Wrexham	Gold Star Taxis
		NFM	Manchester	Taxi
		NFM	Cannock	TNT Carriers
		NFM	Walkden	Star Private Hire
		NFM	Thanet	B.CTaxis
		NFM	Salford	Shopping City Security.
		NFM	Airdrie	Mmoffat Ccars
		NFM	Glasgow	Taxi
		NFM	Jersey	HM Customs & Excise Ch 3
167.9900	167.9900	NFM	Netherlands	Fire Brigades Ch 07
168.0000	172.8000	NFM	Salford	Taxis
		NFM	West Glamorgan	S Wales Bus Co.
		NFM	Preston	Buses
		NFM	Manchester	Taxi
		NFM	Weymouth	Brewers Quay Exhibition
		NFM	Cambridge	Camtax
		NFM	Falkirk	Express Taxis (Express)

Base	Mobile	Mode	Location	User and Notes
		NFM	Glasgow	Eastwood Taxis
		NFM	Bristol	Dail A Cab
		NFM	Stoke On Trent	Abbey Taxis
		NFM	Jersey	Tantivy Holiday Coaches
		NFM	Burnley	Day Rider Couriers
168.0100	168.0100	NFM	Netherlands	Fire Brigades Ch 09
168.0125	168.0125	NFM	Salford	Mainline Taxis
		NFM	Edinburgh	Capital Cabs Ch 1
		NFM	Brighton	Taxis
		NFM	Edinburgh	Taxi
		NFM	Nationwide	Community Repeater
		NFM	Sheffield	Taxis
		NFM	Salford	Redline Taxis
		NFM	Stoke on Trent	Fourstar Taxis
		NFM	London	Taxis
168.0250	172.8250	NFM	Hitchin	Swan Garage
		NFM	Cardiff	PMR
		NFM	Ipswich	Robin Hood Taxis
		NFM	Glasgow	Taxi
168.0300	168.0300	NFM	Netherlands	Fire Brigades Ch 05
168.0375	172.8375	NFM	North West	PMR
		NFM	Edinburgh	Capital Cabs Ch 2
		NFM	Guernsey	D.JMachan Engineering
		NFM	March	Rowe
		NFM	London	New Barnet Cars
		NFM	Glasgow	Taxi
168.0500	168.0500	NFM	Netherlands	Fire Brigades Ch 06
168.0500	172.8500	NFM	Worthing	Taxis
		NFM	Nationwide	Pretty Things Road Crew
		NFM	Oldham	Delta Taxis
		NFM	London Heathrow	Airport Cars
		NFM	Central London	Taxis
		NFM	St Andrews	Golf City Taxis
		NFM	Bristol	Z Cars Taxis
		NFM	Cambridge	A1 Taxis
		NFM	Cowley	Rover Plant Ambulance
		NFM	Worksop	J.J & J.R. Jacksons
168.0625	172.8625	NFM	Peterborough	ABC Taxis
		NFM	SE London	Taxis
		NFM	Manchester, Walkden	Taxis
		NFM	Nationwide	Community Repeater
		NFM	Hull	Hull Daily Mail Paper
168.0700	168.0700	NFM	Netherlands	Fire Brigades Ch 02
168.0750	172.8750	NFM	Liverpool	Taxis
		NFM	Central London	Taxis
		NFM	Heywood	New Embassy Taxis
		NFM	West Bergholt	John Willsher
		NFM	Newport	Reliance Taxis

Base	Mobile	Mode	Location	User and Notes
168.0875	172.8875	NFM	Glasgow	Taxis
		NFM	Ascot	Cooper 24Hr Taxis
		NFM	Stevenage	W.G. Silverton
		NFM	Guernsey	Stan Brouard
		NFM	Guernsey	Unigrow
		NFM	Glasgow	Taxi
		NFM	Cardiff	Taxis
168.0900	168.0900	NFM	Netherlands	Fire Brigades Ch 08
168.1000	172.9000	NFM	Slough	A-2-B Taxis
		NFM	Glasgow	Kingsway Taxis
		NFM	Edinburgh	Taxis
		NFM	Southampton	ESSO Fawley Security
		NFM	Co Durham	Taxi
		NFM	Cleveland	PMR
		NFM	Newark	Taxis
		NFM	Sussex	Palace Pier Security
		NFM	Burnley	Taxis
		NFM	Edinburgh	United Artist Cable TV
		NFM	Tottington	Tram Cars
		NFM	Cardiff	Taxis
		NFM	Hamilton	Wellman Taxis
		NFM	Glasgow	Taxi
		NFM	Bristol	Streamline Taxis
		NFM	Welwyn Garden City	752 Taxis
168.1125	172.9125	NFM	Sunderland	Star Taxis
		NFM	Bromley	Taxis
		NFM	Radcliffe	Centre Radio Cars
		NFM	Glasgow	Head End
		NFM	Heysham	Heysham Radio Taxis
		NFM	Cardiff	Capital Taxis
		NFM	Preston	Evening Gazette
		NFM	Caister	Avenue Taxis
		NFM	Edinburgh	Taxi
		NFM	London	Minicab Firm Woodford
		NFM	Sunderland	Star Taxis
		NFM	Bath	Taxis
168.1250	172.9250	NFM	Edinburgh	Taxis
		NFM	Ipswich	Ipswich Buses Ltd
		NFM	Sheffield	Balfour Beaty
		NFM	Dundry	Brinks Mat Security
168.1325	172.9375	NFM	Gosport	Taxis
		NFM	Manchester Airport	Taxis
		NFM	Edinburgh	Black Cabs
		NFM	Burton-On-Trent	Lift Maintenance
		NFM	Arlesey	Station Cars
		NFM	Manchester	Taxi
		NFM	Aberdeen	Plant Hire
		NFM	Bolton	Breightmet Taxis

Base	Mobile	Mode	Location	User and Notes
		NFM	Edinburgh	Taxi (C)
		NFM	Mansfield	A Line Taxis
		NFM	Stoke on Trent	Sid's Taxis
		NFM	Glasgow	Taxi
168.1500	172.9500	NFM	Benwick	Bank Farms
		NFM	Manchester	Town Cars
		NFM	Dublin	Dublin Cablelink
		NFM	Manchester	Taxi
		NFM	Swansea	S And E Taxis
		NFM	Benwick	Bank Farms
		NFM	Ely	Evans Taxis
		NFM	Hull	Taxis
		AM	Scarborough	Beeline
		NFM	Balthwalles	Royal Welsh Show Security
168.1625	172.9625	NFM	Essex	Minicab Firm
		NFM	Manchester	Taxi
		NFM	Goodwood Race Course	Goodwood Control
		NFM	Aberdeen	Taxi
		NFM	London	Minicab Firm Richmond
		AM	Cleethorpes	Taxis
		NFM	Wisbeach	Ellis & Everard
		NFM	London	Capital Cars
		NFM	Glasgow	Taxi
168.1750	172.9750	NFM	Manchester	PMR
		NFM	Newmarket	Triax
		NFM	Rochdale	Castle Private Hire
		NFM	Bedford	Key Cars
		NFM	Edinburgh	PMR
		NFM	London	Ethnic Deportations
		AM	Grimsby Area	TV Repairs
168.1875	172.9875	NFM	Peterborough	DJ Taxis
		NFM	Blackpool	Black Tax Taxis
		NFM	Levenshulme	White Line Private Hire
		NFM	Abingdon	K-9 Security
		NFM	Sutton	Salisbury Bros.
		NFM	Blackpool	Blacktax
		NFM	Salisbury	Bros Sutton
168.2000	173.0000	NFM	Manchester	Taxis
		NFM	Beswick	UK Cars
		NFM	Reading	1A Cars
		NFM	Glasgow	Taxi
		NFM	Brentwood	TNT Carriers
		NFM	Milton	TNT Carriers
		NFM	Morecambe	PMR
		NFM	Nationwide	Community Repeater
		NFM	Shaftesbury	Hilltop Taxis
		NFM	London	Taxis
		NFM	Peterborough	Rivergate Security

Base	Mobile	Mode	Location	User and Notes
		AM	Grimsby	Taxi
168.2125	173.0125	NFM	Cambridge	Bettacars
		NFM	Dukinfield	Taxis
		NFM	Norfolk	ICL
		NFM	Sheffield	Eagle Taxis
		NFM	Stirling	D & M Taxis (D)
		NFM	Bettacars	Cambridge
		NFM	Norwich	Royal Taxis
		NFM	Glasgow	Taxi
		NFM	Trowbridge	Alpha Taxis
		NFM	Eccles	Zip Dispatch
		NFM	Swinton	Zip Dispatch
		NFM	Manchester	Zip Dispatch
168.2250	173.0250	NFM	Manchester	PMR
		NFM	Peterborough	Rivergate Security
		NFM	West Midlands	Public House Repairs
		NFM	Oldham	Untied Private Hire
		NFM	Manchester	Taxi
		NFM	Jersey	Interlink Delivery
		NFM	March	Central Security
		NFM	Nationwide	Radio Investigations Service
		NFM	Swindon	A2B Taxis
		NFM	March	Central Shopping Security
		NFM	Glasgow	Taxi
		NFM	London	AZ Couriers
		NFM	Blackpool	Green Star Taxis
168.2375	173.0375	NFM	Gt. Yarmouth	Halcyon Shipping
		NFM	Llandudno	Taxi Service
		NFM	Nottingham	Taxis
		NFM	Felling	Taxis
		NFM	Carlisle	City Taxis
		NFM	Great Yarmouth	Halcyon Shipping
		NFM	Nottingham	Holme Pier Water Sports
		NFM	Woodbridge	Taxis
		NFM	Corsham	Taxis

168.2500 - 168.9375 MHz   GOVERNMENT AGENCIES/BRITISH TELECOM SIMPLEX

Base	Mobile	Mode	Location	User and Notes
168.2500	168.2500	NFM	Dudley	Waterfront Security
		NFM	Ferndown	E.G. Hoare
		NFM	Swindon	Cooper's Metals
		NFM	Nationwide	BT Linesmen
		NFM	Nationwide	DTI Radio Investigations
168.2625	168.2625	NFM	Nationwide	BT Cable Laying
		NFM	Alderney	Alderney Electricity
168.2750	168.2750	NFM	Lancashire	RCA
		NFM	Nationwide	DTI Radio Investigations
		NFM	Nationwide	Radiocomms Agency

Base	Mobile	Mode	Location	User and Notes
		NFM	Hampshire	Radiocomms Agency
		NFM	Dorset	Radiocomms Agency
168.2875	168.2875	NFM	Burnley	Taxis
		NFM	Nationwide	Alarms
168.3000	168.3000	NFM	Nationwide	BT Linesmen
		NFM	Nationwide	DTI Radio Investigation
		NFM	Nationwide	BT & Post Office Investigators
		NFM	Nationwide	Royal Mail Security
168.3875	168.3875	NFM	Melksham	Taxis
		NFM	Aberdeen	PMR
		NFM	Formula One Racing	Williams Voice
168.4000	168.4000	NFM	Formula One Racing	Williams Team Voice Link
168.4000	168.9000	NFM	France	TEC Alphapage
168.4375	168.4375	NFM	Aberdeen	Security
168.4750		NFM	Dudley	Hospital Security
168.5500	168.5500	NFM	Belgium	Gendarmerie Ch 1
168.5700	168.5700	NFM	Belgium	Gendarmerie Ch 3
168.5900	168.5900	NFM	Belgium	Gendarmerie Ch 5
		NFM	Netherlands (Airports)	Fire Brigades Ch 17
168.6100	168.6100	NFM	Belgium	Gendarmerie Ch 7
168.6300	168.6300	NFM	Belgium	Gendarmerie Ch 9
168.6500	168.6500	NFM	Belgium	Gendarmerie Ch 11
168.6700	168.6700	NFM	Belgium	Gendarmerie Ch 13
168.6900	168.6900	NFM	Belgium	Gendarmerie Ch 15
168.7100	168.7100	NFM	Belgium	Gendarmerie Ch 17
168.7300	168.7300	NFM	Belgium	Gendarmerie Ch 19
168.7500	168.7500	NFM	Swansea	DSS Fraud Teams
		NFM	Guernsey	Civil Defence Network
		NFM	Jersey	Civil Defence Network
		NFM	Belgium	Gendarmerie Ch 21
168.7700	168.7700	NFM	Belgium	Gendarmerie Ch 23
168.7900	168.7900	NFM	Belgium	Gendarmerie Ch 25
168.8100	168.8100	NFM	Belgium	Gendarmerie Ch 27
168.8125	168.8125	NFM	Nationwide	Police Ops
168.8300	168.8300	NFM	Belgium	Gendarmerie Ch 29
168.8400	168.8400	NFM	Belgium	Gendarmerie Ch 30
168.8500	168.8500	NFM	Swansea City	Royal Mail
		NFM	Netherlands	Fire Brigades Ch 10
168.8600	168.8600	NFM	Belgium	Gendarmerie Ch 32
168.8625	168.8625	NFM	Euro Tunnel, Dover	Shakespeare Clift
		NFM	Jersey Airport	Beauport Aviation Gnd Staff
		NFM	Nationwide	National Seismic Studies
		NFM	Glasgow	Taxi
168.8750	168.8750	NFM	Swansea	DSS Fraud Teams
		NFM	Manchester, Denton	72E6
		NFM	Cardiff	Cardiff Van Hire
168.8800	168.8800	NFM	Belgium	Gendarmerie Ch 34
		NFM	Perth Aerodrome	Ground Services

Base	Mobile	Mode	Location	User and Notes
		NFM	Nationwide	BT Video Set Up Link
168.9000	168.9000	NFM	Jersey	Honorary Police (M2SP)
		NFM	Guernsey	Lesbirel Agricultural Services
		NFM	Jersey	Honorary Police Ch 8
		NFM	Belgium	Gendarmerie Ch 36
168.9125	168.9125	NFM	Newport	DHSS
		NFM	Jersey	Kingslea Hire
168.9200	168.9200	NFM	Belgium	Gendarmerie Ch 38
168.9250	168.9250	NFM	London	Bullion Movement Security
		NFM	Jersey	Honorary Police Ch 7
168.9375	168.9375	NFM	Nationwide	Alarms
168.9400	168.9400	NFM	Belgium	Gendarmerie Ch 40

168.9500 - 169.8375 MHz   PMR HIGH BAND SIMPLEX 12.5 KHZ

Base	Mobile	Mode	Location	User and Notes
168.9500	168.9500	NFM	Jersey	Driving Tests Chase Vehicle
		NFM	Nationwide	British Telecom
168.9600	168.9600	NFM	Belgium	Gendarmerie Ch 42
168.9625	168.9625	NFM	Sheffield City Centre	Bus Instectors
		NFM	Minehead	Butlins Security
		NFM	Worthing	PMR
		NFM	Aberdeen	Docks
		NFM	Ayr	Butlins Security
		NFM	Bury St Edmunds	Rushbrooke Farms
		NFM	Jersey	Industrial (Motors) Ltd
		NFM	Scarborough	Brurowick Pavillion Security
		NFM	Nationwide	BBC Engineering Channel
168.9750	168.9750	NFM	Caversham Park	BBC Monitoring Service
		NFM	Nationwide	Ordinance Survey
		NFM	Newcastle	British Telecom
		NFM	Jersey	Horse Racing Shows
		NFM	Leighton Buzzard	Joseph Arnold
		NFM	London	Wembley Stadium Security
		NFM	Nationwide	BBC Engineering Channel
168.9800	168.9800	NFM	Belgium	Gendarmerie Ch 44
168.9875	168.9875	NFM	Peterborough	Ferry Meadows Rangers
		NFM	Nationwide	BBC Engineering Channel
		NFM	Nationwide	Ordnance Survey
		NFM	Peterborough	Ferry Meadows Rangers
		NFM	Croydon	Crystal Palace Shop. Centre
		NFM	Guernsey	Condor Shipping
		NFM	Preston	Moathouse Hotel
		NFM	Aberdeen	Docks
		NFM	Cambridge	Fitzwilliam College
		NFM	Durham	TNT Carriers
		NFM	Felixstowe	Docks Police
		NFM	Jersey	Harbour (Condor)
		NFM	London	Wembley Stadium Stewards
		NFM	Nationwide	IBA Riggers

Base	Mobile	Mode	Location	User and Notes
		NFM	Nationwide	Ordnance Survey
		NFM	Prestwick Airport	British Aerospace
		NFM	Newport	Steelworks Handhelds
		NFM	Fitzwilliam College	Cambridge University
		NFM	Haverfordwest	Farm PMR
169.0000	169.0000	NFM	Southampton	Dock Security
		NFM	Sheffield	Transport Interchange Sec.
		NFM	Bolton	Council Car Park Attendants
		NFM	Bournemouth	Synagogue Security
		NFM	Cambridge	Trinity College
		NFM	Crewe	Oakley Centre
		NFM	Cheltenham	FMR Investigations
		NFM	Guernsey	PSS Security
		NFM	Killwinning	Water Baliffs
		NFM	Nationwide	RAC Rally
		NFM	Southampton	TNT Carriers
		NFM	Tilbury	Docks Freightliner Terminal
		NFM	Belgium	Gendarmerie Ch 46
169.0125	169.0125	NFM	Lords Cricket Ground	Stewards
		NFM	Nationwide	RAC Rally
		NFM	Wembley Stadium	Merchandise
		NFM	Edinburgh	HMV Record Shop Security
		NFM	Nationwide	Network Q Rally - Subaru
		NFM	Parkeston Quay	Harwich Transport
		NFM	Cornwall	TSBrent
		NFM	Dundee	Tay Bridge Maintenance
		NFM	Jersey	DHL Courier
		NFM	Nationwide	Short Term Lease PMR
		NFM	St Austell	Scrap Car Yard
		NFM	Weymouth	Guardforce Security
169.0200	169.0200	NFM	Belgium	Gendarmerie Ch 48
169.0250	169.0250	NFM	Cambridge	Posthouse Forte Hotel
		NFM	Brighton	Pier And Front
		NFM	Bury St Edmonds	Council
		NFM	Cambridge	Posthouse Forte Hotel
		NFM	Guernsey	Mainland Market Deliveries
		NFM	Hillingdon	Council
		NFM	Humberside Airport	Servisair
		NFM	Jersey	Deliveries
		NFM	Liverpool	Marks & Spenser Security
		NFM	London	Cazenove & Co Stockbrokers
		NFM	Nationwide	RAC Rally
		NFM	Nationwide	St Johns Ambulance Ch B
		NFM	Perth	Security
		NFM	Powys	Powys County Council
		NFM	Prestatyn	Pontins Holiday Camp Sec.
169.0375	169.0375	NFM	Maidstone	Leeds Castle Security Staff
		NFM	Wimbledon LTC	Wimbledon Tennis Champs

Base	Mobile	Mode	Location	User and Notes
		NFM	Clacton	Pier Co
		NFM	Bristol	Fruit Market
		NFM	Fort William	Nevis Range Ski Co.
		NFM	Lochaber	Nevis Rescue Services
		NFM	Penzance	Antenna Riggers
		NFM	Humberside Airport	Servisair Ops
		NFM	Luton Airport	Airline Ops & Ramp
		NFM	Luton Airport	Britannia Ground
		NFM	Manchester	Freightliners Yard Staff
		NFM	Bournemouth	International Centre Security
		NFM	Clacton-on-Sea	Pier Company
		NFM	Jersey	Jersey Zoo
		NFM	Cheltenham	FMR Investigations
		NFM	Plymouth	City Centre Shop Security
		NFM	Tendring	Tendring Hundreds Water
		NFM	Scarborough	Core Security
		NFM	Hull	Hull Rugby Stewards
169.0400	169.0400	NFM	Belgium	Gendarmerie Ch 50
169.0500	169.0500	NFM	Bacton	British Gas Corp
		NFM	Nationwide	RAC Rally
		NFM	England	CEGB
		NFM	Newport	Wimpey Builders
		NFM	Newport	Tarmac Road Repairs
169.0600	169.0600	NFM	Belgium	Gendarmerie Ch 52
169.0625	169.0625	NFM	London	Strocadero Security
		NFM	Carlisle	Portland Centre
		NFM	Brighton	Palace Pier
		NFM	Jersey	Commodore Shipping
		NFM	Lowestoft	Christian Salvesen
		NFM	Nationwide	ICL Computers
		NFM	London, Piccadilly	Troca Dero Security,
169.0750	169.0750	NFM	Rannoch Moor	White Corries Ski Co.
		NFM	Newquay	Hendra Caravan Park
		NFM	Liverpool	Albert Dock Security
		NFM	Llanelli, Pembury	Country Park Rangers
		NFM	Cardiff	PMR
		NFM	Poole	Valiant Security
		NFM	Guernsey	Balfour Beatty Falla
		NFM	London	West Ham FC Security
		NFM	London	Arsenal FC Security
		NFM	London	QPR FC Security
		NFM	Tyneside	Five Star Security
169.0800	169.0800	NFM	Belgium	Gendarmerie Ch 54
169.0875	169.0875	NFM	Newmarket	Bookmakers
		NFM	London	Arsenal FC Security
		NFM	Bolton	Peak Security
		NFM	Plymouth	DSS Security Office
		NFM	Crownhill	DSS Security Office

Base	Mobile	Mode	Location	User and Notes
		NFM	RAF St Mawgan	PSA Agency
		NFM	North West	PMR
		NFM	Jersey	Euro. Golf Championships
		NFM	Guernsey	Allied Heating
		NFM	Guernsey	Louis Dekker Bulbs
		NFM	Plymouth	City Centre Shop Security
		NFM	Nationwide	Limited DHSS Use
		NFM	Nationwide	Red Cross
		NFM	Plymouth	Plymouth Market Security
		NFM	Southampton	Docks
		NFM	Sutton Coldfield	Belfry Golf Course
		NFM	Blackpool	Social Security
		NFM	Abergavenny	Mountain Rescue Team 1
		NFM	Southern England	Mowlen Civil Engineering
169.1000	169.1000	NFM	Cambridge	Medical Research Council
		NFM	Isle Of Arran	NTS Rangers
		NFM	Cambridge	Medical Research Council
		NFM	Fishguard	Stena Sealink
		NFM	Folkestone	Stena Sealink
		NFM	Larne	Stena Sealink
		NFM	Southampton	Stena Sealink
		NFM	Stranraer	Stena Sealink
		NFM	Belgium	Gendarmerie Ch 56
169.1125	169.1125	NFM	University of Kent	Canterbury College
		NFM	Kent	Camber Sands
		NFM	Stanton	Marshalls Quarries
		NFM	Bournemouth	International Centre Security
		NFM	Halesworth	K.W.Thomas
		NFM	StHelier	Reclamation Site
		NFM	East End, London	BNP Book Shop
		NFM	Worksop	Fox Covert Scrap Yard
		NFM	Grimsby	Shopping Centre
		NFM	Weymouth	Hospital Security
169.1200	169.1200	NFM	Belgium	Gendarmerie Ch 58
169.1250	169.1250	NFM	Birkenhead	Shopping Centre Security
		NFM	Plymouth	Plymouth Hospital
		NFM	Sheffield	Radio Sheffield Beacon
		NFM	Scarborough	Scarborough FC Stewards
169.1300		NFM	Grand Prix Circuits	Williams Team Voice Link
169.1375	169.1375	NFM	Hampshire	Council
		NFM	Durris	NTS Rangers
		NFM	Scunthorpe	Balfour Beatty Construction
		NFM	London	Wembley Stadium Security
		NFM	Aberdeen	Bon Accord Centre Security
		NFM	Nationwide	Short Term Lease PMR
		NFM	Nationwide	St John's Ambulances
		NFM	Weymouth	RSPB
169.1400	169.1400	NFM	Belgium	Gendarmerie Ch 60

Base	Mobile	Mode	Location	User and Notes
169.1500	169.1500	NFM	Bournmouth	Beach Wardens
		NFM	Manchester	Pump Services
		NFM	Stanton	East Coast Slag
		NFM	Whitland	Dairy Crest
		NFM	Jersey	Jersey Builders
		NFM	Nationwide	National Trust
		NFM	Worksop	Bassetlaw Hospital
169.1600	169.1600	NFM	Luton Airport	Aircraft Cleaning
		NFM	Belgium	Gendarmerie Ch 62
169.1625	169.1625	NFM	London	Planet Hollywood Security
		NFM	Twickenham	Rugby Stewards
		NFM	Surrey	Council County Engineer
		NFM	Bishop Strotford	Mears Construction
		NFM	Cardigan	Cardi Cabs
		NFM	Haverfordwest	Cardi Cabs
		NFM	Luton Airport	Baggage Handlers
		NFM	London	Wembley Stadium Security
		NFM	Taplow, Cliveden House	Hotel Security
		NFM	Edinburgh	City Surveyors
		NFM	Ayr	Butlins Entertainment
		NFM	Essex	Top Guard International
		NFM	Jersey	Keith Rogers Building
		NFM	Nationwide	Short Term Lease PMR
		NFM	London	DSS Discreet
		NFM	Nationwide	St John's Ambulances Ch 5
		NFM	Bedford	Bedfordshire Festival 1994
169.1750	169.1750	NFM	Peterborough	East of England Show Gnd
		NFM	Ballachulish	Glencoe MR Team
		NFM	Fort William	PMR
		NFM	Snowdon	Mountain Railway
		NFM	Boston	OLGA
		NFM	Martlesham Heath	Department of Energy
		NFM	Guernsey	Ronez (Monmains)
		NFM	Nationwide	Mountain Rescue Scotland
		NFM	East End, London	Bangladeshi Vigilanties
		NFM	Perth	Landscape Gardens Ltd
		NFM	Three Holes	Frank Hartley
		NFM	Martlesham Heath	D.O.E.
		NFM	Cardiff	St Fagans Fock Museum
169.1800	169.1800	NFM	Belgium	Gendarmerie Ch 64
169.1875	169.1875	NFM	Plymouth	Cascade Security
		NFM	Wigan	Statesman Security
		NFM	Killingholme	National Power Security
		NFM	Peterlee	Five Star Taxis
		NFM	Penrith	Market Security
		NFM	Garston	Freightliner terminal
		NFM	Redruth	Land Rover Racing
		NFM	Biggleswade Airfield	Ops

Base	Mobile	Mode	Location	User and Notes
		NFM	London	Wembley Stadium Catering
		NFM	Ingleston	Market Stewards
		NFM	North West	PMR
		NFM	Grand Prix Circuits	Lotus Team Ch 3
		NFM	Jersey	Jersey Lift Engineers
		NFM	Nationwide	NCB Emergencies
		NFM	Nationwide	Short Term Lease PMR
		NFM	Morecambe	Trino's Taxis
		NFM	Perth	Security
		NFM	Brighton	Marina Asda Supermarket
		NFM	London	Public Health Labs
		NFM	Nationwide	St John's Ambulances Ch 6
169.2000	169.2000	NFM	Thanet	Thanet Technical College
		NFM	Bolton	Peak Security
		NFM	Peterborough	Regional College
		NFM	Fort William	BSW Sawmill
		NFM	Huyton	Ferraris Nighclub Security
		NFM	Swansea	F.R.F Motors
		NFM	Edinburgh	Chamber StMuseum
		NFM	Belfast Airport	Ground Services
		NFM	Burnley	Potterton ProdLines Ch 1
		NFM	Sheffield	British Steel
		NFM	Aberdeen	Aberdeen Ice Rink
		NFM	Jersey	Wilson Vets & Animal Shelter
		NFM	Perth	Security
		NFM	Ware	Glaxo Operations
		NFM	Belgium	Gendarmerie Ch 66
169.2125	169.2125	NFM	Dover	District Council
		NFM	Croydon	Water Palace
		NFM	Wigan	Car Park Security
		NFM	Bournemouth	M+J Security
		NFM	Bournemouth	Malibu Club Doormen
		NFM	East Midlands Airport	Airport Security
		NFM	Jersey	Beachguards
		NFM	Stoke on Trent	Stoke City FC Security
169.2200	169.2200	NFM	Belgium	Gendarmerie Ch 68
169.2250	169.2250	NFM	Carlisle	Thomas Graham & Sons
		NFM	Liverpool	Taxi-Taxi Channel
		NFM	Glasgow University	Security
		NFM	North Weald Airfield	Security & Crash Ops
		NFM	Jersey	Hurricaine Despatch
		NFM	Nationwide	RAC Rallies
		NFM	Wigan	Rugby Ground Stewards
		NFM	Orton	Longueville School
169.2375	169.2375	NFM	Liverpool	G.HLee Security
		NFM	England	Water Baliffs
169.2400	169.2400	NFM	Belgium	Gendarmerie Ch 70
169.2500	169.2500	NFM	Southampton	University Security

Base	Mobile	Mode	Location	User and Notes
		NFM	Brecon	Mountain Railway
		NFM	Trafford	Haulage Company
169.2600	169.2600	NFM	Belgium	Gendarmerie Ch 72
169.2625	169.2625	NFM	Felixstowe	Repcon
		NFM	Great Yarmouth	St.Nicholas Hospital
		NFM	Guernsey	Harlequin Hire Cars
		NFM	Hull	Shopping Centre Security
		NFM	Jersey	Builders
169.2750	169.2750	NFM	Isle of Man	Doctors On Call
		NFM	Shoreham Airfield	Tower-Ground
		NFM	East Northamptonshire	Traffic Control
		NFM	London Edmonton	Pickets Lock Centre
		NFM	Stansted Airport	Maintenance
		NFM	Woodbridge	Kemball
		NFM	Shoreham	Airport Ground Vehicles
		NFM	Southend-on-Sea	Technical College
169.2800	169.2800	NFM	Belgium	Gendarmerie Ch 74
169.2875	169.2875	NFM	Croydon	Croydon Health
		NFM	Kettering	Metalforce Ltd
		NFM	Woburn Sands	Plysu Plc
		NFM	Southampton	Dock Stevadores
169.3000	169.3000	NFM	Carlisle	H & H Auction Mart
		NFM	Heathrow Airport	Passenger Services
		NFM	Morecambe	Pleasure Beach Security
		NFM	Birmingham	West Brom FC Stewards
		NFM	Guernsey	Sarnia Hire Cars
		NFM	London Heathrow	Airline Passenger Service
		NFM	Newport	Town Centre Security
		NFM	Belgium	Gendarmerie Ch 76
169.3125	169.3125	NFM	Channel Tunnel	Group 4 Security
		NFM	London	Wembley Stadium Car Parks
		NFM	Nationwide	Network Q Rally - Nissan
		NFM	Jersey	Commodore Shipping
		NFM	Jersey	Otis Lifts
		NFM	Nationwide	Titan Fire Services
		NFM	Wigan	British Waterways
		NFM	Cardiff	PMR
169.3200	169.3200	NFM	Belgium	Gendarmerie Ch 78
169.3250	169.3250	NFM	Bath	Theatre Royal
		NFM	Barton-on-Humber	Peter Birse Construction
		NFM	Newquay	Car Park Attendants
		NFM	Luton Airport	Baggage Handlers
		NFM	Cannock	TNT Carriers
		NFM	Hull	Hull FC Stewards
		NFM	Clevedon	Passanger Traffic Control
		NFM	Exeter	Exeter Cathedral
169.3375	169.3375	NFM	Snetterton	British Auto Racing
		NFM	Kings College	Cambridge University

Base	Mobile	Mode	Location	User and Notes
		NFM	Cornwall	Tarmac
		NFM	Silverstone Airfield	Racetrack Ops
		NFM	Silverstone	Crash Trucks
		NFM	Cambridge	Kings College
		NFM	County Durham	Doctor's Medicall
		NFM	Devon	Tamar Bridge Security
		NFM	Jersey	Island Sports Officials
		NFM	Jersey	Motor Sports Officials
		NFM	Perth	St John's Centre Security
		NFM	Silverstone	RAC General Use
		NFM	London	Cazenove & Co Stockbrokers
169.3400	169.3400	NFM	Belgium	Gendarmerie Ch 80
169.3500	169.3500	NFM	Sussex	St John's Ambulance
		NFM	Luton Airport	Monarch Airlines
		NFM	Bournemouth	Weymouth House Security
		AM	Swansea Airport	Runway & Ground Crews
		NFM	Powys	South Wales Electricity
		NFM	Hull	Humber Bridge Control
169.3600	169.3600	NFM	Belgium	Gendarmerie Ch 82
169.3625	169.3625	NFM	Nationwide	St Johns Ambulance Ch A/1
		NFM	Plymouth	Police Plymouth Argyle FC
		NFM	Nationwide	Dept. of Trade & Industry
		NFM	Deptford	Dispatch Company
		NFM	Burnley	Potterton Security
		NFM	Glasgow	Woyka Timber Mill
		NFM	Burnley	Shopping Centre
		NFM	Whiston	Hexagon (HISS) Security Ltd
		NFM	Preston	Harris Museum
		NFM	Swansea	DSS Fraud Teams
		NFM	Dorset	DADPC Blandford Camp
		NFM	Leighton Buzzard	George Garside Sand
		NFM	Bolton	Bolton FC Stewards
169.3750	169.3750	NFM	Bell College	Saffron Walden
		NFM	Sheffield	Council
		NFM	Carlisle	PMR
		NFM	South Walden	Bell College
		NFM	Sheffield	Council Housing Dept.
169.3800	169.3800	NFM	Belgium	Gendarmerie Ch 84
169.3875	169.3875	NFM	Southwark	Crown Court Security
		NFM	Preston	Council Car Parks
		NFM	Humberside Airport	Tower-Ground
		NFM	Silverstone Airfield	Security & Crash Ops
		NFM	Kent	Prismo Road Surfacing
		NFM	Nottingham	Technical Services
		NFM	Bradford	Chapatti Deliveries
		NFM	Blackpool	Car Park Attendants
		NFM	Nationwide	St Johns Ambulance Ch 2

Base	Mobile	Mode	Location	User and Notes
169.39375 - 169.84375 MHz			**NEW EUROPEAN MESSAGING SERVICE**	
			(ERMES) PMR SIMPLEX 12.5 kHz NFM	
169.4000	169.4000	NFM	Newmarket	Harry Wrass Ltd
		NFM	Gt Yarmouth	Palgrave Brown
		NFM	Belgium	Gendarmerie Ch 86
169.4200	169.4200	NFM	Belgium	Gendarmerie Ch 88
169.4250	169.4250	NFM	Gt Yarmouth	Shipping Co
169.4375	169.4375	NFM	Southampton	Event Control
		NFM	Eastleigh	Taxis
		NFM	South Midlands	Comms Ltd Demo Ch
		NFM	Norwich	TV
		NFM	Jersey, Hotel De France	Conferences
169.4400	169.4400	NFM	Belgium	Gendarmerie Ch 90
169.4500	169.4500	NFM	Wisbeach	J.D. Walker Ltd
169.4600	169.4600	NFM	Belgium	Gendarmerie Ch 92
169.4625	169.4625	NFM	London	Security
		NFM	Tamworth	Road Works
169.4750	169.4750	NFM	Caister	Holiday Camp
		NFM	Stowmarket	Helmingham Est Farms
		NFM	Cambridge University	Christ's College
		NFM	Abergavenny	TV Antenna Riggers
169.4800	169.4800	NFM	Belgium	Gendarmerie Ch 94
169.4875	169.4875	NFM	Grand Prix Circuits	Benetton Voice
		NFM	Nationwide	Red Cross Ambulance
		NFM	Bournmouth	Centurian Security
		NFM	Grimsby	Burns Security
169.5000	169.5000	NFM	Norwich	British Rail
		NFM	Nationwide	Carlink Ferries
		NFM	Belgium	Gendarmerie Ch 96
169.5125	169.5125	NFM	Brandon	F.Hiam Farms
169.5200	169.5200	NFM	Belgium	Gendarmerie Ch 98
169.5250	169.5250	NFM	Woodbridge	Tubbs Building Supplies
		NFM	Luton	Vauxhall Motors
		NFM	Jersey	South Pier Shipyard
169.5375	169.5375	NFM	Nationwide	Whitbread World Race Sec.
		NFM	Cambridge	Council
		NFM	Nationwide	Honda Williams Racing Team
		NFM	Epsom	Race Course
		NFM	Jersey	Rob Thompson Electronics
		NFM	Blackpool	RSmith Leisure Services
		NFM	Burnley	Guardhall Security
169.5400	169.5400	NFM	Belgium	Gendarmerie Ch 100
169.5500	169.5500	NFM	Kings Lynn	Wicken Farm Co.
169.5600	169.5600	NFM	Belgium	Gendarmerie Ch 102
169.5750	169.5750	NFM	Wisbeach	J.D. Walker
		NFM	Folkestone	SIS
		NFM	Chatteris	Nongell Ltd
		NFM	Canterbury	Cathedral security

Base	Mobile	Mode	Location	User and Notes
		NFM	Dorset	Clearway Transport
		NFM	Swansea	Private Detectives
169.5800	169.5800	NFM	Belgium	Gendarmerie Ch 104
169.6000	169.6000	NFM	Luton Airport	Brittania Airways
		NFM	Belgium	Gendarmerie Ch 106
169.6125	169.6125	NFM	Wanton	Morley Farms
169.6200	169.6200	NFM	Belgium	Gendarmerie Ch 108
169.6250	169.6250	NFM	Thetford	H. Fledger
		NFM	Hythe	Nicholls Quarry
		NFM	Dereham	Crane Fruehauf
169.6375	169.6375	NFM	Cumbria	Repeater South Lakes
		NFM	Bournemouth	Farm Security
		NFM	Newhaven Port	Shorrock Security
169.6400	169.6400	NFM	Belgium	Gendarmerie Ch 110
169.6600	169.6600	NFM	Belgium	Gendarmerie Ch 112
169.6625	169.6625	NFM	Ramsgate Harbour	Marine Pollution Control
		NFM	Woolverstone	A.W Mayhew Farms
169.6625	169.6625	NFM	Nottingham	Sheriff Plant Hire
169.6750	169.6750	NFM	Nationwide	DSS Snoopers Ch 01
		NFM	Nottingham	Claredon College
169.6800	169.6800	NFM	Belgium	Gendarmerie Ch 114
169.7000	169.7000	NFM	Nationwide	DSS Snoopers Ch 02
		NFM	Nationwide	DSS Covert
		NFM	Belgium	Gendarmerie Ch 116
169.7200	169.7200	NFM	Belgium	Gendarmerie Ch 118
169.7250	169.7250	NFM	Bournemouth	Southern Despatch Bikes
		NFM	Bethnal Green	Star of David Bacon Factory
		NFM	Jersey	States Telecoms
		NFM	Jersey	Interference Officer
		NFM	Plymouth	St John's Ambulance
169.7375	169.7375	NFM	Birmingham	Bull Ring Security
		NFM	London	Chelsea FC Link
169.7400	169.7400	NFM	Belgium	Gendarmerie Ch 120
169.7500	169.7500	NFM	Jersey	Esso Co
169.7600	169.7600	NFM	Belgium	Gendarmerie Ch 122
169.7625	169.7625	NFM	South Midlands	SMC Demo Channel
		NFM	London, Piccadilly	The Rock Gardens Security
		NFM	Sandwich	Royal St George Golf Club
		NFM	Buckinghamshire	Bucks Council Ch 1
		NFM	Bedlinton	Taxis
		NFM	London	Piccadilly Rock Gardens
169.7750	169.7750	NFM	Bedford	Smith & Co
		NFM	Bishop Stortford	College
169.7800	169.7800	NFM	Belgium	Gendarmerie Ch 124
169.7875	169.7875	NFM	Reading	Council
		NFM	Cambridge	Roy Pett
169.8000	169.8000	NFM	France	C.S.A.
		NFM	Guernsey	Airport Services

Base	Mobile	Mode	Location	User and Notes
		NFM	Bristol	D.O.T.
		NFM	Guernsey	Airport Services
		NFM	Belgium	Gendarmerie Ch 126
169.8100	165.2100	NFM	Germany	Emergency Services Ch 101
169.8125	169.8125	NFM	Guernsey	Aurigny Ground Services
		NFM	Sheffield	N. Gen Hospital Security
		NFM	Birmingham	Aston Villa FC Stewards
169.8200	169.8200	NFM	Belgium	Gendarmerie Ch 128
169.8250	169.8250	NFM	Folkestone	Burstin Hotel
		NFM	Nationwide	DSS Snoopers Ch 03
		NFM	Jersey	Honorary Police
		NFM	Nationwide	Inland Revenue Ch 03
		NFM	Folkestone	Folkestone Hotel
		NFM	Perth	Maintenance
		NFM	Jersey	Honorary Police Ch 6
169.8300	165.2300	NFM	Germany	Emergency Services Ch 102
169.8375	169.8375	NFM	Wisbeach	Corbill Ltd
		NFM	Wisbeach	British Road Services
		NFM	Sheffield	Orchard Square SCS
		NFM	St Austell	ECC Pits
		NFM	London	Wembley Stadium Stewards
		NFM	Oxford	Oxford FC Stewards
		NFM	Burnley	Potterton ProdLines Ch 2
		NFM	Hull, Princes Quay	Carpark Security
169.8400	169.8400	NFM	Belgium	Gendarmerie Ch 130
169.84375 - 173.04375 MHz			PMR High Band Mobiles (Base Split - 4.8 MHz)	
169.8500		NFM	Kings Lynn	British Road Service
169.8500		NFM	Lincoln	Taxis
169.8500	165.2500	NFM	Germany	Emergency Services Ch 103
169.8600	169.8600	NFM	Belgium	Gendarmerie Ch 132
169.8700	165.2700	NFM	Germany	Emergency Services Ch 104
169.8750		NFM	Carlisle	PMR
169.8800	169.8800	NFM	Belgium	Gendarmerie Ch 134
169.8875		NFM	Portsmouth	Buses
169.8900	165.2900	NFM	Germany	Emergency Services Ch 105
169.9000	169.9000	NFM	Belgium	Gendarmerie Ch 136
169.9100	165.3100	NFM	Germany	Emergency Services Ch 106
169.9125	169.9125	NFM	Jersey	Beeline Taxis Channel 2
169.9200	169.9200	NFM	Belgium	Gendarmerie Ch 138
169.9250		NFM	Edinburgh	PMR
169.9250		NFM	Ulverston	McKenna's Taxis
169.9300	165.3300	NFM	Germany	Emergency Services Ch 107
169.9375	169.9375	NFM	Jersey	Land Surveyors & Architects
169.9400	169.9400	NFM	Belgium	Gendarmerie Ch 140
169.9500	165.3500	NFM	Germany	Emergency Services Ch 108
169.9600	169.9600	NFM	Belgium	Gendarmerie Ch 142
169.9625		NFM	Folkestone	Rotunda Park

Base	Mobile	Mode	Location	User and Notes
169.9625		NFM	East Durham	Private Message
169.9625	169.9625	NFM	London	Cazenove & Co Stockbrokers
169.9700	165.3700	NFM	Germany	Emergency Services Ch 109
169.9800	169.9800	NFM	Belgium	Gendarmerie Ch 144
169.9900	165.3900	NFM	Germany	Emergency Services Ch 110
170.0000		NFM	Barrow	BNFL Security
170.0000	170.0000	NFM	Belgium	Gendarmerie Ch 146
170.0100	165.4100	NFM	Germany	Emergency Services Ch 111
170.0200	170.0200	NFM	Belgium	Gendarmerie Ch 148
170.0300	165.4300	NFM	Germany	Emergency Services Ch 112
170.0375		NFM	Greater Manchester	Thameside Council
170.0400	170.0400	NFM	Belgium	Gendarmerie Ch 150
170.0500	165.4500	NFM	Germany	Emergency Services Ch 113
170.0600	170.0600	NFM	Belgium	Gendarmerie Ch 152
170.0700	165.4700	NFM	Germany	Emergency Services Ch 114
170.0750		NFM	Fleetwood	Doctors Paging
170.0800	170.0800	NFM	Belgium	Gendarmerie Ch 154
170.0875		NFM	Wrexham	Apollo Taxis
170.0900	165.4900	NFM	Germany	Emergency Services Ch 115
170.1000	170.1000	NFM	Belgium	Gendarmerie Ch 156
170.1100	165.5100	NFM	Germany	Emergency Services Ch 116
170.1200	170.1200	NFM	Belgium	Gendarmerie Ch 158
170.1300	165.5300	NFM	Germany	Emergency Services Ch 117
170.1400	170.1400	NFM	Belgium	Gendarmerie Ch 160
170.1500	165.5500	NFM	Germany	Emergency Services Ch 118
170.1600	170.1600	NFM	Belgium	Gendarmerie Ch 162
170.1700	165.5700	NFM	Germany	Emergency Services Ch 119
170.1900	165.5900	NFM	Germany	Emergency Services Ch 120
170.2000	170.2000	NFM	Bedford	Building Co.
170.2100	165.6100	NFM	Germany	Emergency Services Ch 121
170.2300	165.6300	NFM	Germany	Emergency Services Ch 122
170.2500	165.6500	NFM	Germany	Emergency Services Ch 123
170.2625		NFM	Worthing	Nynex Cable
170.2700	165.6700	NFM	Germany	Emergency Services Ch 124
170.2875		NFM	Manchester	Taxi
170.2900	165.6900	NFM	Germany	Emergency Services Ch 125
170.3785		NFM	Macclesfield	PMR
170.4000		NFM	Manchester	Taxi
170.4000	171.8000	NFM	Norway	Police
170.5000		NFM	Portsmouth	Taxis
170.5175		NFM	Newmarket	La Hoge Farm
170.6125		NFM	Perren Purth	Taxis
170.9750		NFM	Burnley	Corporation Base
171.1000		NFM	Manchester	Ambulance Service
171.2300	171.3900	NFM	Rijkswaterstaat, Holland	Motorway Maintenance
171.3300	171.3300	NFM	Netherlands	Police Ch 101
171.3500	171.3500	NFM	Netherlands	Police Ch 102
171.3700	171.3700	NFM	Netherlands	Police Ch 103

Base	Mobile	Mode	Location	User and Notes
171.3900	171.3900	NFM	Netherlands	Police Ch 104
171.4100	171.4100	NFM	Netherlands	Police Ch 105
171.4300	171.4300	NFM	Netherlands	Police Ch 106
171.4625		NFM	Barrow	Highways & Cleansing
171.4700	171.4700	NFM	Netherlands	Police Ch 107
171.4750	166.6750	NFM	Southampton	A2B Taxis
171.4900	171.4900	NFM	Netherlands	Police Ch 108
171.5100	171.5100	NFM	Netherlands	Police Ch 109
171.6000		NFM	Worthing	Sussex Ambulances
171.6125		NFM	Isle of Man	Nobles Hospital
171.7000		NFM	Nationwide	BBC O/B Link (OL-94)
		NFM	Manchester	Refuse Collection
171.7100	171.7100	NFM	Netherlands	Police Ch 100
171.8500	171.8500	NFM	Newport	Steelworks Paging
171.9625		NFM	New Biggen	Taxis
172.0000		NFM	Slough	Mars Factory
172.0000	167.2000	NFM	Nationwide	PMR Park And Demo Chan
172.0000	172.0000	NFM	Jersey	Dock Crane Operators
		NFM	Brechin	Builders
172.1250		NFM	Grundon	Waste Disposal
172.1250	172.2750	NFM	Norway	Fire Service Ch 2
172.1400	167.5400	NFM	Germany	Emergency Services Ch 200
172.1500	176.3500	NFM	Haywards Heath	Census Taxis
172.1600	167.5600	NFM	Germany	Emergency Services Ch 201
172.1800	167.5800	NFM	Germany	Emergency Services Ch 202
172.2000	167.6000	NFM	Germany	Emergency Services Ch 203
172.2125		NFM	Manchester	Taxi
172.2200	167.6200	NFM	Germany	Emergency Services Ch 204
172.2400	167.6400	NFM	Germany	Emergency Services Ch 205
172.2600	167.6600	NFM	Germany	Emergency Services Ch 206
172.2800	167.6800	NFM	Germany	Emergency Services Ch 207
172.3000	167.7000	NFM	Germany	Emergency Services Ch 208
172.3125	172.3125	NFM	Jersey	HM Customs & Excise Ch 6
172.3200	167.7200	NFM	Germany	Emergency Services Ch 209
172.3250	172.3250	NFM	Jersey	Fort Regent Channel 4
172.3400	167.7400	NFM	Germany	Emergency Services Ch 210
172.3500	172.3500	NFM	Jersey	Fort Regent Channel 2
172.3600	167.7600	NFM	Germany	Emergency Services Ch 211
172.3750		NFM	Cramlinton	Taxis
172.3800	167.7800	NFM	Germany	Emergency Services Ch 212
172.3900		NFM	Holland	Riot Police
172.4000	167.8000	NFM	Germany	Emergency Services Ch 213
172.4200	167.8200	NFM	Germany	Emergency Services Ch 214
172.4400	167.8400	NFM	Germany	Emergency Services Ch 215
172.4500		NFM	Walsall	Taxi
172.4600	167.8600	NFM	Germany	Emergency Services Ch 216
172.4800	167.8800	NFM	Germany	Emergency Services Ch 217
172.5000	167.9000	NFM	Germany	Emergency Services Ch 218

Base	Mobile	Mode	Location	User and Notes
172.5200	167.9200	NFM	Germany	Emergency Services Ch 219
172.5250		NFM	Carno	Laura Ashley Security
172.5400	167.9400	NFM	Germany	Emergency Services Ch 220
172.5600	167.9600	NFM	Germany	Emergency Services Ch 221
172.5800	167.9800	NFM	Germany	Emergency Services Ch 222
172.6000		NFM	Nationwide	BBC O/B Link (OL-94)
172.6000	168.0000	NFM	Germany	Emergency Services Ch 223
172.6200	168.0200	NFM	Germany	Emergency Services Ch 224
172.6400	168.0400	NFM	Germany	Emergency Services Ch 225
172.6600	168.0600	NFM	Germany	Emergency Services Ch 226
172.6625		NFM	Worthing	Taxis
172.6800	168.0800	NFM	Germany	Emergency Services Ch 227
172.7000	172.7000	NFM	Jersey	HM Customs & Excise Ch 2
172.7000	168.1000	NFM	Germany	Emergency Services Ch 228
172.7200	168.1200	NFM	Germany	Emergency Services Ch 229
172.7400	168.1400	NFM	Germany	Emergency Services Ch 230
172.7600	168.1600	NFM	Germany	Emergency Services Ch 231
172.7800	168.1800	NFM	Germany	Emergency Services Ch 232
172.7875	172.7875	NFM	Jersey	HM Customs & Excise Ch 4
172.8000	168.2000	NFM	Germany	Emergency Services Ch 233
172.8200	168.2200	NFM	Germany	Emergency Services Ch 234
172.8400	168.2400	NFM	Germany	Emergency Services Ch 235
172.8600	168.2600	NFM	Germany	Emergency Services Ch 236
172.8625	172.8625	NFM	Jersey	Beachguards
172.8800	168.2800	NFM	Germany	Emergency Services Ch 237
172.9000	168.3000	NFM	Germany	Emergency Services Ch 238
172.9200	168.3200	NFM	Germany	Emergency Services Ch 239
172.9400	168.3400	NFM	Germany	Emergency Services Ch 240
172.9600	168.3600	NFM	Germany	Emergency Services Ch 241
172.9800	168.3800	NFM	Germany	Emergency Services Ch 242
173.0000		NFM	Norway	Ambulance
		NFM	Nationwide	Low Power Guitar Systems
173.0000	173.5000	NFM	France	TEC Alphakage
173.0000	168.4000	NFM	Germany	Emergency Services Ch 243
173.0200	168.4200	NFM	Germany	Emergency Services Ch 244
173.0250		NFM	Nationwide	DTI Ch 1
173.0400	168.4400	NFM	Germany	Emergency Services Ch 245

173.04375 - 173.09375 MHz   PMR SIMPLEX 12.5 kHz NFM

Base	Mobile	Mode	Location	User and Notes
173.0500		NFM	Nationwide	DTI Ch 2
173.0600	168.4600	NFM	Germany	Emergency Services Ch 246
173.0625		NFM	Nationwide	RAC Network Q Rally
173.0750		NFM	Nationwide	DTI Ch 3
		NFM	Jersey	Stolen Car Detector Systems
173.0800	168.4800	NFM	Germany	Emergency Services Ch 247
173.0875		NFM	Torridon	NTS Rangers
		NFM	Bradford	Asian Youth Club
		NFM	Jersey	Surveyors

Base	Mobile	Mode	Location	User and Notes
173.09375 - 173.9875 MHz			**LOW POWER DEVICES, RADIO DEAF AIDS, BIOLOGICAL TELEMETRY & GARAGE DOOR OPENERS**	
173.1000	168.5000	NFM	Germany	Emergency Services Ch 248
173.1200	168.5200	NFM	Germany	Emergency Services Ch 249
173.1400	168.5400	NFM	Germany	Emergency Services Ch 250
173.1600	168.5600	NFM	Germany	Emergency Services Ch 251
173.1800	168.5800	NFM	Germany	Emergency Services Ch 252
173.1875		NFM	Nationwide	Mobile Alarm Paging
173.2000	168.6000	NFM	Germany	Emergency Services Ch 253
173.2200		NFM	Scotland	Singing Kettle Entertainment
173.2200	168.6200	NFM	Germany	Emergency Services Ch 254
173.2250		NFM	Nationwide	Building Site Alarms
		NFM	Nationwide	Radio Ctrl'd Garage Doors
173.240	168.6400	NFM	Germany	Emergency Services Ch 255
173.2600	168.6600	NFM	Germany	Emergency Services Ch 256
173.2800	168.6800	NFM	Germany	Emergency Services Ch 257
173.3000	168.7000	NFM	Germany	Emergency Services Ch 258
173.3200	168.7200	NFM	Germany	Emergency Services Ch 259
173.3400	168.7400	NFM	Germany	Emergency Services Ch 260
173.3500		NFM	Jersey	School Deaf Aids
173.3500 - 175.0200 MHz			**LIMITED COMMERICAL PMR AND POLICE USAGE CORDLESS MICROPHONES SIMPLEX**	
173.3600	168.7600	NFM	Germany	Emergency Services Ch 261
173.3800	168.7800	NFM	Germany	Emergency Services Ch 262
173.4000		NFM	Jersey	School Deaf Aids
		NFM	Nationwide	Deaf Aids
173.4000	168.8000	NFM	Germany	Emergency Services Ch 263
173.4200	168.8200	NFM	Germany	Emergency Services Ch 264
173.4400	168.8400	NFM	Germany	Emergency Services Ch 265
173.4600	168.8600	NFM	Germany	Emergency Services Ch 266
173.4625		NFM	Jersey	School Deaf Aids
173.4650		NFM	Nationwide	Deaf Aids
173.4800	168.8800	NFM	Germany	Emergency Services Ch 267
173.5000	168.9000	NFM	Germany	Emergency Services Ch 268
173.5200	168.9200	NFM	Germany	Emergency Services Ch 269
173.5400	168.9400	NFM	Germany	Emergency Services Ch 270
173.5450		NFM	Nationwide	Deaf Aids
173.5600	168.9600	NFM	Germany	Emergency Services Ch 271
173.5800	168.9800	NFM	Germany	Emergency Services Ch 272
173.6000		NFM	Nationwide	Yellow Channel
173.6000	169.0000	NFM	Germany	Emergency Services Ch 273
173.6200	169.0200	NFM	Germany	Emergency Services Ch 274
173.6400		NFM	Jersey	School Deaf Aids
		NFM	Nationwide	Deaf Aids
173.6400	169.0400	NFM	Germany	Emergency Services Ch 275
173.6600	169.0600	NFM	Germany	Emergency Services Ch 276

Base	Mobile	Mode	Location	User and Notes
173.6800	169.0800	NFM	Germany	Emergency Services Ch 277
173.7000 - 175.1000 MHz			**RADIO MIRCOPHONES NFM**	
173.7000	169.1000	NFM	Germany	Emergency Services Ch 278
173.7200	169.1200	NFM	Germany	Emergency Services Ch 279
173.7400	169.1400	NFM	Germany	Emergency Services Ch 280
173.7600	169.1600	NFM	Germany	Emergency Services Ch 281
173.7800	169.1800	NFM	Germany	Emergency Services Ch 282
173.8000		NFM	Nationwide	Theatre Radio Microphone
		NFM	Nationwide	Yellow Channel
		NFM	Perth	Church Radio Microphone
173.8000	169.2000	NFM	Germany	Emergency Services Ch 283
173.8200	169.2200	NFM	Germany	Emergency Services Ch 284
173.8250	173.8250	NFM	Newport	Panic-Phone Alarms
173.8400	169.2400	NFM	Germany	Emergency Services Ch 285
173.8600	169.2600	NFM	Germany	Emergency Services Ch 286
173.8800	169.2800	NFM	Germany	Emergency Services Ch 287
173.9000	169.3000	NFM	Germany	Emergency Services Ch 288
173.9200	169.3200	NFM	Germany	Emergency Services Ch 289
173.9400	169.3400	NFM	Germany	Emergency Services Ch 290
173.9500		NFM	Jersey	School Deaf Aids
173.9600	169.3600	NFM	Germany	Emergency Services Ch 291
173.9800	169.3800	NFM	Germany	Emergency Services Ch 292
174.0000		NFM	London	Transport Co.
174.0000	174.5000	NFM	Nationwide	Police Data Link
174.0125		NFM	Nationwide	RAC Network Q Rally
174.0250		NFM	Nationwide	RAC Network Q Rally
174.0375		NFM	Nationwide	RAC Network Q Rally
174.1000		NFM	Nationwide	Phil Collins Radio Mic (2)
		NFM	Nationwide	Red Channel
		NFM	Nationwide	Theatre Radio Microphone
		NFM	Guernsey	Channel TV Radio Mics
174.1100		NFM	Scotland	Singing Kettle Entertainment
174.1180		NFM	Scotland	Singing Kettle Entertainment
174.2875		NFM	Edinburgh	Edinburgh Castle Security
174.3000		NFM	Nationwide	Church Radio Mics
174.4250		NFM	London	Transport Co.
174.5000		NFM	Nationwide	Phil Collins Radio Mic (1)
		NFM	Nationwide	Blue Channel
		NFM	Glasgow	Baptist Church Mic
174.5250		NFM	Nationwide	Low Power Guitar Systems
174.6000		NFM	Nationwide	Channelradio Mics
174.6625		NFM	Aberdeen	ASD
		NFM	Scarborough	Theatre Mic
174.6750		NFM	Nationwide	Channel Radio Mics Green
174.7000		WFM	Jersey	BBC Jersey Radio Mics
174.7700		NFM	Nationwide	Channel Radio Mics
174.8000		NFM	Nationwide	Green Channel

Base	Mobile	Mode	Location	User and Notes
		NFM	Nationwide	Theatre Radio Microphone
		NFM	Southampton	Mecca Bingo Radio Mic
		NFM	Blackpool	St Thomas Church Radio Mic
		NFM	Prescot	Leisure Centre Mics
174.9750		NFM	Dorset	2CR VHF Radio Microphones
175.0000		NFM	Nationwide	Theatre Radio Microphone
		NFM	Nationwide	White Channel
		WFM	Jersey	BBC Jersey Radio Mics
		NFM	St. Helier	Church Radio Microphone
		NFM	Perth	Church Radio Microphone
		NFM	Scotland	Singing Kettle Entertainment
175.0875		NFM	Canvey Island	Trio Radio Cars

175.1500 - 175.3500 MHz   RADIO MIRCOPHONES NFM

175.3000 - 177.1000 MHz   IBA BROADCAST LINKS 12.5 kHz & RADIO MIRCOPHONES NFM

175.4250 - 175.6250 MHz   RADIO MIRCOPHONES NFM

Base	Mobile	Mode	Location	User and Notes
175.5200		NFM	Nationwide	ITV Radio Microphone
176.1875		NFM	Basildon	Taxis
176.4000		NFM	Nationwide	Theatre Radio Microphone
176.6000		NFM	Nationwide	BBC Radio Microphone
176.8000		NFM	Nationwide	BBC News Radio Mics
177.0000		NFM	Nationwide	Theatre Radio Microphone
177.1250		NFM	London	Multi-Business Shared Rep.

177.2000 - 181.7000 MHz   TRUNKED PMR BASE REPEATERS 12.5 kHz (SPLIT + 8.0 kHz)

Base	Mobile	Mode	Location	User and Notes
177.4625	185.4625	NFM	London	Multi-Business Shared Rep.
177.6125	185.6125	NFM	London	Courier Service
		NFM	London Heathrow	Ground Staff
177.9125		NFM	London	London Bus Co.
178.2375		NFM	Stirling	Data Link
178.2625	186.2625	NFM	London	Courier Service
178.3625	186.3625	NFM	London	Courier Service
178.5125	186.5125	NFM	London	Multi-Business Shared Rep.
178.6625	186.6625	NFM	London	Multi-Business Shared Rep.
178.7250		NFM	Tayside	Data Repeater
178.8125	186.8125	NFM	London	Multi-Business Shared Rep.
178.9625	186.9625	NFM	London	Multi-Business Shared Rep.
178.9875	186.9875	NFM	Cumbria	Fire Brigade
179.0250		NFM	Tayside	Data Repeater
179.1125	187.1125	NFM	London	Multi-Business Shared Rep.
179.1875		NFM	Glasgow	Data Link
180.0000		NFM	Nationwide	Illegal Bugging Devices
		NFM	Space	Cosmos 1870 Satellite
180.0125	188.0125	NFM	London	Multi-Business Shared Rep.

Base	Mobile	Mode	Location	User and Notes
180.1250		NFM	Space	Cosmos Satellite
180.4125		NFM	Warwickshire	Warwickshire Parcels Ltd
180.4250	188.4250	NFM	London	Multi-Business Shared Rep.
180.5375		NFM	Manchester	HGV PMR
180.5750	188.5750	NFM	London	Locksmith Ambulances
180.7250	188.7250	NFM	London	Multi-Business Shared Rep.
180.8875		NFM	Walsall	PMR
180.9500	188.9500	NFM	Tayside	Data Repeater
180.9875		NFM	Manchester	PMR
		NFM	North West	PMR
181.1375		NFM	Manchester	Transport PMR
181.2000		NFM	Pocklington	Orchard Taxis
181.5000		NFM	London (Lime Grove)	BBC Feed to TS2 O/B Mobile

181.7000 - 181.8000 MHz   VHF PMR 12.5 kHz NFM SIMPLEX

181.8000 - 183.5000 MHz   VHF PMR 12.5 kHz NFM DUPLEX

Base	Mobile	Mode	Location	User and Notes
182.5000		WFM	France	French TV Channel 5 Sound

183.5000 - 184.5000 MHz   VHF PMR 12.5 kHz NFM SIMPLEX

Base	Mobile	Mode	Location	User and Notes
184.0000		NFM	London	Transport Co.
184.4250		NFM	London	Transport Co.

184.5000 - 185.2000 MHz   RADIO MICROPHONES NFM

Base	Mobile	Mode	Location	User and Notes
184.6000		NFM	Nationwide	BBC News Radio Mics
184.8000		NFM	Nationwide	ITV Radio Microphone
		NFM	Jersey	Channel TV Radio Mics
185.0000		NFM	Nationwide	ITV Radio Microphone
		NFM	Tayside	Radio Tay OB Mics

185.2000 - 189.7000 MHz   VHF M1 PMR MOBILES 12.5 kHz
(SPLIT + 8.0 kHz)

Base	Mobile	Mode	Location	User and Notes
187.0100		WFM	London	Radio Feeder to 100.6 MHz

189.7000 - 189.8000 MHz   VHF PMR 12.5 kHz NFM SIMPLEX

Base	Mobile	Mode	Location	User and Notes
189.7025		NFM	Twickenham	BBC ITV Links Thames TV
189.7813		NFM	Twickenham	Thames TV
189.7938		NFM	Twickenham	BBC ITV Links Thames TV

189.8000 - 191.5000 MHz   VHF PMR 12.5 kHz NFM DUPLEX

Base	Mobile	Mode	Location	User and Notes
190.1500	206.1500	NFM	Penygrain	RETB
190.5000		WFM	France	French TV Channel 6 Sound

191.5000 - 193.2000 MHz   RADIO MICROPHONES NFM

Base	Mobile	Mode	Location	User and Notes
191.9000	191.9000	NFM	Scarborough	Theatre Microphone
192.6000	192.6000	NFM	Nationwide	BBC News Radio Mics
192.8000		WFM	Nationwide	BBC Antiques Roadshow
192.8000	192.8000	NFM	Nationwide	ITV Radio Microphone

Base	Mobile	Mode	Location	User and Notes
193.0000		NFM	London	Transport Co.
193.0000	193.0000	NFM	Nationwide	BBC Radio Microphone
193.1525		NFM	Glasgow	Strathclyde Buses
193.2000 - 199.5000 MHz			RADIO MICROPHONES PMR MOBILES 12.5 KHZ (BASE + 8.0 MHz)	
193.4625		NFM	London	Transport Co.
193.5625		NFM	London	Transport Co.
193.6125		NFM	London	Transport Co.
193.7125		NFM	London	Transport Co.
193.7625		NFM	London	Transport Co.
193.8625		NFM	London	Transport Co.
193.9125		NFM	London	Transport Co.
193.9250		NFM	Walsall	Council
193.9625		NFM	London	Transport Co.
194.0625	205.0625	NFM	Manchester	Metro Link
194.1500		NFM	Walsall	Taxi
194.3125		NFM	London	Transport Co.
194.4250		NFM	London	Transport Co.
194.4750		NFM	Walsall	Trunked PMR
195.0125		NFM	London	Transport Co.
195.2000		NFM	Walney Island	Mobile Coastguard
195.7750		NFM	North West	PMR
196.8125		NFM	London	Transport Co.
196.8500	204.8500	NFM	Louhuichart	RETB
		NFM	Achanalt	RETB
		NFM	Garelochead	RETB
		NFM	Helensburgh Upper	RETB
196.8750		NFM	Walsall	Maintenance
196.9625		NFM	London	Transport Co.
197.0125		NFM	London	Capitol Bus
197.0125	205.0125	NFM	Garve	RETB
197.0500	205.0500	NFM	Achiasheen	RETB
		NFM	Achnasheallach	RETB
		NFM	Strathcarron	RETB
		NFM	Attadale	RETB
		NFM	Stromferry	RETB
		NFM	Duncraig	RETB
		NFM	Plockton	RETB
		NFM	Duirinish	RETB
		NFM	Kyle of Lochalsh	RETB
		NFM	Mallaig	RETB
		NFM	Glenfinnan	RETB
		NFM	Locheilside	RETB
		NFM	Arrochar	RETB
		NFM	Glen Douglas (Loop)	RETB
197.1000	205.1000	NFM	Inverness	RETB
		NFM	Muir of Ord	RETB

Base	Mobile	Mode	Location	User and Notes
		NFM	Dingwall	RETB
		NFM	Morar	RETB
		NFM	Arisaig	RETB
		NFM	Beasdale	RETB
		NFM	Lochailort	RETB
		NFM	Spean Bridge	RETB
		NFM	Roy Bridge	RETB
		NFM	Tulloch	RETB
		NFM	Corrour	RETB
197.1500	205.1500	NFM	Rannoch	RETB
		NFM	Bridge of Orchy	RETB
197.4000	204.9000	NFM	Caersws	RETB
		NFM	Newtown	RETB
		NFM	Welshpool	RETB
		NFM	Shrewsbury	RETB
		NFM	Machynlleth	RETB
		NFM	Ardlui	RETB
		NFM	Sutton Bridge Junction	RETB
197.6500	205.6500	NFM	Darsham	RETB
		NFM	Saxmundham	RETB
197.7500	205.9500	NFM	Dovey Junction	RETB
197.8000	205.8000	NFM	Brampton	RETB
		NFM	Eccles	RETB
197.9000	205.9000	NFM	Westerfield	RETB
		NFM	Woodbridge	RETB
197.9500	205.9500	NFM	Tywtn	RETB
		NFM	Barmouth	RETB
		NFM	Llanaber	RETB
		NFM	Loch Eil O/B	RETB
		NFM	Banavie	RETB
		NFM	Fort William	RETB
198.0000	205.1000	NFM	Braemar	RETB
		NFM	Oulton Broad South	RETB
		NFM	Barmouth	RETB
198.1500	206.1500	NFM	Harlech	RETB
		NFM	Penychain	RETB
		NFM	Portmadoc	RETB
		NFM	Pwllheli	RETB
198.3500	205.3500	NFM	Aberystwyth	RETB
		NFM	Bortu	RETB
		NFM	Dovey Junction	RETB
198.4500		NFM	Isle Of Sheppey	British Rail
198.5000		WFM	France	French TV Channel 7 Sound
198.7625		NFM	London	Medicall
199.1000		NFM	Portsmouth	Taxis
199.1625	165.6375	NFM	London	BT Police Ch 2

199.5000 - 200.5000 MHz   VHF PMR 12.5 KHz NFM SIMPLEX

Base	Mobile	Mode	Location	User and Notes
200.3000		NFM	Scarborough	Theatre Microphone

200.5000 - 201.2000 MHz   RADIO MICROPHONES NFM

Base	Mobile	Mode	Location	User and Notes
200.5000		NFM	Nationwide	Radio Mics
200.6000		NFM	Nationwide	BBC Radio Microphone
		WFM	Nationwide	BBC Antiques Roadshow Mics
200.8000		NFM	Nationwide	ITV News Radio Mics
201.0000		NFM	Nationwide	ITV Radio Microphone
		NFM	Jersey	Channel TV Radio Mics
201.0000	193.0000	NFM	Nationwide	Trunked PMR
201.1125	193.1125	NFM	Nationwide	Trunked PMR
201.1250	193.1250	NFM	Nationwide	Trunked PMR
201.1375	193.1375	NFM	Nationwide	Trunked PMR
201.1500	193.1500	NFM	Nationwide	Trunked PMR
201.1625	193.1625	NFM	Nationwide	Trunked PMR
201.1750	193.1750	NFM	Nationwide	Trunked PMR
201.1875	193.1875	NFM	Nationwide	Trunked PMR

201.2000 - 207.5000 MHz   TRUNKED BASE PMR 12.5 KHZ
(MOBILES - 8.0 MHZ)

Base	Mobile	Mode	Location	User and Notes
201.2000	193.2000	NFM	Nationwide	Trunked PMR
201.2125	193.2125	NFM	Nationwide	Trunked PMR
201.2250	193.2250	NFM	Nationwide	Trunked PMR
201.2375	193.2375	NFM	Nationwide	Trunked PMR
201.2500	193.2500	NFM	Perth	Trunked PMR
		NFM	Nationwide	Trunked PMR
		NFM	Rugby	Electricians
201.2625	193.2625	NFM	Nationwide	Trunked PMR
201.2750	193.2750	NFM	Nationwide	Trunked PMR
201.2875	193.2875	NFM	Nationwide	Trunked PMR
201.3000	193.3000	NFM	Nationwide	Trunked PMR
201.3125	193.3125	NFM	Sheffield	South Yorkshire Transport
		NFM	Central Scottish	Bus Company
		NFM	South Yorkshire	Bus Company
		NFM	Nationwide	Trunked PMR
201.3250	193.3250	NFM	Nationwide	Trunked PMR
201.3375	193.3375	NFM	North West	PMR
		NFM	Nationwide	Trunked PMR
201.3500	193.3500	NFM	Nationwide	Trunked PMR
201.3625	193.3625	NFM	Nationwide	Trunked PMR
		NFM	Central Scottish	Bus Company
		NFM	South Yorkshire	Bus Company
		NFM	Newport	Bus Company
		NFM	London	Bus Company
201.3750	193.3750	NFM	Nationwide	Trunked PMR
201.3875	193.3875	NFM	Nationwide	Trunked PMR
201.4000	193.4000	NFM	North West	PMR
		NFM	Tayside	Trunked PMR

Base	Mobile	Mode	Location	User and Notes
		NFM	Nationwide	Trunked PMR
201.4125	193.4125	NFM	Nationwide	Trunked PMR
		NFM	Gt Manchester	Bus Company
		NFM	Strathclyde	Bus Company
		NFM	Alder Valley	Bus Company
201.4175	193.4375	NFM	Nationwide	Trunked PMR
201.4250	193.4250	NFM	Nationwide	Trunked PMR
201.4500	193.4500	NFM	Nationwide	Trunked PMR
201.4625	193.4625	NFM	London	London Transport
		NFM	Glasgow	Bus Company
		NFM	Nationwide	Trunked PMR
201.4750	193.4750	NFM	Nationwide	Trunked PMR
201.4875	193.4875	NFM	Nationwide	Trunked PMR
201.5000	193.5000	NFM	Nationwide	Trunked PMR
		NFM	London	Securiplan Plc Security
201.5125	193.5125	NFM	London	London Transport
		NFM	Cardiff	Bus Company
		NFM	West Yorkshire	Bus Company
		NFM	West Midlands	Bus Company
		NFM	Nationwide	Trunked PMR
201.5250	193.5250	NFM	Hull	Council Housing Repairs
		NFM	Hull	Mobile Doctors Service
		NFM	South Yorkshire	Trunked PMR
201.5375	193.5375	NFM	Nationwide	Trunked PMR
201.5500	193.5500	NFM	Tayside	Data Link/Trunked PMR
		NFM	Nationwide	Trunked PMR
201.5625	193.5625	NFM	Manchester	Metrolink Control
		NFM	Nationwide	Trunked PMR
		NFM	Yorkshire	Bus Company
		NFM	West Scotland	Bus Company
		NFM	London	Bus Company
		NFM	Northampton	Bus Company
201.5750	193.5750	NFM	Nationwide	Trunked PMR
201.5875	193.5075	NFM	Nationwide	Trunked PMR
201.6000	193.6000	NFM	Nationwide	Trunked PMR
201.6125	193.6125	NFM	London	London Transport
		NFM	Strathclyde	Bus Company
		NFM	Manchester	Bus Company
		NFM	Glasgow	Strathclyde Buses
201.6250	193.6250	NFM	Nationwide	Trunked PMR
201.6375	193.6375	NFM	Nationwide	Trunked PMR
201.6500	193.6500	NFM	Nationwide	Trunked PMR
201.6625	193.6625	NFM	Birmingham	West Midlands Bus Travel
		NFM	London	London Transport
		NFM	Strathclyde	Bus Company
		NFM	Cardiff	Bus Company
		NFM	London	Bus Company
		NFM	Darlington	Bus Company

Base	Mobile	Mode	Location	User and Notes
		NFM	Chester	Bus Company
		NFM	Gt Manchester	Bus Company
		NFM	Lancashire	Squires Transport
201.6750	193.6750	NFM	Nationwide	Trunked PMR
201.6875	193.6875	NFM	Manchester	Transport
		NFM	Nationwide	Trunked PMR
201.7000	193.7000	NFM	Tayside	Data Link/Trunked PMR
		NFM	Nationwide	Trunked PMR
201.7125	193.7125	NFM	London	London Transport
		NFM	Tyne & Wear	Bus Company
		NFM	Cardiff	Bus Company
		NFM	Nationwide	Trunked PMR
201.7250	193.7250	NFM	Nationwide	Trunked PMR
201.7375	193.7375	NFM	Nationwide	Trunked PMR
201.7500	193.7500	NFM	Nationwide	Trunked PMR
201.7625	193.7625	NFM	Rotherham	South Yorkshire Transport
		NFM	London	London Transport
		NFM	South Yorkshire	Bus Company
		NFM	Scotland	Midland Scottish
		NFM	Nationwide	Trunked PMR
201.7750	193.7750	NFM	Nationwide	Trunked PMR
201.7875	193.7875	NFM	Nationwide	Trunked PMR
201.8000	193.8000	NFM	Nationwide	Trunked PMR
		NFM	London	Security Company
201.8125	193.8125	NFM	Nationwide	Ch 42
		NFM	Gt Manchester	United
		NFM	London	United
		NFM	West Midlands	United
201.8250	193.8250	NFM	Nationwide	Band III Channel
201.8375	193.8375	NFM	North West	PMR
		NFM	Nationwide	Trunked PMR
201.8500	193.8500	NFM	Tayside	Trunked PMR/Data
		NFM	Nationwide	Band III Channel
201.8625	193.8625	NFM	London	London Transport
		NFM	Strathclyde	Buses
		NFM	London	Buses
		NFM	Nationwide	Band III Channel 40
		NFM	Glasgow	Strathclyde Buses
201.8750	193.8750	NFM	Nationwide	Band III Channel
201.8875	193.8875	NFM	Manchester	Transport
		NFM	Nationwide	Trunked PMR
201.9000	193.9000	NFM	Nationwide	Trunked PMR
201.9125	193.9125	NFM	London	London Transport
		NFM	York	Buses
		NFM	Warrington	Buses
		NFM	London	Buses
		NFM	West Yorkshire	Buses
		NFM	Nationwide	Band III Channel 30

Base	Mobile	Mode	Location	User and Notes
201.9250	193.9250	NFM	Nationwide	Trunked PMR
201.9375	193.9375	NFM	Nationwide	Trunked PMR
		NFM	W Yorkshire	Trunked Radio System
201.9500	193.9500	NFM	Nationwide	Trunked PMR
201.9625	193.9625	NFM	London	London Transport
		NFM	Yorkshire	Buses
		NFM	Scotland	West Scottish
		NFM	Bristol	Buses
		NFM	Wooler	Buses
		NFM	Manchester	GM Buses
201.9750	193.9750	NFM	Nationwide	Trunked PMR
201.9875	193.9875	NFM	North West	PMR
		NFM	Nationwide	Trunked PMR
		NFM	Ipswich	Radio Anglia
202.0000	194.0000	NFM	Tayside	Trunked PMR
		NFM	Nationwide	Trunked PMR
202.0125	194.0125	NFM	London	London Transport
		NFM	Bristol	Buses
		NFM	Tyne & Wear	Buses
		NFM	Derby	Buses
		NFM	Nationwide	Band III Channel
		NFM	Manchester	GM Buses
202.0250	194.0250	NFM	Nationwide	Band III Channel
202.0375	194.0375	NFM	Nationwide	Band III Channel
202.0500	194.0500	NFM	Nationwide	Band III Channel
202.0625	194.0625	NFM	North West	PMR
		NFM	London	London Transport
		NFM	Manchester	Metrolink Control
		NFM	Sheffield	South Yorkshire Transport
		NFM	Nationwide	Band III Channel 59
202.0750	194.0750	NFM	Nationwide	Band III Channel
202.0875	194.0875	NFM	Nationwide	Trunked PMR
202.1000	194.1000	NFM	Nationwide	Trunked PMR
202.1125	194.1125	NFM	nationwide	National Express Buses
		NFM	Nationwide	Trunked PMR
202.1250	194.1250	NFM	Nationwide	Trunked PMR
		NFM	W Yorkshire	Trunked Radio System
202.1375	194.1375	NFM	North West	PMR
		NFM	Nationwide	Trunked PMR
202.1500	194.1500	NFM	Tayside	Data Link/Trunked PMR
		NFM	Nationwide	Band III Channel
202.1625	194.1625	NFM	Manchester	Transport
		NFM	Birmingham	West Midlands Bus Travel
		NFM	Nationwide	Band III Channel 38
		NFM	Nationwide	National Express Buses
		NFM	Manchester	GM Buses
202.1750	194.1750	NFM	Nationwide	Band III Channel
202.1875	194.1875	NFM	Nationwide	Trunked PMR

Base	Mobile	Mode	Location	User and Notes
		NFM	Blackpool	PMR
202.2000	194.2000	NFM	North West	PMR
		NFM	Nationwide	Trunked PMR
202.2125	194.2125	NFM	Birmingham	West Midlands Bus Travel
		NFM	London	London Transport
		NFM	Scotland	East Scottish
		NFM	West Yorkshire	Buses
		NFM	Hull	Buses
		NFM	Nationwide	Trunked PMR
		NFM	Sheffield	Trams
202.2250	194.2250	NFM	Nationwide	Trunked PMR
202.2375	194.2375	NFM	Nationwide	Band III Channel
202.2500	194.2500	NFM	Nationwide	Trunked PMR
202.2625	194.2625	NFM	West Yorkshire	Northern General
		NFM	Maidstone	Buses
		NFM	Ely	Buses
		NFM	Nationwide	Trunked PMR
		NFM	Manchester	GM Buses
202.2750	194.2750	NFM	Nationwide	Trunked PMR
202.2875	194.2875	NFM	London	London Transport
		NFM	Nationwide	Trunked PMR
202.3000	194.3000	NFM	Nationwide	Trunked PMR
		NFM	Portsmouth	Taxis
202.3125	194.3125	NFM	Manchester	Bus
		NFM	London	London Transport
		NFM	Gt Manchester	Buses
		NFM	Tyne & Wear	Buses
		NFM	Nationwide	Trunked PMR
		NFM	Manchester	GM Buses
202.3175	194.3175	NFM	London	London Transport
		NFM	London	Revenue Inspectors Ch 2
202.3250	194.3250	NFM	Nationwide	Trunked PMR
202.3375	194.3375	NFM	Nationwide	Trunked PMR
202.3500	194.3500	NFM	Nationwide	Trunked PMR
202.3625	194.3625	NFM	Sheffield	South Yorkshire Transport
		NFM	London	London Transport
		NFM	Gt Manchester	Buses
		NFM	Tyne & Wear	Buses
		NFM	Nationwide	Band III Channel 32
		NFM	Manchester	GM Buses
202.3750	194.3750	NFM	Nationwide	Trunked PMR
202.3875	194.3875	NFM	Nationwide	Trunked PMR
202.4000	194.4000	NFM	Nationwide	Trunked PMR
202.4125	194.4125	NFM	Nationwide	Band III Channel
202.4250	194.4250	NFM	Nationwide	Band III Channel
		NFM	W Yorkshire	Trunked Radio System
202.4375	194.4375	NFM	North West	PMR
		NFM	Nationwide	Trunked PMR

Base	Mobile	Mode	Location	User and Notes
		NFM	Nationwide	Trunked PMR
202.4500	194.4500	NFM	Nationwide	Trunked PMR
202.4625	194.4625	NFM	London	London Transport
		NFM	Gt. Manchester	Buses
		NFM	Midlands	Buses
		NFM	Nationwide	Band III Channel 31
		NFM	Manchester	GM Buses
202.4750	194.4750	NFM	Nationwide	Trunked PMR
202.5000	194.5000	NFM	Nationwide	Trunked PMR
202.5125	194.5125	NFM	Merseyside	Buses
		NFM	East Kent	Buses
		NFM	Tayside	Buses
		NFM	South Wales	Buses
		NFM	Nationwide	Band III Channel
202.5250	194.5250	NFM	North West	PMR
		NFM	Nationwide	Trunked PMR
202.5375	194.5375	NFM	Nationwide	Trunked PMR
202.5500	194.5500	NFM	Nationwide	Trunked PMR
202.5625	194.5625	NFM	Nationwide	Trunked PMR
		NFM	W Yorkshire	Trunked Radio System
202.5750	194.5750	NFM	Nationwide	Trunked PMR
202.5875	194.5875	NFM	North West	PMR
		NFM	Nationwide	Trunked PMR
202.6000	194.6000	NFM	Nationwide	Trunked PMR
202.6125	194.6125	NFM	North West	PMR
		NFM	Nationwide	Trunked PMR
202.6175	194.6075	NFM	Nationwide	Trunked PMR
202.6250	194.6250	NFM	Nationwide	Trunked PMR
202.6500	154.6500	NFM	Nationwide	Trunked PMR
202.6625	194.6625	NFM	Nationwide	Trunked PMR
202.6750	194.6750	NFM	Nationwide	Trunked PMR
202.6875	194.6875	NFM	Nationwide	Trunked PMR
202.7000	194.7000	NFM	Nationwide	Trunked PMR
202.7125	194.7125	NFM	Nationwide	Trunked PMR
202.7250	194.7250	NFM	Nationwide	Trunked PMR
202.7375	194.7375	NFM	North West	PMR
		NFM	Nationwide	Trunked PMR
202.7500	194.7500	NFM	Nationwide	Trunked PMR
		NFM	Stockport	Breakdown Recovery
202.7625	194.7625	NFM	Nationwide	Trunked PMR
202.7750	194.7750	NFM	Nationwide	Trunked PMR
202.7875	194.7875	NFM	Nationwide	Trunked PMR
202.8000	194.8000	NFM	Nationwide	Trunked PMR
202.8125	194.8125	NFM	Nationwide	Trunked PMR
202.8250	194.8250	NFM	Nationwide	Trunked PMR
202.8375	194.8375	NFM	Nationwide	Trunked PMR
202.8500	194.8500	NFM	Nationwide	Trunked PMR
202.8625	194.8625	NFM	Nationwide	Trunked PMR

Base	Mobile	Mode	Location	User and Notes
		NFM	W Yorkshire	Trunked Radio System
202.8750	194.8750	NFM	Nationwide	Trunked PMR
202.8875	194.8875	NFM	Nationwide	Trunked PMR
202.9000	194.9000	NFM	Nationwide	Trunked PMR
202.9125	194.9125	NFM	Nationwide	Trunked PMR
202.9250	194.9250	NFM	Nationwide	Trunked PMR
202.9375	194.9375	NFM	Nationwide	Trunked PMR
202.9500	194.9500	NFM	Nationwide	Trunked PMR
202.9625	194.9625	NFM	Nationwide	Trunked PMR
		NFM	West Yorkshire	Buses
		NFM	Fife	Buses
		NFM	London	Buses
		NFM	Devon	Buses
		NFM	West Midlands	Buses
202.9756	194.9750	NFM	Nationwide	Trunked PMR
202.9875	194.9875	NFM	Nationwide	Trunked PMR
203.0000	195.0000	NFM	Nationwide	Trunked PMR
		NFM	London	R & I Blue Buses
203.0125	195.0125	NFM	London	London Transport
		NFM	Sheffield	Trams
		NFM	Nationwide	Trunked PMR
		NFM	West Yorkshire	Buses
		NFM	Hampshire	Buses
		NFM	London	Buses
		NFM	Scotland	East Scottish
203.0250	195.0250	NFM	Nationwide	Trunked PMR
203.0375	195.0375	NFM	Manchester	Rescue & Recovery
		NFM	Nationwide	Trunked PMR
203.0500	195.0500	NFM	Nationwide	Trunked PMR
203.0625	195.0625	NFM	London	Buses
		NFM	West Yorkshire	Buses
		NFM	Devon	Buses
		NFM	Tyne & Wear	Buses
		NFM	Nationwide	Trunked PMR
203.0750	195.0750	NFM	North West	PMR
		NFM	Nationwide	Band III Channel
203.0875	195.0875	NFM	Nationwide	Band III Channel
203.1000	195.1000	NFM	Nationwide	Band III Channel
203.1125	195.1125	NFM	Gt. Manchester	Buses
		NFM	Strathclyde	Buses
		NFM	Maidstone	Buses
		NFM	Devon	Buses
		NFM	Nationwide	Trunked PMR
203.1250	195.1250	NFM	Nationwide	Trunked PMR
203.1375	195.1375	NFM	Nationwide	Trunked PMR
203.1500	195.1500	NFM	Nationwide	Trunked PMR
203.1625	195.1625	NFM	Plymouth	Western National Buses
		NFM	London	Buses

Base	Mobile	Mode	Location	User and Notes
		NFM	Nationwide	Band III Channel
		NFM	Yorkshire	Yorkshire Traction
203.1750	195.1750	NFM	Nationwide	Trunked PMR
203.1875	195.1875	NFM	Nationwide	Band III Channel
		NFM	W Yorkshire	Trunked Radio System
203.2000	195.2000	NFM	Nationwide	Band III Channel
203.2125	195.2125	NFM	Sheffield	South Yorkshire Transport
		NFM	Nationwide	Band III Channel
203.2250	195.2250	NFM	Nationwide	Band III Channel
203.2375	195.2375	NFM	North West	PMR
		NFM	Manchester	Bus Company
203.2500	195.2500	NFM	North West	PMR
		NFM	Nationwide	Band III Channel
		NFM	Nationwide	Band III Channel
203.2575	195.2175	NFM	Nationwide	Band III Channel
203.2625	195.2625	NFM	London	London Transport Emergency
		NFM	Nationwide	Band III Channel
		NFM	Chesterfield	Buses
		NFM	Hartlepool	Buses
		NFM	London	Buses
203.2750	195.2750	NFM	Nationwide	Band III Channel
203.2875	195.2875	NFM	Nationwide	Band III Channel
203.3000	195.3000	NFM	Nationwide	Band III Channel
203.3125	195.3125	NFM	London	London Transport
		NFM	Lancaster	Buses
		NFM	Nationwide	Band III Channel 37
203.3250	195.3250	NFM	Nationwide	Band III Channel
203.3375	195.3375	NFM	Nationwide	Band III Channel
		NFM	W Yorkshire	Trunked Radio System
203.3500	195.3500	NFM	Nationwide	Band III Channel
203.3625	195.3625	NFM	London	London Transport
		NFM	Burnley	Buses
		NFM	Nationwide	Band III Channel 36
203.3675	195.3875	NFM	Nationwide	Trunked PMR
203.3750	195.3750	NFM	Nationwide	Band III Channel
		NFM	Nationwide	British Rail
203.4000	195.4000	NFM	North West	PMR
		NFM	Nationwide	Trunked PMR
203.4125	195.4125	NFM	Nationwide	Trunked PMR
203.4250	195.4250	NFM	Nationwide	Trunked PMR
203.4375	195.4375	NFM	North West	PMR
		NFM	Nationwide	Trunked PMR
203.4500	195.4500	NFM	Nationwide	Trunked PMR
203.4625	195.4625	NFM	Nationwide	Trunked PMR
		NFM	W Yorkshire	Trunked Radio System
203.4750	195.4750	NFM	Nationwide	Trunked PMR
203.4875	195.0000	NFM	North West	PMR
		NFM	Nationwide	Band III Channel

Base	Mobile	Mode	Location	User and Notes
203.5000	195.5000	NFM	Nationwide	Trunked PMR
203.5125	195.5125	NFM	Nationwide	Trunked PMR
		NFM	W Yorkshire	Trunked Radio System
203.5250	193.5250	NFM	Nationwide	Trunked PMR
203.5375	195.5375	NFM	Nationwide	Trunked PMR
203.5500	195.5500	NFM	Nationwide	Trunked PMR
203.5625	195.5625	NFM	Nationwide	Trunked PMR
		NFM	Pocklington	Peter Winn Tyres
203.5750	195.5750	NFM	Nationwide	Trunked PMR
203.5875	195.5875	NFM	North West	PMR
		NFM	Nationwide	Trunked PMR
203.6000	195.6000	NFM	Nationwide	Trunked PMR
203.6125	195.6125	NFM	Nationwide	Trunked PMR
		NFM	W Yorkshire	Trunked Radio System
203.6250	195.6250	NFM	North West	PMR
		NFM	Nationwide	Trunked PMR
203.6375	195.6375	NFM	Nationwide	Trunked PMR
203.6500	195.6500	NFM	Nationwide	Trunked PMR
203.6625	195.6625	NFM	London	London Transport
		NFM	Sheffield	South Yorkshire Transport
		NFM	South Yorkshire	Buses
		NFM	Central Scotland	Buses
		NFM	Cynon Valley	Buses
		NFM	Nationwide	Band III Channel 60
203.6750	195.6750	NFM	Nationwide	Trunked PMR
203.6875	195.6875	NFM	Nationwide	Trunked PMR
203.7000	195.7000	NFM	Nationwide	Trunked PMR
203.7125	195.7125	NFM	London	London Transport
		NFM	Nationwide	Trunked PMR
		NFM	Gt Manchester	Buses
		NFM	Tyne & Wear	Buses
203.7250	195.7250	NFM	Nationwide	Trunked PMR
203.7375	195.7375	NFM	Nationwide	Band III Channel
203.7500	195.7500	NFM	Nationwide	Trunked PMR
203.7625	195.7625	NFM	Midlands	Tec & Development
		NFM	Nationwide	Band III Channel
203.7750	195.7750	NFM	North West	PMR
		NFM	Nationwide	Band III Channel
203.7875	195.7875	NFM	Nationwide	Trunked PMR
203.8000	195.8000	NFM	Nationwide	Trunked PMR
203.8125	195.8125	NFM	Nationwide	Trunked PMR
		NFM	Ribble	Buses
		NFM	Cardiff	Buses
		NFM	West Midlands	Buses
203.8250	195.8250	NFM	Manchester	Transport
		NFM	Nationwide	Band III Channel
203.8375	195.6375	NFM	Nationwide	Band III Channel
203.8500	195.8500	NFM	North West	PMR

Base	Mobile	Mode	Location	User and Notes
		NFM	Nationwide	Trunked PMR
203.8625	195.6625	NFM	West Yorkshire	Buses
		NFM	Halton	Buses
		NFM	Oxford	Buses
		NFM	Nationwide	Band III Channel
203.8675	195.8875	NFM	Nationwide	Band III Channel
203.8750	195.8750	NFM	North West	PMR
		NFM	Nationwide	Band III Channel
203.9000	195.9000	NFM	Nationwide	Trunked PMR
203.9125	195.9125	NFM	West Yorkshire	Buses
		NFM	West Midlands	Buses
		NFM	Reading	Buses
		NFM	Scotland	Highland Scottish Buses
		NFM	Nationwide	Trunked PMR
203.9250	195.9250	NFM	Nationwide	Trunked PMR
203.9375	195.9375	NFM	Nationwide	Band III Channel
203.9500	195.9500	NFM	Nationwide	Trunked PMR
203.9625	195.9625	NFM	Nationwide	Band III Channel
203.9750	195.9750	NFM	North West	PMR
		NFM	Nationwide	Trunked PMR
		NFM	London	Security Company
203.9875	195.9875	NFM	Nationwide	Trunked PMR
204.0000	196.0000	NFM	Nationwide	Trunked PMR
204.0125	196.0125	NFM	Nationwide	Trunked PMR
204.0250	196.0250	NFM	Aberdeen	PMR
		NFM	Nationwide	Trunked PMR
204.0375	196.0375	NFM	Nationwide	Band III Channel
204.0500	196.0500	NFM	Nationwide	Trunked PMR
204.0625	196.0625	NFM	Nationwide	Trunked PMR
204.0750	196.0750	NFM	Nationwide	Band III Channel
204.0875	196.0875	NFM	Nationwide	Trunked PMR
204.1000	196.1000	NFM	Nationwide	Trunked PMR
204.1125	196.1125	NFM	Nationwide	Trunked PMR
204.1250	196.1250	NFM	Nationwide	Trunked PMR
		NFM	Glasgow	Trunked PMR
204.1375	196.1375	NFM	Nationwide	Trunked PMR
204.1500	196.1500	NFM	Nationwide	Trunked PMR
204.1625	196.1625	NFM	Nationwide	Trunked PMR
204.1750	196.1750	NFM	Nationwide	Band III Channel
204.1875	196.1875	NFM	Nationwide	Trunked PMR
		NFM	Edinburgh	PMR
204.2000	196.2000	NFM	Nationwide	Trunked PMR
204.2125	196.2125	NFM	Nationwide	Trunked PMR
204.2250	196.2250	NFM	Nationwide	Band III Channel
		NFM	Hull	Council Repairs
		NFM	Hull	Doctors On Call
204.2375	196.2375	NFM	Nationwide	Trunked PMR
		NFM	Edinburgh	PMR

Base	Mobile	Mode	Location	User and Notes
204.2500	196.2500	NFM	North West	PMR
		NFM	Nationwide	Band III Channel
204.2625	196.2625	NFM	Nationwide	Band III Channel
204.2750	196.2750	NFM	Nationwide	Trunked PMR
		NFM	Glasgow	Trunked PMR
204.2875	196.2875	NFM	Nationwide	Trunked PMR
204.3000	196.3000	NFM	Nationwide	Trunked PMR
204.3125	196.3125	NFM	North West	PMR
		NFM	Nationwide	Band III Channel
204.3250	196.3250	NFM	Nationwide	Trunked PMR
204.3375	196.3375	NFM	Nationwide	Trunked PMR
204.3500	196.3500	NFM	Nationwide	Trunked PMR
204.3625	196.3625	NFM	Nationwide	Trunked PMR
204.3750	196.3750	NFM	Nationwide	Trunked PMR
204.3875	196.3875	NFM	Nationwide	Trunked PMR
		NFM	W Yorkshire	Trunked Radio System
204.4000	196.4000	NFM	North West	PMR
		NFM	Nationwide	Trunked PMR
204.4125	196.4125	NFM	Nationwide	Trunked PMR
204.4250	196.4250	NFM	Nationwide	Trunked PMR
204.4375	196.4375	NFM	Nationwide	Trunked PMR
204.4500	196.4500	NFM	North West	Transport
		NFM	Nationwide	Trunked PMR
204.4625	196.4625	NFM	Nationwide	Trunked PMR
204.4750	196.4750	NFM	Nationwide	Trunked PMR
204.4875	196.4875	NFM	Nationwide	Trunked PMR
		NFM	Glasgow	Trunked PMR
204.5000	196.5000	NFM	Nationwide	Trunked PMR
		NFM	W Yorkshire	Trunked Radio System
204.5125	196.5125	NFM	Nationwide	Trunked PMR
204.5250	196.5250	NFM	Nationwide	Trunked PMR
		NFM	W Yorkshire	Trunked Radio System
204.5375	196.5375	NFM	Nationwide	Trunked PMR
		NFM	Taunton	Data & PMR Voice
204.5500	196.5500	NFM	Nationwide	Trunked PMR
204.5625	196.5625	NFM	North West	PMR
		NFM	Nationwide	Trunked PMR
204.5750	196.5750	NFM	North West	PMR
		NFM	Nationwide	Trunked PMR
204.5875	196.5875	NFM	Tayside	Data Link
		NFM	Nationwide	Trunked PMR
		NFM	W Yorkshire	Trunked Radio System
204.6000	196.6000	NFM	Nationwide	Trunked PMR
		NFM	Blackpool	PMR
204.6125	196.6125	NFM	North West	PMR
		NFM	Nationwide	Trunked PMR
204.6250	196.6250	NFM	Nationwide	Trunked PMR
204.6375	196.6375	NFM	Nationwide	Trunked PMR

Base	Mobile	Mode	Location	User and Notes
204.6500	196.6500	NFM	Aberdeen	PMR
		NFM	Nationwide	Trunked PMR
		NFM	W Yorkshire	Trunked Radio System
204.6625	196.6625	NFM	Nationwide	Trunked PMR
204.6750	196.6750	NFM	Nationwide	Trunked PMR
204.6875	196.6875	NFM	Nationwide	Trunked PMR
		NFM	Taunton	Data & PMR Voice
		NFM	Glasgow	Trunked PMR
204.7000	196.7000	NFM	Nationwide	Trunked PMR
204.7125	196.7125	NFM	Birmingham	West Midlands Bus Travel
		NFM	Scotland	Tec & Development
		NFM	Nationwide	Band III Channel 55
204.7250	196.7250	NFM	Nationwide	Trunked PMR
204.7375	196.7375	NFM	Tayside	Data Link
		NFM	Nationwide	Trunked PMR
204.7500	196.7500	NFM	North West	PMR
		NFM	Nationwide	Trunked PMR
204.7625	196.7625	NFM	Birmingham	West Midlands Bus Travel
		NFM	Nationwide	Band III Channel 26
		NFM	London	Buses
		NFM	Bristol	Buses
		NFM	Gt Manchester	Buses
		NFM	Tyne & Wear	Buses
204.7750	196.7750	NFM	Nationwide	Trunked PMR
204.7875	196.7875	NFM	Nationwide	Trunked PMR
		NFM	Edinburgh	PMR
204.8000	196.8000	NFM	Nationwide	Trunked PMR
204.8125	196.8125	NFM	Manchester	Bus
		NFM	London	London Transport
		NFM	Ribble	Buses
		NFM	Midlands	Buses
		NFM	Sotland	Buses
		NFM	Cleveland	Buses
		NFM	Nationwide	Band III Channel 53
		NFM	Manchester	GM Buses
204.8250	196.8250	NFM	Nationwide	Trunked PMR
204.8375	196.8375	NFM	Nationwide	Trunked PMR
		NFM	Blackpool	Vehicle Recovery
		NFM	Edinburgh	PMR
204.8500	196.8500	NFM	Nationwide	British Rail
		NFM	Nationwide	Trunked PMR
		NFM	Merseyside	Merseyside Electric
		NFM	Newport	British Rail
204.8625	196.8625	NFM	London	London Transport
		NFM	Nationwide	Band III Channel
204.8750	196.8750	NFM	Nationwide	Trunked PMR
		NFM	Glasgow	Trunked PMR
204.8875	196.8875	NFM	North West	PMR

Base	Mobile	Mode	Location	User and Notes
		NFM	Nationwide	Trunked PMR
204.9000	196.9000	NFM	Caersws	Mid Wales Railway Line RETB
		NFM	Nationwide	British Rail Channel 353
		NFM	Nationwide	Trunked PMR
204.9125	196.9125	NFM	London	London Transport
		NFM	Nationwide	Band III Channel 29
		NFM	Gt. Manchester	Buses
		NFM	Tyne & Wear	Buses
		NFM	Manchester	GM Buses
204.9250	196.9250	NFM	Nationwide	Trunked PMR
204.9375	196.9375	NFM	Nationwide	Trunked PMR
		NFM	Edinburgh	PMR
204.9500	196.9500	NFM	Tayside	Data Link
		NFM	Nationwide	British Rail Channel 357
204.9625	196.9625	NFM	Manchester	Bus Company
		NFM	Birmingham	West Midlands Bus Travel
		NFM	London	London Transport
		NFM	West Riding	Buses
		NFM	Scotland	West Scottish Buses
		NFM	Nationwide	Band III Channel 62
		NFM	Manchester	GM Buses
204.9750	196.9750	NFM	Nationwide	Trunked PMR
204.9875	196.9875	NFM	Nationwide	Trunked PMR
		NFM	Blackpool	RAC
205.0000	197.0000	NFM	Nationwide	British Rail Channel 361
		NFM	Newport	British Rail
205.0125	197.0125	NFM	Sheffield	South Yorkshire Transport
		NFM	Birmingham	West Midlands Bus Travel
		NFM	London	Buses
		NFM	Portsmouth	Blue Ankiral Buses
		NFM	Nationwide	Band III Channel 10
205.0250	197.0250	NFM	North West	PMR
		NFM	Nationwide	Trunked PMR
205.0375	197.0375	NFM	Tayside	Data Link
		NFM	Nationwide	Trunked PMR
		NFM	W Yorkshire	Trunked Radio System
205.0500	197.0500	NFM	North West	PMR
		NFM	Nationwide	British Rail Channel 365
		NFM	London	Buses
		NFM	Nationwide	Trunked PMR
		NFM	Fort William	British Rail
205.0625	197.0625	NFM	Manchester	City Bus Inspectors
		NFM	Plymouth	City Buses
		NFM	Nationwide	Band III Channel 57
		NFM	South	Tec & Development.
205.0750	197.0750	NFM	North West	PMR
		NFM	Nationwide	Trunked PMR
205.0875	197.0875	NFM	Nationwide	Trunked PMR

Base	Mobile	Mode	Location	User and Notes
205.1000	197.1000	NFM	Nationwide	British Rail Channel 369
		NFM	Nationwide	Trunked PMR
		NFM	Yorkshire	British Rail
205.1125	197.0125	NFM	Nationwide	Trunked PMR
		NFM	Nationwide	Bus National Emergency
205.1250	197.1250	NFM	Nationwide	Trunked PMR
205.1375	197.1375	NFM	Nationwide	Trunked PMR
		NFM	Taunton	Data & PMR Voice
205.1500	197.1500	NFM	Nationwide	BR Cab Channel
		NFM	Nationwide	British Rail Channel 373
		NFM	Newtown	Mid Wales Railway Line RETD
		NFM	Shrewsbury	Mid Wales Railway Line RETD
		NFM	Welshpool	Mid Wales Railway Line RETD
		NFM	Westbury	Mid Wales Railway Line RETD
		NFM	Sutton Bridge Junction	MWL RETD
205.1625	197.1625	NFM	Nationwide	Trunked PMR
		NFM	W Yorkshire	Trunked Radio System
205.1750	197.1750	NFM	North West	PMR
		NFM	Nationwide	Trunked PMR
205.1875	197.1875	NFM	Tayside	Data Link
		NFM	Nationwide	Trunked PMR
205.2000	197.2000	NFM	Nationwide	British Rail Channel 377
		NFM	Newport	British Rail
205.2125	197.2125	NFM	Nationwide	Trunked PMR
205.2250	197.2250	NFM	Nationwide	Trunked PMR
205.2315	197.2375	NFM	Nationwide	Trunked PMR
205.2500	197.2500	NFM	Nationwide	BR Cab Channel
		NFM	Nationwide	British Rail Channel 381
205.2625	197.2625	NFM	Nationwide	Trunked PMR
		NFM	Blackpool	PMR
205.2750	197.2750	NFM	Nationwide	Trunked PMR
		NFM	W Yorkshire	Trunked Radio System
205.2875	197.2875	NFM	Nationwide	Trunked PMR
205.3000	197.3000	NFM	Nationwide	British Rail Channel 385
205.3125	197.3125	NFM	Nationwide	Band III Channel
		NFM	W Yorkshire	Trunked Radio System
205.3250	197.3250	NFM	Nationwide	Band III Channel
		NFM	W Yorkshire	Trunked Radio System
205.3375	197.3375	NFM	North West	PMR
		NFM	Nationwide	Trunked PMR
205.3500	197.3500	NFM	Dovey Junction	MWL RETD
		NFM	Aberyswyth	Mid Wales Railway Line RETD
		NFM	Borth	Mid Wales Railway Line RETD
		NFM	Nationwide	BR Cab Channel
		NFM	Nationwide	British Rail Channel 389
205.3625	197.3625	NFM	Manchester	Transport
		NFM	Nationwide	Trunked PMR
205.3750	197.3750	NFM	Nationwide	Trunked PMR

Base	Mobile	Mode	Location	User and Notes
205.3875	197.3875	NFM	Nationwide	Trunked PMR
		NFM	Edinburgh	PMR
205.4000	197.4000	NFM	Machynlleth	Mid Wales Railway Line RETD
		NFM	Sutton Bridge Junction	MWL RETD
		NFM	Nationwide	British Rail Channel 393
		NFM	Newtown	Mid Wales Railway Line RETD
		NFM	Shrewsbury	Mid Wales Railway Line RETD
		NFM	Welshpool	Mid Wales Railway Line RETD
		NFM	Westbury	Mid Wales Railway Line RETD
		NFM	Nationwide	Trunked PMR
205.4125	197.4125	NFM	Nationwide	Trunked PMR
205.4250	197.4250	NFM	Weymouth	Heavy Breakdown Recovery
		NFM	Nationwide	Trunked PMR
		NFM	W Yorkshire	Trunked Radio System
205.4375	197.4375	NFM	Nationwide	Trunked PMR
		NFM	Blackpool	PMR
		NFM	Taunton	Data & PMR Voice
205.4500	197.4500	NFM	Nationwide	British Rail Channel 397
		NFM	Nationwide	Trunked PMR
205.4625	197.4625	NFM	Crosville	Buses
		NFM	Scotland	Midland Scottish Buses
		NFM	Southdown	Buses
		NFM	Preston	Buses
		NFM	Nationwide	Trunked PMR
		NFM	Brighton	Buses
205.4750	197.4750	NFM	Nationwide	Trunked PMR
205.4875	197.4875	NFM	Nationwide	Trunked PMR
205.5000	197.5000	NFM	Nationwide	British Rail Channel 401
		NFM	Nationwide	Trunked PMR
205.5125	197.5125	NFM	Nationwide	Trunked PMR
		NFM	Merseyside	Buses
		NFM	Central Scotland	Buses
		NFM	Gosport	Buses
		NFM	Fareham	Buses
205.5250	197.5250	NFM	Nationwide	Trunked PMR
205.5375	197.5375	NFM	Nationwide	Trunked PMR
		NFM	W Yorkshire	Trunked Radio System
205.5500	197.5500	NFM	Nationwide	British Rail Channel 405
		NFM	Nationwide	Trunked PMR
205.5625	197.5625	NFM	North West	PMR
		NFM	Crosville	Buses
		NFM	Lothian	Buses
		NFM	Colchester	Buses
		NFM	Nationwide	Band III Channel
		NFM	Manchester	GM Buses
205.5750	197.5750	NFM	North West	PMR
		NFM	Nationwide	Trunked PMR
205.5875	197.5875	NFM	Nationwide	British Rail Channel

Base	Mobile	Mode	Location	User and Notes
		NFM	W Yorkshire	Trunked Radio System
205.6000	197.6000	NFM	Nationwide	British Rail Channel 409
		NFM	Nationwide	BR Cab Channel
		NFM	Nationwide	Trunked PMR
205.6125	197.6125	NFM	Nationwide	Band III Channel 9
		NFM	Crosville	Buses
		NFM	Eastbourne	Buses
		NFM	Ribble	Buses
		NFM	Ipswich	Buses
		NFM	Manchester	GM Buses
205.6250	197.6250	NFM	Nationwide	Trunked PMR
205.6375	197.6375	NFM	North West	PMR
		NFM	Nationwide	Trunked PMR
205.6500	197.6500	NFM	Nationwide	British Rail Channel 413
205.6625	197.6625	NFM	Merseyside	Buses
		NFM	Bournemouth	Buses
		NFM	London	Buses
		NFM	Scotland	East Scottish Buses
		NFM	Nationwide	Trunked PMR
205.6750	197.6750	NFM	Nationwide	BR Cab Channel
		NFM	Nationwide	British Rail Channel 415
		NFM	Nationwide	Trunked PMR
205.6875	197.6875	NFM	Nationwide	Trunked PMR
		NFM	W Yorkshire	Trunked Radio System
205.7000	197.7000	NFM	Nationwide	BR Cab Channel
		NFM	Nationwide	British Rail Channel 417
205.7125	197.7125	NFM	Nationwide	Band III Channel 17
		NFM	Crosville	Buses
		NFM	Lothian	Buses
		NFM	Portmouth	Buses
		NFM	Manchester	GM Buses
205.7250	197.7250	NFM	Nationwide	Trunked PMR
		NFM	Nationwide	British Rail Channel 419
		NFM	Newport	British Rail
205.7375	197.7375	NFM	Nationwide	Band III Channel
205.7500	197.7500	NFM	Nationwide	British Rail Channel 421
205.7625	197.7625	NFM	Nationwide	Band III Channel
		NFM	Gt Manchester	Buses
		NFM	East Yorkshire	Buses
		NFM	Isle of Wight	Buses
205.7750	197.7750	NFM	Nationwide	Trunked PMR
205.7875	197.7875	NFM	Nationwide	Trunked PMR
205.8000	197.8000	NFM	Nationwide	BR Cab Channel
		NFM	Nationwide	British Rail Channel 425
205.8125	197.8125	NFM	Birmingham	West Midlands Bus Travel
		NFM	Nationwide	National Express
		NFM	Nationwide	Band III Channel 14
205.8250	197.8250	NFM	Nationwide	Trunked PMR

Base	Mobile	Mode	Location	User and Notes
		NFM	London	Thamesway Buses
		NFM	London	TNT Couriers
205.8375	197.8375	NFM	Tayside	Data Link
		NFM	Nationwide	British Rail Channel 428
		NFM	Nationwide	Trunked PMR
		NFM	Cardiff	British Rail
205.8500	197.8500	NFM	Nationwide	British Rail
		NFM	W Yorkshire	Trunked Radio System
205.8625	197.8625	NFM	Nationwide	National Express
		NFM	Nationwide	Band III Channel
205.8750	197.8750	NFM	Nationwide	Trunked PMR
205.8875	197.8875	NFM	Nationwide	Trunked PMR
		NFM	Taunton	Data
205.9000	197.9000	NFM	Nationwide	BR Cab Channel
		NFM	Nationwide	British Rail Channel 433
		NFM	London	Thamesway Buses
		NFM	Nationwide	British Rail
205.9125	197.9125	NFM	London	Thamesway Buses
		NFM	Merseyside	Buses
		NFM	Gt. Yarmouth	Buses
		NFM	Southampton	Buses
		NFM	Nationwide	Trunked PMR
205.9250	197.9250	NFM	Nationwide	Trunked PMR
205.9375	197.9375	NFM	Tayside	Data Link
		NFM	Nationwide	Trunked PMR
		NFM	Edinburgh	PMR
205.9500	197.9500	NFM	Nationwide	BR Cab Channel
		NFM	Nationwide	British Rail Channel 437
		NFM	Fort William	British Rail
205.9625	197.9625	NFM	Nationwide	Band III Channel
		NFM	Manchester	GM Buses
205.9750	197.9750	NFM	Nationwide	Trunked PMR
205.9875	197.9875	NFM	Nationwide	Trunked PMR
206.0000	198.0000	NFM	Nationwide	BR Cab Channel
		NFM	Nationwide	British Rail Channel 441
		NFM	Nationwide	Trunked PMR
		NFM	Edgehill	British Rail
206.0125	198.0125	NFM	Birmingham	West Midlands Bus Travel
		NFM	Merseyside	Buses
		NFM	East Scotland	Buses
		NFM	East Kent	Buses
		NFM	South Wales	Buses
		NFM	Nationwide	Trunked PMR
206.0250	198.0250	NFM	Nationwide	Trunked PMR
206.0375	198.0375	NFM	Nationwide	Trunked PMR
206.0625	198.0625	NFM	Birmingham	West Midlands Bus Travel
		NFM	Glasgow	Bus Company
		NFM	Nationwide	Trunked PMR

Base	Mobile	Mode	Location	User and Notes
		NFM	Blackpool	Buses
		NFM	Strathclyde	Buses
		NFM	Southdown	Buses
		NFM	Wales	Buses
206.0750	198.0750	NFM	Nationwide	Trunked PMR
206.0875	198.0875	NFM	Nationwide	Trunked PMR
		NFM	Edinburgh	PMR
206.1000	198.1000	NFM	North West	PMR
		NFM	Nationwide	British Rail Channel 449
		NFM	Nationwide	British Rail Ch 26
		NFM	London	Data
		NFM	Manchester	Data
		NFM	Brecon	Data
206.1125	198.1125	NFM	Merseyside	Buses
		NFM	Strathclyde	Buses
		NFM	Southdown	Buses
		NFM	Nationwide	Trunked PMR
206.1250	198.1250	NFM	Nationwide	Trunked PMR
206.1375	198.1375	NFM	Nationwide	Trunked PMR
206.1500	198.1500	NFM	Tayside	Data Link
		NFM	Nationwide	BR Cab Channel
		NFM	Nationwide	British Rail Channel 453
		NFM	Nationwide	British Rail Ch 27
206.1625	198.1625	NFM	Birmingham	West Midlands Bus Travel
		NFM	Bristol	City Line Buses (Minibuses)
		NFM	London	London Transport Talking Clock
		NFM	Manchester	City Bus Inspectors
		NFM	Nationwide	Band III Channel
		NFM	London	Bus Talking Clock
		NFM	Gt Manchester	Northern General.
		NFM	Manchester	GM Buses
206.1750	198.1750	NFM	Nationwide	Trunked PMR Ch 455
206.1875	198.1875	NFM	Nationwide	Trunked PMR Ch 456
206.2000	198.2000	NFM	Nationwide	British Rail Ch 28
206.2125	198.2125	NFM	North West	PMR
		NFM	Birmingham	West Midlands Bus Travel
		NFM	London	London Transport Stanford Hill
		NFM	Manchester	GM Buses
206.2500	198.2500	NFM	Nationwide	British Rail Channel 461
206.2625	198.2625	NFM	Birmingham	West Midlands Bus Travel
		NFM	London	London Transport Stockwell
206.2875	198.2875	NFM	W Yorkshire	Trunked Radio System
206.3000	198.3000	NFM	Nationwide	BR Cab Channel
		NFM	Nationwide	British Rail Channel 465
206.3375		NFM	North West	PMR
206.5000		WFM	France	French TV Channel 8 Sound
206.5125		NFM	Manchester	Lorries
206.5250		NFM	Stockport	Engineers

Base	Mobile	Mode	Location	User and Notes
206.5875		NFM	North West	PMR
206.6625		NFM	North West	PMR
206.6750		NFM	North West	PMR
206.7625		NFM	Stockport	PMR
206.8875		NFM	North West	PMR
206.9125		NFM	Macclesfield	Delivery

207.5000 - 208.5000 MHz   **RADIO MICROPHONES NFM**

Base	Mobile	Mode	Location	User and Notes
208.3000		NFM	Jersey	BBC Radio Jersey

208.5000 - 216.0000 MHz   **VHF B3 PMR BASE REPEATERS 12.5 kHz (SPLIT + 8.0 MHz) OUTSIDE BROADCAST RADIO MICROPHONES**

Base	Mobile	Mode	Location	User and Notes
208.6000		NFM	Nationwide	BBC Radio 1 Roadshow Mics
		WFM	Nationwide	BBC Antiques Roadshow Mics
208.8000	208.8000	NFM	Nationwide	ITV Radio Microphone
209.0000	209.0000	NFM	Nationwide	BBC Radio Microphone
209.1500		NFM	Jersey	PC Gartmore Speech
211.7500		NFM	Manchester	Taxis
212.2000		NFM	Wolverhampton	Beacon Radio O/B
213.3000		WFM	London	Towndown Radio Feeder
213.8750		NFM	Silverstone	BBV Outside Broadcasts
213.9500		WFM	London	BBC Radio Car O/B
214.0250		NFM	Castle Donington	Grand Prix Radio O/B Link
214.1000		WFM	London	BBC Radio Car O/B
214.5000		WFM	France	French TV Channel 9 Sound

217.5000 - 230.0000 MHz   **FUTURE DIGITAL BROADCASTING BAND DAB**

216.0000 - 225.0000 MHz   **VHF M3 PMR MOBILES 12.5 kHz (SPLIT + 8.0 MHz) RADIO MICROPHONES**

Base	Mobile	Mode	Location	User and Notes
216.8000		WFM	Nationwide	BBC Antiques Roadshow Mics
224.1000		NFM	Sheffield	BBC Radio Sheffield O/B
224.2181		USB	Scotland	BBC Studio Feed
224.23125		NFM	Bristol	BBC O/B Talkback
224.2320		NFM	Scotland	BBC Clean Feed from Glasgow

225.0000 - 399.9750 MHz   **MILITARY AERONAUTICAL COMMUNICATIONS**

Base	Mobile	Mode	Location	User and Notes
225.2000	225.2000	AM	Nationwide	RAF Discreet

225.5000 -227.0000 MHz   **BBC DAB TEXT TRANSMISSIONS (SOUTH EAST ENGLAND ONLY)**

Base	Mobile	Mode	Location	User and Notes
225.6480		DAB	London	BBC Radio Ch12B
226.5000	226.5000	NFM	Alnwick	Police Helicopter
226.6000	226.6000	AM	RNAS Portland	Royal Navy

Base	Mobile	Mode	Location	User and Notes
227.0000 - 241.0000 MHz			TACTICAL MILITARY EXERCISE COMMUNICATIONS 25 kHz	
230.0500	230.0500	AM	RAF Buchan	Air Defence Region Ops
		AM	RAF West Drayton	London Military (Dover/Lydd)
230.1500	230.1500	AM	RAF Boulmer	Air Defence Region Ops
230.6000	230.6000	AM	Nationwide	Air-Air
		AM	Nationwide	Air Defence Region
230.6500	230.6500	AM	Nationwide	RAF AWACS Ops
231.0750	231.0750	AM	Nationwide	Air Defence Region
231.2250	231.2250	AM	Holland	Dutch Military
231.2500	231.2500	AM	Nationwide	Air Defence Region
231.3500	231.3500	AM	Nationwide	USAF Ops
231.3750	231.3750	AM	RAF Valley	4FTS Air-Air
231.5500	231.5500	AM	RAF Buchan	Air Defence Region Ops
231.6000	231.6000	AM	Nationwide	NATO Air-Air
231.6250	231.6250	AM	RAF West Drayton	London Mil. (Pole Hill/Irish Sea)
231.9750	231.9750	AM	RAF West Drayton	London Military (Seaford/Hurn)
232.0750	232.0750	AM	Donna Nook	Range Secondary
232.3000	232.3000	AM	Nationwide	AWACS Ops
232.3500	232.3500	AM	RAF Neatishead	Air Defence Region Ops
232.5500	232.5500	AM	RAF Neatishead	Air Defence Region Ops
232.7000	232.7000	AM	RAF Neatishead	Air Defence Region Ops
233.0000	233.0000	AM	Royal Navy	Ship-Air
233.1500	233.1500	AM	RAF Portreath	Air Defence Region Ops
233.2000	233.2000	AM	Royal Navy	Ship-Air
233.7000	233.7000	AM	RAF Mildenhall	USAF Air-Air
233.8000	233.8000	AM	RAF West Drayton	London Mil. (London Upper)
233.9250	233.9250	AM	RNAS Portland	Royal Navy
234.6500	234.6500	AM	Cumbria	RAF Low Flying Air-Air
		AM	Nationwide	RAF AWACS Ops
234.9000	234.9000	AM	Nationwide	RAF Volmet
235.0500	235.0500	AM	RAF West Drayton	London Mil (London Upper)
235.2500	235.2500	AM	Nationwide	USAF Displays
237.5000		NFM	Nationwide	Dynamic Sciences Surv.
237.8500	237.8500	AM	HMS Invincible	Air-Deck
240.3000	240.3000	AM	Nationwide	Air-Air Refuelling
240.3000	240.3000	AM	RAF Neatishead	Radar
240.4000	240.4000	AM	AARA 1 (NW Scotland)	Refuelling Primary
		AM	AARA 7 (SW England)	Refuelling Primary
		AM	AARA 10 (NW Scotland)	Refuelling Primary
241.0000	241.0000	AM	Nationwide	Forward Air Controllers
		AM	RAF Coningsby	Air-Air
241.1750	241.1750	AM	Cowden	Range Primary
241.4500	241.4500	AM	RAF Manston	Dispatcher
241.6000	241.6000	AM	Castle Martin	Range Air-Ground
241.6250	241.6250	AM	RAF Benson	Talkdown
241.6500		AM	RAF Linton-On-Ouse	ATIS
241.7750	241.7750	AM	RAF Cowden	Range

Base	Mobile	Mode	Location	User and Notes
241.8250	241.8250	AM	RAF Aldergrove	RAF Ops
		AM	RAF St Mawgan	Tower
241.8500	241.8500	AM	RAF Neatishead	Radar Ops
		AM	RAF Topcliffe	Ground
241.9500	241.9500	AM	RNAS Culdrose	Approach
242.0500	242.0500	AM	Nationwide	Red Arrows Display
242.0750	242.0750	AM	RAF Lakenheath	Dep Con
		AM	RAF Wittering	Air-Air
242.1500	242.1500	AM	RAF Lakenheath	Defence Exercises
242.2000	242.2000	AM	Nationwide	Red Arrows Display
242.2750	242.2750	AM	Nationwide	Air Defence Region
242.3250		AM	RAF Cottesmore	DATIS
242.4000	242.4000	AM	RAF Leuchars	111 Sqn Air-Air
242.4500	242.4500	AM	RAF Wittering	1 Sqn Ops (Willard Ops)
242.5500	242.5500	AM	RAF Coningsby	5 Sqn Ops
242.6000	242.6000	AM	Warton	Test Flights
		AM	Nationwide	Patroulle De France Displays
243.0000	243.0000	AM	International	Air Distress
243.3250	243.3250	AM	RAF Leeming	11 Sqn Air-Air
243.4500	243.4500	AM	Nationwide	Red Arrows Display
243.4750	243.4750	AM	Nationwide	USAF Ops
243.6000	243.6000	AM	RAF Lakenheath	Radar
243.8000	243.8000	AM	RAF Aerodrome	Radio Failure Frequency

243.9450 - 244.2500 MHz   US AFSATCOM DOWN LINKS

Base	Mobile	Mode	Location	User and Notes
243.9450		NFM	AFSATCOM F2	NB Channel 11
243.9550		NFM	AFSATCOM F2	NB Channel 12
243.9600		NFM	AFSATCOM F2	NB Channel 13
243.9650		NFM	AFSATCOM F2	NB Channel 14
243.9700		NFM	AFSATCOM F2	NB Channel 15
243.9750		NFM	AFSATCOM F2	NB Channel 16
243.9800		NFM	AFSATCOM F2	NB Channel 17
243.9850		NFM	AFSATCOM F2	NB Channel 18
243.9900		NFM	AFSATCOM F2	NB Channel 19
243.9950		NFM	AFSATCOM F2	NB Channel 20
244.0000		NFM	AFSATCOM F2	NB Channel 21
244.0100		NFM	AFSATCOM F2	NB Channel 22
244.0450		NFM	AFSATCOM F3	NB Channel 11
244.0550		NFM	AFSATCOM F3	NB Channel 12
244.0600		NFM	AFSATCOM F3	NB Channel 13
244.0650		NFM	AFSATCOM F3	NB Channel 14
244.0700		NFM	AFSATCOM F3	NB Channel 15
244.0750		NFM	AFSATCOM F3	NB Channel 16
244.0800		NFM	AFSATCOM F3	NB Channel 17
244.0850		NFM	AFSATCOM F3	NB Channel 18
244.0900		NFM	AFSATCOM F3	NB Channel 19
244.0950		NFM	AFSATCOM F3	NB Channel 20
244.1000		NFM	AFSATCOM F3	NB Channel 21

Base	Mobile	Mode	Location	User and Notes
244.1100		NFM	AFSATCOM F3	NB Channel 22
244.1450		NFM	AFSATCOM F1	NB Channel 11
244.1550		NFM	AFSATCOM F1	NB Channel 12
244.1600		NFM	AFSATCOM F1	NB Channel 13
244.1650		NFM	AFSATCOM F1	NB Channel 14
244.1700		NFM	AFSATCOM F1	NB Channel 15
244.1750		NFM	AFSATCOM F1	NB Channel 16
244.1800		NFM	AFSATCOM F1	NB Channel 17
244.1850		NFM	AFSATCOM F1	NB Channel 18
244.1900		NFM	AFSATCOM F1	NB Channel 19
244.1950		NFM	AFSATCOM F1	NB Channel 20
244.2000		NFM	AFSATCOM F1	NB Channel 21
244.2100		NFM	AFSATCOM F1	NB Channel 22
244.2750	244.2750	AM	RAF Waddington	AWACS Wing Ops
244.3000	244.3000	AM	RAF Valley	4FTS Air-to-Air
244.4250	244.4250	AM	RAF Northolt	Ops
244.6000	244.6000	AM	Nationwide	UK Distress
		AM	Plymouth	Plymouth Rescue

244.6500 - 248.8000 MHz			TACTICAL MILITARY EXERCISE COMMUNICATIONS 25 kHz	
244.6500	244.6500	AM	AARA 6 (S North Sea)	Air-Air Refuelling
		AM	RAF Buchan	Air Defence Region Ops
		AM	RAF Neatishead	Air Defence Region Ops
244.6750	244.6750	AM	Nationwide	4 Sqn Air-Air
244.7000	244.7000	AM	RAF Neatishead	Air Defence Region Ops
244.8750	244.8750	AM	RAF Leconfield	Leconfield Rescue
244.9000	244.9000	AM	RAF Leeming	11 Sqn Air-Air
245.0500	245.0500	AM	RAF Boulmer	Air Defence Region Ops
245.1000		AM	Nationwide	RAF Personal Locator Beacons
246.0500	246.0500	AM	Nationwide	Air-Air Refuelling
246.4500	246.4500	AM	Nationwide	Displays
246.7000	246.7000	AM	Nationwide	Forward Air Controllers
247.0000	247.0000	AM	RAF Boulmer	Air Defence Region
247.2750	247.2750	AM	Nationwide	Air Defence Region
247.7000	247.7000	AM	Nationwide	Forward Air Controllers
248.1000	248.1000	AM	RAF Neatishead	Air Defence Region Ops
248.1500	248.1500	AM	RAF Lakenheath	493FS Discreet
248.2750	248.2750	AM	RAF Lakenheath	48FW Air-to-Air
248.3000	248.3000	AM	Nationwide	Airborne Intercept Cmd
		AM	Nationwide	RAF AWACS Ops
248.4000	248.4000	AM	RAF Buchan	Air Defence Region Ops
248.8000	248.8000	AM	Nationwide	Sharks Helicopter Display

248.8500 - 249.3500 MHz			US AFSATCOM DOWN LINKS	
248.8500	302.4500	NFM	MARISAT	Channel 1
248.8750	302.4750	NFM	MARISAT	Channel 2
248.9000	302.5000	NFM	MARISAT	Channel 3

Base	Mobile	Mode	Location	User and Notes
248.9250	302.5250	NFM	MARISAT	Channel 4
248.9500	302.5500	NFM	MARISAT	Channel 5
248.9750	302.5750	NFM	MARISAT	Channel 6
249.0000	302.7000	NFM	MARISAT	Channel 7
249.0000		NFM	Nationwide	Dynamic Sciences Surv.
249.0250	302.7250	NFM	MARISAT	Channel 8
249.0500	302.7500	NFM	MARISAT	Channel 9
249.0750	302.7750	NFM	MARISAT	Channel 10
249.1000	302.8000	NFM	MARISAT	Channel 11
249.1250	302.8250	NFM	MARISAT	Channel 12
249.1500	302.8500	NFM	MARISAT	Channel 13
249.1750	302.8750	NFM	MARISAT	Channel 14
249.2000	302.9000	NFM	MARISAT	Channel 15
249.2250	302.9250	NFM	MARISAT	Channel 16
249.2500	302.9500	NFM	MARISAT	Channel 17
249.2750	302.9750	NFM	MARISAT	Channel 18
249.3000	303.0000	NFM	MARISAT	Channel 19
249.3250	303.0250	NFM	MARISAT	Channel 20
249.3500	303.0500	NFM	MARISAT	Channel 21
249.4750	249.4750	AM	Prestwick	Scottish Military
249.5250		AM	RAF Leeming	ATIS
249.5750		AM	RAF Leuchars	DATIS
249.6000	249.6000	AM	RAF Marham	617 Sqn Ops (Nigger Ops)
249.6250	249.6250	AM	RAF West Drayton	London Military
249.6750	249.6750	AM	RAF West Drayton	London Military
249.7000		NFM	Nationwide	Dynamic Sciences Surv.
		AM	RAF Lakenheath	ATIS
249.7250	249.7250	AM	RNAS Yeovilton	D School
249.7500	249.7500	AM	RAF Midlenhall	Command Post Backup
249.8000		NFM	Nationwide	Dynamic Sciences Surv.
249.8000	249.8000	AM	RAF Chivenor	7FTS Air-Air
249.8500	249.8500	AM	RAF Waddington	Departures
249.9500	249.9500	AM	RAF Brawdy	Brawdy Rescue
250.0500	250.0500	AM	RAF Cranwell	Zone
		AM	RAF Lossiemouth	Talkdown
250.1500	250.1500	AM	Nationwide	Forward Air Controllers
250.2750	250.2750	AM	RAF West Drayton	London Military

250.3500 - 250.6500 MHz   US FLTSATCOM FLEET BROADCAST DOWN LINKS

Base	Mobile	Mode	Location	User and Notes
250.3500	291.3500	NFM	FLTSATCOM	Channel W1
250.4500	291.4500	NFM	FLTSATCOM F1	Channel X1
250.4750	250.4750	AM	Nationwide	Sharks Helicopter Display Team
250.5500	291.5500	NFM	FLTSATCOM F3	Channel Y1
250.6500	291.6500	NFM	FLTSATCOM F2	Channel Z1
250.6750	250.6750	AM	RAF Lakenheath	48FW Air-to-Air
250.7000	250.7000	AM	Nationwide	Air Defence Region

Base	Mobile	Mode	Location	User and Notes
250.9000		NFM	Nationwide	Dynamic Sciences Surv
251.2000	251.2000	AM	RNAS Culdrose	Kilderkin Ops
251.3750	251.3750	AM	RAF Wittering	20 Sqn Ops (Bronze Ops)
251.5000	251.5000	AM	Nationwide	USAF Displays
251.6000		NFM	Nationwide	Dynamic Sciences Surv
251.6250	251.6250	AM	RAF West Drayton	London Military
251.6500	251.6500	AM	Nationwide	Air Defence Region
251.7250	251.7250	AM	RAF Newton	Approach
251.7500	251.7500	AM	Nationwide	Air Defence Region
251.8000		NFM	Nationwide	Dynamic Sciences Surv
251.8500	292.8500	NFM	FLTSATCOM	Channel W 2
251.9000		NFM	Nationwide	Dynamic Sciences Surv
251.9500	292.9500	NFM	FLTSATCOM F1	Channel X 2
252.0500	293.0500	NFM	FLTSATCOM F3	Channel Y 2
252.1000	252.1000	AM	North Sea	ACMI Range Show Ground 1
252.1500	293.1500	NFM	FLTSATCOM F2	Channel Z 2
252.4000	252.4000	AM	Nationwide	Air Defence Region
252.4500	225.4500	AM	RAF Valley	4FTS Air-Air
252.4625	252.4625	AM	Prestwick	Scottish Military
252.8000	252.8000	AM	RAF Chivenor	Chivenor Rescue
252.9000	252.9000	AM	RAF Dishforth	AAC Ops
		AM	Arran	Police Helicopter
		AM	Colchester Garrison	Tower
		AM	Nationwide	Silver Eagles Helicopter Team
253.0000		NFM	Nationwide	Dynamic Sciences Surv
253.1000	253.1000	AM	RAF Lakenheath	Rapcon
253.3000	253.3000	AM	Nationwide	Forward Air Controllers
253.5000	253.5000	AM	Netheravon	Salisbury Plain
253.5500	294.5500	NFM	FLTSATCOM	Channel W 3
253.6500	294.6500	NFM	FLTSATCOM F1	Channel X 3
253.7500	294.7500	NFM	FLTSATCOM F3	Channel Y 3
253.8000	253.8000	AM	Nationwide	NATO SAR Training
253.8500	294.8500	NFM	FLTSATCOM F2	Channel Z 3
253.9000		NFM	Nationwide	Dynamic Sciences Surv
254.0750	254.0750	AM	RAF Marham	2 Sqn Air-to-Air
254.2000	254.2000	AM	RAF Shawbury	Zone
		AM	RAF Lossiemouth	Splash
254.2250	254.2250	AM	RAF West Drayton	London Military
254.2500	254.2500	AM	RAF Coltishall	Talkdown
254.3500	254.3500	AM	Nationwide	NATO Air-Air
254.4000	254.0000	AM	RAF Lossiemouth	15 Sqn Ops
		AM	RAF Marham	27 Sqn Ops (Nellie Ops)
254.4250	254.4250	AM	Nationwide	Air Defence Region
254.4750	254.4750	AM	RAF Brize Norton	ATIS
254.5000	254.5000	AM	Aberporth	Range Tertiary
254.5250	254.5250	AM	RAF Church Fenton	Approach
254.6500	254.6500	AM	RAF Lyneham	Ops
254.6750	254.6750	AM	RAF Coningsby	5 Sqn Ops (Maple Ops)

Base	Mobile	Mode	Location	User and Notes
254.7500	254.7500	AM	RAF Brawdy	Zone Departures
254.8250	254.8250	AM	RAF West Drayton	London Military
254.8750	254.8750	AM	RAF Mildenhall	Approach
254.9000	254.9000	AM	RAF West Drayton	London Military
255.1000	255.1000	AM	Nationwide	RAF Falcons Parachutists
		AM	Weston on the Green	Weston Radio
		AM	Nationwide	Forward Air Controllers
255.2500	296.2500	NFM	FLTSATCOM	Channel W 4
255.2750	255.2750	AM	RAF Lakenheath	48FW Aux
255.3500	296.3500	AM	FLTSATCOM F1	Channel X 4
255.4000	255.4000	AM	RAF West Drayton	London Military
		AM	RAF Leuchars	Approach
255.4500	296.4500	AM	FLTSATCOM F3	Channel Y 4
255.5500	296.5500	AM	FLTSATCOM F2	Channel Z 4
255.6000	255.6000	AM	RAF Topcliffe	Director
255.7000	255.7000	AM	RAF West Drayton	London Military
255.8500	255.8500	AM	RAF Cottesmore	Air-to-Air
256.0000	256.0000	AM	Royal Navy	Ship-Air
		AM	Farnborough	PAR
256.1000	256.1000	AM	Royal Navy	Ship-Air
256.1250	256.1250	AM	MoD Filton	Approach
256.6000		NFM	Nationwide	Dynamic Sciences Surv
256.8500	297.8500	NFM	FLTSATCOM	Channel W 5
256.9000	256.9000	AM	Nationwide	Forward Air Controllers
256.9500	297.9500	AM	FLTSATCOM F1	Channel X 5
257.0500	298.0500	AM	FLTSATCOM F3	Channel Y 5
257.1000	257.1000	AM	RAF Brize Norton	Brize Radar
257.1500	298.1500	AM	FLTSATCOM F2	Channel Z 5
257.2000	257.2000	AM	Nationwide	Forward Air Controllers
		AM	Otterburn	Range Primary
257.2250	257.2250	AM	RAF West Drayton	London Military
257.7500	257.7500	AM	RAF Alconbury	Alconbury Metro
		AM	RAF Mildenhall	Mildenhall Metro
257.8000	257.8000	AM	RAF Brawdy	Tower
		AM	RAF Brize Norton	Tower
		AM	RAF Church Fenton	Tower
		AM	RAF Cottesmore	Tower
		AM	RAF Cranwell	Tower
		AM	RAF Fairford	Tower
		AM	RAF Greenham Common	Tower
		AM	RAF Kinloss	Tower
		AM	RAF Lakenheath	Tower
		AM	RAF Leeming	Tower
		AM	RAF Linton-on-Ouse	Tower
		AM	RAF Manston	Tower
		AM	RAF Marham	Tower
		AM	RAF Newton	Tower
		AM	RAF Northolt	Tower

Base	Mobile	Mode	Location	User and Notes
		AM	RAF Odiham	Tower
		AM	RAF St Athan	Tower
		AM	RAF Shawbury	Tower
		AM	RAF Topcliffe	Tower
		AM	RAF Valley	Tower
		AM	RAF Waddington	Tower
		AM	RAF Wittering	Tower
		AM	Nationwide	Forward Air Controllers
258.0500	258.0500	AM	Nationwide	Air-Air Tanker Ops
258.3000	258.3000	AM	Nationwide	Forward Air Controllers
258.3500	299.3500	NFM	FLTSATCOM	Channel W 6
258.4000	258.4000	AM	AARA 10 (NW Scotland)	Air-Air Refuelling
258.4500	299.4500	NFM	FLTSATCOM F1	Channel X 6
258.5000	258.5000	AM	Nationwide	AWACS
258.5500	299.5500	NFM	FLTSATCOM F3	Channel Y 6
258.6500	299.6500	NFM	FLTSATCOM F2	Channel Z 6
258.7750	258.7750	AM	RAF Chivenor	7FTS Air-Air
258.8000	258.8000	AM	Nationwide	British Army Air-Air
		AM	RAF Benson	60 Sqn Air-Air
258.8250	258.8250	AM	RAF Mildenhall	Tower
258.8500	258.8500	AM	RAF Lossiemouth	Lossie Departures
258.9250	258.9250	AM	RAF Leuchars	Tower
258.9750	258.9750	AM	RAF Newton	Ground
259.0000	259.0000	AM	RNAS Aberporth	Aberporth Information
		AM	MoD Farnborough	PAR
		AM	MoD West Freugh	Radar
259.0250	259.0250	AM	Teesside	Radar
259.0750	259.0750	AM	RAF Marham	2 Sqn Ops (Melbourne Ops)
259.1000	259.1000	AM	RAF Neatishead	Air Defence Region Ops
259.1750	259.1750	AM	Prestwick	Scottish Military
259.5250	259.5250	AM	Nationwide	RAF Discreet
259.6000	259.6000	AM	RAF Neatishead	Air Defence Region Ops
259.7000	259.7000	NFM	International	Space Shuttle Down Link
259.7250	259.7250	AM	Prestwick	Scottish Military
259.7500	259.7500	AM	RNAS Culdrose	Talkdown
259.7750	259.7750	AM	Prestwick	Scottish Military
259.8000	259.8000	AM	RNAS Yeovilton	D School
259.8250	259.8250	AM	RAF Dishforth	Tower
259.8500	259.8500	AM	RAF Leuchars	Ground
259.8750	259.8750	AM	RAF Linton-on-Ouse	Talkdown
		AM	RAF Benson	Talkdown
259.9250	259.9250	AM	RAF Greenham Common	Ground
259.9500	259.9500	AM	RAF Brawdy	Ground
		AM	RAF Woodvale	Tower
259.9750	259.9750	AM	RAF Fairford	Ground
		AM	RAF Kinloss	Director
		AM	RAF Lossiemouth	Director
260.0000	260.0000	AM	RAF St Mawgan	Ops

Base	Mobile	Mode	Location	User and Notes
		AM	Cowden	Range
260.0250	260.0250	AM	RAF West Drayton	London Military
260.1500	260.1500	AM	Nationwide	Air Defence Region

260.3000 - 262.5500 MHz US FLTSATCOM WIDEBAND DOWN LINK

Base	Mobile	Mode	Location	User and Notes
260.3500	293.9500	NFM	FLTSATCOM F1	WB Channel A/X 1
260.3750	293.9750	NFM	FLTSATCOM F1	WB Channel A/X 2
260.4000	294.0000	NFM	FLTSATCOM F1	WB Channel A/X 3
260.4250	294.0250	NFM	FLTSATCOM F1	WB Channel A/X 4
260.4500	294.0500	NFM	FLTSATCOM F1	WB Channel A/X 5
260.4750	294.0750	NFM	FLTSATCOM F1	WB Channel A/X 6
260.5000	294.1000	NFM	FLTSATCOM F1	WB Channel A/X 7
260.5250	294.1250	NFM	FLTSATCOM F1	WB Channel A/X 8
260.5500	294.1500	NFM	FLTSATCOM F1	WB Channel A/X 9
260.5750	294.1750	NFM	FLTSATCOM F1	WB Channel A/X 10
260.6000	294.2000	NFM	FLTSATCOM F1	WB Channel A/X 11
260.6250	294.2250	NFM	FLTSATCOM F1	WB Channel A/X 12
260.6500	294.2500	NFM	FLTSATCOM F1	WB Channel A/X 13
260.6750	294.2750	NFM	FLTSATCOM F1	WB Channel A/X 14
260.7000	294.3000	NFM	FLTSATCOM F1	WB Channel A/X 15
260.7250	294.3250	NFM	FLTSATCOM F1	WB Channel A/X 16
260.7500	294.3500	NFM	FLTSATCOM F1	WB Channel A/X 17
260.7750	294.3750	NFM	FLTSATCOM F1	WB Channel A/X 18
260.8000	294.4000	NFM	FLTSATCOM F1	WB Channel A/X 19
260.8250	294.4250	NFM	FLTSATCOM F1	WB Channel A/X 20
260.8500	294.4500	NFM	FLTSATCOM F1	WB Channel A/X 21
260.9500	260.9500	AM	RAF Coningsby	Air-to-Air
261.0000	261.0000	AM	RAF West Drayton	London Military
261.0250	261.0250	AM	RAF West Drayton	London Military
261.0500	261.0500	AM	RAF Barkston Heath	Director
261.0750	261.0750	AM	RAF Leeming	23 Sqn Ops (Red Ops)
261.2000		AM	RAF Marham	ATIS
261.4500	295.0500	NFM	FLTSATCOM F3	WB Channel B/Y 1
261.4750	295.0750	NFM	FLTSATCOM F3	WB Channel B/Y 2
261.5000	295.1000	NFM	FLTSATCOM F3	WB Channel B/Y 3
261.5250	295.1250	NFM	FLTSATCOM F3	WB Channel B/Y 4
261.5500	295.1500	NFM	FLTSATCOM F3	WB Channel B/Y 5
261.5750	295.1750	NFM	FLTSATCOM F3	WB Channel B/Y 6
261.6000	295.2000	NFM	FLTSATCOM F3	WB Channel B/Y 7
261.6250	295.2250	NFM	FLTSATCOM F3	WB Channel B/Y 8
261.6500	295.2500	NFM	FLTSATCOM F3	WB Channel B/Y 9
261.6750	295.2750	NFM	FLTSATCOM F3	WB Channel B/Y 10
261.7000	295.3000	NFM	FLTSATCOM F3	WB Channel B/Y 11
261.7250	295.3250	NFM	FLTSATCOM F3	WB Channel B/Y 12
261.7500	295.3500	NFM	FLTSATCOM F3	WB Channel B/Y 13
261.7750	295.3750	NFM	FLTSATCOM F3	WB Channel B/Y 14
261.8000	295.4000	NFM	FLTSATCOM F3	WB Channel B/Y 15
261.8250	295.4250	NFM	FLTSATCOM F3	WB Channel B/Y 16

Base	Mobile	Mode	Location	User and Notes
261.8500	295.4500	NFM	FLTSATCOM F3	WB Channel B/Y 17
261.8750	295.4750	NFM	FLTSATCOM F3	WB Channel B/Y 18
261.9000	295.5000	NFM	FLTSATCOM F3	WB Channel B/Y 19
261.9250	295.5250	NFM	FLTSATCOM F3	WB Channel B/Y 20
261.9500	295.5500	NFM	FLTSATCOM F3	WB Channel B/Y 21
262.0500	295.6500	NFM	FLTSATCOM F2	WB Channel C/Z 1
262.0750	295.6750	NFM	FLTSATCOM F2	WB Channel C/Z 2
262.1000	295.7000	NFM	FLTSATCOM F2	WB Channel C/Z 3
262.1250	295.7250	NFM	FLTSATCOM F2	WB Channel C/Z 4
262.1500	295.7500	NFM	FLTSATCOM F2	WB Channel C/Z 5
262.1750	295.7750	NFM	FLTSATCOM F2	WB Channel C/Z 6
262.2000	295.8000	NFM	FLTSATCOM F2	WB Channel C/Z 7
262.2250	295.8250	NFM	FLTSATCOM F2	WB Channel C/Z 8
262.2500	295.8500	NFM	FLTSATCOM F2	WB Channel C/Z 9
262.2750	295.8750	NFM	FLTSATCOM F2	WB Channel C/Z 10
262.3000	295.9000	NFM	FLTSATCOM F2	WB Channel C/Z 11
262.3250	295.9250	NFM	FLTSATCOM F2	WB Channel C/Z 12
262.3500	295.9500	NFM	FLTSATCOM F2	WB Channel C/Z 13
262.3750	295.9750	NFM	FLTSATCOM F2	WB Channel C/Z 14
262.4000	296.0000	NFM	FLTSATCOM F2	WB Channel C/Z 15
262.4250	296.0250	NFM	FLTSATCOM F2	WB Channel C/Z 16
262.4500	296.0500	NFM	FLTSATCOM F2	WB Channel C/Z 17
262.4750	296.0750	NFM	FLTSATCOM F2	WB Channel C/Z 18
262.5000	296.1000	NFM	FLTSATCOM F2	WB Channel C/Z 19
262.5250	296.1250	NFM	FLTSATCOM F2	WB Channel C/Z 20
262.5500	296.1500	NFM	FLTSATCOM F2	WB Channel C/Z 21
262.6500	262.6500	AM	RAF Valley	4FTS Air-Air
262.7000	262.7000	AM	RAF Church Fenton	Tower
262.7250	262.7250	AM	RAF Lossiemouth	TWCU Air-to-Air
262.9000	262.9000	AM	RAF Cottesmore	Talkdown
262.9250	262.9250	AM	RNAS Yeovilton	Royal Navy Ops
262.9500	262.9500	AM	RAF Coningsby	Director
262.9750	262.9750	AM	RAF West Drayton	London Mil
263.0750	263.0750	AM	RAF West Drayton	London Mil
263.1500	263.1500	AM	Nationwide	Air Defence Region
263.5000		AM	Boscombe Down (MoD)	ATIS
263.5500	297.1500	NFM	FLTSATCOM	WB Channel W 1
263.5750	297.1750	NFM	FLTSATCOM	WB Channel W 2
263.6000	297.2000	NFM	FLTSATCOM	WB Channel W 3
263.6250	297.2250	NFM	FLTSATCOM	WB Channel W 4
263.6500	297.2500	NFM	FLTSATCOM	WB Channel W 5
263.6750	297.2750	NFM	FLTSATCOM	WB Channel W 6
263.7000	297.3000	NFM	FLTSATCOM	WB Channel W 7
263.7250	297.3250	NFM	FLTSATCOM	WB Channel W 8
263.7500	297.3500	NFM	FLTSATCOM	WB Channel W 9
263.7750	297.3750	NFM	FLTSATCOM	WB Channel W 10
263.8000	297.4000	NFM	FLTSATCOM	WB Channel W 11
263.8250	297.4250	NFM	FLTSATCOM	WB Channel W 12

Base	Mobile	Mode	Location	User and Notes
263.8500	297.4500	NFM	FLTSATCOM	WB Channel W 13
263.8750	297.4750	NFM	FLTSATCOM	WB Channel W 14
263.9000	297.5000	NFM	FLTSATCOM	WB Channel W 15
263.9250	297.5250	NFM	FLTSATCOM	WB Channel W 16
263.9500	297.5500	NFM	FLTSATCOM	WB Channel W 17
263.9750	297.5750	NFM	FLTSATCOM	WB Channel W 18
264.0000	297.6000	NFM	FLTSATCOM	WB Channel W 19
264.0250	297.6250	NFM	FLTSATCOM	WB Channel W 20
264.0500	297.6500	NFM	FLTSATCOM	WB Channel W 21
264.1000	264.1000	AM	RAF Lakenheath	Radar
264.2000	264.2000	AM	Nationwide	Forward Air Controllers
264.4000	264.4000	AM	Nationwide	RAF AWACS Ops
264.4750	264.4750	AM	RAF West Drayton	London Military (Clacton)
264.6750	264.6750	AM	RAF Lakenheath	MATZ Crossing
265.2500	306.2500	NFM	FLTSATCOM	Channel W 7
265.3500	306.3500	NFM	FLTSATCOM F1	Channel X 7
265.4500	306.4500	NFM	FLTSATCOM F3	Channel Y 7
265.5500	306.5500	NFM	FLTSATCOM F2	Channel Z 7
265.8500	265.8500	AM	Nationwide	Air-Air Refuelling
265.9000	265.9000	AM	Nationwide	Air Defence Region
266.2750	266.2750	AM	RAF Lakenheath	494FS Discreet
266.4500	266.4500	AM	RAF Neatishead	Air Defence Region Ops
266.5000	266.5000	AM	Nationwide	USAF Air-Air Refuelling
266.5500	266.5500	AM	RAF Neatishead	Air Defence Region Ops
266.7500	307.7500	NFM	FLTSATCOM	Channel W 8
266.8000		NFM	Nationwide	Dynamic Sciences Surv
266.8500	307.8500	NFM	FLTSATCOM F1	Channel X 8
266.9500	307.9500	NFM	FLTSATCOM F3	Channel Y 8
267.0500	308.0500	NFM	FLTSATCOM F2	Channel Z 8
267.4000		NFM	Nationwide	Dynamic Sciences Surv
267.4000	267.4000	AM	RAF Mildenhall	Tower Discreet
267.5500	267.5500	AM	RAF Boulmer	Air Defence Region Ops
		AM	RAF Neatishead	Air Defence Region Ops
267.9000	267.9000	AM	Nationwide	NATO Air-to-Air
268.1500	309.1500	NFM	FLTSATCOM	Channel W 9
268.2500	309.2500	NFM	FLTSATCOM F1	Channel X 9
268.3500	309.3500	NFM	FLTSATCOM F3	Channel Y 9
268.4000		NFM	Nationwide	Dynamic Sciences Surv
268.4000	268.4000	AM	RAF Brawdy	Talkdown
		AM	Holland	Dutch Military
268.4500	309.4500	NFM	FLTSATCOM F2	Channel Z 9
268.5750	268.5750	AM	Prestwick	Scottish Military
268.6000	268.6000	AM	RAF Coltishall	6 Sqn Ops
268.6500	368.6500	AM	RAF Valley	4FTS Air-to-Air
268.6750	268.6750	AM	RAF Chivenor	7FTS Air-Air
268.7000	268.7000	AM	RAF Coningsby	Wing Ops
268.7750	268.7750	AM	RAF Leuchars	Finals
		AM	RAF Valley	Valley Radar

Base	Mobile	Mode	Location	User and Notes
268.8000		NFM	Nationwide	Dynamic Sciences Surv
268.8250	268.8250	AM	RAF Benson	Approach
268.9250	268.9250	AM	RAF Chinevor	Ops
269.0000	269.0000	AM	Nationwide	Rakie Radar
269.0000		NFM	Nationwide	Dynamic Sciences Surv
269.0750	269.0750	AM	RAF Lakenheath	Command Post
269.1000	269.1000	AM	RAF Shawbury	Tower
269.1250	269.1250	AM	RAF Woodford	Approach
269.6500	310.6500	NFM	FLTSATCOM	Channel W 10
269.7500	269.7500	AM	Nationwide	RAF Discreet
269.7500	310.7500	NFM	FLTSATCOM F1	Channel X 10
269.8500	310.8500	NFM	FLTSATCOM F3	Channel Y 10
269.9000		NFM	Nationwide	Dynamic Sciences Surv
269.9500	310.9500	NFM	FLTSATCOM F2	Channel Z 10
270.0000	270.0000	AM	RAF West Drayton	London Military
		NFM	Space	NASA Space Shuttle
270.0250	270.0250	AM	RAF Odiham	7 Sqn Air-Air
270.9000		NFM	Nationwide	Dynamic Sciences Surv
271.5000		AM	Nationwide	ATC Channel U4
271.8000		NFM	Nationwide	Dynamic Sciences Surv
272.0750	272.0750	AM	RNAS Portland	Royal Navy Exercises
272.2250	272.2250	AM	Nationwide	Air Defence Region
273.0000		AM	Nationwide	ATC Channel U3
273.5250	273.5250	AM	RNAS Portland	Royal Navy
273.9000		NFM	Nationwide	Dynamic Sciences Surv
273.9000	273.9000	AM	Nationwide	NATO Low-Level Flying
274.4000		NFM	Nationwide	Dynamic Sciences Surv
274.8500	274.8500	AM	Nationwide	Forward Air Controller
275.3500	275.3500	AM	Nationwide	USAF Displays
		AM	RAF West Drayton	London Military (Central)
275.4500	275.4500	AM	RAF Cottesmore	Air-to-Air
275.4750	275.4750	AM	RAF West Drayton	London Military
275.5500	275.5500	AM	RAF Cranwell	3FTS Air-to-Air
275.6250	275.6250	AM	Prestwick	Scottish Mil
275.7500	275.7500	AM	Nationwide	Air Defence Region
275.8000		NFM	Nationwide	Dynamic Sciences Surv
275.8000	275.8000	AM	RAF Upavon	Tower
275.8750	275.8750	AM	RAF Coningsby	Tower
275.9000	275.9000	AM	RAF Leuchars	111 Sqn Ops (Sabre Ops)
275.9750	275.9750	AM	RAF Coltishall	Talkdown
276.0000	276.0000	AM	RAF Greenham Common	Ground
276.0750	276.0750	AM	RAF Chetwynd	Shawbury Approach
		AM	RAF Shawbury	Approach
276.1250	276.1250	AM	RAF Cosford	Approach
276.1750	276.1750	AM	RAF Odiham	ATIS
276.2000	276.2000	AM	RAF Valley	4FTS Air-to-Air
		AM	RAF Ty Croes	ADR Air-Ground
276.2250	276.2250	AM	RAF Lakenheath	48FW Ops

Base	Mobile	Mode	Location	User and Notes
276.2500	276.2500	AM	RNAS Yeovilton	801 Sqn Air-Air
276.6000		NFM	Nationwide	Dynamic Sciences Surv
276.6500	276.6500	AM	RAF Neatishead	Air Defence Region Ops
276.8250	276.8250	AM	RAF Ternhill	Approach
276.8500	276.8500	AM	MoD Boscombe Down	PAR
277.0000	277.0000	AM	Nationwide	NATO Magic Surveillance
		AM	Royal Navy	Ship-Air
277.0750	277.0750	AM	RAF Mildenhall	ATIS
277.1250	277.1250	AM	RAF West Drayton	London Military
277.2250	277.2250	AM	RAF St Athan	Approach
277.3000	277.3000	AM	RAF Leuchars	43 Sqn Ops (Golf Ops)
277.4000	277.4000	AM	Nationwide	Air Defence Region
277.4500	277.4500	AM	RAF Cottesmore	Air-to-Air
277.4750	277.4750	AM	Wattisham	Director
		AM	RAF Waddington	Director
277.5000	277.5000	AM	Aberporth	Range Tertiary
277.7500	277.7500	AM	Nationwide	Air Defence Region
277.7750	277.7750	AM	RAF West Drayton	London Military
277.9000	277.9000	AM	RAF Chivenor	7FTS Air-Air
277.9500	277.9500	AM	RAF West Drayton	London Military (Dover/Lydd)
278.0250	278.0250	AM	RAF West Drayton	London Military
278.1500	278.1500	AM	RAF West Drayton	London Military
278.8500	278.8500	AM	Nationwide	RAF AWACS Ops
278.9000		NFM	Nationwide	Dynamic Sciences Surv
279.0000		NFM	Space	Space Shuttle Down Link
279.1750	279.1750	AM	RAF West Drayton	London Mil
279.2250	279.2250	AM	RAF West Drayton	London Mil
279.2500	279.2500	AM	RAF Lakenheath	Radar
279.3000	279.3000	AM	RAF West Drayton	London Military
279.3250	279.3250	AM	MoD Boscombe Down	ATIS
279.3500	279.3500	AM	RAF Benson	Tower
279.4750	279.4750	AM	RAF West Drayton	London Military
279.5250	279.5250	AM	Nationwide	Air Defence Region
279.7250	279.7250	AM	Nationwide	Air Defence Region
280.0750	280.0750	AM	Nationwide	Tactical
280.4000	280.4000	AM	Nationwide	Forward Air Controllers
		AM	Otterburn	Range Secondary
280.6000		NFM	Nationwide	Dynamic Sciences Surv
280.7250	280.7250	AM	RAF Lakenheath	Aux-08 "Bite"
281.1000	281.1000	AM	Nationwide	Air Defence Region
281.1500	281.1500	AM	Lyme Bay	Range Primary
281.2000	281.2000	AM	Royal Navy	Ship-Air
281.5500	281.5500	AM	Nationwide	Air-Air
281.7250	281.7250	AM	RNAS Portland	Naval Exercises
281.8000	281.8000	AM	Nationwide	Displays
282.0000	282.0000	AM	RAF Cranwell	Director
282.1250	282.1250	AM	RAF West Drayton	London Mil
282.2500	282.2500	AM	Netheravon	Salisbury Plain

Base	Mobile	Mode	Location	User and Notes
282.8000	282.8000	AM	RAF Boulmer	Boulmer Rescue
		AM	RAF Leconfield	Leconfield Rescue
		AM	RAF Valley	SAR Approach
		AM	RNAS Portland	Portland Radio
		AM	Nationwide	NATO SAR
283.4250	283.4250	AM	RAF Swinderby	Approach
283.4500	283.4500	AM	Nationwide	9 Sqn Air-Air
283.4750	283.4750	AM	Anglia	Anglian Radar
283.5250	283.5250	AM	RAF West Drayton	London Mil
283.5750	283.5750	AM	RAF Waddington	Zone
		AM	Wattisham	Director
283.6000	283.6000	AM	Nationwide	17 Sqn Air-Air
283.6500	283.6500	AM	Nationwide	Air Defence Region
283.6750	283.6750	AM	RAF West Drayton	London Mil
283.9000	283.9000	AM	RAF Lossiemouth	Safety
284.3000	284.3000	AM	RAF West Drayton	London Mil
284.6000	284.6000	AM	Newcastle	Radar Approach
284.8750	284.8750	AM	RAF West Drayton	London Mil
284.9000	284.9000	AM	RAF Lakenheath	Maintenance
284.9500	284.9500	AM	RAF Lyneham	LTW Air-Air
284.9750	284.9750	AM	Nationwide	Air Defence Region
285.0250	285.0250	AM	RAF Leuchars	Ops
285.0500	285.0500	AM	RAF Waddington	Tower
285.0750	285.0750	AM	Prestwick	Scottish Military
285.1000	285.1000	AM	Nationwide	FRADU Discreet
285.1500	285.1500	AM	RAF Cranwell	Talkdown
285.1750	285.1750	AM	RAF West Drayton	London Mil

285.5000 - 290.5000 MHz   TACTICAL MILITARY EXERCISE COMMUNICATIONS 25 KHZ

Base	Mobile	Mode	Location	User and Notes
285.6500	285.6500	AM	RAF Neatishead	Air Defence Region Ops
285.7500	285.7500	AM	RAF Buchan	Air Defence Region Ops
285.8500	285.8500	AM	RAF Boulmer	Boulmer Rescue
286.6500	286.6500	AM	RAF Lossiemouth	12 Sqn Air-Air
286.9000	286.9000	AM	RAF Buchan	Air Defence Region Ops
287.2500	287.2500	AM	Nationwide	RAF Air-Air Tanker Ops
287.6500	287.6500	AM	RAF Neatishead	Air Defence Region Ops
		AM	Royal Navy	Ship-Air
287.7000	287.7000	AM	Nationwide	Air Defence Region
288.4000	288.4000	AM	RAF Boulmer	Air Defence Region Ops
		AM	RAF Neatishead	Air Defence Region Ops
		AM	SE Scotland	Combat Air Patrol Area B
288.6000	288.6000	AM	Nationwide	USAF AWACS Ops
		AM	Nationwide	USAF Air-Air
289.0500	289.0500	AM	RAF Boulmer	Air Defence Region Ops
289.2500	289.2500	AM	RAF Lossiemouth	16 Sqn Air-Air
289.3500	289.3500	AM	RAF Neatishead	Air Defence Region Ops
290.0500	290.0500	AM	RAF Neatishead	Air Defence Region Ops

Base	Mobile	Mode	Location	User and Notes
290.3750	290.3750	AM	Nationwide	Air Defence Region
290.5750	290.5750	AM	RAF West Drayton	London Military
290.6000	290.6000	AM	RAF Coltishall	Radar
290.7000	290.7000	AM	RAF West Drayton	London Military
290.8000	290.8000	AM	RAF Coningsby	Air-Air
290.8250	290.8250	AM	RAF Lakenheath	Radar
290.8500	290.8500	AM	RAF Coningsby	29 Sqn Ops (Triplex Ops)
290.9250	290.9250	AM	RAF West Drayton	London Military
290.9500	290.9500	AM	Netheravon	Tower
		AM	North Sea	ACMI Range Show Ground 4
291.0000	291.0000	AM	Prestwick Airport	Navy Prestwick
291.0750	291.0750	AM	Nationwide	Air Defence Region
291.1250	291.1250	AM	Wattisham	Approach
291.2250	291.2250	AM	RAF Lossiemouth	15 Sqn Air-to-Air
291.6500	291.6500	AM	MoD Boscombe Down	Approach
291.6750	291.6750	AM	RAF Waddington	DATIS
291.7000	291.7000	AM	RAF Barkston Heath	Departures
291.8000	291.8000	AM	West Drayton	London Military (LJAO)
291.9500	291.9500	AM	RAF Marham	Approach
292.4500	292.4500	AM	RAF Boulmer	Air Defence Region Ops
292.4750	292.4750	AM	RAF Leuchars	Director
292.5000	292.5000	AM	Salisbury Plain	Air-Ground
292.5250	292.5250	AM	West Drayton	London Military
292.6000	292.6000	AM	West Drayton	London Military
292.6750	292.6750	AM	Prestwick	Scottish Military
292.7000	292.7000	AM	RAF Leeming	Zone Radar
292.8000	292.8000	AM	RAF Linton-on-Ouse	Departures
293.4250	293.4250	AM	RAF Coltishall	Zone
293.5250	293.5250	AM	RAF West Drayton	London Military
293.5750	293.5750	AM	RAF West Drayton	London Military
293.7250	293.7250	AM	RAF Lakenheath	Aux-07 493FS
293.7750	293.7750	AM	RAF Marham	Radar
293.9750	293.9750	AM	RAF West Drayton	London Military
294.9000	294.9000	AM	RAF West Drayton	London Military
295.8500	295.8550	AM	Prestwick	Scottish Military
296.4000	296.4000	AM	Nationwide	Air Defence Region
296.5750	296.5750	AM	Nationwide	RAF/USAF Discreet
296.7250	296.7250	AM	RAF Coltishall	Ground
		AM	RNAS Culdrose	705 Sqn Air-Air
296.7500	296.7500	AM	RAF Waddington	Radar
296.8000	296.8000	AM	International	Space Shuttle Down Link
296.9000	296.9000	AM	RAF Neatishead	Air Defence Region Ops
		AM	RAF Cranwell	Ground
298.6500	298.6500	AM	Nationwide	Air Defence Region
299.1000	299.1000	AM	RAF Boulmer	Boulmer Rescue
299.4000	299.4000	AM	RAF Brawdy	Tower
		AM	Boscombe Down (MoD)	Ground
		AM	RNAS Culdrose	Ground

Base	Mobile	Mode	Location	User and Notes
		AM	RAF Lossiemouth	Ground
299.5000	299.5000	AM	AARA 3 (N North Sea)	Air-Air Refuelling
299.7000	299.7000	AM	Nationwide	Air Defence Region
299.9000	299.9000	AM	RAF Alconbury	9RW/U2 Tactical
299.9750	299.9750	AM	RAF West Drayton	London Military

Base	Mobile	Mode	Location	User and Notes
300.0000	300.0000	AM	RAF Lakenheath	Air-Air
300.0500	300.0500	AM	Portland Exercise Area	Ops
300.1000	300.1000	AM	RAF Lyneham	LTW Air-Air
300.0750	300.0750	AM	RAF Lakenheath	492FS Bowler Ops
300.1500	300.1500	AM	RAF Benbecula	Air Defence Region Ops
300.1750	300.1750	AM	RNAS Portland	Radar
300.2000	300.2000	AM	RAF Lakenheath	492FS Air-to-Air
300.2500	300.2500	AM	DRA Boscombe Down	ETPS Tester Ops
300.3500	300.3500	AM	RAF Northolt	ATIS
300.4250	300.4250	AM	RAF Linton-on-Ouse	Tower
300.4500	300.4500	AM	RAF Odiham	Talkdown
300.4750	300.4750	AM	RAF Lyneham	Director
300.5750	300.5750	AM	RAF Waddington	Director
300.6000	300.6000	AM	Warton	Ops
300.6250	300.6250	AM	RAF Cranwell	3FTS Air-to-Air
300.6500	300.6500	AM	RAF Neatishead	Air Defence Region Ops
300.7750	300.7750	AM	RAF Church Fenton	Approach
300.8000	300.8000	AM	Nationwide	NATO Low Level
300.8250	300.8250	AM	RAF Lakenheath	Dispatcher
		AM	Lilstock Range (D119)	Range Control
300.8750	300.8750	AM	RAF Leeming	11 Sqn Ops (Black Ops)
300.9250	300.9250	AM	RAF Coningsby	Talkdown

300.9500 - 308.9500 MHz			TACTICAL MILITARY EXERCISE COMMUNICATIONS 25 kHz	
300.9500	300.9500	AM	Nationwide	Air Defence Region
301.3250	301.3250	AM	RAF Lakenheath	Air-Air
304.0000		NFM	Worldwide	USAF Satcom Downlink
305.9000	305.9000	AM	RNAS Culdrose	750 Sqn Ops
306.4000	306.4000	AM	RAF Lakenheath	Operations
306.5000	306.5000	AM	AARA 6 (S North Sea)	Air-Air Refuelling
306.6500	306.6500	AM	SW Scotland	Combat Air Patrol Area C
307.0000	307.0000	AM	RAF Neatishead	Air Defence Region Ops
307.4000	307.4000	AM	RAF Cottesmore	TTTE Ops
307.6000	307.6000	AM	RAF Neatishead	Air Defence Region Ops
307.8000	307.8000	AM	RAF Fairford	Command Post
307.8000	307.8000	AM	Stanford	Stanford Ops
308.0000	308.0000	AM	AARA 3 (N North Sea)	Air-Air Refuelling
308.7500	308.7500	AM	RAF Chinevor	Ops
309.0750	309.0750	AM	RAF Lakenheath	Radar
309.5500	309.5500	AM	RAF Chetwynd	Ternhill Tower
309.6250	309.6250	AM	RAF Odiham	Tower
309.6500	309.6500	AM	RAF Valley	4FTS Air-to-Air
		AM	Nationwide	AWACS
309.6750	309.6750	AM	RAF Waddington	Talkdown
309.7250	309.7250	AM	RAF Topcliffe	Tower
309.8750	309.8750	AM	RAF Leeming	Talkdown
310.0000	310.0000	AM	RAF Aldergrove	Approach

Base	Mobile	Mode	Location	User and Notes
		AM	AARA 2 (N North Sea)	Air-Air Refuelling
310.9000	310.9000	AM	Nationwide	17 Sqn Air-Air
311.2000	311.2000	AM	RAF Valley	4FTS Air-Air
311.3000	311.3000	AM	Warton	Tower
		AM	RAF Lossiemouth	12 Sqn Air-Air
311.3250	311.3250	AM	RAF Kinloss	Director
		AM	RAF Lossiemouth	Lossie Director
		AM	RNAS Yeovilton	Yeovil Ground
311.4000	311.4000	AM	RAF Binbrook	Tower
311.4750	311.4750	AM	Nationwide	USAF Air-Air
311.8250	311.8250	AM	RAF Lossiemouth	15 Sqn Air-to-Air
		AM	RAF Cranwell	ATIS
311.9500	311.9500	AM	RAF Wittering	Ground
311.9750	311.9750	AM	Nationwide	USAF General Air-Air
312.0000	312.0000	AM	Middle Wallop	Wallop Approach
312.0750	312.0750	AM	RAF Cottesmore	Approach
312.2250	312.2250	AM	RAF Coningsby	Approach
		AM	RAF Coningsby	Stud 13
312.3250	312.3250	AM	RAF Manston	Talkdown
312.3500	312.3500	AM	RAF Northolt	Tower
312.4000	312.4000	AM	RAF Lossiemouth	Talkdown
312.4250	312.4500	AM	RAF Mildenhall	Command Post
312.5000	312.5000	AM	RAF Waddington	Approach
312.5500	312.5500	AM	RAF Marham	Ops
312.6750	312.6750	AM	Middle Wallop	Director
312.7000	312.7000	AM	RNAS Merryfield	Tower
312.8000	312.8000	AM	RAF Woodvale	Approach
313.1000	313.1000	AM	RAF Valley	4FTS Air-Air

314.0000 - 315.0000 MHz　　TACTICAL MILITARY EXERCISE
COMMUNICATIONS 25 kHz

Base	Mobile	Mode	Location	User and Notes
314.4750	314.4750	AM	Nationwide	Air Defence Region
315.0000	315.0000	AM	RAF Neatishead	NATO AWACS Coord
315.5250	315.5250	AM	MoD Farnborough	Radar
315.5500	315.5500	AM	Edinburgh	UAS Air-Air
315.5750	315.5750	AM	RAF Lakenheath	Dep Con
315.6500	315.6500	AM	RNAS Lee-on-Solent	Tower
315.7500	315.7500	AM	RAF Abingdon	SRE
315.8500	315.8500	AM	RAF Neatishead	Air Defence Region Ops
315.9750	315.9750	AM	RAF Odiham	Odiham Information

316.1000 - 327.1000 MHz　　TACTICAL MILITARY EXERCISE
COMMUNICATIONS 25 kHz

Base	Mobile	Mode	Location	User and Notes
316.3500	316.3500	AM	AARA 8 (North Sea)	Air-Air Refuelling
316.6000	316.6000	AM	AARA 4 (N North Sea)	Air-Air Refuelling
316.7000	316.7000	AM	RAF Lakenheath	493FS Air-to-Air
316.7500	316.7500	AM	Nationwide	USAF Air-Air
316.8000	316.8000	AM	RAF Lossiemouth	Orange Alert

Base	Mobile	Mode	Location	User and Notes
316.8750		AM	RAF St Mawgan	DATIS
317.2000	317.2000	AM	AARA 4 (N North Sea)	Air-Air Refuelling
317.3750	317.3750	AM	RAF Lakenheath	48FW Air-to-Air
317.5000	317.5000	AM	Nationwide	Air Defence Region
317.8500	317.8500	AM	Nationwide	Air Defence Region
		AM	Nationwide	RAF AWACS Ops
318.5500	318.5500	AM	Nationwide	Air-Air Refuelling
		AM	RAF Boulmer	Air Defence Region Ops
318.7500	318.7500	AM	RAF Neatishead	Air Defence Region Ops
319.4000	319.4000	AM	RAF Neatishead	Air Defence Region Ops
319.6000	319.6000	AM	Royal Navy	Ship-Air
322.2000	322.2000	AM	Nationwide	USAF Air-Air
322.4000	322.4000	NFM	Nationwide	TADIL-A Data Link
322.9500	322.9500	AM	Nationwide	USAF Displays
		AM	East Anglia	USAF Talk-through
		AM	Nationwide	AWACS
323.2000	323.2000	AM	Nationwide	USAF Air-Air
325.2000	325.2000	AM	Nationwide	RAF Discreet

326.5000 - 328.6000 MHz   RADIO ASTRONOMY

326.9000	326.9000	AM	AARA 5 (North Sea)	Air-Air Refuelling

329.1500 - 335.0000 MHz   AERONAUTICAL ILS GLIDESLOPECOMPONENT

329.1500		AM	Nationwide	Glideslope (Localiser 108.95 MHz)
		AM	Woodford	Runway 25
329.3000		AM	Nationwide	Glideslope (Localiser 108.90 MHz)
		AM	Cranfield	Runway 22
		AM	Edinburgh	Runway 07/25
		AM	Kerry	Runway 07/25
329.4500		AM	Nationwide	Glideslope (Localiser 110.55 MHz)
		AM	Filton	Runway 10/28
329.6000		AM	Nationwide	Glideslope (Localiser 110.50 MHz)
		AM	Bournemouth	Runway 08/26
		AM	London/Stansted	Runway 05/23
329.7500		AM	Nationwide	Glideslope (Localiser 108.55 MHz)
329.9000		AM	Nationwide	Glideslope (Localiser 108.50 MHz)
		AM	RAF Benson	Runway 19
330.0500		AM	Nationwide	Glideslope (Localiser 110.75 MHz)
330.2000		AM	Nationwide	Glideslope (Localiser 110.70 MHz)
		AM	Cardiff	Runway 12/30
		AM	Connaught	Runway 27
		AM	London/Heathrow	Runway 23
		AM	RAF Coningsby	Runway 26
330.3500		AM	Nationwide	Glideslope (Localiser 108.75 MHz)
		AM	Humberside	Runway 21
330.5000		AM	Nationwide	Glideslope (Localiser 108.70 MHz)
		AM	RAF Leuchars	Runway 27
		AM	RAF St Mawgan	Runway 31

Base	Mobile	Mode	Location	User and Notes
		AM	RAF Shawbury	Runway 19
330.6500		AM	Nationwide	Glideslope (Localiser 110.95 MHz)
330.8000		AM	Nationwide	Glideslope (Localiser 110.90 MHz)
		AM	Belfast/Aldergrove	Runway 17
		AM	Jersey	Runway 09
		AM	Leeds & Bradford	Runway 32/14
		AM	London/Gatwick	Runway 08R/26L
		AM	Norwich	Runway 27
		AM	Ronaldsway	Runway 27
330.9500		AM	Nationwide	Glideslope (Localiser 111.95 MHz)
331.2500		AM	Nationwide	Glideslope (Localiser 109.15 MHz)
		AM	Luton	Runway 08/28
331.3000		AM	Nationwide	Glideslope (Localiser 111.90 MHz)
		AM	RAF Brize Norton	Runway 08/26
331.4000		AM	Nationwide	Glideslope (Localiser 109.10 MHz)
331.5500		AM	Nationwide	Glideslope (Localiser 111.15 MHz)
331.7000		AM	Nationwide	Glideslope (Localiser 111.10 MHz)
		AM	RAF Fairford	Runway 09/27
		AM	RAF Lossiemouth	Runway 23
		AM	RAF Waddington	Runway 21
		AM	Wattisham	Runway 23
331.8500		AM	Nationwide	Glideslope (Localiser 109.35 MHz)
332.0000		AM	Nationwide	Glideslope (Localiser 109.30 MHz)
		AM	Glasgow	Runway 23
		AM	RAF Church Fenton	Runway 24
332.1500		AM	Nationwide	Glideslope (Localiser 111.35 MHz)
332.3000		AM	Nationwide	Glideslope (Localiser 111.30 MHz)
		AM	Hatfield	Runway 24
		AM	Perth	Runway 21
		AM	Teesside	Runway 23
332.4500		AM	Nationwide	Glideslope (Localiser 109.55 MHz)
332.6000		AM	Nationwide	Glideslope (Localiser 109.50 MHz)
		AM	London/Heathrow	Runway 09R/27L
		AM	Manchester	Runway 06/24
		AM	Plymouth	Runway 31
		AM	Shannon	Runway 24
332.7500		AM	Nationwide	Glideslope (Localiser 111.55 MHz)
		AM	Newcastle	Runway 07/25
332.9000		AM	Nationwide	Glideslope (Localiser 111.50 MHz)
		AM	RAF Coltishall	Runway 22
333.0500		AM	Nationwide	Glideslope (Localiser 109.75 MHz)
		AM	Coventry	Runway 23
333.2000		AM	Nationwide	Glideslope (Localiser 109.70 MHz)
		AM	Belfast/Aldergrove	Runway 25
		AM	Beauvais	Runway 31
		AM	Dinard	Runway 36
		AM	RAF Cranwell	Runway 27
		AM	RAF Kinloss	Runway 26

Base	Mobile	Mode	Location	User and Notes
		AM	RAF Lyneham	Runway 25
		AM	RAF Valley	Runway 14
333.3500		AM	Nationwide	Glideslope (Localiser 111.75 MHz)
		AM	Liverpool	Runway 09/27
333.5000		AM	Nationwide	Glideslope (Localiser 111.70 MHz)
		AM	RAE Boscombe Down	Runway 24
333.6500		AM	Nationwide	Glideslope (Localiser 109.95 MHz)
333.8000		AM	Nationwide	Glideslope (Localiser 109.90 MHz)
		AM	Aberdeen/Dyce	Runway 16/34
		AM	Cherbourg	Runway 29
		AM	Cork	Runway 17/35
		AM	East Midlands	Runway 09/27
		AM	Exeter	Runway 26
		AM	Stornoway	Runway 18
		AM	Warton	Runway 26
333.9500		AM	Nationwide	Glideslope (Localiser 108.35 MHz)
334.1000		AM	Nationwide	Glideslope (Localiser 108.30 MHz)
		AM	Bedford	Runway 27
		AM	Deauville	Runway 30
		AM	RAF Lakenheath	Runway 24
334.2500		AM	Nationwide	Glideslope (Localiser 110.15 MHz)
334.2500		AM	Bristol	Runway 09/27
334.4000		AM	Nationwide	Glideslope (Localiser 110.10 MHz)
		AM	Birmingham	Runway 15/33
		AM	Glasgow	Runway 05
		AM	RAF Marham	ILS Runway 24
		AM	Rennes	Runway 29
334.5500		AM	Nationwide	Glideslope (Localiser 108.15 MHz)
		AM	Blackpool	Runway 28
		AM	Lydd	Runway 22
334.7000		AM	Nationwide	Glideslope (Localiser 108.10 MHz)
		AM	Guernsey	Runway 09/27
		AM	RAF Abingdon	Runway 36
		AM	RAF Chivenor	Runway 28
		AM	RAF Mildenhall	Runway 11/29
334.7500	334.750	AM	RAF Neatishead	MRSA
334.8500		AM	Nationwide	Glideslope (Localiser 110.35 MHz)
335.0000		AM	Nationwide	Glideslope (Localiser 110.30 MHz)
		AM	Jersey	Runway 27
		AM	London/Heathrow	Runway 09L/27R
		AM	Prestwick	Runway 13/31
		AM	RAF Cottesmore	Runway 23
		AM	RAF Leeming	Runway 16

335.4000 - 399.9000 MHz   UHF MILITARY AVIATION 25 KHZ

Base	Mobile	Mode	Location	User and Notes
336.2250	336.2250	AM	Manobier	Range
336.2750	336.2750	AM	MoD Farnborough	Approach
336.3250	336.3250	AM	Hawarden	Tower

Base	Mobile	Mode	Location	User and Notes
336.3500	336.3500	AM	RAF Kinloss	Tower
		AM	RAF Leeming	Talkdown
		AM	RAF Marham	Ground
336.3750	336.3750	AM	RAF Cottesmore	Ground
336.4750	336.4750	AM	MoD Filton	Director
		AM	Warton	Approach
336.5250	336.5250	AM	RAF St Athan	Tower
336.5500	336.5500	AM	RAF St Mawgan	Talkdown
337.5750	337.5750	AM	RAF Fairford	Tower
337.6000	337.6000	AM	Jurby	Range Primary
337.7250	337.7250	AM	RAF Valley	Director
337.7500	337.7500	AM	RAF Cranwell	Ground
		AM	RAF Lossiemouth	Tower
		AM	RNAS Portland	Tower
		AM	RNAS Prestwick	Navy Prestwick
337.8250	337.8250	AM	RAF Leeming	Approach
337.8500	337.8500	AM	East Scotland	Combat Air Patrol Area A
337.8750	337.8750	AM	RAF Cottesmore	Talkdown
337.9000	337.9000	AM	RAF Marham	Tower
		AM	RAF Shawbury	Ground
337.9250	337.9250	AM	MoD Bedford	Tower
		AM	MoD West Freugh	Tower
337.9500	337.9500	AM	RAF Wittering	Talkdown
337.9750	337.9750	AM	RAF Coningsby	Talkdown

338.0000 - 397.9500 MHz   TACTICAL MILITARY COMMUNICATIONS 25 kHz

338.0000 - 338.5000 MHz   TACTICAL MILITARY EXERCISE
COMMUNICATIONS 25 kHz

Base	Mobile	Mode	Location	User and Notes
338.2000	338.2000	NFM	Nationwide	TADIL-A Data Link
338.6250	338.6250	AM	RAF Manston	Manston Director
338.6500	338.6500	AM	RAF Brize Norton	Brize Talkdown
338.6750	338.6750	AM	RAF Lakenheath	Radar
338.8250	338.8250	AM	RAF Ternhill	Tower
338.8500	338.8500	AM	RAF Leeming	Ground
338.8750	338.8750	AM	RNAS Yeovilton	Yeovil Director
		AM	RNAS Predannack	Tower
339.9500	339.9500	AM	RAF Coltishall	Tower
		AM	RNAS Culdrose	Radar
339.9750	339.9750	AM	RNAS Yeovilton	Talkdown
340.0250	340.0250	AM	RAF Linton-on-Ouse	Ground
		AM	RAF Lyneham	Zone
340.1000	340.1000	AM	RAF St Athan	Talkdown
340.1500	340.1500	AM	RAF Brawdy	Talkdown
340.1750	340.1750	AM	RAF Lyneham	Ground
		AM	RAF Valley	Tower
340.2000	340.2000	AM	RAF Church Fenton	Ground

Base	Mobile	Mode	Location	User and Notes
340.2500	340.2500	AM	Warton	Special Tasks-Test Flying
340.3000	340.3000	AM	Central Wales	Combat Air Patrol Area F
340.3250	340.3250	AM	RAF Greenham Common	Tower
		AM	RAF Benson	Ground
340.4250	340.4250	AM	RAF Lakenheath	493FS Aux-08 (Iceman)
340.4500	340.4500	AM	RAF Neatishead	MRSA
340.4750	340.4750	AM	RAF Cranwell	Cranwell Approach
340.5250	340.5250	AM	RAF Barkston Heath	Barkston Approach
340.5500	340.5500	AM	North Sea	ACMI Range Show Ground 3
340.5750	340.5750	AM	RAF Cottesmore	Approach
341.6750	341.6750	AM	Nationwide	Air Defence Region
342.0250	342.0250	AM	MoD Filton	Tower
342.0750	342.0750	AM	RAF Barkston Heath	Barkston Tower
342.1000	342.1000	AM	RAF Valley	4FTS Air-Air
342.1250	342.1250	AM	RAF Waddington	Ground
342.1500	342.1500	AM	RAF Chinevor	7FTS Ops
342.1750	342.1750	AM	Donna Nook	Range Primary
342.2000	342.2000	AM	Warton	Radar
342.2500	342.2500	AM	RAF Coltishall	Director
342.4500	342.4500	AM	RAF Brize Norton	Brize Approach
342.6500	342.6500	AM	RAF Neatishead	Air Defence Region Ops
		AM	Nationwide	RAF AWACS Ops
343.2000	343.2000	AM	RAF Ty Croes	ADR Air-Ground
343.3000	343.3000	AM	RAF Neatishead	Air Defence Region Ops
		AM	RAF Lakenheath	493FS Aux-08 (Crusty)
343.4250	343.4250	AM	Wattisham	Tower
		AM	RAF Lakenheath	Air-Air
343.4750	343.4750	AM	RAF Lakenheath	48FW Aux
343.6000	343.6000	AM	RAF Croughton	Croughton Radio
		AM	RAF Lakenheath	493FS
343.6750	343.6750	AM	RAF Lakenheath	494FS Panther Ops
		AM	RAF Leeming	11 Sqn Air-Air
343.7000	343.7000	AM	Warton	Radar
344.0000	344.0000	AM	RAF Abingdon	SRE
		AM	RAF Benson	Approach
		AM	RAF Brize Norton	Director
		AM	RAF Coningsby	Director
		AM	RAF Cranwell	Director
		AM	RAF Leeming	Director
		AM	RAF Lyneham	Director
		AM	RAF Manston	Director
		AM	RAF Marham	Director
		AM	RAF St Athan	Director
		AM	RAF St Mawgan	Director
		AM	RAF Shawbury	Radar
		AM	RAF Valley	Director
		AM	RAF Waddington	Director
		AM	RAF Wittering	Director

Base	Mobile	Mode	Location	User and Notes
344.2000	344.2000	AM	Warton	Radar
		AM	RAF Lossiemouth	16 Sqn Air-Air
344.3500	344.3500	AM	RAF Manston	Tower
		AM	RAF Topcliffe	Director
		AM	RNAS Yeovilton	Talkdown
344.4250	344.4250	AM	RAF Chivenor	7FTS Air-Air
344.4500		AM	RAF Lossiemouth	DATIS
344.4750	344.4750	AM	RAF Linton-on-Ouse	Director
344.5000	344.5000	AM	Warton	Operations (Boffin Ops)
344.5750	344.5750	AM	RAF Leeming	Tower
344.6000	344.6000	AM	RAF Abingdon	Tower
344.6250	344.6250	AM	RAF Coningsby	Approach
344.7000	344.7000	AM	RAF Marham	13 Sqn Air-to-Air
344.7500	344.7500	AM	RAF Cottesmore	Air-to-Air
344.8000	344.8000	AM	RAF Mildenhall	Command Post
344.9750	344.9750	AM	RAF Northolt	Approach
345.0000 - 356.0000 MHz			**TACTICAL MILITARY EXERCISE**	
			COMMUNICATIONS 25 kHz	
345.0000	345.0000	AM	RAF Neatishead	Air Defence Region Ops
345.0250	345.0250	AM	RAF Lyneham	Zone
345.1000	345.1000	AM	RAF Wittering	20 Sqn Ops
345.2000	345.2000	AM	Larkhill	Range Primary
349.1750	259.1750	AM	Prestwick	Scottish Mil
352.4750	352.4750	AM	Nationwide	AWACS
353.0000	353.0000	AM	RAF Boulmer	Air Defence Region Ops
353.0500	353.0500	AM	RAF Buchan	Air Defence Region Ops
353.2000	353.2000	AM	RAF Ternhill	Approach
353.5500	353.5000	AM	Aberdeen	Radar
		AM	DRA Boscombe Down	Gauntlet Ops
354.4500	354.4500	AM	RNAS Portland	Naval Exercises
355.0250	355.0250	AM	Nationwide	Forward Air Controllers
355.9750	355.9750	AM	Nationwide	31 Sqn Air-Air
356.1750	356.1750	AM	Wattisham	Talkdown
356.2000	356.2000	AM	Aberporth	Range Primary
356.2750	356.2750	AM	RAF Halton	Halton Aero Club
356.4000	356.4000	AM	RAF Valley	4FTS Air-Air
356.7250	356.7250	AM	RAF Leeming	Seagull Ops
356.8500	356.8500	AM	Nationwide	RAF AWACS Ops
356.8750	356.8750	AM	RAF Brize Norton	Brize Director
356.9750	356.9750	AM	RAF Shawbury	Talkdown
357.1250	357.1250	AM	RAF Cosford	Tower
357.1500	357.1500	AM	RAF Wittering	Tower
357.1750	357.1750	AM	RAF St Athan	Radar
357.2000	357.2000	AM	RAF St Mawgan	Approach
357.3750	357.3750	AM	RAF Topcliffe	Approach
357.4000	357.4000	AM	MoD Farnborough	Tower

Base	Mobile	Mode	Location	User and Notes
357.4750	357.4750	AM	RAF Brize Norton	Brize Ops
357.6000	357.6000	AM	Nationwide	AWACS
358.4750	358.4750	AM	RAF Kinloss	Ops
358.4750	358.4750	AM	Northern England	Combat Air Patrol Area D West
358.5000	358.5000	AM	RAF Brawdy	Director
358.5250	358.5250	AM	RAF Linton-on-Ouse	Talkdown
358.5500	358.5500	AM	RAF Coningsby	Ground
		AM	Castle Martin	Range Air-Ground
358.5750	358.5750	AM	Woodford	Tower
358.6000	358.6000	AM	RAF Fairford	Fairford Metro
358.6500	358.6500	AM	RAF Leeming	Director
358.6750	358.6750	AM	RAF Lakenheath	Tower
		AM	RAF Valley	Talkdown
358.7000	358.7000	AM	RNAS Culdrose	Talkdown
358.7250	358.7250	AM	RAF Cottesmore	Director
358.7500	358.7500	AM	RAF Mona	Tower
358.8000	358.8000	AM	RAF Abingdon	Benson Zone
		AM	RAF Benson	Zone
358.8500	358.8500	AM	RAF Church Fenton	Director
358.9250	268.5750	AM	Prestwick	Scottish Mil
359.4000	359.4000	AM	North Sea	ACMI Range Show Ground 2
359.4250	359.4250	AM	RNAS Portland	Naval Exercises
359.5000	359.5000	AM	RAF Lyneham	Approach
359.8250	359.8250	AM	Wattisham	Talkdown
359.8750	359.8750	AM	RAF Wittering	Approach
360.5500	360.5500	AM	RAF St Mawgan	Director
360.7250	360.7250	AM	RAF Barkston Heath	Talkdown
360.7500	360.7500	AM	RAF Colerne	Ground
360.7750	360.7750	AM	Manobier	Range
361.1000	361.1000	AM	RAF Leeming	11 Sqn Air-Air
361.9750	361.9750	AM	North Sea	ACMI Range Show Ground 5
362.0500	362.0500	AM	Salisbury Plain	Salisbury Ops
362.1250	362.1250	AM	RAF Lakenheath	Ram Rod
362.1750	362.1750	AM	RAF Lossiemouth	15 Sqn Air-to-Air
362.2000	362.2000	AM	MoD Bedford	Approach
362.2250	362.2250	AM	Netheravon	Approach
362.3000	362.3000	AM	RAF Abingdon	Approach
		AM	RAF Benson	Approach
		AM	RAF Brawdy	Approach
		AM	RAF Brize Norton	Brize Approach
		AM	RAF Church Fenton	Fenton Approach/Radar
		AM	RAF Coningsby	Approach
		AM	RAF Cosford	Approach
		AM	RAF Cranwell	Approach
		AM	RAF Dishforth	Approach
		AM	RAF Fairford	Brize Radar
		AM	Inverness Airport	Approach
		AM	RAF Kemble	Approach

Base	Mobile	Mode	Location	User and Notes
		AM	RAF Kinloss	Approach
		AM	RAF Leeming	Approach
		AM	RAF Leuchars	Approach
		AM	RAF Linton-on-Ouse	Approach
		AM	RAF Lossiemouth	Approach
		AM	RAF Lyneham	Approach
		AM	RAF Manston	Approach
		AM	RAF Marham	Approach
		AM	RAF Mildenhall	Approach
		AM	RAF Newton	Approach
		AM	RAF Northolt	Approach
		AM	RAF St Athan	Approach
		AM	RAF St Mawgan	Approach
		AM	RAF Shawbury	Approach
		AM	RAF Ternhill	Approach
		AM	RAF Topcliffe	Approach
		AM	RAF Valley	Approach
		AM	RAF Waddington	Approach
		AM	RAF Wittering	Approach
		AM	RNAS Portland	Approach/Radar/Tower
		AM	RNAS Yeovilton	Approach/Director

362.5000 - 364.5000 MHz   TACTICAL MILITARY EXERCISE COMMUNICATIONS 25 KHZ

Base	Mobile	Mode	Location	User and Notes
362.5250	362.5250	AM	RAF Valley	4FTS Air-Air
362.6750	362.6750	AM	RAF Linton-on-Ouse	Approach
362.8250	362.8250	AM	Nationwide	Air Defence Region
362.9000	362.9000	AM	RAF Wittering	1/20 Sqn Air-to-Air
362.9750	362.9750	AM	RAF Coningsby	Ransack Ops
364.2000	364.2000	AM	RAF Neatishead	Air Defence Region Ops
		AM	Nationwide	NATO Magic Surveillance
		AM	Nationwide	RAF AWACS Ops
		AM	Faroe Islands	Pole Star
364.6500	364.6500	AM	RAF Leeming	25 Sqn Ops (Silver Ops)
		AM	RNAS Yeovilton	D School
364.8000	364.8000	AM	RAF Coltishall	Wing Ops
364.8250	364.8250	AM	Middle Wallop	Talkdown
364.8500	364.8500	AM	RAF Valley	4FTS Air-Air
364.9750	364.9750	AM	RAF Coningsby	56 Sqn Ops (Ransack Ops)
		AM	North Sea	Combat Air Patrol Area E
365.0250	365.0250	AM	RAF Valley	4FTS Air-to-Air
365.0500	365.0500	AM	RAF Coningsby	Air-to-Air
365.0750	365.0750	AM	RAF Ternhill	Approach
365.1000	365.1000	AM	RAF Mildenhall	Dispatcher

| 365.5000 | 369.5000 | MHz | Tactical Military Exercise Communications 25 kHz | |
| 365.6750 | 275.6750 | AM | RAF West Drayton | London Military |

Base	Mobile	Mode	Location	User and Notes
366.2250	366.2250	AM	Manorbick	Range Primary
366.6000	366.6000	AM	RNAS Culdrose	750 Sqn Ops
366.7250	366.7250	AM	RAF Church Fenton	PAR
367.1250	367.1250	AM	Nationwide	Air Defence Region
367.9500	367.9500	AM	RAF Brawdy	Approach
368.3000	368.3000	AM	RAF Wittering	1 Sqn Air-Air
369.0000	369.0000	AM	RAF Marham	13 Sqn Ops (Dagger Ops)
369.0500	369.0500	AM	Northern England	Combat Air Patrol Area D East
369.1250	369.1250	AM	Nationwide	Air Defence Region
369.1500	369.1500	AM	RAF Spadeadam	Ops
369.1750	369.1750	AM	Nationwide	Air Defence Region
369.3750	369.3750	AM	RAF Lakenheath	493FS Discreet
369.6500	369.6500	AM	East Anglia	USAF Talk-through
369.8750	369.8750	AM	RNAS Yeovilton	Radar
369.9000	369.9000	AM	RAF Coningsby	56 Sqn Ops (Lion Ops)
370.0000	370.0000	AM	RNAS Predannack	Tower
370.0250	370.0250	AM	RAF Leuchars	Finals
370.0500	370.0500	AM	RAF Cottesmore	Tower
		AM	RAF Kinloss	Talkdown
370.0750	370.0750	AM	RAF Leuchars	Finals
370.1000	370.1000	AM	MoD Boscombe Down	Tower
370.3000	370.3000	AM	MoD Llanbedr	PAR
		AM	RAF Brize Norton	Brize Ground
370.9500	370.9500	AM	RAF Mildenhall	AMC Ops
371.2000	371.2000	AM	RAF Fairford	Command Post
		AM	Nationwide	Air Defence Region
372.0500	372.0500	AM	RAF Neatishead	Air Defence Region Ops
372.2500	372.2500	AM	RAF Chivenor	7FTS Air-Air
372.3000		AM	RNAS Culdrose	ATIS
372.3250	372.3250	AM	RAF Valley	Valley Approach
372.3500	372.3500	AM	RAF Coltishall	54 Sqn Ops (Lion Ops)
372.4250	372.4250	AM	HMS Cambridge	Royal Navy
372.6250	372.6250	AM	Middle Wallop	Wallop Tower
372.6500	372.6500	AM	RNAS Yeovilton	Tower
		AM	RAF Lossiemouth	617 Sqn Air-Air

373.0000 - 375.0000 MHz			**TACTICAL MILITARY EXERCISE**	
			COMMUNICATIONS 25 kHz	
373.1000	373.1000	AM	Nationwide	Air Defence Region
374.3000	284.3000	AM	RAF West Drayton	London Mil
374.4250	374.4250	AM	RAF Lakenheath	493FS Discreet
375.2000	375.2000	AM	RAF Lyneham	Talkdown
375.3000	375.3000	AM	RAF Swinderby	Tower
375.3250	375.3250	AM	RAF Church Fenton	Director
375.4250	375.4250	AM	RAF Newton	Tower
375.5000	375.5000	AM	RAF Northolt	Talkdown
375.5250	375.5250	AM	RAF Kinloss	Talkdown
376.5750	376.5750	AM	RAF Cottesmore	Departure Control

Base	Mobile	Mode	Location	User and Notes
		AM	RAF Wittering	Dep Control
376.6000	376.6000	AM	Jurby	Range Secondary
376.6250	376.6250	AM	RAF Brize Norton	Director
		AM	RAF St Mawgan	Grounds
376.6500	376.6500	AM	RAF Lossiemouth	Approach
		AM	RAF Kinloss	Approach
377.6000	377.6000	AM	Nationwide	Red Arrows Display
378.1000	378.1000	AM	Nationwide	RAF AWACS Ops
378.1500	378.1500	AM	RAF Wittering	1 Sqn Air-Air
378.2000	378.2000	AM	RAF Neatishead	MRSA
379.0250	379.0250	AM	RAF Manston	Approach
379.2000	379.2000	AM	Aberporth	Range Secondary
379.2750	379.2750	AM	RAF Coltishall	Approach
379.3750	379.3750	AM	RAF Coningsby	Air-to-Air
379.4000	379.4000	AM	Aberporth	Range Secondary
379.4250	379.4250	AM	RAF Northolt	Director
379.4750	379.4750	AM	RAF Fairford	Dispatcher
379.5000	379.5000	AM	RNAS Culdrose	Radar
379.5250	379.5250	AM	RAF Cranwell	Tower
379.6500	379.6500	AM	RAF Marham	Talkdown
379.6750	379.6750	AM	RAF Dishforth	Approach
379.7000	379.7000	AM	RAF Mona	Approach
379.7500	379.7500	AM	RNAS Yeovilton	ATIS
		AM	Nationwide	RAF AWACS Ops
379.8000	379.8000	AM	Teesside	Tower
379.8750	379.8750	AM	Pembury	Range Primary
379.9000	379.9000	AM	Nationwide	RAF AWACS Ops
379.9750	379.9750	AM	MoD Farnborough	Ops
380.0250	380.0250	AM	MoD Boscombe Down	Approach
380.1250	380.1250	AM	RAF St Athan	Director
380.1500	380.1500	AM	RAF Mildenhall	Ground
380.1750	380.1750	AM	MoD Llanbedr	Tower
380.2000	380.2000	AM	Nationwide	AAC Eagles Air to Air
380.2250	380.2250	AM	RNAS Culdrose	Tower
380.8000	380.8000	AM	Nationwide	Air-Air Refuelling
380.8750	380.8750	AM	Nationwide	Air Defence Region
380.9500	380.9500	AM	RAF Wittering	Approach
381.0000	381.0000	AM	RAF Lyneham	ATIS
381.0750	381.0750	AM	RAF Linton-on-Ouse	Departures
381.1000	381.1000	AM	RAF Waddington	Raven
381.1250	381.1250	AM	MoD Boscombe Down	PAR
381.1500	381.1500	AM	RAF Coltishall	41 Sqn Ops
381.2000	381.2000	AM	RAF Brize Norton	Tower
381.3000	381.3000	AM	Nationwide	USAF AWACS Ops
381.5750	381.5750	AM	Nationwide	USAF AWACS Ops
382.6750	382.6750	AM	Prestwick	Scottish Mil
382.9000	382.9000	AM	HMS Drake (Plymouth)	Royal Navy
383.1500	383.1500	NFM	Nationwide	TADIL-A Data Link

Base	Mobile	Mode	Location	User and Notes
383.2250	383.2250	AM	RAF Wittering	Talkdown
383.2750	383.2750	AM	Tain	Range Primary
383.3750	383.3750	AM	Nationwide	RAF Discreet
383.4750	383.4750	AM	RAF Cranwell	Talkdown
		AM	RAF West Drayton	London Mil
383.5250	383.5250	AM	MoD West Freugh	Approach
383.6000	383.6000	AM	RAF Valley	Air-to-Air
383.6250	383.6250	AM	MoD Bedford	Approach
385.4000	385.4000	AM	RAF Brize Norton	Talkdown
		AM	RAF Church Fenton	Fenton Talkdown
		AM	RAF Leeming	Talkdown
		AM	RAF Lyneham	Talkdown
		AM	RAF Manston	Talkdown
		AM	RAF Marham	Talkdown
		AM	RAF Northolt	Talkdown
		AM	RAF Odiham	Talkdown
		AM	RAF St Athan	Talkdown
		AM	RAF St Mawgan	Talkdown
		AM	RAF Shawbury	Talkdown
		AM	RAF Topcliffe	Talkdown
		AM	RAF Valley	Talkdown
		AM	RAF Waddington	Talkdown
386.5000	386.5000	AM	RAF St Athan	Ground
386.6500	386.6500	AM	RAF Leuchars	43 Sqn Air-Air
386.6750	386.6750	AM	MoD Llanbedr	Approach
386.7250	386.7250	AM	RAF Church Fenton	Talkdown
		AM	MoD Bedford	PAR
386.7750	386.7750	AM	MoD Farnborough	Radar
		AM	RAF Odiham	Radar
386.8250	386.8250	AM	RAF Lyneham	Tower
386.8750	386.8750	AM	RAF Shawbury	Radar
386.9000	386.9000	AM	RAF Valley	Ground
387.5500	387.5500	AM	RAF Lossiemouth	16 Sqn Air-Air
388.0000	388.0000	AM	Nationwide	Sharks Helicopter Displays
393.2000	393.2000	AM	RAF West Drayton	London Military
393.4750	393.4750	AM	RAF Coningsby	Air-to-Air
394.0500	394.0500	AM	DRA Boscombe Down	Gauntlet Ops
397.8500	397.8500	AM	Nationwide	RAF AWACS Ops
397.9750	397.9750	AM	RAF Lakenheath	Ground
398.1000	398.1000	AM	RAF Lossiemouth	Approach
398.2000	398.2000	AM	RAF Lakenheath	Command Post
398.2500	398.2500	AM	Nationwide	NATO Air-Air
398.3500	398.3500	AM	RAF Lakenheath	Rapcon
398.6050		NFM	Nationwide	Illegal Bugging Devices
398.8750	398.8750	AM	Nationwide	Air Defence Region
399.4550		NFM	Nationwide	Illegal Bugging Devices

399.9000 -400.0500 MHZ   RADIO NAVIGATION SATELLITE DOWN LINKS

Base	Mobile	Mode	Location	User and Notes
400.1000		NFM	Nationwide	Satellite Satellite Std. Frequency

400.1500 - 401.0000 MHz   SATELLITE DOWN LINKS & TELEMETRY

Base	Mobile	Mode	Location	User and Notes
401.0000		NFM	Nationwide	RAF Target Telemetry

401.0000 - 406.1000 MHz   MOBILE SATELLITE TERMINAL UP LINK

Base	Mobile	Mode	Location	User and Notes
402.1135		NFM	Forties B	BP Weather Station
406.0000		AM	International	Distress Frequency

406.0000 - 406.1000 MHz   SATELLITE UPLINKS NFM

Base	Mobile	Mode	Location	User and Notes
406.0000		NFM	Nationwide	Ship's EPIRB
406.0250		AM	Nationwide	RAF Locator Beacons
406.1000		AM	International	Distress Frequency Monitored by UK USA & JAPAN

406.1000 - 410.0000 MHz   RADIO ASTRONOMY, NORTH SEA RADIO POSITIONS BEACONS AND US EMBASSY CLOSE PROTECTION TEAMS

Base	Mobile	Mode	Location	User and Notes
406.1500		NFM	Nationwide	US Navy On-Board Comms
406.4250	406.4250	NFM	RAF Lakenheath	Ops
		NFM	RAF Mildenhall	Medics
406.5500		NFM	Nationwide	US Navy On-Board Comms
406.6250	406.6250	NFM	RAF Lakenheath	Ops
406.6250	406.6250	NFM	RAF Mildenhall	Ops
		NFM	RAF Fairford	Tower-Ground
406.8750	406.8750	NFM	RAF Mildenhall	Fire Channel
406.9500		NFM	Nationwide	US Navy On-Board Comms
407.2750	407.2750	NFM	RAF Fairford	Ops
		NFM	RAF Mildenhall	Ops
407.3500		NFM	Nationwide	US Navy On-Board Comms
407.4250	407.4250	NFM	London	US Embassy
407.4750		NFM	RAF Chicksands	Security Ch 1
407.7250		NFM	London	US Embassy
407.7500		NFM	RAF Mildenhall	Channel 1
408.0000	421.0000	NFM	Statfjord A & B	Mobil To Hotel
408.1250		NFM	Nationwide	US Presidential Advance Team
408.2750	408.2750	NFM	London	US Embassy
408.3000		NFM	Jersey	Data Link
408.5500		NFM	Nationwide	US Presidential Guard
408.7250	408.7250	NFM	RAF Lakenheath	Ops
		NFM	RAF Mildenhall	Ops
408.8250		NFM	RAF Mildenhall	Ops
409.0250	416.5500	NFM	RAF Lakenheath	Trunked Voice
		NFM	RAF Mildenhall	Trunked Voice
		NFM	RAF Lakenheath	Security Police
		NFM	RAF Mildenhall	Main Gate Police

Base	Mobile	Mode	Location	User and Notes
410.0000 - 425.0000 MHz			**MOD, USAF & MOULD USE 25 kHz**	
			FORMULA ONE RACING TEAM LINKS	
410.0000	410.0000	NFM	Nationwide	USAF Base Common
410.2700	410.2700	NFM	RAF Mildenhall	Base Ops
		NFM	RAF Fairford	Ground Maintenance
410.2750	416.9000	NFM	RAF Lakenheath	Trunked Voice
		NFM	RAF Mildenhall	Trunked Voice
410.2875	410.2875	NFM	RAF Lakenheath	Ground Maintenance
410.3250		NFM	RAF Mildenhall	Ops
410.4750	410.4750	NFM	RAF Fairford	Ground Support
		NFM	RAF Fairford	Ops
		NFM	RAF Alconbury	Ops
410.5000		NFM	RAF Lakenheath	Ops
		NFM	RAF Mildenhall	Phone Patches
410.5250	410.5250	NFM	Portsmouth	Navy Provosts
410.6000	410.6000	NFM	RAF Fairford	Base Security
		NFM	RAF Mildenhall	Ground
		NFM	RAF Upper Heyford	77 TS Mobile
		NFM	RAF Mildenhall	Ops
410.6750	410.6750	NFM	RAF Fairford	Base Security
		NFM	RAF Chicksands	Fire Ch 4
410.7500		NFM	RAF Fairford	Ground Support
410.7700	410.7700	NFM	RAF Mildenhall	Ops
410.7750	417.5500	NFM	RAF Lakenheath	Trunked Voice
		NFM	RAF Mildenhall	Trunked Voice
		NFM	RAF Lakenheath	Ops
410.7800	410.7800	NFM	RAF Mildenhall	Ops
410.7875	410.7875	NFM	RAF Lakenheath	Ops
410.8000	410.8000	NFM	RAF Fairford	Base Security
		NFM	RAF Mildenhall	Fuel Tankers
		NFM	RAF Lakenheath	Ops
		NFM	RAF Chicksands	Base Ops
410.8500		NFM	RAF Mildenhall	Ops
410.9000	410.9000	NFM	Nationwide	MoD Transport
		NFM	RAF Mildenhall	Command Network
		NFM	RAF Lakenheath	Ops
		NFM	RAF Upper Heyford	79 TS Mobile
411.0000	411.0000	NFM	RAF Fairford	Tanker Ops
411.1250	411.1250	NFM	RAF Lakenheath	Red Net
411.1500	411.1500	NFM	RAF Mildenhall	Ops
		NFM	RAF Upper Heyford	USAF Ground
		NFM	RAF Mildenhall	USAF Police
411.1750	411.1750	NFM	Leicester	City Council
411.1875		NFM	RAF Lakenheath	Ops
411.2500	411.2500	NFM	RAF Lakenheath	MTD
		NFM	RAF Mildenhall	Security
411.2750	411.2750	NFM	RAF Lakenheath	Yellow Net
411.3000	411.3000	NFM	RAF Lakenheath	Base Ops

Base	Mobile	Mode	Location	User and Notes
411.4000		NFM	RAF Mildenhall	Ops
411.4250	417.7500	NFM	RAF Lakenheath	Trunked Voice (Nitro)
411.4250	417.7500	NFM	RAF Mildenhall	Trunked Voice
411.4750		NFM	RAF Mildenhall	Ops
411.5000	411.5000	NFM	RAF Mildenhall	Strategic Command
411.5000	426.0000	NFM	Statfjord A & C	Mobil To Hotel
411.5750	411.5750	NFM	RAF Mildenhall	Maintenance
		NFM	RAF Lakenheath	Ground Maintenance
411.6000	411.6000	NFM	RAF Lakenheath	Base Ops
411.6250	411.6250	NFM	RAF Lakenheath	Fire Paging
		NFM	RAF Mildenhall	9th Recon Wing Ops
		NFM	RAF Mildenhall	Fire Paging
411.6750	418.3500	NFM	RAF Lakenheath	Trunked Voice
		NFM	RAF Mildenhall	Trunked Voice
		NFM	RAF Lakenheath	Ops
		NFM	RAF Mildenhall	Trucked Network
		NFM	RAF Chicksands	Security Ch 2
411.7000	411.7000	NFM	RAF Lakenheath	Base Ops
411.7250	418.4000	NFM	RAF Lakenheath	Trunked Voice
		NFM	RAF Mildenhall	Trunked Voice (Bandit)
		NFM	RAF Mildenhall	Ops
411.7750	411.7750	NFM	RAF Mildenhall	Security
		NFM	RAF Lakenheath	Ops
411.8000	411.8000	NFM	RAF Lakenheath	Ops
		NFM	RAF Mildenhall	Security
		NFM	RAF Lakenheath	Ops
411.9000	411.9000	NFM	RAF Mildenhall	Security
412.1750	412.1750	NFM	RAF Lakenheath	Transit Alert
		NFM	RAF Mildenhall	Maintenance
		NFM	RAF Lakenheath	Ops
412.2750	412.2750	NFM	RAF Fairford	USAF Ground
412.2750	418.5000	NFM	RAF Lakenheath	Trunked Voice (Dispatch)
		NFM	RAF Mildenhall	Trunked Voice
		NFM	RAF Mildenhall	Trucked Network
412.3750		NFM	RAF Mildenhall	Services Squadron
412.4750		NFM	RAF Fairford	Ops
412.5250		NFM	Brecon	MoD Mould Repeater
412.5500	412.5500	NFM	RAF Lakenheath	Command Network
		NFM	RAF Mildenhall	Base Ops
412.5875		NFM	RAF Lakenheath	Ops
412.7750	412.7750	NFM	RAF Mildenhall	Ops
412.8000	412.8000	NFM	RAF Mildenhall	Ops
412.8375		NFM	Brecon	MoD Mould Repeater
412.9000	412.9000	NFM	RAF Mildenhall	Ops
413.0000	413.0000	NFM	RAF Mildenhall	Ops
		NFM	RAF Mildenhall	USAF Police
413.0750	413.0750	NFM	RAF Upper Heyford	USAF Ground
		NFM	RAF Lakenheath	Scrambled

Base	Mobile	Mode	Location	User and Notes
		NFM	RAF Mildenhall	Transit Alert
413.0800	413.0800	NFM	RAF Lakenheath	Base Ops
413.1000	413.1000	NFM	Nationwide	USAF Displays
413.1200	413.1200	NFM	RAF Lakenheath	Base Ops
413.1250	413.1250	NFM	RAF Upper Heyford	USAF Ground
		NFM	RAF Mildenhall	Ops
413.1500	413.1500	NFM	Nationwide	USAF Base Common
413.1750	413.1750	NFM	RAF Mildenhall	Dispatch
		NFM	RAF Lakenheath	Ops
		NFM	RAF Upper Heyford	USAF Ground
413.2000		NFM	RAF Chicksands	Command & Control Ch 8
413.2750		NFM	RAF Fairford	Ground Support
		NFM	RAF Fairford	FI Control
413.3000		NFM	RAF Mildenhall	Ground
413.3700	413.3700	NFM	RAF Mildenhall	Base Ops
413.3750	418.6500	NFM	RAF Lakenheath	Trunked Data Signalling
		NFM	RAF Mildenhall	Trunked Data Signalling
		NFM	RAF Lakenheath	Ops
413.4000	413.4000	NFM	RAF Upper Heyford	USAF Ground
413.4250	413.4250	NFM	Malvern (MoD)	Security
413.4500	413.4500	NFM	Nationwide	MoD Transport
		NFM	Nationwide	MoD Transport
413.5000	428.0500	NFM	Statfjord B & C	Mobil To Flotel
413.7000		NFM	RAF Mildenhall	Ground
413.7500	413.7500	NFM	RAF Mildenhall	Maintenance
413.7750	413.7750	NFM	RAF Lakenheath	Base Ops
413.8000	413.8000	NFM	Nationwide	Nuclear Security
		NFM	RAF Mildenhall	Ops
		NFM	RAF Upper Heyford	USAF Ground
		NFM	RAF Mildenhall	Ops
413.8500		NFM	RAF Mildenhall	Ground
413.9000	413.9000	NFM	RAF Mildenhall	Maintenance
414.1500	414.1500	NFM	RAF Mildenhall	Command Network
		NFM	RAF Upper Heyford	USAF Ground
		NFM	RAF Lakenheath	Base Ops
		NFM	RAF Mildenhall	Ops
414.2500		NFM	RAF Mildenhall	Ground
414.3000	414.3000	NFM	RAF Fairford	USAF Base Security
		NFM	RAF Mildenhall	AMC Ops
		NFM	RAF Lakenheath	Base Ops
414.3000	414.9000	NFM	RAF Mildenhall	Base Ops
		NFM	RAF Fairford	Ops
		NFM	London	US Embassy
414.4000		NFM	RAF Mildenhall	Ground
414.4875		NFM	Grand Prix Circuits	McLaren Team Voice Link
414.7000	414.7000	NFM	RAF Lakenheath	Security
414.9800	414.9800	NFM	RAF Lakenheath	Ops
415.3500		NFM	RAF Fairford	Ops

Base	Mobile	Mode	Location	User and Notes
415.4000		NFM	RAF Mildenhall	Ground
415.5625		NFM	Belfast	British Miltary Data Link
415.7000	407.8500	NFM	Nationwide	Air Force One Air-Ground
415.7500		NFM	RAF Mildenhall	Ground
415.9875		NFM	Grand Prix Circuits	McLaren Team Voice Link
416.0000	416.0000	NFM	Newport	Moss Car Alarms Remote
416.2175		NFM	Newmarket	RAF Security
416.4750	413.0000	NFM	RAF Mildenhall	Ops
		NFM	RAF Lakenheath	Ops
		NFM	RAF Chicksands	Enlisted Spouses Assoc.
416.5500	416.5500	NFM	RAF Lakenheath	Base Ops
		NFM	RAF Mildenhall	Ops
416.5875		NFM	RAF Mildenhall	Crash Ops
416.7000		NFM	RAF Mildenhall	Ground
416.9000		NFM	RAF Lakenheath	Security (Dispatch)
417.2000	417.2000	NFM	RAF Mildenhall	Base Ops
417.3000	417.3000	NFM	RAF Lakenheath	Security
417.5250		NFM	RAF Lakenheath	Ops
		NFM	RAF Mildenhall	Aircrew Reception
417.5300	417.5300	NFM	RAF Lakenheath	Base Ops
417.5750	417.5750	NFM	RAF Fairford	Military Police
417.9375		NFM	Manchester	Mould
418.0000	418.0000	NFM	Newport	Moss House Alarms
418.2000		NFM	Normandy	French Marine Ch 16 Link
418.2250		NFM	RAF Mildenhall	Ops
418.2300	418.2300	NFM	RAF Lakenheath	Base Ops
418.3000		NFM	Jersey	Data Link
418.3250		NFM	Nationwide	US Presidential Guard
418.3500		NFM	RAF Lakenheath	Operations
418.5000		NFM	RAF Lakenheath	Engineering (Spectre 1)
419.2750		NFM	RAF Mildenhall	Scrambled
		NFM	RAF Lakenheath	Scrambled
419.6250		NFM	Newmarket	RAF Security
419.9875		NFM	Grand Prix Circuits	McLaren Team Voice Link
420.0125		NFM	Manchester	Mould
420.4750		NFM	Nationwide	Grand Prix Minarde Team
421.5625		NFM	Manchester	Mould
421.7875		NFM	Manchester	Mould
421.9125		NFM	Strathclyde	Mould
421.9875		NFM	Strathclyde	Mould
422.1375	422.1375	NFM	london	Trooping the Colour 1994.
422.3625		NFM	Strathclyde	Mould
422.9500	428.4500	NFM	Glasgow	Taxis
423.0000	408.5000	NFM	Flotel	Mobil To Statfjord A & B
424.2500	424.2500	NFM	Belfast	Police Mobile Data Link
424.7500	424.7500	NFM	Northern Ireland	Special Branch

Base	Mobile	Mode	Location	User and Notes
425.0000 - 425.5000 MHz			**PMR MOBILE 12.5 KHZ NFM**	
			(SPLIT + 20.5 MHz)	
425.2625		NFM	London	Medicall
425.2875		NFM	London	Medicall NW London
425.3000		NFM	London	British Rail
425.4875		NFM	Dorset	2CR UHF Radio Microphones
425.5000 - 429.0000 MHz			**PMR MOBILE 12.5 KHZ NFM**	
			(SPLIT + 14.5 MHz)	
425.6000		NFM	Manchester	PMR
425.7025		NFM	London	Burglar Alarms
426.0000	411.5000	NFM	Hotel	Mobil To Statfjord A & C
426.0750		NFM	Glasgow	MOD HQ Security
426.9500		NFM	Glasgow	Medicall
427.1750		NFM	Manchester	PMR
427.8125		NFM	Manchester	ITN O/B Studio Link
428.0000	413.5000	NFM	Hotel	Mobil To Statfjord B & C
428.2625		NFM	London	Medicall
428.3250		NFM	RAF Chicksands	Disaster Repeater Ch 7
428.6750		NFM	London	Gas Board Engineers
428.7000		NFM	London	Gas Board Engineers
		NFM	Glasgow	Barra's Security
428.7125		NFM	London	Gas Board Engineers
428.7625		NFM	Gerrards Cross	Gas Board Engineers
429.0000 - 430.0000 MHz			**MOD RADIOLOCATION BEACONS**	
429.0875		NFM	Strathclyde	Mould
429.1125		NFM	Strathclyde	Mould
430.0000 - 431.0000 MHz			**MOD ALLOCATION**	
430.9000	430.9000	NFM	RAF Newton	Base Security
433.0000 - 434.0000 MHz			**MOD MOULD REPEATERS 12.5 KHZ**	
433.0000 - 440.0000 MHz			**70CM AMATEUR RADIO BAND**	
433.0000	434.6000	NFM	Bishop Stortford	Repeater (GB3SV)
		NFM	Boston	Repeater (GB3SO)
		NFM	Bracknell	Repeater (GB3BN)
		NFM	Bulbarrow Hill	Repeater (GB3DT)
		NFM	Charing	Repeater (GB3CK)
		NFM	Exeter	Repeater (GB3EX)
		NFM	Farnborough	Repeater (GB3KB)
		NFM	Llandudno	Repeater (GB3LL)
		NFM	Malvern	Repeater (GB3MS)
		NFM	Milton Keynes	Repeater (GB3MK)
		NFM	Newcastle	Repeater (GB3NT)
		NFM	Norwich	Repeater (GB3NR)
		NFM	Pendle Forest	Repeater (GB3PF)

Base	Mobile	Mode	Location	User and Notes
		NFM	Perth	Repeater (GB3PU)
		NFM	Scarborough	Repeater (GB3NY)
		NFM	Sheffield	Repeater (GB3US)
		NFM	Wolverhampton	Repeater (GB3WN)
433.0125		NFM	Birmingham	Mould
		NFM	Strathclyde	Mould
433.0250	434.6250	NFM	Hemel Hempstead	Repeater (GB3BV)
433.0500	434.6500	NFM	Aberdeen	Repeater (GB3BA)
		NFM	Aylesbury	Repeater (GB3AV)
		NFM	Belfast	Repeater (GB3UL)
		NFM	Corby	Repeater (GB3CI)
		NFM	Crawley	Repeater (GB3AV)
		NFM	Flyde Coast	Repeater (GB3CF)
		NFM	Huddersfield	Repeater (GB3HD)
		NFM	Lincoln	Repeater (GB3LS)
		NFM	London	Repeater (GB3LV)
		NFM	Margate	Repeater (GB3EK)
		NFM	Plymouth	Repeater (GB3CH)
		NFM	Portsmouth	Repeater (GB3CH)
		NFM	Stoke on Trent	Repeater (GB3ST)
		NFM	Stourbridge	Repeater (GB3OS)
		NFM	Wells	Repeater (GB3NN)
		NFM	Yeovil	Repeater (GB3YL)
433.0750	434.6750	NFM	Hull	Repeater (GB3HU)
		NFM	London	Repeater (GB3HL)
		NFM	Taunton	Repeater (GB3VS)
433.1000	434.7000	NFM	Anglesey	Repeater (GB3AN)
		NFM	Bath	Repeater (GB3UB)
		NFM	Elgin	Repeater (GB3KM)
		NFM	Goole	Repeater (GB3GC)
		NFM	High Wycombe	Repeater (GB3HZ)
		NFM	Ipswich	Repeater (GB3IH)
		NFM	Isle of Wight	Repeater (GB3IW)
		NFM	Kings Lynn	Repeater (GB3KL)
		NFM	Knockmore	Repeater (GB3KM)
		NFM	Leicester	Repeater (GB3LE)
		NFM	Linlithgow	Repeater (GB3OH)
		NFM	Manchester	Repeater (GB3MA)
		NFM	Pembroke	Repeater (GB3SP)
		NFM	Wrotham	Repeater (GB3NK)
433.1250	434.7250	NFM	Gloucester	Repeater (GB3GH)
		NFM	Huntingdon	Repeater (GB3OV)
		NFM	London	Repeater (GB3NW)
		NFM	Scunthorpe	Repeater (GB3WJ)
		NFM	West Sussex	Repeater (GB3HY)
433.1375		NFM	Birmingham	Mould
		NFM	Strathclyde	Mould
433.1500	434.7500	NFM	Barnsley	Repeater (GB3SY)

Base	Mobile	Mode	Location	User and Notes
		NFM	Bedford	Repeater (GB3BD)
		NFM	Brighton	Repeater (GB3SR)
		NFM	Canterbury	Repeater (GB3SK)
		NFM	Hornsea	Repeater (GB3HA)
		NFM	London	Repeater (GB3LW)
		NFM	Mold	Repeater (GB3CR)
		NFM	Newtown	Repeater (GB3CW)
		NFM	Nottingham	Repeater (GB3NM)
		NFM	Port Talbot	Repeater (GB3WG)
		NFM	Rugby	Repeater (GB3ME)
		NFM	Salisbury	Repeater (GB3SW)
433.1625		NFM	Strathclyde	Mould
433.1875		NFM	Strathclyde	Mould
433.2000	434.8000	NFM	Warwickshire	Repeater (GB3EH)
		NFM	Telford	Repeater (GB3TF)
433.2250	434.8250	NFM	Bury St Edmunds	Repeater (GB3BE)
		NFM	Salisbury	Repeater (GB3SW)
		NFM	Greenock	Repeater (GB3PG)
433.2500	434.8500	NFM	Ashmansworth	Repeater (GB3AW)
		NFM	Banstead	Repeater (GB3NS)
		NFM	Benbecula	Repeater (GB3NU)
		NFM	Blackhill	Repeater (GB3ML)
		NFM	Bristol	Repeater (GB3BS)
		NFM	Danbury	Repeater (GB3ER)
		NFM	Dundee	Repeater (GB3DD)
		NFM	Leamington Spa	Repeater (GB3MW)
		NFM	Little Weighton	Repeater (GB3HU)
		NFM	Liverpool	Repeater (GB3LI)
		NFM	Luton	Repeater (GB3LT)
		NFM	Peterborough	Repeater (GB3PB)
		NFM	Peterhead	Repeater (GB3PD)
		NFM	Queensbury	Repeater (GB3WY)
		NFM	Wirksworth	Repeater (GB3DY)
433.2625		NFM	Strathclyde	Mould
433.2750	434.8750	NFM	Chatham	Repeater (GB3RE)
		NFM	Devon	Repeater (GB3SH)
		NFM	Grantham	Repeater (GB3GR)
		NFM	Grimsby	Repeater (GB3GY)
		NFM	Hinckley	Repeater (GB3HT)
		NFM	Hitchin	Repeater (GB3HN)
		NFM	Leeds	Repeater (GB3LA)
		NFM	Lewes	Repeater (GB3LR)
		NFM	East Manchester	Repeater (GB3WP)
		NFM	Reading	Repeater (GB3BK)
		NFM	Southampton	Repeater (GB3NF)
		NFM	Stafford	Repeater (GB3ZI)
		NFM	Sunderland	Repeater (GB3DC)
		NFM	Swaffham	Repeater (GB3AH)

Base	Mobile	Mode	Location	User and Notes
433.2875		NFM	Birmingham	Mould
433.3000	434.9000	NFM	Barkway	Repeater (GB3PT)
		NFM	Bolton	Repeater (GB3MT)
		NFM	Chesterfield	Repeater (GB3EE)
		NFM	Guildford	Repeater (GB3GF)
		NFM	Leicester	Repeater (GB3RY)
		NFM	Tamworth	Repeater (GB3TH)
		RTTY	Nationwide	Channel SU17
433.3250	434.9250	NFM	Carlisle	Repeater (GB3CA)
		NFM	Daventry	Repeater (GB3XX)
		NFM	Gidea Park	Repeater (GB3GU)
		NFM	Guernsey	Repeater (GB3GU)
		NFM	Hatfield	Repeater (GB3VH)
		NFM	Leek	Repeater (GB3SM)
		NFM	Louth	Repeater (GB3LC)
		NFM	Swindon	Repeater (GB3TD)
		NFM	Worksop	Repeater (GB3DS)
		NFM	York	Repeater (GB3CY)
433.3500	434.9500	NFM	Aberdeen	Repeater (GB3AB)
		NFM	Birmingham	Repeater (GB3CB)
		NFM	Cambridge	Repeater (GB3PY)
		NFM	Colchester	Repeater (GB3CE)
		NFM	Edinburgh	Repeater (GB3ED)
		NFM	Glasgow	Repeater (GB3GL)
		NFM	Hastings	Repeater (GB3HE)
		NFM	Hawick	Repeater (GB3HK)
		NFM	Horsham	Repeater (GB3HO)
		NFM	Ilfracombe	Repeater (GB3ND)
		NFM	Leeds	Repeater (GB3WF)
		NFM	Lowestoft	Repeater (GB3YL)
		NFM	Middlesborough	Repeater (GB3TS)
		NFM	Stanmore	Repeater (GB3HR)
		NFM	Staveley	Repeater (GB3LF)
		NFM	Stockport	Repeater (GB3MR)
		NFM	Weymouth	Repeater (GB3SD)
433.3750	434.9750	NFM	Berkshire	Repeater (GB3BF)
		NFM	Bournemouth	Repeater (GB3SZ)
		NFM	Cardiff	Repeater (GB3SG)
		NFM	Hereford	Repeater (GB3HC)
		NFM	Omagh	Repeater (GB3OM)
		NFM	Oxford	Repeater (GB3OX)
		NFM	Preston	Repeater (GB3PP)
		NFM	Shrewsbury	Repeater (GB3LH)
		NFM	St Austell	Repeater (GB3HB)
		NFM	Wakefield	Repeater (GB3WU)
		NFM	Wisbech	Repeater (GB3WI)
		NFM	Sudbury	GB3SU Repeater
433.3875		NFM	Strathclyde	Mould

Base	Mobile	Mode	Location	User and Notes
433.4000	435.0000	NFM	Hereford	Repeater (GB3HC)
433.4375		NFM	Strathclyde	Mould
433.5000	433.5000	NFM	Nationwide	Channel SU20 Calling
433.6250		NFM	Nationwide	CH4 The Big Breakfast O/B
433.7000		NFM	Leicester	Raynet

433.7200 - 434.5120 MHz   VEHICLE RADIO KEYS

Base	Mobile	Mode	Location	User and Notes
433.7250		NFM	Leicester	Raynet
433.7750	433.7750	NFM	Mildenhall	Raynet
433.8750		NFM	RAF Mildenhall	Ops

435.0000 - 438.0000 MHz   AMATEUR SATELLITES & RAF CADETS

Base	Mobile	Mode	Location	User and Notes
435.0750		NFM	Space	Oscar 14
435.1500		NFM	Space	Oscar 19 Data
435.2500		NFM	Space	Oscar 14
435.6250	435.6250	NFM	Nationwide	RAF Cadets Channel U2
435.7250	435.7250	NFM	Nationwide	RAF Cadets Channel U5
435.7500	435.7500	NFM	Nationwide	RAF Cadets NATO Channel U1
435.7500		AM	Nationwide	ATC Channel U1
435.9100		NFM	Space	Oscar 20 Beacon
435.9750		NFM	Space	Polar Bear 8688A
437.6875		NFM	Glasgow	PMR
437.8875	437.8875	NFM	London	Capital Radio Relay

438.0000 - 440.0000 MHz   AMATEUR RADIO BAND

Base	Mobile	Mode	Location	User and Notes
438.0750		NFM	RAF Mildenhall	Ops
438.3500	445.3500	NFM	Ekofisk	Senter Phillips
438.4000	445.4000	NFM	Ekofisk	Senter Phillips
438.4500	445.4500	NFM	Ekofisk	Senter Phillips
438.5000	445.5000	NFM	Ekofisk	Senter Phillips
438.5500		NFM	Edinburgh	Sky TV Sound Relay
438.5750	438.4750	NFM	HMP Highpoint	Storno 4000
438.6000	445.6000	NFM	Ekofisk	Senter Phillips
439.0000	446.0000	NFM	Ekofisk	Senter Phillips
439.2000	446.2000	NFM	Valhall Field	Amoco
439.2250	446.2250	NFM	Ekofisk	Senter Phillips
439.2750	446.2750	NFM	Valhall Field	Amoco
439.4500	446.4500	NFM	Valhall Field	Amoco
439.8500		NFM	Ayrshire	Amateur Packet Link

440.0125 - 443.4875 MHz   PMR BASE REPEATERS 12.5 KHZ
(SPLIT - 14.5 MHz)

Base	Mobile	Mode	Location	User and Notes
440.0250		NFM	Heathrow Airport	Ground Staff
440.0375	425.5375	NFM	London	RAM Mobile Data Network
440.0500	425.6500	NFM	Leicester	City Council Depots
440.0500	425.5500	NFM	Lanarkshire	Monklands Direct Works
440.0500		NFM	Gatley	Electric Board
		NFM	Leicester	Council Depot

Base	Mobile	Mode	Location	User and Notes
440.0750	440.0750	NFM	Dover	HM Customs
440.0750	425.5750	NFM	London	Wandsworth Council Parks
		NFM	Liverpool	Liverpool Ranger Service
		NFM	Newcastle	Highways
		NFM	London	Council
		NFM	North West	PMR
440.1000	425.6000	NFM	Barrow	VSEL Submarine Guards
		NFM	Leicester	City Council 24hr Repairs
		NFM	London	Wimbledon Borough Council
		NFM	Glasgow	Parcel Firm
		NFM	Liverpool	Mersey Tunnel Police Ch 1
		NFM	Leicester	Council Repairs
440.1125	425.6125	NFM	London	RAM Mobile Data Network
440.1250	425.6250	NFM	Nationwide	TNT Offices
		NFM	Glasgow	PMR
		NFM	Walsall	PMR
		NFM	Watford	Watford Borough Council
		NFM	Wigan	Emergency Repairs
		NFM	Glasgow	Waste Collection
440.1750	425.6750	NFM	London	London Transport Buses
		NFM	Liverpool	Mersey Tunnel Police Ch 1
		NFM	Wallasey	Mersey Tunnel Police Ch 1
		NFM	Mersey Tunnel	Police
440.1875	425.6875	NFM	London	RAM Mobile Data Network
		NFM	Edinburgh Airport	Beacon
440.2000	425.7000	NFM	Greenford	Glaxo Fire and Security
		NFM	London Gatwick	Delta Airlines
		NFM	Wilton	ICI
440.2250	425.7250	NFM	Birmingham	NEC Security & Maintenance
		NFM	London	London Transport Buses
		NFM	Hull	Hull Telephone Repairs
		NFM	Glasgow	Regional Council
		NFM	Manchester	Data Relay
		NFM	Bexley	L.B. Bexley
		NFM	Newcastle	Highways
440.2625	425.7625	NFM	London	RAM Mobile Data Network
440.2750	425.7750	NFM	Liverpool	Mersey Port Police
		NFM	Heathrow Airport	Trunked Network
440.2875	425.7875	NFM	London	RAM Mobile Data Network
440.3000	425.8000	NFM	Wilton	ICI
		NFM	Glasgow	Data Link
		NFM	Heathrow Airport	Trunked Network
440.3125	425.8125	NFM	London	RAM Mobile Data Network
440.3250	425.8250	NFM	London	London Transport Buses
440.3375	425.8375	NFM	London	RAM Mobile Data Network
		NFM	Glasgow	Data Link
		NFM	Newcastle	The Metro Centre Data Link
440.3500	425.8500	NFM	London Heathrow	Ground Staff

Base	Mobile	Mode	Location	User and Notes
		NFM	Heathrow Airport	Trunked Network
440.4000	425.9000	NFM	Surrey	Ambulance Incident Control
		NFM	London	RAM Mobile Data Network
		NFM	Co. Durham	Taxis
440.4250	425.9250	NFM	Aberdeen	PMR
		NFM	Glasgow	PMR
		NFM	Heathrow Airport	Ground Staff
440.4625	425.9625	NFM	London	RAM Mobile Data Network
440.4750	425.9750	NFM	London	London Transport Buses
		NFM	Wilton	ICI
		NFM	M6	Motorway Maintenance
440.4875	425.9875	NFM	London	RAM Mobile Data Network
		NFM	West Perthshire	Data Link
440.5000	426.0000	NFM	London	London Transport Buses
		NFM	Glasgow	PMR
440.5250	426.0250	NFM	London	London Transport Buses
440.5375	426.0375	NFM	London	PMR Parking/Demo
440.5500	426.0500	NFM	London	London Transport Buses
440.5750	426.0750	NFM	London	London Taxis North/Central
		NFM	Glasgow	PMR
		NFM	Gateshead	Metro Centre Security
		NFM	Manchester	Construction Company
		NFM	Wigan	Park Wardens
		NFM	Glasgow	TOA Taxis Ch 1 (Data)
440.5875	426.0875	NFM	London	London Taxis N1/N7
440.6000	426.1000	NFM	London	London Taxis WC/SW1
		NFM	Glasgow	Taxi
		NFM	Glasgow	TOA Taxis Ch 2 (Data)
		NFM	Knowsley	Council Security
440.6250	426.1250	NFM	London	London Taxis Gt London
		NFM	Glasgow	TOA Taxis Ch 3 (Voice)
		NFM	Glasgow	Taxis
		NFM	Birmingham	NEC Catering
440.6500	426.1500	NFM	London	London Taxis Gt London
		NFM	Edinburgh	Radio Cabs
		NFM	Birmingham	NEC Catering
440.6625	426.1625	NFM	Edinburgh	Taxis
440.6750	426.1750	NFM	Edinburgh	Taxis
		NFM	London	Taxis
		NFM	Birmingham	NEC Traffic
		NFM	Edinburgh	Radio Cabs
440.7000	426.2000	NFM	London	Centracom Ltd
		NFM	Sutton	Taxis
440.7250	426.2250	NFM	London	Central London Messanger
		NFM	London	London Taxis
		NFM	Edinburgh	Taxis
		NFM	Edinburgh	Taxis
		NFM	Edinburgh	Taxis

Base	Mobile	Mode	Location	User and Notes
		NFM	Birmingham	NEC Maintenance
		NFM	Edinburgh	Acolade Cars
440.7500	426.2500	NFM	London	Taxis
		NFM	Gatwick Airport	HM Customs & Excise
		NFM	Manchester Airport	Customs
440.7625	426.2625	NFM	London Heathrow	NMRL CBS Tristar House
		NFM	Saddleworth	PMR
		NFM	North West	PMR
440.7750	440.7750	NFM	Nationwide	HM Customs & Excise Ch. 1
440.7750	426.2750	NFM	Nationwide	HM Customs & Excise Ch. 4
		NFM	Manchester Airport	Customs & Immigration
		NFM	Heathrow Airport	Main Customs Net
		NFM	Luton Airport	Customs
440.7875	426.2875	NFM	North West	PMR
440.8000	426.3000	NFM	London	Security Company
		NFM	Saddleworth	PMR
		NFM	Central London	Taxis
		NFM	Swansea	HM Customs
440.8250	440.8250	NFM	Nationwide	HM Customs & Excise Ch 2
		NFM	North-West	Covert Customs Surveillance
440.8250	426.3250	NFM	Nationwide	HM Customs & Excise Ch 5
		NFM	London Heathrow	HM Customs Surveillance
		NFM	Shoreham	HM Customs & Excise
		NFM	Heathrow Airport	Customs Surveillance Training
440.8500	440.8500	NFM	Nationwide	HM Customs & Excise Ch 3
440.8500	426.3500	NFM	Nationwide	HM Customs & Excise Ch 6
		NFM	Newhaven	HM Customs & Excise
		NFM	Southampton Docks	HUM Customs (Aztec)
		NFM	Heathrow Airport	Customs
440.8750	426.3750	NFM	Nationwide	HM Customs & Excise Ch 7
		NFM	N London	Taxis
440.9000	426.4000	NFM	Wilton	ICI
		NFM	Manchester	Construction/Repairs
		NFM	Gatley	PMR
		NFM	Heathrow Airport	Trunked Network
		NFM	Birmingham	Rackhams Security
		NFM	North West	PMR
440.9250	426.4250	NFM	London	Taxis
		NFM	Manchester	PMR
		NFM	Stockport	Local Authority
		NFM	Liverpool	Council Security
		NFM	Manchester	North West Water
440.9375	426.4375	NFM	London	Taxis
440.9500	426.4500	NFM	Wilton	ICI
		NFM	Heathrow Airport	Trunked Network
440.9750	426.4750	NFM	Viewpark	Denton Security
440.9875	426.4875	NFM	North London	Taxis
		NFM	Hendon	Couriers

Base	Mobile	Mode	Location	User and Notes
441.0000	426.5000	NFM	Nationwide	Xerox Copiers
		NFM	City of Westminster	Traffic Wardens
		NFM	Co. Durham	Radio Engineers
		NFM	Plumstead	Taxis
		NFM	Birmingham	NEC Maintenance
441.0250	426.5250	NFM	Leicester	Leicester Buses
441.0375		NFM	Heathrow Airport	Trunked Network
441.0500	426.5500	NFM	Aberdeen	PMR
		NFM	Saddleworth	PMR
		NFM	London	Builders
		NFM	Heathrow Airport	Trunked Network
441.0750	426.5750	NFM	London Heathrow	Ground Staff
		NFM	Birmingham Airport	Ground Staff
		NFM	Glasgow	Council
		NFM	Chester	PMR
		NFM	SE London	Couriers
		NFM	Gatwick Airport	Trunked Network
		NFM	Heathrow Airport	Trunked Network
441.1000	426.6000	NFM	Nationwide	MediCall
		NFM	London	Medicall
441.1125	426.6125	NFM	Heathrow Airport	Trunked Network
441.1250	426.1250	NFM	Birmingham Airport	Armed Police
		NFM	West Midlands	Security Firm
		NFM	Gatwick Airport	Trunked Network
441.1500	426.6500	NFM	Birmingham Airport	AirCall
		NFM	London	Courier Company
		NFM	Saddleworth	Haulage Firm
		NFM	Edinburgh	Taxis
		NFM	Central London	Taxis
441.1750	426.6750	NFM	Coatbridge	Shanks McEwan Skip Hire
		NFM	West Perthshire	Builders
		NFM	Luton	Communications Repeater
		NFM	Denton	FMR Investigations
		NFM	Glasgow	Vehicle Removal Unit
		NFM	Strathclyde	Ship Hire
		NFM	Bootle	PMR
		NFM	Co. Durham	TV Engineers
		NFM	Glasgow	Security
		NFM	Middlesborough	Prichard Security
		NFM	Manchester	Pub Machine Suppliers
441.2000	426.7000	NFM	Cambridge	Community Repeater
		NFM	Dorking	Keynet CBS
		NFM	Manchester	TV Repairs
		NFM	Birmingham	Police CID Scrambled
		NFM	Manchester	Couriers
441.2250	426.7250	NFM	Glasgow	PMR
		NFM	London	CBS Car Telephones
		NFM	Glasgow	PMR

Base	Mobile	Mode	Location	User and Notes
		NFM	Heathrow Airport	Trunked Network
441.2500	426.7500	NFM	London Heathrow	Ground Staff
		NFM	Waltham-on-Wolds	Nat Radiofone CBS
		NFM	Leicester	Nat Radiofone CBS
		NFM	Pontop Pike	Nat Radiofone CBS
		NFM	Glasgow Warlaw Hill	Nat Radiofone CBS
		NFM	Aberdeen	Nat Radiofone CBS
		NFM	Manchester	Nat Radiofone CBS
		NFM	Bradford	Nat Radiofone CBS
		NFM	Newcastle	Highways
		NFM	Tyneside	Couriers
		NFM	Preston	B.D. Electronics
		NFM	Gatwick Airport	Trunked Network
		NFM	Heathrow Airport	Trunked Network
		NFM	North West	PMR
441.2750	441.2750	NFM	Glasgow	PMR
		NFM	Bootle	PMR
		NFM	Stoke-On-Trent	Skip Hire
		NFM	Gatwick Airport	Trunked Network
441.3000	426.8000	NFM	London	Security Company
		NFM	Newcastle	Security Firm
		NFM	London Hilton	Nat Radiofone CBS
		NFM	Glasgow	PMR
441.3250	426.8250	NFM	Glasgow	PMR
		NFM	Co. Durham	Private Security
		NFM	Gatwick Airport	Trunked Network
441.3500	426.8500	NFM	Crewe	Taxis
		NFM	Home Moss Penine	Nat Radiofone CBS
		NFM	Glasgow	Security
		NFM	Gatwick Airport	Trunked Network
		NFM	Heathrow Airport	Trunked Network
441.3750	426.8750	NFM	London	Met. Police SAV Repeater
		NFM	London	Metropolitan Police Repeater
		NFM	Manchester	Plant Company
		NFM	Manchester	Private Company
		NFM	Tyne & Wear	Security Firm
		NFM	Newcastle	Security Firm
441.4000	426.9000	NFM	Sheffield	PMR
		NFM	London	Met. Police SAV Repeater
		NFM	London	Metropolitan Police Repeater
		NFM	St Annes	Taxis
441.4375	426.9375	NFM	London	Courier Company
		NFM	Nottinghamshire	Steetley Haulage Ltd
441.4500	426.9500	NFM	Manchester Airport	TNT Carriers
		NFM	Glasgow	Paramedics
441.4750	426.9750	NFM	Aberdeen	PMR
		NFM	Edinburgh	PMR
		NFM	Burnley	Breakdown Recovery

Base	Mobile	Mode	Location	User and Notes
		NFM	Blackburn	Garage Recovery
441.5000	427.0000	NFM	Turners Hill	Nat Radiofone CBS
		NFM	Glasgow	Nat Radiofone CBS
		NFM	Aberdeen	Nat Radiofone CBS
		NFM	London	Taxis
441.5250	427.0250	NFM	Glasgow	Security Company
		NFM	Highgate	Nat Radiofone CBS
		NFM	Glasgow	Games Machines Firm
		NFM	Tyneside	Safe-Guard Security
		NFM	Lanark	Security Firm
		NFM	Newcastle	Security Firm
		NFM	Glasgow	Security
		NFM	Preston	Drinks Machine Suppliers
		NFM	Manchester	Motoring Organisation
441.5500	427.0500	NFM	Sheffield	Nat Radiofone CBS
		NFM	Frodsham	Nat Radiofone CBS
		NFM	Heathrow Airport	Trunked Network
441.5750	427.0750	NFM	Manchester	NSPCC Investigation Branch
		NFM	Manchester	Harcross Building Supplies
		NFM	Gatley	PMR
		NFM	North West	PMR
441.6250	427.1250	NFM	Aberdeen	PMR
		NFM	London	Courier
441.6500	427.1500	NFM	Aberdeen	PMR
		NFM	London	PMR
441.6500	441.6500	NFM	Alba	FSU Chevron Shuttle DGP Data
		NFM	Central London	Taxis
441.6625		NFM	Saddleworth	PMR
		NFM	Skelmersdale	Couriers
		NFM	Blackpool	Delivery Firm
441.6750		NFM	Manchester	Security
		NFM	London	Taxis
		NFM	North West	PMR
441.7000	427.2000	NFM	Waltham-on-Wolds	Nat Radiofone CBS
		NFM	Stoke	Nat Radiofone CBS
		NFM	Manchester	PMR
		NFM	Heathrow Airport	Trunked Network
		NFM	North West	PMR
441.7125	427.2125	NFM	Saddleworth	PMR
441.7250	427.2250	NFM	Glasgow	PMR
		NFM	South London	NMRL CBS
		NFM	Saddleworth	PMR
		NFM	Glasgow	Medicall
441.7375	427.2375	NFM	Sheffield	PMR
441.7500	427.2500	NFM	London	Medicall
441.7750	427.2750	NFM	Sheffield	PMR
441.8000	427.3000	NFM	Heathrow Airport	Trunked Network
441.8125	427.3125	NFM	London	Haulage

Base	Mobile	Mode	Location	User and Notes
441.8150	427.8125	NFM	SE London	Builders
441.8250	427.3250	NFM	London (Victoria)	Minicabs
		NFM	London	Taxis
441.8500	427.3500	NFM	Liverpool	Expo Boarding-Up Service
		NFM	London	Delivery Service
441.8750	427.3750	NFM	Pontop	Nat Radiofone CBS
		NFM	London	Met. Police SAV Repeater
441.8750	441.8750	NFM	London	Metropolitan Police Repeater
441.8750	427.3750	NFM	SE London	Taxis
441.9000	427.4000	NFM	London Hilton	NMRL CBS 2
		NFM	Glasgow	PMR
441.9250	427.4250	NFM	Turners Hill	Nat Radiofone CBS
		NFM	Glossop	PMR
		NFM	North West	PMR
441.9500	427.4500	NFM	SE London	Taxis
		NFM	Heathrow Airport	Trunked Network
441.9750	427.4750	NFM	London	Bus Tour Company
		NFM	London	Crime Prevention Guards
		NFM	Gatley	PMR
442.0000	427.7000	NFM	London Hilton	NMRL CBS 2
		NFM	Gatley	Breakdown Service
		NFM	Heathrow Airport	Trunked Network
		NFM	North West	PMR
442.0500	427.7500	NFM	W London	Couriers
442.0750	427.7750	NFM	Turners Hill	Nat Radiofone CBS
442.1000	427.6000	NFM	London	Circle Security
442.1000	442.1000	NFM	Birmingham	Security
		NFM	Walsall	Mercia Lifting Gear
442.1250	427.8250	NFM	Waltham-on-Wolds	Nat Radiofone CBS
442.1500	427.6500	NFM	London	Security Company
		NFM	Chelmsford	Boreham Tyre Services
442.1750	427.6750	NFM	London	Police Car Pound
		NFM	London	London Wheel Clamping
		NFM	Stoke	Doctors on Call
442.2000	427.7000	NFM	London	Blackheath Cleansing Dept
		NFM	Manchester	Construction Company
442.2750	427.7750	NFM	London	BBC TV Talkback
442.2875	427.7875	NFM	London	BBC Radio 5 Talkback
		NFM	London	BBC TV Talkback
442.3250	427.8250	NFM	London	BBC TV Talkback
442.3375	427.8375	NFM	London	BBC TV Talkback
442.3625	427.8625	NFM	London	BBC TV Talkback
442.3865	427.8865	NFM	London	BBC TV Talkback
442.3875	427.8875	NFM	London	ITN Talkback
442.4250	427.8250	NFM	London	ITN Reverse Prog Circuit
		NFM	London	ITN
442.43125		NFM	Birmingham	ITN Talkback
442.4375	427.9375	NFM	London	ITV Talkback

Base	Mobile	Mode	Location	User and Notes
442.4500	427.9500	NFM	London	ITV Talkback
442.4625	427.9625	NFM	London	ITN Reverse Prog Circuit*
442.4750	427.9750	NFM	Grays	ITN MCR
442.4875	427.9875	NFM	London	ITN Talkback
442.5000	428.0000	NFM	London	ITN News Talkback
442.5250	428.0250	NFM	Wilton	ICI
		NFM	London	Hackney Council
442.5375	428.0375	NFM	North West	PMR
442.5625	428.0625	NFM	London	BBC TV Talkback
442.5875	428.0875	NFM	London	Pilkenton Security
		NFM	Gt Manchester	Skip Co.
		NFM	North West	PMR
442.6125	428.1125	NFM	Wembley	Actonian School of Motoring
		NFM	Hounslow	Hounslow Car Spares
442.6250	428.1250	NFM	London	Royal London Hospital
		NFM	London Heathrow	Ground Staff
		NFM	Greenwich	National Maritime Museum
		NFM	London	British Museum
442.6750	428.1750	NFM	Liverpool	Inshore Lifeboats
		NFM	Wilton	ICI
		NFM	Clydebank	Clyde Shopping Centre Security
		NFM	Heathrow Airport	Ground Repeater
		NFM	Heathrow Airport	Trunked Network
442.7250	428.2250	NFM	London Gatwick	American Airlines
		NFM	Wilton	ICI
442.7500	428.2500	NFM	London Heathrow	Quantas
442.7750	428.2750	NFM	Croydon	Whitgift Security
		NFM	Glasgow	Collins Books
		NFM	Heathrow Airport	Trunked Network
442.8000	428.3000	NFM	Glasgow	Electricians
		NFM	Heathrow Airport	Trunked Network
442.8500	428.3500	NFM	London Gatwick	Virgin Ops
		NFM	Glasgow	Trojan Security
442.8750	428.3750	NFM	Heathrow Airport	Trunked Network
442.9000	428.4000	NFM	Glasgow	Glasgow Transport
		NFM	London Hilton	NMRL CBS 2
		NFM	Glasgow	Taxi
		NFM	SE London	Taxis
442.9125	428.4125	NFM	Glasgow	Glasgow Transport
442.9250	428.4250	NFM	Glasgow	TOA Taxis
		NFM	Nottinghamshire	Target Express Parcels
		NFM	Central London	Taxis
442.9500	428.4500	NFM	Glasgow	Taxis
443.0000	428.5000	NFM	Wilton	ICI
		NFM	London	Tate Gallery Security
443.0500	428.5500	NFM	London	Videotron Cable TV
		NFM	Sunbury	RCA Records
		NFM	London Gatwick	Continental Ops

Base	Mobile	Mode	Location	User and Notes
443.0875	428.5875	NFM	London	Coach Company
443.1000	428.6000	NFM	Merseyside	Guardrite Security
443.1500	428.6500	NFM	London	Builders
		NFM	Surrey	Radiofone
443.1750	428.6750	NFM	London	Haulage
443.1875	428.6875	NFM	London	Minicabs
443.2625	428.6625	NFM	Surrey	Radiofone
		NFM	Manchester	Washing Machine Repairs
		NFM	Surrey	Radiofone
443.3750	428.9750	NFM	SE London	Plumbers
443.4125	428.9125	NFM	London	Minicabs
443.4375	428.9375	NFM	London	Pizza Delivery Company
443.4500	428.9500	NFM	Heathrow Airport	Ground Repeater
443.4625	428.9625	NFM	London	Pizza Delivery Company
443.4750	428.9750	NFM	Watford	Watford Borough Council
443.4875	428.9875	NFM	London	International Couriers

443.5000 - 445.3000 MHz   MoD RADIOLOCATION & BASE COMMS 25 kHz

Base	Mobile	Mode	Location	User and Notes
443.5750	443.5750	NFM	Whitehall	Military Police
		NFM	London	Military Police
443.6750	443.6750	NFM	Whitehall	Military Police
		NFM	London	Military Police
443.7500		NFM	Colchester	36 DWS REME
444.0250		NFM	Colchester	36 DWS REME
444.0500		NFM	RAF Fairford	IAT Tanker Ops
444.0750		NFM	Nationwide	Radiocommunications Agency
444.2750	449.5750	NFM	RAF Fairford	IAT Campsite
444.3000	449.6000	NFM	RAF Fairford	IAT Chalets
444.3250		NFM	Colchester	36 DWS REME
444.3750	449.6750	NFM	RAF Fairford	IAT Communicatons
444.5000	449.8000	NFM	RAF Fairford	IAT Exhibition Control
444.5500	449.8500	NFM	RAF Fairford	IAT Admissions
444.6500		NFM	Colchester	36 DWS REME

445.0000 - 447.9875 MHz   SHOP & POST OFFICE SECURITY 25 kHz

Base	Mobile	Mode	Location	User and Notes
445.0375	445.0375	NFM	Nationwide	Security Express
445.1500		NFM	Birmingham	British Rail Post Office
445.1875		NFM	Portsmouth	Marine Re-fuelling
445.2500		NFM	Aberdeen	BBC Film Crews
445.3500	438.3500	NFM	Ekofisk	Senter Phillips
445.4000	438.4000	NFM	Ekofisk	Senter Phillips
445.4225		NFM	Lothian and Borders	Police
445.4500	438.4500	NFM	Ekofisk	Senter Phillips
445.5000	438.5000	NFM	Ekofisk	Senter Phillips
445.5125		NFM	London	Post Office
445.5250	425.0250	NFM	W London	Taxis
445.5500	445.5500	NFM	Plymouth	Post Office Security
		NFM	Glasgow	Taxis

Base	Mobile	Mode	Location	User and Notes
445.5625		NFM	Liverpool	PMR
445.5750	425.0750	NFM	Glasgow	Courier Service
445.5875		NFM	Bootle	Security Firm
445.6000		NFM	Newcastle	Trunked PMR
		NFM	Kensington	Council Traffic Wardens
445.6000	438.6000	NFM	Ekofisk	Senter Phillips
445.6000	445.6000	NFM	SE London	Borough Traffic Wardens
445.6500		NFM	Heathrow Airport	British Airways Engineering
445.6750	425.1750	NFM	London	High Court Security
445.7000		NFM	Nationwide	MediCall
		NFM	Newcastle	Trunked PMR
445.7250	425.2250	NFM	London	Underground Stations Ch 1
		NFM	London Underground	Chancery Lane
		NFM	London	DER Repeater (Crystal Palace)
		NFM	London Underground	Aldgate East
		NFM	London Underground	Bayswater
		NFM	London Underground	Cannon Street
		NFM	London Underground	Earls' Court
		NFM	London Underground	Embankment
		NFM	London Underground	Euston
		NFM	London Underground	Gloucester Road
		NFM	London Underground	Hamersmith
		NFM	London Underground	Holburn
		NFM	London Underground	Kings Cross
		NFM	London Underground	Leicester Square
		NFM	London Underground	Liverpool Street
		NFM	London Underground	Mile End
		NFM	London Underground	Moorgate
		NFM	London Underground	Sloane Square
		NFM	London Underground	South Kensington
		NFM	London Underground	St James's Park
		NFM	London Underground	Temple
		NFM	London Underground	Tottenham Crt Rd
		NFM	London Underground	Tower Hill
		NFM	London Underground	Victoria
		NFM	London Underground	Whitechapel
		NFM	London Heathrow	Underground
445.7500	425.2500	NFM	London	Medicall
		NFM	London Underground	Liverpool Street
445.7625	425.2625	NFM	London	Medicall
445.7750	425.2750	NFM	London Underground	Gloucester Road
		NFM	London Underground	Paddington
		NFM	London Underground	Stations Channel 2
		NFM	London Underground	Westminster
		NFM	London Underground	Blackfriars
		NFM	London Underground	Edgeware Road
		NFM	London Underground	Embankment
		NFM	London Underground	Goldhawk Road

Base	Mobile	Mode	Location	User and Notes
		NFM	London Underground	Hamersmith
		NFM	London Underground	Ladbrooke Grove
		NFM	London Underground	Latimar Grove
		NFM	London Underground	Royal Oak
		NFM	London Underground	Shepards Bush
		NFM	London Underground	Wembley Park
		NFM	London Underground	Westbourne Park
445.7750	445.7750	NFM	Nationwide	HM Customs & Excise
445.7875		NFM	London	Medicall
		NFM	Manchester	Transport PMR
445.8000	425.3000	NFM	London Underground	Ladbrooke Grove
		NFM	London Underground	Mansion House
		NFM	London Underground	Stations Channel 3
		NFM	London Underground	Bow Road
		NFM	London Underground	Farringdon
		NFM	London Underground	High St Kensington
		NFM	Heathrow Airport	Ground Repeater
445.8250	425.3250	NFM	Nationwide	Customs & Excise
		AM	Nationwide	DoT Motorway Spot Checks
		NFM	Glasgow	Skypack
		NFM	Central London	Couriers
445.8375	445.8375	NFM	Nationwide	BBC
445.8500	445.8500	NFM	Nationwide	Customs & Excise
445.9000	445.9000	NFM	Nationwide	BBC O/B Link (OL-94)
		NFM	Nationwide	BBC
445.9125		NFM	Manchester	Debt Collectors
445.9625		NFM	Manchester	PMR
		NFM	Bootle	Site Deliveries
		NFM	Preston	Haulage
		NFM	North West	PMR
445.9750		NFM	Newcastle	Trunked PMR
		NFM	Tyneside	Fencing Contractors
446.0000		WFM	Sheffield	BBC Radio Sheffield O/B
		NFM	Solihull	Business Park Security
446.0000	439.0000	NFM	Ekofisk	Senter Phillips
446.0500		NFM	Edinburgh	Stevenson College Janitors
446.1250		NFM	Guildford	Debenhams Security
		NFM	Nottingham	Debenhams Security
		NFM	Stapeley	Stapeley Water Gardens
446.2000	439.2000	NFM	Valhall Field	Amoco
		NFM	Edinburgh	Virgin Record Shop Security
446.2250	439.2250	NFM	Ekofisk	Senter Phillips
		NFM	Lewisham	Lewisham Shopping Centre
446.2500		NFM	Gatwick	Thomas Cook
446.2625		NFM	Edinburgh	The Gyle Centre Security
446.2750	446.2750	NFM	Luton Airport	TNT Carriers
446.2750	439.2750	NFM	Valhall Field	Amoco
446.3000		NFM	London	Capital Radio Flying Eye

Base	Mobile	Mode	Location	User and Notes
		NFM	Edinburgh	Lorry Loaders
446.3500		NFM	Chelmsley Wood	Security
446.4000		NFM	Nationwide	Radio Investigations Service
446.4500		NFM	Nationwide	British Pipeline Agency
		NFM	Thetford	British Pipeline Agency
		NFM	Nationwide	Radio Investigations Service
446.4500	439.4500	NFM	Valhall Field	Amoco
446.4750	452.2500	NFM	Nationwide	Fire Brigade Channel 2
		NFM	Dorset	Fire Brigade
446.5000 - 447.5000 MHz			**IBA, BBC and MoD Allocations**	
446.5625		NFM	Essex	BBC Radio Essex Links
		WFM	London	BBC-TV London Marathon
446.6375		NFM	Stoke on Trent	Radio Stoke O/B
		NFM	Nationwide	BBC Local Radio Talkback
		NFM	Nottinghamshire	Radio Nottingham O/B
446.6875	446.6275	NFM	Nationwide	BBC
446.7000		NFM	London	Medicall
446.7375	446.7375	NFM	Nationwide	BBC
		NFM	Nationwide	BBC Local Radio Talkback
		NFM	Manchester	BBC GMR O/B
446.7875		NFM	London	BBC Radio 5 Talkback
		NFM	Belfry (Ryder Cup)	BBC Radio 5
446.8375		NFM	Derbyshire	Radio Derby Outside Broadcast
		NFM	Nationwide	BBC Local Radio Talkback
446.9000		NFM	London	British Rail Post Office (Euston)
446.9375		NFM	Nationwide	BBC Local Radio Talkback
446.9375	141.3000	NFM	Leicester	BBC Radio Leicester O/B
446.9375	446.9375	NFM	Nationwide	BBC
447.0000		NFM	Silverstone	Japanese TV Talkback
		NFM	Denmark	Police
447.0875		NFM	Birmingham	BRMB/Xtra O/B
		NFM	Stoke on Trent	Signal Radio O/B
		NFM	Hull	Viking Radio O/B
447.0875	447.0875	NFM	Birmingham	ILR X-tra AM
447.08925		NFM	London	Independant Radio Talkback
447.13125		NFM	Manchester	Piccadilly Gold
447.1875	447.1875	NFM	Blackpool	Radio Wave O/B
		NFM	London	Independant Radio Talkback
		NFM	Hull	Viking Radio O/B
		NFM	Stockport	Signal Cheshire
447.2375		NFM	Salisbury	Spire FM
447.2875		NFM	London	Independant Radio Talkback
447.3375		NFM	Birmingham	Buzz FM Outside Broadcasts
447.4000		NFM	Silverstone	US TV Talkback
447.4250		NFM	Ferrybridge	Engineering Talkback
		NFM	Yorkshire	Yorkshire Television
		NFM	Liverpool	Brookside Studio

Base	Mobile	Mode	Location	User and Notes
447.4300		WFM	Sheffield	Yorkshire TV O/B
447.4375		NFM	Leeds	Yorkshire TV O/B
447.4500		NFM	Denmark	Police Speed Traps
447.4750		NFM	London	Independant Radio Talkback
		NFM	Denmark	Traffic Police
447.4875	447.4875	NFM	Liverpool	Brookside TV Director
447.5000		NFM	London	Independant Radio Talkback
		NFM	Silverstone	US TV Talkback
447.5250	447.5250	NFM	Merseyside	Ambulance Handhelds
447.5500		NFM	Aberystwyth	Radio 1 Roadshow OB Talkback
447.8000		NFM	Denmark	Traffic Police

448.00625 - 448.99375 MHz   PMR [LONDON ONLY] (MOBILES - 17 MHz)

Base	Mobile	Mode	Location	User and Notes
448.0250		NFM	London	Taxis
448.0750		NFM	E London	Taxis
448.1250		NFM	London	Motorbike Couriers
448.2250	451.2250	NFM	Birmingham	French Diplomatic Service
448.25625		NFM	London	London Hilton Trunking System
448.5000		NFM	Central London	Contract Wheel Clampers
448.5750		NFM	London	Rotherhithe Couriers
448.6000		NFM	City of Westminster	Traffic Wardens (Papa Sierra)
448.8750	431.8750	NFM	Tunbridge Wells	The Wells

449.0000 - 450.0000 MHz   MoD RADIOLOCATION BEACONS

Base	Mobile	Mode	Location	User and Notes
449.4125		NFM	Manchester	ITN O/B Studio Link
449.6625		NFM	London	Carlton TV Talkback
449.7250		NFM	Rhyl	Police (WA)

**450.0000 - 452.9750 MHz   POLICE MOBILE PMR SYSTEM
ENGLAND & WALES)**

Base	Mobile	Mode	Location	User and Notes
450.0250	464.0250	NFM	Wilmslow	Police
		NFM	Mansfield	Police Channel 1
		NFM	London	Notting Hill Carnival 1
450.0250	450.0250	NFM	Brent Spar	Shell
450.0500	450.0500	NFM	England & Wales	Police Channel 77
		NFM	Sheffield	Police Sheffield Wed FC Security
		NFM	Bournemouth	Police Bournemouth FC
		NFM	London	Police Arsenal FC
450.0500	464.0500	NFM	England & Wales	Police Channel 61
		NFM	Chichester	Police
		NFM	London	Police Wembley FC
		NFM	Luton	Police Luton Town FC
		NFM	Blackpool	Police Special Events
		NFM	Wolverhampton	Police Wolverhampton FC
		NFM	London	Police Chelsea FC
		NFM	Ashford	Police (Tour de France)
		NFM	Oldham	Police Oldham FC
		NFM	City of London	Divisional Support Units

Base	Mobile	Mode	Location	User and Notes
		NFM	Wirral	Police (Tranmere Rov) Ch 1
450.0500	450.0500	NFM	Tranmere	Police Tranmere Rovers FC
		NFM	West Midlands	Police Dog Handlers
		NFM	Blackpool	Police Football Control
		NFM	Leicester	Police (Coventry FC)
		NFM	Milton Keynes	Police MK Bowl Security
		NFM	Carlisle	Police (Football Security)
450.0750	464.0750	NFM	Blackpool	Police Blackpool FC
		NFM	Luton Airport	Police
450.0750	450.0750	NFM	Hove	Police
		NFM	England & Wales	Channel 78
		NFM	Blackpool	Police Special Events
		NFM	Bolton	Police Bolton Wanderers FC
		NFM	Sheffield	Police Sheffield United Sec
		NFM	England & Wales	Police Channel 62
		NFM	London	Police Millwall FC
		NFM	Port Vale	Police Port Vale FC
		NFM	Goodwood	Police Race Course (M2KB)
		NFM	Scarborough	Police Scarborough FC
		NFM	Brighton	Police Brighton & Hove FC
		NFM	London	Police Tottenhan FC
		NFM	Milford Haven	Police
		NFM	West Midlands	Police Motorway Accidents
		NFM	Shoreham	Police
		NFM	Stoke on Trent	Police Stoke City FC
		NFM	Hove	Police
		NFM	Birmingham	Police (Aston Villa FC)
		NFM	Tamworth	Police (Encrypted)
		NFM	Birmingham	Police (Birmingham City FC)
		NFM	Folkestone	Police
450.1250	464.1250	NFM	England & Wales	Police Channel 63
		NFM	England & Wales	Police Special Events Only
		NFM	Ashford	Police (Tour de France)
		NFM	Plymouth	Police Operational Support
450.1250	450.1250	NFM	England & Wales	Police Channel 79
		NFM	Thames Valley	Police Scrambled
		NFM	Blackpool	Police Special Events
		NFM	Charlton	Police Charlton FC
		NFM	Leicester	Police Leicester City FC
		NFM	London	Police QPR FC
		NFM	London	Police West Ham FC
		NFM	Southend on Sea	Police Southend Utd FC
		NFM	W Bromwich	Police W Bromich FC
		NFM	Portsmouth	Police (Fratton Park)
		NFM	Plymouth	Police Special Ops
		NFM	West Bromwich	Police (W Bromwich FC)
450.1500	464.1500	NFM	England & Wales	Police Channel 64
		NFM	England & Wales	Police Special Events

Base	Mobile	Mode	Location	User and Notes
		NFM	Tunbridge Wells	Police (Tour de France)
		NFM	London	Police Crystal Palace FC
		NFM	Brentford	Police Brentford FC
		NFM	Stockport	Police Stockport FC
		NFM	Suffolk	Police Events
		NFM	Beeston	Police Encrypted
		NFM	Plymouth	Police Ward
		NFM	Burnley	Police Football Security
		NFM	Liverpool	Police (Liverpool FC) Ch 1
		NFM	Liverpool	Police (Everton FC) Ch 1
450.1500	450.1500	NFM	England & Wales	Police Channel 80
		NFM	Manchester	Police (Part Time Use)
		NFM	London	Met Police Testing (MP2MT)
		NFM	Thames Valley	Police
		NFM	Blackpool	Police CID
		NFM	Bradford	Police Bradford City FC
		NFM	Charlton	Police Charlton FC
		NFM	Sunderland	Police Sunderland FC
		NFM	Walsall	Police Walsall FC
		NFM	Plymouth	Police Special Ops
450.1750	464.1750	NFM	England & Wales	Police Channel 65
		NFM	England & Wales	Police Special Events
		NFM	Folkestone	Police (Tour de France)
		NFM	Southend	Police Southend United FC
		NFM	Stoke on Trent	Police Stoke City FC
		NFM	London	Notting Hill Carnival 2
		NFM	Wirral	Police (Tranmere Rov) Ch 1
		NFM	South Wales	BR Transport Police
450.1750	450.1750	NFM	England & Wales	Channel 81
		NFM	London	Police Arsenal FC
		NFM	Port Vale	Police Port Vale FC
		NFM	London	Police Fulham FC
		NFM	London	Police Chelsea FC
450.2000	464.2000	NFM	London	Police Tottenham Hotspur
		NFM	England & Wales	Police Channel 66
		NFM	Gillingham	Police Gillingham FC
		NFM	Ipswich	Police Ipswich FC
		NFM	Manchester	Police Man United FC
		NFM	Leeds	Police
		NFM	London	Police Millwall FC
		NFM	Portsmouth	Police (Portsmouth FC)
		NFM	Tunbridge Wells	Police (Tour de France)
		NFM	Portsmouth	Police (Fratton Park)
		NFM	Blackpool	Police Special Events
		NFM	Liverpool	Police (Liverpool FC) Ch 2
		NFM	Liverpool	Police (Everton FC) Ch 2
450.2000	450.2000	NFM	England & Wales	Police Channel 82
		NFM	Gloucester	Police

Base	Mobile	Mode	Location	User and Notes
		NFM	Maidstone	Police
450.2250	450.2250	NFM	England & Wales	Police Channel 83
450.2250	464.2250	NFM	England & Wales	Police Channel 67
		NFM	London	Police West Ham FC
		NFM	Brands Hatch	Police Security
		NFM	Blackpool	Police Special Events
		NFM	England & Wales	Police Special Events
450.2250	464.1250	NFM	Manchester (Moss Side)	Police Drugs Squad
		NFM	Manchester	Police (Part Time Use)
		NFM	London	Police Crystal Palace FC
		NFM	Bolton	Police Bolton Wanderers FC
		NFM	Brighton	Police Area Incident Channel
450.2250	450.2250	NFM	Hull	Police Hull Kingston Rovers
		NFM	Southampton	Police (Southampton FC)
		NFM	Nottingham	Police (Nott's Forest FC)
		NFM	Milton Keynes	Police MK Bowl Security
		NFM	Brighton	Police CID Special Ops
450.2500	450.2500	NFM	England & Wales	Police Channel 84
		NFM	London	Police Crystal Palace FC
		NFM	Blackpool Conference	Army Bomb Squad
450.2500	464.1500	NFM	Brighton	Police Area Incident Channel
450.2500	464.2500	NFM	England & Wales	Police Channel 68
		NFM	England & Wales	Police Special Events
		NFM	Colchester	Police (Foxtrot)
		NFM	Doncaster	Police Doncaster Rovers FC
		NFM	Tunbridge Wells	Police (Tour de France)
		NFM	Bognor Regis	Police
		NFM	Brockenhurst	Police
		NFM	Gainsborough	Police (E)
		NFM	Plymouth	Police Football Control
		NFM	RAF Fairford	IAT Fire Control
450.2750	464.2750	NFM	England & Wales	Police Channel 69
		NFM	Gwynedd	Fire Brigade
450.3000	450.3000	NFM	England & Wales	Fire Command Channel 70
450.3125		NFM	Rhyl	Police (WA)
450.3250	450.3250	NFM	London	Met Police
450.3750	450.3750	NFM	London	Met Police
450.4000	450.4000	NFM	London	Met Police
450.4500	450.4500	NFM	London	Met Police
450.5250		NFM	Irlam	Police
450.5750		NFM	Llandudno	Police (WA)
		NFM	Colwyn Bay	Police (WA)
		NFM	Warrington	Police
		NFM	St Helens	Police
450.6000		NFM	Portsmouth	Police
450.6250	450.6250	NFM	England & Wales	Police Channel 88 Air-Ground
		NFM	West Sussex	Police Helicopter (Hotel 900)
		NFM	Hampshire	Police Optica (Boxer 10)

Base	Mobile	Mode	Location	User and Notes
		NFM	England & Wales	Police Air to Ground Ch 88
		NFM	England & Wales	Fire Brigade Channel 8
		NFM	Skelmersdale	Police Helicopter
		NFM	Merseyside	Police (Encrypted)
		NFM	Merseyside	Police Helicopter (M1)
		NFM	Luton Airport	Police Air Support Unit (XA99)
		NFM	Herefordshire	Police Helicopter
		NFM	Shropshire	Police Helicopter
		NFM	South Wales	Police Helicopter (WO99)
		NFM	West Midlands	Police Helicopter (AO1)
		NFM	Merseyside	Police Helicopter (M1)
450.6750	450.6750	NFM	England & Wales	Police Channel 89 Air-Ground
		NFM	England & Wales	Fire Brigade Channel 9
		NFM	Northampton	Police Helicopter
		NFM	Leicester	Police Helicopter
		NFM	Warickshire	Police Helicopter
		NFM	Lancashire	Police Helicopter
450.8000		NFM	Liverpool Toxteth	Police
		NFM	West Midlands	Police Motorway Incident Unit
		NFM	Gatley	Police
		NFM	Merseyside	Police Drug Squad (Encrypted)
		NFM	Gt Manchester	Police (Encrypted)
450.8250		NFM	Salwick	AEA Police
		NFM	North Wales	Police (D)
		NFM	Rhyl	Police (WA)
450.8500	450.8500	NFM	Manchester Ringway	Police
		NFM	Manchester Airport	Police
		NFM	Barton Airfield	Police Helicopter
451.0000	464.9000	NFM	Various Areas	Police
451.0250	464.9250	NFM	England & Wales	Police Channel T1
451.0500	464.9500	NFM	England & Wales	Police Channel T2
451.0500	451.0500	NFM	Sunderland AFC	Police Security
451.0750	451.0750	NFM	Hendon	Police Training College
451.0750	464.9750	NFM	England & Wales	Police Channel T3
		NFM	Hendon	Police Radio Training
451.1000	465.0000	NFM	England & Wales	Police Channel T4
451.1000	465.0000	NFM	England & Wales	Antenna Rigging & Testing
		NFM	Preston	Police
451.1250	465.0125	NFM	England & Wales	Police Channel T5
451.1250	465.0125	NFM	England & Wales	Bomb Disposal Unit (Bravo)
451.1250	465.1250	NFM	London	Notting Hill Carnival 4
451.1500	451.1500	NFM	England & Wales	Police Channel 00
		NFM	England & Wales	Police Covert Surveillance
451.1750	465.0750	NFM	England & Wales	Police Channel 87
		NFM	Portsmouth	Police
		NFM	North Wales	Police (A)
		NFM	Cosham	Police
		NFM	Colwyn Bay	Police (WA)

Join the **Police Scanner Club!**

☐ *Police Scanning News*
☐ **Keep up with the latest developments**
☐ **Latest frequencies**

By joining the Police Scanner Club you will have the latest information covering the police and other emergency services. The latest frequencies and changes will be published in the *Police Scanner News* which will be sent to members three times a year starting in July. Packed with the latest radio news and developments in technology you will be ahead of the rest, and will be able to share the latest changes and frequencies in you area with other members. That's not all! From time to time as a member you will receive free publications, bulletin service and special offers!

Membership is only £10 a year which starts every July.
Available by subscription only.

JOIN BY THE 31ST JULY TO RECEIVE A FREE POLICE BANDPLAN!

Interproducts
8 Abbot Street, Perth, PH2 0EB
Tel. and Fax: 01738-441199

Base	Mobile	Mode	Location	User and Notes
451.2000	465.1000	NFM	England & Wales	Police Channel 86
		NFM	Ashford	Police (JZ)
		NFM	Manchester Longsight	Police
		NFM	Manchester Gorton	Police
		NFM	Manchester Greenheys	Police
		NFM	Manchester Levenshulme	Police
		NFM	Manchester Moss Side	Police
		NFM	Manchester Whalley	Police
		NFM	Warrington	Police
		NFM	Walsall	Traffic Wardens
		NFM	Liverpool	Police
		NFM	Wirral	Police
		NFM	Wallsey	Police
		NFM	New Brighton	Police
		NFM	Pow-t-Ffordd	Police
		NFM	Wallasey	Police (A1)
451.2250	465.1250	NFM	England & Wales	Police Channel 85
		NFM	Manchester	Police (Gorton)
		NFM	Ashford	Police (DA)
		NFM	Warrington	Police
		NFM	Cleveland	Police
451.2500	465.1500	NFM	England & Wales	Police Channel 84
		NFM	London	Police Diplomatic Protection
451.2750	464.8750	NFM	Humberside	Police Channel 02
		NFM	England & Wales	Police Reserve Channel B
451.2750	465.1750	NFM	England & Wales	Police Channel 05
		NFM	Manchester Bredbury	Police
		NFM	Manchester Brinnington	Police
		NFM	Manchester Cheadle	Police
		NFM	Manchester Ch. Hulme	Police
		NFM	Manchester Hazel Grove	Police
		NFM	Manchester Marple	Police
		NFM	Manchester Reddish	Police
		NFM	Stockport	Police
		NFM	Birmingham Airport	Police (M2YMEA)
451.2750	465.8750	NFM	England & Wales	Police Reserve Channel B
		NFM	Cheadle	Police
		NFM	Thames Valley	Police
		NFM	Stockport	Police
		NFM	Broadstairs	Police (E/E) Ch 5
		NFM	Margate	Police (E/D) Ch 5
451.3000	451.3000	NFM	England & Wales	Optica Surveillance Air-Ground
		NFM	England & Wales	Police Channel 71 Optica
		NFM	Thames Valley	Police
		NFM	England & Wales	Police Motorcycle Training
451.3000	465.2000	NFM	England & Wales	Police Airborne
		NFM	Gatwick	Police Immigration
		NFM	West Yorksshire	Ambulance Hand Held

Base	Mobile	Mode	Location	User and Notes
451.3000	465.2000	NFM	Cwmbran	Police Training College
		NFM	Trowbridge	Police Speed Traps
451.3125	465.2652	NFM	Newport	Newport Rangers
		NFM	Hastings	Police (H)
451.3250	465.2250	NFM	England & Wales	Police Channel 07
		NFM	England & Wales	CID Covert
		NFM	England & Wales	Police Airborne
		NFM	England & Wales	Police CID SOCO
		NFM	England & Wales	Police Engineers
		NFM	England & Wales	Police Speed Traps
		NFM	England & Wales	Police TV Units
		NFM	Essex	Police Helicopter (H900)
		NFM	Kent	Police (Tour de France)
		NFM	London	HM Customs/Police Link
		NFM	England & Wales	CID Covert Channel 07
		NFM	Heysham (Port)	Special Branch
451.3250	465.3250	NFM	Thames Valley	Police Traffic
		NFM	Gatwick	Armed Police Tactical Liaison
		NFM	London Heathrow	Armed Police Tactical Liaison
		NFM	Scarborough	Special Constabules/CID Overt
		NFM	Plymouth Airport	Fire Appliance
		NFM	Neath	Police
		NFM	N Wales	Police Helicopter (W1)
		NFM	Ingoldmells	Police
451.3500	465.2500	NFM	Birmingham Airport	Immigration
		NFM	England & Wales	Police Channel 08
		NFM	England & Wales	HM Prisons
		NFM	Gatwick	Police Immigration
		NFM	London	Police Port Authority of London
		NFM	Newhaven	HM Immigration
		NFM	Stansted Airport	Immigration
		NFM	Heathrow Airport	Immigration
451.3750	465.2750	NFM	England & Wales	Police Channel 09
		NFM	Abergele	Police
		NFM	Acklington	HMP Acklington (M2MU)
		NFM	Basildon	Police
		NFM	Birmingham	HMP Winson Green
		NFM	Canvey Island	Police
		NFM	Cardiff	Police
		NFM	Farnborough	Police
		NFM	Gloucester	Police
		NFM	High Wycombe	Police (AE)
		NFM	HMP Feltham	
		NFM	HMP Littlehey	
		NFM	Holbeck	Police
		NFM	Horley	Police
		NFM	Leeds	Police (Holbeck)
		NFM	Liverpool	Police

Base	Mobile	Mode	Location	User and Notes
		NFM	London	HMP Pentonville
		NFM	Manchester Arndale	Police
		NFM	Manchester Bootle Street	Police
		NFM	Manchester City Centre	Police
		NFM	Manchester Newton St.	Police
		NFM	Marlow	Police
		NFM	Rye	Police (M2KBEO+ER)
		NFM	Norfolk	HMP Wayland
		NFM	Northampton	Police
		NFM	Nottingham	Police City Centre
		NFM	Pembroke	Police
		NFM	Renishaw	Police
		NFM	Spalling	Police
		NFM	St Asaph	Police
		NFM	Wisbech	Police
		NFM	Bangor	Police
		NFM	North Wales	Police Mobile Repeater
		NFM	Stockton-on-Tees	HMP Stockton
		NFM	Droitwich	Police
		NFM	Milford Haven	Police
		NFM	Andover	Police
		NFM	Leeds Holbeck	Police
		NFM	Cleveland	HMP Homehouse
		NFM	Frankley	Police (RA)
		NFM	Buckley	Police
		NFM	Full Sutton	HMP Full Sutton
451.4000	451.4000	NFM	England & Wales	Police/Fire Link Channel 97
		NFM	England & Wales	Fire Services Channel 01
451.4000	465.3000	NFM	England & Wales	Police Channel 10
		NFM	Guernsey	Fire Brigade
451.4000	465.4000	NFM	London	Fire Brigade
		NFM	Falmouth	Police
		NFM	Newquay	Police
		NFM	Edinburgh	Fire Brigade
451.4000	451.0000	NFM	Newport	Radio Auth. Surveilance
451.4250	465.3250	NFM	England & Wales	Police Channel 11
		NFM	Aylesbury	Police (AA)
		NFM	Birmingham Acocks Gn	Police
		NFM	Birmingham Dunstall Rd	Police
		NFM	Bristol	Police
		NFM	Catherton	Police
		NFM	Connah's Quay	Police
		NFM	Ecclesfied, S. Yorkshire	Police (F2)
		NFM	Essex	Police
		NFM	Faringdon	Police
		NFM	Gloucestershire	Police
		NFM	Grays	Police
		NFM	HMP Guys Marsh	Young Offenders (2BV)

Base	Mobile	Mode	Location	User and Notes
		NFM	Leeds	Police
		NFM	Liverpool St Helens	Police
		NFM	Long Eaton	Police
		NFM	Manchester Ancoats	Police
		NFM	Manchester Blackley	Police
		NFM	Manchester Bradford	Police
		NFM	Manchester Cheetham	Police
		NFM	Manchester Collyhurst	Police
		NFM	Manchester Harpurhey	Police
		NFM	Manchester Newton H.	Police
		NFM	Nationwide	Immigration
		NFM	Newbury	Police (M2FA)
		NFM	Nottingham	Police Eastwood
		NFM	Portsmouth	Police
		NFM	Pudsey	Police
		NFM	Reading East	Police (EX)
		NFM	Reading West	Police (EA)
		NFM	Rossington	Police
		NFM	Stansted Airport	Police (GF/GM)
		NFM	Suffolk	HMP Hollesley Bay
		NFM	Thames Valley	Police (AB)
		NFM	Wantage	Police
		NFM	Wendover	Police
		NFM	Whitley Bay	Police (M2LBC2)/(H1)
		NFM	Witney	Police
		NFM	Wolverhampton	Police North (M2YMG)
		NFM	Malton	Police
		NFM	Portsmouth, Ferry Point	Police
		NFM	Wickford	Police
		NFM	Stansted Airport	Police
		NFM	HMP Hollesley Gay	
		NFM	Haverigg	HMP Millom
		NFM	Malton	Police
		NFM	Leeds Pudsey	Police
		NFM	Portsmouth	Immigration
		NFM	New Furry	Police
		NFM	Speke	Police (D1)
		NFM	Garston	Police (D2)
451.4250	465.3250	NFM	Belfast	Ulster Folk & Transport Mus
451.4500	451.4500	NFM	England & Wales	Police/Fire Link Channel 99
		NFM	England & Wales	Fire Services Channel 3
451.4500	465.3500	NFM	England & Wales	Channel 12
		NFM	England & Wales	Police Channel 12
		NFM	Mersyside	Prescot Police Comms
		NFM	Dudley	Police
		NFM	Merseyside	Police (Encrypted)
451.4500	465.4500	NFM	England	Fire Service Channel 02
451.4750	451.4750	NFM	England	General Fire Incidents Ch 4

Base	Mobile	Mode	Location	User and Notes
451.4750	465.3750	NFM	England & Wales	Police Channel 13
		NFM	Alton	Police
		NFM	Basingstoke	Police
		NFM	Billericay	Police
		NFM	Brighton	Crown Court
		NFM	Burnham	Police (CC)
		NFM	Campsfield	Detention Centre
		NFM	Cleveland	Police
		NFM	Greyshott	Police
		NFM	Harrogate	Police
		NFM	Hull	Police
		NFM	Humberside	Police
		NFM	Ilkley	Police
		NFM	Isle of Wight	Police Relay
		NFM	Keithley	Police
		NFM	London	HMP Wandsworth
		NFM	Maidenhead	Police (M2CG)
		NFM	Manchester Chadderton	Police
		NFM	Manchester Failsworth	Police
		NFM	Manchester Royton	Police
		NFM	Manchester Uppermill	Police
		NFM	Newcastle	Police
		NFM	Oldham	Police
		NFM	Petersfield	Police
		NFM	Ripley	Police
		NFM	South Godstone	Police
		NFM	Thames Valley	Police
		NFM	Throne, S. Yorkshire	Police (A2)
		NFM	Tonbridge	Police (CC)
		NFM	Uttoxeter	Police
		NFM	Wakefield	HMP Wakefield
		NFM	Wallsend	Police (M2LBC3)/(I1)
		NFM	Walsall	Police (M2YMH)
		NFM	Wickford	Police
		NFM	Cleveland, Eston	Police
		NFM	Walsall	Police (M2YMHX)
		NFM	Aldridge	Police (M2YMHX)
		NFM	Erlestoke	HMP Erlestoke
451.5000	465.4000	NFM	England & Wales	Police Channel 14
451.5250	465.4250	NFM	Birkenhead	Police
		NFM	Birmingham Solihull	Police (M2YML)
		NFM	Bradford Laisterdyke	Police
		NFM	Cardiff Central	Police (WY)
		NFM	Carterton	Police (FJ)
		NFM	Collyhurst	Police
		NFM	Essex	Police
		NFM	Godalming	Police (WO)
		NFM	Grays	Police

Base	Mobile	Mode	Location	User and Notes
		NFM	Hazelmere	Police (WO)
		NFM	Huntingdon	Police
		NFM	Long Eaton	Police
		NFM	Manchester Collyhurst	Police
		NFM	Mexborough	Police (A3)
		NFM	Miles Platting	Police
		NFM	Plymouth	Police
		NFM	Shirley	Police
		NFM	Stafford	Police
		NFM	Thames Valley	Police
		NFM	West Bridgford	Police
		NFM	W Midlands, Birmingham Rd	Police
		NFM	Wirral	Police
		NFM	Wirley	Police (FI)
		NFM	Wolverhampton	Police (M2YMG)
		NFM	Weymouth	Police
451.5250	451.5250	NFM	England & Wales	Fire Breathing Apparatus 6
451.5250	465.4250	NFM	England & Wales	Police Channel 15
		NFM	Adwick	Police
		NFM	Birkenhead	Police
		NFM	Birtley	Police (K2)
		NFM	Bristol	Traffic Wardens
		NFM	Blaydon	Police (K3)
		NFM	Eastchurch	HMP Elmley
		NFM	Faringdon	Police
		NFM	Farncombe	Police
		NFM	Manchester Ancoats	Police
		NFM	Manchester Blackley	Police
		NFM	Manchester Bradford	Police
		NFM	Manchester Cheetham	Police
		NFM	Manchester Collyhurst	Police
		NFM	Manchester Harpurhey	Police
		NFM	Manchester Newton H.	Police
		NFM	Newcastle	Police
		NFM	Nottingham	Police
		NFM	Oxford	Police
		NFM	Poole	Police
		NFM	Southampton	Police
		NFM	Whickham	Police (K1)
		NFM	Witney	Police
		NFM	Basildon	Police
		NFM	Malvern	Police
		NFM	Oldhill	Police
		NFM	Southampton City	Police
		NFM	Plymouth	Police VHF-UHF Repeater
		NFM	Solihull	Police
		NFM	Wirral	Police
		NFM	Solihull	Police (L1)

Base	Mobile	Mode	Location	User and Notes
		NFM	Wolverhampton	Police (G3)
		NFM	Birkenhead	Police (A2)
451.5375	465.4375	NFM	Merseyside	Police (Encrypted)
451.5500	451.5500	NFM	England & Wales	Police Channel 02
451.5500	465.4500	NFM	England & Wales	Police Channel 16
		NFM	London	Police Diplomatic Protection
451.5750	465.6750	NFM	England & Wales	Police Channel 17
		NFM	Accrington	Police
		NFM	Avon	Police (M2QP)
		NFM	Bradford	Police
		NFM	Castelford	Police
		NFM	Dover	Dover Detention Centre
		NFM	Dudley	Police (M2YMJ)
		NFM	Faringdon	Police (M2FE)
		NFM	Farnham	Police (WF)
		NFM	Garstang	Police
		NFM	Gosforth	Police (M2LBB5)
		NFM	Haslingden	Police
		NFM	HMP Latchmere House	
		NFM	Worcestershire	HMP Long Lartin
		NFM	HMP Ranby	
		NFM	HMP Swinton	
		NFM	HMP Walton	
		NFM	Jesmond	Police
		NFM	Kenton	Police (G3)
		NFM	Lancaster	Police
		NFM	Liverpool	HMP
		NFM	Rochester	Borstal
		NFM	Sedgley	Police
		NFM	Somerset	Police
		NFM	S Yorkshire	HMP Lindholme
		NFM	Swindon	Police
		NFM	Taunton	Police
		NFM	Telford	Police
		NFM	Thames Valley	Police
		NFM	Torpoint	Police B Division
		NFM	Wantage	Police (FF)
		NFM	Warrington	Police (D2)
		NFM	Yorkshire (M62)	Police
		NFM	Southampton West	Police
		NFM	London	HMP Pentonvill
		NFM	Breiley Hill	Police
		NFM	Whitehaven	Police
		NFM	Bradford Central	Police
		NFM	Eastleigh	Police
		NFM	Romsey	Police
		NFM	Saltash	Police
		NFM	Wellingborough	HM Prison

Base	Mobile	Mode	Location	User and Notes
		NFM	Cleveland	HMP Kirklevington
		NFM	Milton Keynes	HMP Woodhill
451.6000	465.5000	NFM	England & Wales	Police Channel 18
		NFM	Birmingham Central	Police (M2YMF)
		NFM	HMP North Sea Camp	
		NFM	Lancaster	Police
		NFM	Maidstone	Police
		NFM	Manchester Altrincham	Police
		NFM	Manchester Sale	Police
		NFM	Manchester Stretford	Police
		NFM	Manchester Trafford	Police
		NFM	Manchester Urmston	Police
		NFM	Nottinghamshire	HMP Whatton
		NFM	Oldham	Police
		NFM	Ramsgate	Police
		NFM	Sale	Police
		NFM	Southwick	Police (M1) Encrypted
		NFM	Southwood	Police (F3)
		NFM	Sunderland	Police (M2LBF3)
		NFM	Addlestone	Police (NA)
		NFM	Wellingborough	Police
		NFM	W. Midlands, Steelhouse	Police
		NFM	W. Midlands, Bradford St	Police
		NFM	Middlesbrough	Police
		NFM	Cradley Heath	Police
		NFM	Preston	Police
451.6125	451.6125	NFM	England & Wales	Fire Breathing Apparatus 2
		NFM	Plymouth Airport	Fire Appliance
451.6250	465.5250	NFM	England & Wales	Police Channel 19
		NFM	Blackpool	Police Football Control
		NFM	Brighton	Police Special Ops
		NFM	Cambridge	Police Football Control
		NFM	Derby	Police Vice Squad
		NFM	Derby	Police Derby City FC
		NFM	Dover	Police Operations Centre
		NFM	Dyfed	Police Helicopter (X99)
		NFM	Essex	Police
		NFM	Gatwick	Police M2KB Special Ops
		NFM	Gt Manchester	Police Surveillance
		NFM	Guernsey	Police Channel 2
		NFM	Ipswich	Police Mobile Repeater
		NFM	Leicester	Police
		NFM	Nationwide	CID Use
		NFM	Nationwide	Police National Emergencies
		NFM	Nationwide	Police Special Events
		NFM	Slough	Police
		NFM	Stoke on Trent	Police
		NFM	Tenterden	Police

Base	Mobile	Mode	Location	User and Notes
		NFM	Thames Valley	Police Special Events
		NFM	West Sussex	Police Emergency Use
		NFM	Yorkshire	Police Football Control
		NFM	Peterborough	Police Ops
		NFM	Birmingham	Police (NEC Motor Show)
		NFM	Kendal	Ploce
		NFM	Kendal	Ploce
451.6375	465.5375	NFM	Oxford	Police
451.6500	465.5500	NFM	England & Wales	Police Channel 20
		NFM	Bagshot	Police
		NFM	Cambridge	Police Mobile Repeater
		NFM	Caterham	Police
		NFM	Chiddingford	Police
		NFM	Cornwall	Police Mobile Repeater
		NFM	Devon	Police Mobile Repeater
		NFM	Hertfordshire	Police Mobile Repeater
		NFM	Humberside	Police Mobile Repeater
		NFM	Lincolnshire	Police Mobile Repeater
		NFM	Lowestoft	Police
		NFM	Merseyside	Police Mobile Repeater
		NFM	Northumberland	Police Repeaters
		NFM	Nottinghamshire	Police Mobile Repeater
		NFM	Poole	Police RCS Encrypted Cougar
		NFM	St Ives	Police
		NFM	Shirehall	Police Link
		NFM	South Wales	Police Mobile Repeater
		NFM	South Yorkshire	Police Mobile Repeater
		NFM	Staffordshire	Police Mobile Repeater
		NFM	Thames Valley	Police Mobile Repeater
		NFM	Tyne and Wear	Police Repeaters
		NFM	Ulverstone	Police
		NFM	West Mercia	Police
		NFM	West Midlands	Police Mobile Repeater
		NFM	West Sussex	Police Mobile Repeater
		NFM	West Yorkshire	Police Mobile Repeater
		NFM	Weybridge	Police
451.6250	465.5250	NFM	Conwy Valley	Police Mobile Repeater
		NFM	Gatwick Airport	Police Ch.19
		NFM	Co Durham	Police (LA)
451.6750	465.5750	NFM	England & Wales	Police Channel 21
		NFM	Barnsley	Police
		NFM	Benfleet	Police
		NFM	Bishop Stortford	Police
		NFM	Bradford	Police
		NFM	Canvey Island	Police
		NFM	Cardiff Central	Police
		NFM	Chipping Norton	Police
		NFM	City Of London	Police Channel 2 (AJ)

Base	Mobile	Mode	Location	User and Notes
		NFM	Cornwall	Police (Mobile Repeater)
		NFM	Cosham	Police
		NFM	Devon	Police Mobile Repeater
		NFM	Gateshead South	Police
		NFM	Havant	Police
		NFM	Henley	Police (M2EE)
		NFM	Kirky in Ashfield	Police
		NFM	Leicester	Police
		NFM	Liverpool	Police
		NFM	Mansfield	Police
		NFM	Matlock	Police
		NFM	Newcastle	Police (M2LBB3)/(F1)
		NFM	Northwich	Police (E1)
		NFM	Pangbourne	Police
		NFM	Portsmouth	Police
		NFM	Reading	Police (EG)
		NFM	Redditch	Police
		NFM	Shinfield	Police
		NFM	Stoke on Trent	Police
		NFM	Sutton	Police
		NFM	Sutton in Ashfield	Police
		NFM	Tamworth	Police
		NFM	Theale	Police
		NFM	Twyford	Police
		NFM	Welwyn Garden City	Police
		NFM	Wokingham	Police
		NFM	Woodley	Police (EB)
		NFM	Portsmouth	Police
		NFM	Glossop	Police
		NFM	Buxton	Police
		NFM	Tamworth	Police (Encrypted)
		NFM	Merseyside	Police (Encrypted)
		NFM	Merseyside	Police (Encrypted)
		NFM	Merseyside	Police HQ Div A
451.7000	465.6000	NFM	England & Wales	Police Channel 22
		NFM	Arnold	Police
		NFM	Birmingham Bourneville	Police (M2YMB)
		NFM	Burscough	Police
		NFM	Chorley	Police
		NFM	Coppull	Police
		NFM	Dorking	Police (ED)
		NFM	Durham	Police (BD)
		NFM	Gillingham	Police (BB)
		NFM	Gt Manchester Eccles	Police
		NFM	Gt Manchester Broughton	Police
		NFM	Gt Manchester L.. Hulton	Police
		NFM	Gt Manchester Pendleton	Police
		NFM	Gt Manchester Salford	Police

Base	Mobile	Mode	Location	User and Notes
		NFM	Gt Manchester Swinton	Police
		NFM	Gt Manchester Walkden	Police
		NFM	Leatherhead	Police (EL)
		NFM	Rainham	Police (BB)
		NFM	Sheffield	Police (E1)
		NFM	Southampton	Police
		NFM	Thames Valley	Police
		NFM	Ashford	Police
		NFM	Bitterne	Police
		NFM	Folkestone	Police
451.7250	465.6250	NFM	England & Wales	Police Channel 23
		NFM	Ammanford	Police
		NFM	Birmingham	Police NEC Security
		NFM	Blackpool	Police
		NFM	Brighton	Police Conference Security
		NFM	Cardiff	Police Special Events
		NFM	Cheadle Hume	Police
		NFM	Humberside	Police Football Control
		NFM	Leicester	Police
		NFM	Manchester	Police
		NFM	Northumberland	Police Mobile (M2LBX+Y)
		NFM	Suffolk	Police Special Events
		NFM	Thames Valley	Police
		NFM	Wakefield	Police HQ
451.7250	465.7250	NFM	London	Notting Hill Carnival 3
451.7500	465.6500	NFM	England & Wales	Police Channel 24
		NFM	Birmingham Ward End	Police (M2YME)
		NFM	Blackpool	Police
		NFM	Bramford	Police
		NFM	Burnley	Police
		NFM	Bury	Police
		NFM	Cardiff	Police L Division (WY)
		NFM	Ely	Police
		NFM	Flint	Police
		NFM	Gt Manchester Birch	Police
		NFM	Gt Manchester Motorway	Police
		NFM	Gt Manchester Prestwich	Police
		NFM	Gt Manchester Radcliffe	Police
		NFM	Gt Manchester Ramsbottom	Police
		NFM	Gt Manchester Whitefield	Police
		NFM	Hinckley	Police
		NFM	Kirkham	Police
		NFM	Liverpool Huyton	Police
		NFM	Lytham	Police
		NFM	Market Harborough	Police
		NFM	Melksham	Police
		NFM	Middleton	Police
		NFM	Peterlee	Police (BE)

Base	Mobile	Mode	Location	User and Notes
		NFM	Retford	Police
		NFM	Salisbury	HMP Salisbury
		NFM	Skegness	Police
		NFM	St Annes	Police
		NFM	Thames Valley	Police
		NFM	Warton	Police
		NFM	Weeton	Police
		NFM	Worksop	Police
		NFM	Bournemouth	Police
		NFM	Rochford	Police
		NFM	Notty Ash	Police
		NFM	Peterlee	Police
		NFM	Merseyside	Police (Encrypted)
		NFM	Merseyside	Police HQ Div D
		NFM	Boscombe	Police
		NFM	Croxteth	Police (C1)
451.7750	465.6750	NFM	England & Wales	Fire Breathing App Ch3
		NFM	England & Wales	Police Channel 25
		NFM	Blackpool	Police Conference Security
		NFM	Brighton	Brighton Crown Court
		NFM	Cambridge	Police Special Branch
		NFM	England & Wales	Police Emergency Channel
		NFM	Farnborough	Police Air Show Security
		NFM	Gt Manchester	Police Surveillance
		NFM	Hull	Police Football Control
		NFM	Lancashire	Police Emergency Channel
		NFM	Leicester	Police
		NFM	Maidstone	Police
		NFM	Northumberland	Police Mobile (M2LBX+Y)
		NFM	RAF Lakenheath	Police Base Security
		NFM	Rotherham	Police Football Control
		NFM	Suffolk	Police FHQ Repeater
		NFM	Sunninghill	Police
		NFM	Thames Valley	Police Special Events
		NFM	Lincoln	Police
		NFM	Cardiff	Police CID
		NFM	Merseyside	Police (Encrypted)
		NFM	Merseyside	Police HQ Div F
451.7750	465.7250	NFM	London	Notting Hill Carnival 5
451.8000	465.7000	NFM	England & Wales	Police Channel 26
		NFM	Ainsdale	Police
		NFM	Birmingham Acock's Green	Police (M2YME)
		NFM	Bolton	Police
		NFM	Burton-on-Trent	Police
		NFM	Crosby	Police
		NFM	Felling	Police (M2LBD2)/(J2)
		NFM	Formby	Police
		NFM	Gateshead	Police Stadium Area

Base	Mobile	Mode	Location	User and Notes
		NFM	Gloucester	Police
		NFM	Gt Manchester Astley Bridge	Police
		NFM	Gt Manchester Breightmet	Police
		NFM	Gt Manchester Farnworth	Police
		NFM	Gt Manchester Horwich	Police
		NFM	Gt Manchester Mi. Hulton	Police
		NFM	Gt Manchester Westh.n	Police
		NFM	New Forest	Police
		NFM	Leeds Gipton	Police
		NFM	Liverpool Marsh Lane	Police
		NFM	Manchester Airport	Police
		NFM	Ringwood	Police
		NFM	Seacroft	Police
		NFM	Southampton Totton	Police
		NFM	Southport	Police
		NFM	Thames Valley	Police
		NFM	Wallington	Police
		NFM	Oldbury	Police
		NFM	Leeds Killingbeck	Police
		NFM	New Forest	Police
		NFM	Merseyside	Police (Encrypted)
		NFM	Merseyside	Police HQ Div B
		NFM	Bootle	Police (B1)
		NFM	Southport	Police (B2)
451.8250	465.7250	NFM	England & Wales	Police Channel 27
		NFM	Abingdon	Police
		NFM	Ashford	Sandgate Police Centre
		NFM	Barry	Police
		NFM	Bispham	Police
		NFM	Blyth	Police (M2LBC5)
		NFM	Bristol	Police
		NFM	Canning	Police
		NFM	Canterbury	HMP Canterbury
		NFM	Cowley	Police (BC)
		NFM	Cleveleys	Police
		NFM	Eastchurch	HMP Swaleside
		NFM	Eastleigh	Police
		NFM	Eccleshall	Police
		NFM	Egham	Police
		NFM	Fleetwood	Police
		NFM	Frampton Cotterill	Police
		NFM	Gloucester	Police
		NFM	Gt Manchester Heywood	Police
		NFM	Gt Manchester Kirkholt	Police
		NFM	Gt Manchester Littleborough	Police
		NFM	Gt Manchester Middleton	Police
		NFM	Gt Manchester Milnrow	Police
		NFM	Harlow	Police

Base	Mobile	Mode	Location	User and Notes
		NFM	HMP Coldingley	
		NFM	Langley	Police (CE)
		NFM	Neath	Police
		NFM	Nelson Colne	Police
		NFM	Newcastle	Police
		NFM	Oxford	Police (BA)
		NFM	Pendle	Police
		NFM	Port Talbot	Police
		NFM	Poulton le Fyde	Police
		NFM	Rochdale	Police
		NFM	Slough	Police HQ (CA)
		NFM	Spennymoor	Police (AL)
		NFM	Stratford-Upon-Avon	Police
		NFM	Tadcaster	Police
		NFM	Thames Valley	Police
		NFM	Wigan	Police
		NFM	Woodsetts	Police (E2)
		NFM	Yate	Police
451.8250	445.7250	NFM	Corringham	Police
		NFM	South Ockendon	Police
451.8250	465.7250	NFM	Bristol	Police CID
		NFM	Wombourne	Police
451.8500	465.7500	NFM	England & Wales	Police Channel 28
		NFM	Amersham	Police
		NFM	Aylesbury	Police
		NFM	Beaconsfield	Police (AC)
		NFM	Bletchley	Police (DG)
		NFM	Buckingham	Police (DB)
		NFM	Congleton	Police
		NFM	Gerrards Cross	Police (AC)
		NFM	Grays	Police
		NFM	Havant	Police
		NFM	Horndean	Police
		NFM	HMP Armley	
		NFM	HMP Morton Hall	
		NFM	Lincoln	Police
		NFM	Macclesfield	Police (C1)
		NFM	Milton Keynes	Police
		NFM	Nottingham	HMP Nottingham
		NFM	Ormskirk	Police
		NFM	Stanley	Police (CH)
		NFM	Thames Valley	Police
		NFM	Waterlooville	Police
		NFM	Wednesbury	Police (M2YMK)
		NFM	Bristol	Police
		NFM	Manchester	Police
		NFM	Smethwick	Police
451.8500	465.8500	NFM	London	Notting Hill Carnival 6

Base	Mobile	Mode	Location	User and Notes
451.8750	465.7750	NFM	England & Wales	Police Channel 29
		NFM	Boroughbridge	Police
		NFM	Bournemouth	Police Football Security
		NFM	Cambridge	Police
		NFM	City of London	Police
		NFM	Cosham	Police
		NFM	Farnborough	Police Air Show Security
		NFM	Gloucester	Police
		NFM	Kent	Police Depot Emergencies
		NFM	Lakenheath	Police
		NFM	Lancashire	Police Emergency Channel
		NFM	Nationwide	Police Command Vehicles
		NFM	Northumberland	Police Mobile (M2LBX+Y)
		NFM	Portsmouth	Police
		NFM	Southend	Police
		NFM	Southsea	Police
		NFM	Suffolk	Police Special Events
		NFM	Thames Valley	Police
		NFM	Wigston	Police (CA/W)
		NFM	Wolverhampton	Police
451.8750	451.8750	NFM	Peterborough	Police Crowd Control
		NFM	Liverpool	Police Hooligan Van
451.9000	465.8000	NFM	England & Wales	Police Channel 30
		NFM	Bury	Police
		NFM	Camberley	Police (NC)
		NFM	Coventry South	Police (M2YMM)
		NFM	Dover	Police Special Branch
		NFM	Egham	Police (NE)
		NFM	Fletchamstead	Police
		NFM	Folkestone	Police Special Branch
		NFM	Gt Manchester Birch	Police
		NFM	Gt Manchester Motorway Post	Police
		NFM	Gt Manchester Prestwich	Police
		NFM	Gt Manchester Radcliffe	Police
		NFM	Gt Manchester Ramsbottom	Police
		NFM	Gt Manchester Whitefield	Police
		NFM	Horsforth	Police
		NFM	HMP Holloway	
		NFM	Leeds	Police
		NFM	Liverpool Kirby	Police
		NFM	Newcastle	Police
		NFM	Portsmouth	Police Scrambled
		NFM	Thames Valley	Police
		NFM	Wednesfield	Police (M2YMG)
		NFM	Wolverhampton	Police
		NFM	Darlington	Police
		NFM	Steel House Lane	Police
		NFM	Leeds Horsforth	Police

Base	Mobile	Mode	Location	User and Notes
		NFM	Colchester	Military Prision
		NFM	Ormskirk	Police
		NFM	Holywell	Police
		NFM	Mostyn	Police
451.9250	465.8250	NFM	England & Wales	Police Channel 31
		NFM	Blackpool Divisional HQ	Police
		NFM	Bracknell	Police (M2CH)
		NFM	Buckingham	Police (DB)
		NFM	Buckley	Police
		NFM	Crowthorne	Police (M2CF)
		NFM	Ely	Police
		NFM	England & Wales	HM Prisons
		NFM	Gt Manchester Eccles	Police
		NFM	Gt Manchester Hr. Broughton	Police
		NFM	Gt Manchester Little Hulton	Police
		NFM	Gt Manchester Pendleton	Police
		NFM	Gt Manchester Salford	Police
		NFM	Gt Manchester Swinton	Police
		NFM	Gt Manchester Walkden	Police
		NFM	Hackenthorpe	Police (E1)
		NFM	Hatfield	Police
		NFM	Hungerford	Police (FB)
		NFM	Lancaster	HMP
		NFM	Langley	Police
		NFM	Milton Keynes	Police
		NFM	Morley	Police
		NFM	Newbury (FA)	Police
		NFM	Newcastle	Police (M2LBB1)
		NFM	Newport Pagnell	Police (DD)
		NFM	Northallerton	Police
		NFM	Redhill	Police (ER)
		NFM	Reigate	Police (ER)
		NFM	Saxmundham	Police (VL)
		NFM	Southend	Police
		NFM	Stafford	Police
		NFM	Thatcham	Police
		NFM	Welwyn Garden City	Police
		NFM	Wolverton	Police
		NFM	Dorking	Police
		NFM	Dorchester	Police
		NFM	Coalville	Police
		NFM	Kirby	Police
		NFM	Coalville	Police
		NFM	Caergwle	Police
451.9500	465.8500	NFM	England & Wales	Police Channel 32
		NFM	England & Wales	Mobile Repeaters
		NFM	Aldershot	Police
		NFM	Ash	Police

Base	Mobile	Mode	Location	User and Notes
		NFM	Bewdley	Police
		NFM	Birmingham Kings Heath	Police
		NFM	Brownhills	Police
		NFM	Farnborough	Police Air Show Security
		NFM	Forest Hill	Police (M2LBC4)/(I2)
		NFM	Kings Heath	Police (M2YMB)
		NFM	Lancashire	Police Spare Channel
		NFM	Leeds Garforth	Police
		NFM	Lichfield	Police
		NFM	Long Benton	Police
		NFM	Mytchett	Police
		NFM	Newark	Police
		NFM	Redditch	Police
		NFM	Stourport	Police
		NFM	Thames Valley	Police
		NFM	Widnes	Police (D1)
		NFM	Hitchin	Police
		NFM	Leeds Garforth	Police
		NFM	Plymouth	Police Response Team
		NFM	Blackpool	Police
		NFM	Bournemouth	Police
451.9750	465.8750	NFM	Burnley	Police
452.0000	465.9000	NFM	Leyland	Police
452.0500	465.9500	NFM	Skelmersdale	Police
452.1250	465.1250	NFM	Nationwide	Engineering Test Channel
452.1500	466.0500	NFM	Morecambe Bay	Police
		NFM	Thames Valley	Police Special Use
		NFM	Brentwood	Police
452.1750	466.0750	NFM	Preston	Police
452.2000		NFM	Nationwide	National Power Leaky Feeders
452.2250	466.1250	NFM	Blackburn	Police
452.2500	446.4750	NFM	England & Wales	Fire Service Channel 02
		NFM	England & Wales	Police Use
452.2500	452.2500	NFM	Powys	Fire Brigade
		NFM	England & Wales	Police Channel 73
452.2750	465.9250	NFM	England & Wales	Police Channel 57
		NFM	England & Wales	Police Reserve Channel A
		NFM	Gt Manchester Chadderton	Police
		NFM	Gt Manchester Failsworth	Police
		NFM	Gt Manchester Royton	Police
		NFM	Gt Manchester Uppermill	Police
		NFM	Oldham	Police
		NFM	Thames Valley	Police
		NFM	Merseyside	Armed Police (TH)
452.3000	465.9000	NFM	England & Wales	Police Channel 60
		NFM	England & Wales	Police Reserve Channel C
		NFM	Northwich	Police
		NFM	Bridgnorth	Police

Base	Mobile	Mode	Location	User and Notes
		NFM	Thames Valley	Police
		NFM	Manchester	Police
		NFM	Winsford	Police
		NFM	Portsmouth	Diplomatic Protection
452.3125	457.3125	NFM	Nationwide	Grand Prix Team
452.3250	466.2250	NFM	Darwin	Police
		NFM	Sale	Police
		NFM	Urmston	Police
		NFM	Manchester	Police
452.3250	452.3250	NFM	England & Wales	Police Channel 06
		NFM	England & Wales	Police Channel 74
		NFM	Thames Valley	Police Support Units
		NFM	Nationwide	Police Radio Engineers
		NFM	Nationwide	Police Covert
452.3500	466.2500	NFM	England & Wales	Police Channel 59
		NFM	England & Wales	Police Reserve Channel B
		NFM	Houhgton	Police (O2) Encrypted
		NFM	Liverpool Huyton	Police
		NFM	Gt Manchester Ashton-U-Lyne	Police
		NFM	Gt Manchester Denton	Police
		NFM	Gt Manchester Droylsden	Police
		NFM	Gt Manchester Hyde	Police
		NFM	Gt Manchester Mottram	Police
		NFM	Gt Manchester Stalybridge	Police
		NFM	Thames Valley	Police
		NFM	Thameside	Police
		NFM	Cannock	Police
		NFM	Merseyside	Police (Encrypted)
452.3625	452.3625	NFM	England & Wales	Fire Services Channel 2
452.3750	452.3750	NFM	England & Wales	Channel 75
		NFM	England & Wales	Police Channel 75
		NFM	England & Wales	Tactical Firearms Unit
		NFM	Jersey	Tactical Firearms Unit Ch 1
452.3750	466.2750	NFM	England & Wales	Channel 76
		NFM	England & Wales	Police Channel 76
		NFM	England & Wales	Tactical Firearms Unit
		NFM	Jersey	Tactical Firearms Unit Ch 2
		NFM	County Durham	HMP Frankland
452.3750	452.3750	NFM	Scarborough	Police CID
		NFM	Jersey	Tactical Firearms Unit
452.4000	466.3000	NFM	England & Wales	Police Channel 33
		NFM	Attercliffe	Police (D2)
		NFM	Birmingham	HMP Digbeth
		NFM	Birmingham Central	Police (M2YMF)
		NFM	Bolton	Police
		NFM	Burnley	Police
		NFM	Cambridge	Police
		NFM	Canterbury	HMP Canterbury

Base	Mobile	Mode	Location	User and Notes
		NFM	Derby	Police (O1)
		NFM	Digbeth	Police
		NFM	East Dereham	Police
		NFM	East Sussex	HMP Prisons
		NFM	Epping	Police
		NFM	Exeter	Police (Delta Control)
		NFM	Great Yarmouth	Police
		NFM	Gt Manchester Arndale Centre	Police
		NFM	Gt Manchester Bootle Street	Police
		NFM	Gt Manchester City Centre	Police
		NFM	Gt Manchester Newton St	Police
		NFM	Harpenden	Police
		NFM	Hebburn	Police (L4)
		NFM	Huddersfield	Police
		NFM	Hull	Police
		NFM	Humberside	Police
		NFM	Hunstanton	Police
		NFM	Huntingdon	Police
		NFM	Jarrow	Police (M2LBE2)
		NFM	Lancaster	HMP
		NFM	Leicester	HMP Welford Rd
		NFM	Liverpool Marsh Lane	Police
		NFM	London	HMP Wandsworth
		NFM	London	HMP Wormwood Scrubs
		NFM	Neots	Police
		NFM	Newcastle	Police
		NFM	Norwich	Police
		NFM	Pickering	Police
		NFM	Plymouth	Police
		NFM	Portland Bill	HM Borstal
		NFM	Sheffield Attercliffe	Police (F3)
		NFM	Shipley	Police
		NFM	St Albans	Police
		NFM	St Austell	Police
		NFM	Stafford	HMP Stafford
		NFM	Sussex	Ford Open Prison
		NFM	Sussex	HMP Lewes
		NFM	Sussex	HMP Northeye
		NFM	Swansea	HMP Swansea
		NFM	Swindon	Police
		NFM	Thames Valley	Police
		NFM	Thetford	Police
		NFM	West Midlands, Bradford St	Police
		NFM	York	Police
		NFM	Portsmouth	Police (Encrypted)
		NFM	Birmingham Aiport	Police
		NFM	Huddersfield	Police
		NFM	Padiham	Police

Base	Mobile	Mode	Location	User and Notes
		NFM	Portsmouth	Police (Fratton Park)
		NFM	Merseyside	Police (Encrypted)
		NFM	Merseyside	Police HQ Div B
		NFM	Crosby	Police (B3)
		NFM	York	Traffic Wardens
452.4000	466.5000	NFM	St Austell	Police
452.4000	466.4500	NFM	Windermere	Police
		NFM	Woodbridge	Police
		NFM	Maghull	Police
452.4000	452.4000	NFM	Lancashire	Drug Squad
452.4250	466.3250	NFM	England & Wales	Police Channel 34
		NFM	Bedworth	Police
		NFM	Bradford Queenshouse	Police
		NFM	Bridgend	Police
		NFM	Channel Tunnel	French Police
		NFM	Derby South West	Police (O2)
		NFM	Gt Manchester Altrincham	Police
		NFM	Gt Manchester Sale	Police
		NFM	Gt Manchester Stretford	Police
		NFM	Gt Manchester Trafford	Police
		NFM	Gt Manchester Urmston	Police
		NFM	Hadleigh	Police
		NFM	Ipswich	Police Ispwich FC Spotters
		NFM	Leyland	Police
		NFM	London	HMP Wormwood Scrubs
		NFM	Malton	Police
		NFM	Manningham	Police
		NFM	Preston HQ	Police (BD)
		NFM	Scarborough	Police
		NFM	Stockton on Tees	Police
		NFM	Thames Valley	Police
		NFM	Wombwell	Police (B2)
		NFM	Gosport	Police
452.4250	466.4500	NFM	London	Notting Hill Carnival 7
		NFM	Portsmouth	Police
		NFM	Bradford Queenshouse	Police
		NFM	Fareham	Police
		NFM	Fareham	Taxis
		NFM	Preston	Police
		NFM	Gosport	Police
452.4375	466.3375	NFM	London Orpington	Police
452.4500	466.3500	NFM	England & Wales	Police Channel 35
		NFM	Amersham	Police (AD)
		NFM	Birmingham	Police
		NFM	Boroughbridge	Police
		NFM	Bradford Odsal	Police
		NFM	Bridgend	Police
		NFM	Briglington	Police

Base	Mobile	Mode	Location	User and Notes
		NFM	Cheltenham	Police
		NFM	Chesham	Police (AH)
		NFM	Colwyn Bay	Police
		NFM	Derby Central	Police
		NFM	Dorking	Police (ED)
		NFM	Eastbourne	Police (M2KBEO+EE)
		NFM	Egbaston	Police (M2YMB)
		NFM	Ely	Police
		NFM	Exmouth	Police
		NFM	Farnborough	Police
		NFM	Farringdon	Police (N1) Encrypted
		NFM	Fleet	Police
		NFM	Gorleston-on-Sea	Police
		NFM	Gt Manchester Heywood	Police
		NFM	Gt Manchester Kirkholt	Police
		NFM	Gt Manchester Littleborough	Police
		NFM	Gt Manchester Middleton	Police
		NFM	Gt Manchester Milnrow	Police
		NFM	Gt Yarmouth	Police
		NFM	Sheffield Hammerton Rd	Police (F1)
		NFM	Hillsborough	Police
		NFM	Hull	Police
		NFM	Huntingdon	Police
		NFM	Knutsford	Police
		NFM	Leatherhead	Police (EL)
		NFM	Liverpool	Police
		NFM	London Chequers	Police (AZ)
		NFM	Medway	Police
		NFM	Norwich Rural	Police
		NFM	Nottingham Radford Rd	Police
		NFM	Rochdale	Police
		NFM	Ryhope	Police (N2) Encrypted
		NFM	Speke	Police
		NFM	Stroud	Police
		NFM	Sunderland	Police (M2LBF2)
		NFM	Thirsk	Police
		NFM	West Midlands, Belgrave Rd	Police
		NFM	Westbury	Police
		NFM	West Worcester	Police
		NFM	Wilmslow	Police (C2)
		NFM	Salisbury City	Police
		NFM	Dover	Police
		NFM	Folkestone	Police
		NFM	Deal	Police
		NFM	Medway Towns	Police
		NFM	North Wales	Police
		NFM	Halewood	Police
		NFM	Digbeth	Police

Base	Mobile	Mode	Location	User and Notes
		NFM	Frome	Police
		NFM	Bradford Odsal	Police
		NFM	Ruabun	Police
452.4625	466.3625	NFM	Northumbria	Police Car-Car (M2LB)
452.4750	466.3750	NFM	England & Wales	Police Channel 36
		NFM	Beumont Leys	Police
		NFM	Birmingham Brierley Hill	Police (M2YMJ)
		NFM	Brierley Hill	Police
		NFM	Brighton	Police (M2KBCO+CB)
		NFM	Broadmoor Secure Hospital	
		NFM	Caterham	Police
		NFM	Chelmsley Wood	Police
		NFM	Farnborough	Police Air Show Security
		NFM	Kingswinford	Police
		NFM	Durham	HMP Frankland (M2NE)
		NFM	North Watford	Police
		NFM	Oxley	Police
		NFM	Oxted	Police
		NFM	Rawmarsh	Police (C2)
		NFM	Shrewsbury	Police
		NFM	Skelmersdale	Police
		NFM	Thames Valley	Police
		NFM	Lloyd House Central	Police
		NFM	Ormskirk	Police
		NFM	Bootle	Police
		NFM	New Forest	Police
452.5000	466.4000	NFM	England & Wales	Police Channel 37
		NFM	Aldershot	Police
		NFM	Barton on Humber	Police
		NFM	Bicester	HMP Bullingdon
		NFM	Braintree	Police
		NFM	Bristol	Police
		NFM	Byker	Police (E1)
		NFM	Carmarthen	Police
		NFM	Chelmsford	HMP Chelmsford (PG)
		NFM	Clacton-on-Sea	Police
		NFM	East Grinstead	Police
		NFM	Farnborough	Police
		NFM	Fleet	Police
		NFM	Gt Manchester Airport	Police
		NFM	Gt Manchester Baguley	Police
		NFM	Gt Manchester Benchill	Police
		NFM	Gt Manchester Chorlton	Police
		NFM	Gt Manchester Didsbury	Police
		NFM	Gt Manchester Northenden	Police
		NFM	Gt Manchester Northern Moor	Police
		NFM	Gt Manchester Rusholme	Police
		NFM	Gt Manchester Withington	Police

Base	Mobile	Mode	Location	User and Notes
		NFM	Gt Yarmouth	Police
		NFM	Hailsham	Police (M2KBEO+EA)
		NFM	Harbourne	Police (M2YMC)
		NFM	Harpenden	Police
		NFM	Haverfordwest	Police
		NFM	Headingley	Police
		NFM	Heaton	Police (E3)
		NFM	HMP Ashford	
		NFM	Hove	Police (M2KBCO+CH)
		NFM	Lancashire	Police Spare Channel
		NFM	Landywood	Police
		NFM	Leeds Weetwood	Police
		NFM	Letchwood	Police
		NFM	Liverpool City Centre	Police
		NFM	London	HMP Brixton
		NFM	Longsight	Police
		NFM	Loughborough	Police (B/L)
		NFM	March	Police
		NFM	Market Drayton	Police
		NFM	Newcastle	Police (M2LBB2)
		NFM	Newtown	Police
		NFM	Northampton	Police
		NFM	Preston	HMP Preston
		NFM	St Albans	Police
		NFM	South Killingholme	Police
		NFM	Swanley	Police
		NFM	Thames Valley	Police
		NFM	Walker	Police (E2)
		NFM	Whitchurch	Police
		NFM	Winterton	Police
		NFM	Worcester	Police (CA)
		NFM	Brighton	Police
		NFM	Weymouth	Police
		NFM	West Kingsdown	Police
		NFM	Swanscombe	Police
		NFM	Colchester	Prison
		NFM	Kirkdale	Police
		NFM	Bishop Auckland	Police (AA)
		NFM	Merseyside	Police (Encrypted)
		NFM	Merseyside	Police HQ Div A
		NFM	Wellington	Police (JA)
		NFM	Wem	Police (JF)
		NFM	Whitchurch	Police (JG)
		NFM	Market Drayton	Police (JH)
		NFM	Walton	Police (C4)
		NFM	Preston	Police
452.5250	466.4250	NFM	England & Wales	Police Channel 38
		NFM	England & Wales	Special Use Channel 88

Base	Mobile	Mode	Location	User and Notes
		NFM	Various Areas	Channel 38
		NFM	Nationwide	Police Special Use
		NFM	Nationwide	Police Airborne
		NFM	Newport	Police Ch 2
		NFM	Redcar	Police
		NFM	Gt Manchester	Police
		NFM	Stockport	Police
452.5375	452.5375	NFM	England & Wales	Fire/Police Link Reptrs Ch 8
452.5500	466.4500	NFM	England & Wales	Police Channel 39
		NFM	Banbury	Police (BD)
		NFM	Barnstable	Police
		NFM	Bicester	Police (BE)
		NFM	Canvey Island	Police
		NFM	Carlisle	Police Encrypted
		NFM	Carlton	Police
		NFM	Cuxwold Aerodrome	Police
		NFM	Dishforth	Police
		NFM	Gt Manchester Ashton-U-Lyne	Police
		NFM	Gt Manchester Denton	Police
		NFM	Gt Manchester Droylsden	Police
		NFM	Gt Manchester Hyde	Police
		NFM	Gt Manchester Mottram	Police
		NFM	Gt Manchester Stalybridge	Police
		NFM	Hanley	Police
		NFM	Hessle	Police
		NFM	Hull	Police
		NFM	Kings Lynn	Police
		NFM	Leeds	Police
		NFM	Liverpool	Police
		NFM	Luton	Police
		NFM	Luton Airport	Police
		NFM	March	Police
		NFM	Milford Haven	Police
		NFM	Millgarth	Police
		NFM	Newport	Police
		NFM	Newton Abbot	Police
		NFM	Newton Aycliffe	Police (AK)
		NFM	Norwich	British Transport Police
		NFM	Nottingham	Police
		NFM	Rotherham	Police (C1)
		NFM	Smethwick	Police (M2YMK)
		NFM	Swindon	Police
		NFM	Thames Valley	Police
		NFM	Thameside	Police
		NFM	Uckfield	Police (M2KBCU+EU)
		NFM	Whitby	Police
		NFM	Wilmslow	Police
		NFM	Woking	Police (NW)

Base	Mobile	Mode	Location	User and Notes
		NFM	Tubrook	Police
		NFM	Newport	Police Ch 1
		NFM	Soho Road	Police
		NFM	Trowbridge	Police
		NFM	Leeds Millgarth	Police
		NFM	Southampton City	Police CID
		NFM	Witby	Police
		NFM	Merseyside	Police (Encrypted)
		NFM	Merseyside	Police HQ Div D
		NFM	Rhos	Police
452.5750	466.4750	NFM	England & Wales	Police Channel 40
		NFM	Bacup	Police
		NFM	Basingstoke	Police
		NFM	Billericay	Police
		NFM	Bradford Toller Lane	Police
		NFM	Canterbury	Police
		NFM	Gt Man. Ashton-in-M'field	Police
		NFM	Gt Manchester Hindley	Police
		NFM	Gt Manchester Leigh	Police
		NFM	Gt Manchester Lower Ince	Police
		NFM	Gt Manchester Pemberton	Police
		NFM	Gt Manchester Standish	Police
		NFM	Gt Manchester Tyldesley	Police
		NFM	Hexham	Police (B1)
		NFM	Nationwide	British Transport Police
		NFM	Morecambe	Police
		NFM	Morpeth	Police (M2LBA1)
		NFM	Newhaven Docks	Police Special Branch
		NFM	Portsmouth Docks	Police
		NFM	Rawtenstall	Police
		NFM	Rossendale	Police
		NFM	Sevenoaks	Police
		NFM	Thames Valley	Police
		NFM	Waterfoot	Police
		NFM	Welwyn Garden City	Police
		NFM	Wickford	Police
		NFM	Wigan	Police
		NFM	Stockton-on-Tees	Police
		NFM	Lancaster	Police
		NFM	Bradford Toller Lane	Police
		NFM	Gosport	Police
		NFM	Wigan	Police
452.5875	452.4875	NFM	London Chislehurst	Police
452.6000	466.5000	NFM	England & Wales	Police Channel 41
		NFM	Alnwick	Police (M2LBA3)
		NFM	Ascot	Police (M2CB)
		NFM	Berkhamstead	Police
		NFM	Birmingham W. Bromwich	Police (M2YMK)

Base	Mobile	Mode	Location	User and Notes
		NFM	Bognor Regis	Police (WO)
		NFM	Bristol	Police
		NFM	Bromsgrove	Police
		NFM	Buckinghamshire	HMP Grendon
		NFM	Bury St Edmunds	Police
		NFM	Canterbury	Police
		NFM	Cardiff	Police
		NFM	Crewe	Police (B1)
		NFM	Derby	Police
		NFM	Droitwich	Police
		NFM	Exeter	Police
		NFM	Fallowfields	Police
		NFM	Felixstowe	Police
		NFM	Fulwood	Police
		NFM	Glenfield	Police
		NFM	Gravesend	Police
		NFM	Grimsby	Police
		NFM	Gt Manchester Gorton	Police
		NFM	Gt Manchester Greenheys	Police
		NFM	Gt Manchester Levenshulme	Police
		NFM	Gt Manchester Longsight	Police
		NFM	Gt Manchester Moss Side	Police
		NFM	Gt Manchester Whalley Range	Police
		NFM	Hastings	Police (M2KBEO+EH)
		NFM	Haverhill	Police
		NFM	Hemel Heamstead	Police
		NFM	Hertford	Police
		NFM	Holmfirth	Police
		NFM	Hook	Police
		NFM	Leamington Spa	Police
		NFM	Leicester	Police
		NFM	Leiston	Police
		NFM	Midhurst	Police (M2KBWO,C,M)
		NFM	Mildenhall	Police
		NFM	Nantwich	Police
		NFM	Northfleet	Police
		NFM	Petworth	Police (M2KBWO, C, M, P)
		NFM	Preston	Police
		NFM	Rubery	Police
		NFM	Scunthorpe	Police
		NFM	Seaham	Police (BF)
		NFM	Selsey	Police (M2KBWO, C)
		NFM	Stavely	Police
		NFM	Stow	Police
		NFM	Swansea	Police
		NFM	Syston	Police (B/S)
		NFM	Thames Valley	Police
		NFM	Tring	Police

Base	Mobile	Mode	Location	User and Notes
		NFM	Wallasey	Police
		NFM	Ware	Police
		NFM	Windsor	Police (CD)
		NFM	Worksop	Police
		NFM	Chichester	Police
		NFM	West Bromwich	Police
		NFM	Darlington	Police (DJ) Encrypted
		NFM	Preston	Police
452.6250	466.5250	NFM	England & Wales	Police Channel 42
		NFM	Barrow-in-Furness	Police (BB)
		NFM	Benwell	Police (F1)
		NFM	Chichester	Police (M2KBWO, C)
		NFM	Cumbria South Lakes	Police (BB)
		NFM	Erdington	Police (M2YMD)
		NFM	Gt Manchester Eccles	Police
		NFM	Gt Manchester Hr. Broughton	Police
		NFM	Gt Manchester Little Hulton	Police
		NFM	Gt Manchester Pendleton	Police
		NFM	Gt Manchester Salford	Police
		NFM	Gt Manchester Swinton	Police
		NFM	Gt Manchester Walkden	Police
		NFM	Habrough	Police
		NFM	Immingham	Police
		NFM	Kendal	Police
		NFM	Leicester City Centre	Police
		NFM	Malvern	Police
		NFM	Mansfield	Police Encrypted
		NFM	Newburn	Police (M2LBB4)
		NFM	Newcastle	Police
		NFM	Scotswood	Police (F1)
		NFM	Stoke on Trent	Police
		NFM	Swinton	Police (K2)
		NFM	Tamworth	Police
		NFM	Thames Valley	Police
		NFM	Wigston	Police (CA)
		NFM	Yorkshire	Police Tec. Support Units
		NFM	Shoreham-by-Sea	Police
		NFM	Wolverhampton	Police
		NFM	Hove	Police
		NFM	Shoreham	Police
		NFM	Carlisle	Police
452.6375	452.6375	NFM	England	General Fire Incidents
452.6375	466.5375	NFM	Oprington	Police
		NFM	St Mary Cray	Police
		NFM	Chislehurst	Police
		NFM	Biggin Hill	Police
		NFM	Farnborough	Police
452.6500	466.5500	NFM	England & Wales	Police Channel 43

Base	Mobile	Mode	Location	User and Notes
		NFM	Arundel	Police
		NFM	Baskingstoke	Police
		NFM	Bedford	Police
		NFM	Bexhill	Police
		NFM	Birmingham Aldridge & Bnhills	Police (M2YMH)
		NFM	Blackburn	Police
		NFM	Bodmin	Police
		NFM	Brentwood	Police
		NFM	Bridgend	Police
		NFM	Bristol	Police
		NFM	Bridgnorth	Police
		NFM	Brighton	Police HQ
		NFM	Cambourne	Police
		NFM	Chapletown	Police
		NFM	Chelmsford	Police
		NFM	Chester	Police (A1)
		NFM	Colchester	Police
		NFM	Coventry	Police
		NFM	Crowborough	Police (M2KBNR)
		NFM	Derby City Centre	Police(O3)
		NFM	Durham	HMP Durham (M2MW)
		NFM	Ely	Police
		NFM	Gateshead Metro Centre	Police (M2LBD1)/(J1)
		NFM	Gosport	Police
		NFM	Hagley	Police
		NFM	Hartlepool	Police
		NFM	Helston	Police
		NFM	Hemel Hempstead	Police
		NFM	HMP Holloway	
		NFM	Hoddesdon	Police
		NFM	Kidderminster	Police
		NFM	Leicester	Police (452.8750 Alternate)
		NFM	Lewes HQ	Police
		NFM	Lincoln	HMP Lincoln
		NFM	Littlehampton	Police (M2KBWO, L)
		NFM	London Camden Town	Police
		NFM	Longbridge	Police
		NFM	Longton	Police
		NFM	Morpeth	Police
		NFM	Newcastle	Police
		NFM	Nuneaton	Police (M2YJN)
		NFM	Preston	Police
		NFM	Portsmouth	Police
		NFM	Sheffield	Police
		NFM	Shrewsbury	HMP Shrewsbury (M2JY)
		NFM	Swansea	Police
		NFM	Thames Valley	Police
		NFM	Telford	Police

Base	Mobile	Mode	Location	User and Notes
		NFM	Truro	Police
		NFM	Ware	Police
		NFM	West Bar	Police (E3)
		NFM	West Sussex HQ	Police
		NFM	West Yorkshire	Police Mobile Repeaters
		NFM	Woodbridge	Police
		NFM	Walsall	Police
		NFM	Portsmouth	Police
		NFM	Bootle	HMP Bootle
		NFM	Liskeard	Police Town Net
		NFM	Chester City	Police
		NFM	Wigton	Police
		NFM	Liverpool	HMP Liverpool
		NFM	Christchurch	Police
		NFM	Rhymney Valley	Police
		NFM	New Town	Police
452.6750	466.5750	NFM	England & Wales	Police Channel 44
		NFM	Ashington	Police (M2LBA6)
		NFM	Aston	Police (M2YMD1)
		NFM	Birmingham Stoney Stanton	Police
		NFM	Baskingstoke	Police
		NFM	Coventry North	Police (M2YMM)
		NFM	Cuxwold Aerodrome	Police
		NFM	Debenham	Police (VL)
		NFM	Dover	Police Special Branch
		NFM	Gt Manchester Airport	Police
		NFM	Gt Manchester Baguley	Police
		NFM	Gt Manchester Benchill	Police
		NFM	Gt Manchester Chorlton	Police
		NFM	Gt Manchester Didsbury	Police
		NFM	Gt Manchester Northenden	Police
		NFM	Gt Manchester Northern Moor	Police
		NFM	Gt Manchester Rusholme	Police
		NFM	Gt Manchester Withington	Police
		NFM	Grantham	Police
		NFM	Hollbeach	Police
		NFM	Maltby	Police (C3)
		NFM	Newbury	Police (G2)
		NFM	Rotherham	Police
		NFM	Thames Valley	Police
		NFM	W Midlands, Steelhouse Lane	Police
		NFM	West Midlands, Queens Rd	Police
		NFM	Middlesbrough	Police
		NFM	Telford	Police
		NFM	Middlesborough	Police (M2)
		NFM	Merseyside	Police (Encrypted)
452.7000	466.6000	NFM	England & Wales	Police Channel 45
		NFM	Barrow In Furness	Police

Base	Mobile	Mode	Location	User and Notes
		NFM	Battle	Police
		NFM	Birmingham	Police
		NFM	Bognor Regis	Police (M2KBNO)
		NFM	Boston	Police
		NFM	Bristol	Police
		NFM	Burgess Hill	Police
		NFM	Cambridge City Centre	Police
		NFM	Chipping Norton	Police (BF)
		NFM	Congleton	Police (B2)
		NFM	Cheshire	Police
		NFM	Doncaster	Police
		NFM	Dover	HM Immigration
		NFM	Easingwood	Police
		NFM	Essex	Police
		NFM	Grays	Police
		NFM	Guildford	Police (WG)
		NFM	Halesowen & Stourbridge	Police (M2YMJ)
		NFM	Halifax	Police
		NFM	Harrogate	Police
		NFM	Hayworth Heath	Police (M2KBNO, NA)
		NFM	Hucknall	Police
		NFM	Kettering	Police
		NFM	Knaresborough	Police
		NFM	Lancing	Police
		NFM	Leighton Buzzard	Police
		NFM	Liverpool	Police
		NFM	Liverpool St Helens	Police
		NFM	Merseyside, St Helens	Police
		NFM	Newark	Police
		NFM	Peterborough	Police
		NFM	Scarborough	Police
		NFM	Shoreham	Police
		NFM	South Shields	Police (M2LBE1)/(L1)
		NFM	Sutton Coldfield	Police (M2YMD)
		NFM	Thames Valley	Police
		NFM	West Midlands, Halsowen	Police
		NFM	West Midlands	Police (M2KBNO, B)
		NFM	Woodstock	Police
		NFM	Stockton	Police
		NFM	Bilston	Police
		NFM	Salisbury	Police
		NFM	Chippenham	Police
		NFM	Halifax	Police
		NFM	Merseyside	Police (Encrypted)
		NFM	Merseyside	Police HQ Div E
		NFM	Flint	Police
		NFM	Worthing	Police
		NFM	Irby	Police (A3)

Base	Mobile	Mode	Location	User and Notes
452.7250	466.6250	NFM	England & Wales	Police Channel 46
		NFM	Birmingham	Police
		NFM	Bloxwich	Police (M2YMH)
		NFM	Cleckheaton	Police
		NFM	Cleethorpes	Police
		NFM	Cowes	Police
		NFM	Coventry Central	Police (M2YMM)
		NFM	Grimsby	Police
		NFM	Gt Manchester	HMP Strangeways
		NFM	Guernsey	HMP Les Nicholles
		NFM	Horsham	Police (M2KBNO, H)
		NFM	Houghton le Spring	Police
		NFM	Liverpool Toxteth	Police
		NFM	Mold	Police
		NFM	Ryde	Police
		NFM	Stechford	Police
		NFM	Stockport	Police
		NFM	Thames Valley	Police
		NFM	Tunstall	Police
		NFM	Washington	Police (O1) Encrypted
		NFM	West Midlands, Littel Park St	Police
		NFM	Willenhall	Police
		NFM	Washington	Police (M2LBF4)
		NFM	Keswick	Police
		NFM	Isle of Wight	Police
		NFM	Wednesbury	Police
		NFM	Cleckheaton	Police
		NFM	Bloxwich	Police (M2YMHX)
		NFM	Brownhills	Police (M2YMHX)
		NFM	Willenhall	Police (M2YMHX)
		NFM	Darlaston	Police (M2YMHX)
		NFM	Cheshire	HMP Risley
		NFM	Broadmoor	HMP Broadmoor
		NFM	Wrexham	Police
		NFM	Sittingbourne	Police
452.7375	465.6375	NFM	Westerham	Police
452.7500	466.6500	NFM	England & Wales	Police Channel 47
		NFM	Baldock	Police
		NFM	Beverley	Police
		NFM	Birmingham Yardley	Police (M2YME)
		NFM	Blackwater	Police
		NFM	Boston	Police
		NFM	Bridgeford	Police
		NFM	Brighton	Police CID
		NFM	Bury St Edmonds	Police
		NFM	Camberley	Police (NC)
		NFM	Cardiff	Police
		NFM	Chelmsford	Police

Base	Mobile	Mode	Location	User and Notes
		NFM	Dartford	Police
		NFM	Egham	Police (NE)
		NFM	Gatwick	Police
		NFM	Guernsey	Police (M2GY)
		NFM	Goole	Police
		NFM	Gt Manchester Bredbury	Police
		NFM	Gt Manchester Brinnington	Police
		NFM	Gt Manchester Cheadle	Police
		NFM	Gt Manchester Cheadle Hulme	Police
		NFM	Gt Manchester Hazel Grove	Police
		NFM	Gt Manchester Marple	Police
		NFM	Gt Manchester Reddish	Police
		NFM	Guernsey	Police (M2GY)
		NFM	Hadleigh	Police
		NFM	Halifax	Police
		NFM	Hitchin	Police
		NFM	Ilkley	Police
		NFM	Ipswich Div HQ	Police
		NFM	Keithley	Police
		NFM	Leicester Wigston	Police
		NFM	Lewes	Police (M2KBEO, L)
		NFM	Lowestoft	Police
		NFM	Mexborough	Police
		NFM	Needham Market	Police
		NFM	Newmarket	Police
		NFM	Nottingham	Police
		NFM	Oxhey	Police
		NFM	Rickmansworth	Police
		NFM	Royston	Police
		NFM	Sheerness	Police
		NFM	Stockport	Police
		NFM	Sudbury	Police
		NFM	Sullbridge	Police (F1)
		NFM	Sunderland	Police (M2LBF1) Encrypted
		NFM	Swansea	Police
		NFM	Thames Valley	Police
		NFM	Tonbridge	Police
		NFM	Tunbridge Wells	Police
		NFM	Wakefield	Police
		NFM	Worthing	Police (M2KBWO, WW)
		NFM	Bristol	Police
		NFM	Lancing	Police
		NFM	Pontypool	Police
		NFM	Darlaston	Police
		NFM	Lancing	Police
		NFM	Arundel	Police
		NFM	Littlehampton	Police
		NFM	Bath	Police

Base	Mobile	Mode	Location	User and Notes
		NFM	Wakefield	Police
		NFM	Merseyside	Police (Encrypted)
		NFM	Gatwick Airport	Police (GatPol)
		NFM	Boston	Police
		NFM	Dover	Police
452.7750	466.6750	NFM	England & Wales	Police Channel 48
		NFM	Basildon	Police
		NFM	Beeston	Police
		NFM	Birkenhead	Police
		NFM	Birmingham	Police
		NFM	Burslem	Police
		NFM	Dewsbury	Police
		NFM	Ellesmere Port	Police (A2)
		NFM	Gt Manchester Ringway	Police
		NFM	Handsworth	Police (M2YMC)
		NFM	Ripon	Police
		NFM	Thames Valley	Police
		NFM	West Midlands, Thornhill Rd	Police
		NFM	Redcar	Police
		NFM	Pitsea	Police
		NFM	Tipton	Police
		NFM	Dewsbury	Police
		NFM	Ellesmere Port	Police
		NFM	Wallsey	Police
		NFM	Jonnstown	Police
		NFM	Ellesmere Port	Police
452.8000	466.7000	NFM	England & Wales	Police Channel 49
		NFM	Abingdon	Police (FH)
		NFM	Beeston	Police
		NFM	Berwick-upon-Tweed	Police (M2LBA2)
		NFM	Blundiston	HMP
		NFM	Brighouse	Police
		NFM	Camborne	Police
		NFM	Chester le Street	Police (CG)
		NFM	City Of London	Police
		NFM	Cornwall	Police
		NFM	Crawley	Police (M2KBNO, NC)
		NFM	Didcot	Police (M2FC)
		NFM	Dyfed	Police
		NFM	Evesham	Police
		NFM	Falmouth	Police
		NFM	Gt Manchester Salford West	Police Encrypted
		NFM	Harwich	Police
		NFM	Haverfordwest	Police
		NFM	Hayle	Police
		NFM	Hemsworth	Police
		NFM	Horsham	Police
		NFM	Hull	HMP Hull

Base	Mobile	Mode	Location	User and Notes
		NFM	Ipswich	Police
		NFM	Landywood	Police (M2YMC)
		NFM	Leicester Beumont Leys	Police (A/B)
		NFM	Liverpool Walton Lane	Police
		NFM	Llanelly	Police
		NFM	London	Police
		NFM	Louth	Police
		NFM	Maidstone	HMP Maidstone
		NFM	Newbury	Police
		NFM	Newcastle	Police
		NFM	Newhaven	Police (M2KBEO, EN)
		NFM	North Shields	Police (M2LBC1)
		NFM	Norwich	HMP Norwich
		NFM	Penry	Police
		NFM	Penzance	Police
		NFM	Pontefract	Police
		NFM	Powys	Police
		NFM	Seaford	Police
		NFM	Skipton	Police
		NFM	St Ives	Police
		NFM	Stevenage	Police
		NFM	Stoke on Trent	Police
		NFM	Stradishall	HMP High Point
		NFM	Telford	Police
		NFM	Thames Valley	Police
		NFM	Truro	Police
		NFM	Wallingford	Police
		NFM	Watford	Police
		NFM	Wellington	Police
		NFM	Witham	Police
		NFM	Abingdon	Police (FH)
		NFM	New Quay	Police
		NFM	Grantham	Police
		NFM	Bristol	HMP Horfield
		NFM	Warton	Police
		NFM	Willenhall	Police
		NFM	Brighouse	Police
		NFM	Berwick	Police
		NFM	Merseyside	Police (Encrypted)
		NFM	Merseyside	Police HQ Div C
		NFM	Preston	HMP
		NFM	Rhyl	Police
		NFM	Turbrook	Police (C2)
452.8250	466.7250	NFM	England & Wales	Police Channel 50
		NFM	England & Wales	Police Special Use
		NFM	Jersey	HMP La Moye Ch 1
		NFM	Nationwide	Police Vehicle Trackers
452.8250	466.6750	NFM	Jersey	HMP La Moye

Base	Mobile	Mode	Location	User and Notes
452.8500	466.7500	NFM	England & Wales	Police Channel 51
		NFM	Altrincham	Police
		NFM	Bromborough	Police
		NFM	Jersey	Police Special Events
		NFM	England & Wales	Police Vehicle Trackers
		NFM	England & Wales	Police Special Use
		NFM	Witham	Police
452.8500	466.7000	NFM	Jersey	Diplomatic Protection
452.8750	455.7750	NFM	England & Wales	Police Channel 52
		NFM	Bolton	Police
		NFM	Chelmsley Wood	Police (M2YML)
		NFM	Farnworth	Police
		NFM	Gt Manchester Astley Bridge	Police
		NFM	Gt Manchester Breightmet	Police
		NFM	Gt Manchester Farnworth	Police
		NFM	Gt Manchester Horwich	Police
		NFM	Gt Manchester Middle Hulton	Police
		NFM	Gt Manchester Westhoughton	Police
		NFM	Leicester Central	Police (C/A)
		NFM	N. Yorkshire	Police Link-Ravenscar Ch. 4
		NFM	Poole	Police Encrypted
		NFM	Rayleigh	Police
		NFM	Southend on Sea	Police
		NFM	Thames Valley	Police
		NFM	Winchester	Police
		NFM	Coventry	Police
		NFM	Bolton	Police
		NFM	Christchurch	Police
452.9000	466.8000	NFM	England & Wales	Police Channel 53
		NFM	Barrow In Furness	Police
		NFM	Chester le Street	Police (CG)
		NFM	Gt Man. Ashton-in-M'field	Police
		NFM	Gt Manchester Hindley	Police
		NFM	Gt Manchester Leigh	Police
		NFM	Gt Manchester Lower Ince	Police
		NFM	Gt Manchester Pemberton	Police
		NFM	Gt Manchester Standish	Police
		NFM	Gt Manchester Tyldesley	Police
		NFM	Leigh	Police
		NFM	Mid Glamorgan	Police
		NFM	Thames Valley	Police
		NFM	Wigan	Police
		NFM	Burton Down	Police
452.9250	452.9250	NFM	England & Wales	Police Channel 05
		NFM	Warrington	Police
		NFM	Lymm	Police
452.9250	466.7750	NFM	Jersey	Traffic Wardens
452.9250	466.8250	NFM	England & Wales	Police Channel 54

Base	Mobile	Mode	Location	User and Notes
		NFM	Christchurch	Police
		NFM	Derby	Police
		NFM	Ely	Police
		NFM	Essex	Police
		NFM	Ipswich	Police
		NFM	Leicester	Police
		NFM	South Yorkshire	Police Mobile Repeater
		NFM	Thames Valley	Police
		NFM	Linconshire	Police Mobile Repeater
		NFM	West Mercia	Police
		NFM	South Hams	Police VHF-UHF Repeater
		NFM	Warwickshire	Police Mobile Repeater
452.9500	466.8500	NFM	England & Wales	Police Channel 55
		NFM	Badsworth	Police
		NFM	Kidsgrove	Police
		NFM	Minsthorpe	Police
		NFM	N Yorkshire	Police Link-Ravenscar Ch. 2
		NFM	Pontefract	Police
		NFM	Runcorn	Police (E2)
		NFM	South Yorkshire	Police Mobile Repeater
		NFM	Thames Valley	Police
		NFM	Widnes	Police
		NFM	Newport	Traffic Police
452.9750	452.9750	NFM	England & Wales	Police Channel 01
452.9750	466.8250	NFM	Jersey	Tactical Firearms Unit Ch 3
		NFM	Jersey	HMP La Moye Ch 2
452.9750	466.8750	NFM	England & Wales	Police Channel 56
		NFM	England & Wales	Police Miscellaneous
		NFM	Scarborough	Police
		NFM	Blyth	Police (M2LBC5)
		NFM	Bolton	Police
		NFM	Gt Manchester Astley Bridge	Police
		NFM	Gt Manchester Breightmet	Police
		NFM	Gt Manchester Farnworth	Police
		NFM	Gt Manchester Horwich	Police
		NFM	Gt Manchester Middle Hulton	Police
		NFM	Gt Manchester Westhoughton	Police
		NFM	Horwich	Police
		NFM	Thames Valley	Police
		NFM	Crook Weardale	Police (AB)
		NFM	Bolton	Police Ch 2

453.0000 - 454.0000 MHz			PMR MOBILE BAND 12.5 kHz (SPLIT + 6.5 MHz)	
453.0000	466.9000	NFM	Nationwide	British Rail Transport Police
453.0250	459.5250	NFM	Felixstowe	Harbour Channel
		NFM	Guernsey	Harbour Channel
		NFM	Harwich	Harbour Channel

Base	Mobile	Mode	Location	User and Notes
		NFM	Bolton	Shopping Centre Security
		NFM	Leicester	Shopping Centre Security
		NFM	Jersey	Shell Aviation Fuel Supplies
		NFM	Moray Firth	Beatrice Alpha Platform
		NFM	Nigg Bay	Oil Terminal Control
		NFM	Stansted Airport	Trunked Network
		NFM	Staverton	Staverton Airport Ground
		NFM	Felixstowe	Harbour Channel
		NFM	Beatrice A	BP
		NFM	Beryl B	Mobil Temp. Const. Facility
		NFM	Middlesborough	BSC Ros Railways
		NFM	Leicester	High Street Security
		NFM	Stansted Airport	Ground Repeater
		NFM	Heathrow Airport	Ground Repeater
		NFM	Gloucester Airport	Ground Control
		NFM	Edinburgh	Waverley Market Security
453.0250	453.0250	NFM	Lomond	Amoco CTCSS 131.8 Hz
		NFM	NW Hutton	Amoco
		NFM	North Everest	Amoco CTCSS 131.8 Hz
		NFM	Nigg Terminal	BP
		NFM	Fulmar FSU	Shell
453.0375	459.5375	NFM	Heathrow Airport	Airline & BAA Ops
453.0500	459.5500	NFM	Bournemouth	Winfaith Security
		NFM	Guernsey	Princess Elizabeth Hospital
		NFM	Hull	Royal Infirmary Security
		NFM	Leicester, Brecon Hill	Park Rangers
		NFM	Nationwide	Air Rangers
		NFM	Nationwide	R.R. Security
		NFM	Nationwide	Shopping Centre Security
		NFM	Peterborough	Peter Brotherhood
		NFM	Brighton	Shop Security
		NFM	Luton Airport	catering & Refuellers
		NFM	Immingham	Coal Products Docking
		NFM	Heathrow Airport	Airline & BAA Ops
		NFM	Alba Chevron	ANP PABX Interface - Mobiles
		NFM	Brighton	American Express
		NFM	Blackpool	Premier Cabs
		NFM	Burnley	Burnley & Pendle Buses
		NFM	Coventry	Car Park Attendants
		NFM	Leicester	Park Rangers
		NFM	Luton Airport	Fuel & Catering
		NFM	Edinburgh	Royal Infirmary Porters
		NFM	North West	PMR
		NFM	Stoke On Trent	Roebuck Centre
453.0500	453.0500	NFM	Brent Spar	Shell
453.0500	467.5500	NFM	Magor	Whitbread Beer Secuirty
453.0625	459.5625	NFM	Kent	Medway Shop Security
453.0750	453.0750	NFM	Montrose A	Amoco

Base	Mobile	Mode	Location	User and Notes
		NFM	NW Hutton	Amoco
453.0750	459.5750	NFM	Bacton	Amoco
		NFM	Billingham	ICI
		NFM	Carnforth	Wimpey Quarry
		NFM	Coryton	Shell Haven Oil Refinery
		NFM	Felixstowe	Quay Shipping
		NFM	Harwich	Quay Shipping
		NFM	Heathrow Airport	Airline & BAA Ops
		NFM	Jersey	Harbour/Marina Ch 2
		NFM	March	March Ground Services
		NFM	Middlesborough	ICI Ammonia Base
		NFM	Nationwide	British Rail
		NFM	Oxford	Oxford Univ. Science Area
453.0750	460.1750	NFM	Bristol	Portland Dock Control
453.1000	459.6000	NFM	Beeston	Boots
		NFM	Blackpool	Local Health Authority
		NFM	Blackpool	Tramcar Inspectors
		NFM	Cowley	Rover Plant Channel 1
		NFM	London	Docklands Security
		NFM	Maltby	Buttlers Roadstone
		NFM	Moray Firth	Beatrice Bravo Platform
		NFM	Peterborough	Queensgate SCS
		NFM	South Walden	Schering Agrochemicals
		NFM	Telford	Shopping Centre Security
		NFM	Heathrow Airport	Indian Language Channel
		NFM	Beatrice B	BP
		NFM	Heather A	Unocal
		NFM	Glasgow	Ibrox Match Control
		NFM	Keynsham	Fry's Chocolate
		NFM	Fleetwood	Tram Inspectors
		NFM	Southampton	Hospital Transport Ch 1
		NFM	Edinburgh	Rocksteady Security
		NFM	Belfast	Queen's University Security
453.1125	459.6125	NFM	Manchester	Council
453.1250	459.6250	NFM	Cowley	Rover Plant Channel 4
		NFM	Coventry	Orchards Security
		NFM	Dover	Western Docks Jetfoil
		NFM	East Midlands Airport	British Midland
		NFM	Guernsey	St. Sampson's Harbour
		NFM	Harwich	Carless Solvents
		NFM	Jersey	British Midland Handling
		NFM	Nationwide	British Rail
		NFM	Nigg Bay	Oil Terminal Fire Channel
		NFM	Norwich	Colmans Foods
		NFM	Humber	Conoco Oil Refinery
		NFM	Heathrow Airport	Airline & BAA Ops
453.1250		NFM	Viking Field	Conoco
		NFM	Speke	Halewood Ford Plant Sec.

Base	Mobile	Mode	Location	User and Notes
453.1250	453.1250	NFM	Dover	Western Docks
		NFM	Nigg Terminal	BP
		NFM	Murchison	Conoco
		NFM	Glasgow Airport	British Midland
453.1375	459.6375	NFM	London	Police Dartford Tunnel
		NFM	Morecambe	Data Link
		NFM	Manchester	Data Link
453.1500	459.6500	NFM	Fleetwood	P & O Security
		NFM	London	City Security
		NFM	London	Metro Bus Orpington
		NFM	Sheffield	Council Cleansing Dept
		NFM	Whittlesey	McCain Intenational
		NFM	Heathrow Airport	Airline & BAA Ops
		NFM	Wiltshire	Reading Cable TV
		NFM	Wigan	Central Park Rugby OB
		NFM	Swindon	Council Maintenance
		NFM	Birmingham Airport	Ops
		NFM	Edinburgh	City Centre Couriers
453.1625	459.6625	NFM	Aberdyfi	Lifeboat
453.1750	453.1750	NFM	Moray Firth	Beatrice Alpha Platform
453.1750	459.6750	NFM	Bacton	Shell UK Ltd.
		NFM	Bedford	3M UK
		NFM	Bristol	Bus Inspectors
		NFM	Cardiff	Docks Security
		NFM	Coventry	Courtaulds Security
		NFM	Essex	County Council
		NFM	Ipswich	Docks Security
		NFM	Nationwide	British Rail
		NFM	Sheffield	City Parks Security
		NFM	Suffolk	County Council
		NFM	Billingham	ICI
		NFM	Grimsby	Tioxide UK Chemical Plant
		NFM	Bacton	Shell
		NFM	Inde J	Shell
		NFM	Inde K	Shell
		NFM	Leman B	Shell
		NFM	St. Fergus	Shell
		NFM	Cardiff	Docks Security
		NFM	Edinburgh	Royal Infirmary Security
453.1750	453.1750	NFM	Lomond	Amoco CTCSS 131.8 Hz
		NFM	NW Hutton	Amoco
		NFM	North Everest	Amoco CTCSS 131.8 Hz
		NFM	Beatrice A	BP
		NFM	St. Fergus	Shell
453.2000	453.2000	NFM	Murchison	Conoco
		NFM	Jersey Harbour	Shell Fuel Supplies
453.2000	459.7000	NFM	Ipswich	British Rail Transport Police
		NFM	Birmingham	Taxi Co

Base	Mobile	Mode	Location	User and Notes
		NFM	Fleetwood	Plumbers
		NFM	Glasgow	City Centre Council Patrol
		NFM	North West	PMR
		NFM	Boston	Acorn Cabs
		NFM	Hull	Hospital Porters
		NFM	Milton Keynes	MK Security
		NFM	Plymouth	City Bus Inspectors
		NFM	Portsmouth	Taxis
		NFM	Ramsbottom	Civic Private Hire
		NFM	Rotherham	Bus Inspectors
453.2125	459.7125	NFM	Nationwide	British Rail
		NFM	Morecambe	Data Link
		NFM	Dundee	Data Link
453.2250	453.2250	NFM	Alba Chevron	FSU Shuttle Operations
453.2250	459.7250	NFM	Eider	Shell
		NFM	Heathrow Airport	Airline & BAA Ops
		NFM	Jersey	Harbour Ch 1
		NFM	London Heathrow	Heathrow Tower
		NFM	Ninian South	Chevron
		NFM	Tilbury	Rover Security
		NFM	Peterborough	Aggregate Company
453.2500	453.2500	NFM	Clyde A	BP
		NFM	Murchison	Conoco
		NFM	Brae N	Marathon
		NFM	Whiston	Whiston Hospital Security
453.2500	459.7500	NFM	Leeds	Traffic Wardens
		NFM	Heathrow Airport	Airline & BAA Ops
		NFM	Gatwick Airport	Airline & BAA Ops
		NFM	London (Central)	Traffic Wardens
		NFM	Gatwick Airport	Ground Repeater
		NFM	Belfast	Ulster Folk & Transport Mus.
453.2625	459.7625	NFM	Newcastle	Data Link
453.2750	453.2750	NFM	Brent B	Shell
453.2750	459.7750	NFM	Leman BH	Shell Base
		NFM	Heathrow Airport	Airline & BAA Ops
		NFM	Heathrow Airport	Ground Repeater
		NFM	Middlesborough	British Steel Medics
		NFM	Nationwide	Ambulance Emergency
		NFM	Oxford	Ambulance Service
		NFM	West Sussex	Ambulance Incident Vehicle
453.3000	453.3000	NFM	Liverpool	Buses
		NFM	Lomond	Amoco CTCSS 131.8 Hz
		NFM	Montrose A	Amoco
		NFM	NW Hutton	Amoco
		NFM	North Everest	Amoco CTCSS 131.8 Hz
		NFM	Magnus	BP
		NFM	Brae N	Marathon
453.3000	459.8000	NFM	Liverpool	Merseybus Inspectors

Base	Mobile	Mode	Location	User and Notes
		NFM	Bagg	Company Security
		NFM	Humberside	Lindsey Oil Refinery
453.3125	459.8125	NFM	Perth	Data Link
453.3250	459.8250	NFM	March	St Mary's Hospital Security
		NFM	Manchester	Doctors on Call
		NFM	East Sussex	Ambulance Incident Vehicle
		NFM	Manchester	District Nurse
		NFM	Stansted Airport	Ground Repeater
		NFM	Heathrow Airport	Ground Repeater
		NFM	North West	PMR
453.3500	453.3500	NFM	Murchison	Conoco
		NFM	Brae N	Marathon
453.3500	459.8500	NFM	Walsall	Council Works Yard
		NFM	Nottingham	City Engineers
		NFM	London	Security Co.
		NFM	Humberside Airport	Bond Helicopters
453.3625	459.8625	NFM	Nationwide	DSS
453.3750	453.3750	NFM	Liverpool	All Docks Handhelds
453.3750	459.8750	NFM	Cowley	Rover Plant Channel 2
		NFM	Nationwide	DSS
		NFM	Immingham	Lindsey Oil Fire Service
		NFM	Humberside	Conoco Oil Ref. Fire & Sec
		NFM	Cambridge	Addenbrooks Porters
		NFM	Luton Airport	Luggage Handlers Ch 5
		NFM	Port Talbot	BP Works
453.3875	459.8875	NFM	Nationwide	DSS
453.4000	453.4000	NFM	Nigg Terminal	BP
		NFM	Ninian North	Chevron
453.4000	459.9000	NFM	Ipswich	Port Authority
		NFM	Jersey Airport	Esso Refuelling
		NFM	Nationwide	British Rail
		NFM	Nigg Bay	Oil Terminal Maintenance
		NFM	Nottingham	Formans
		NFM	Oxford	Oxford Univ. Science Area
		NFM	Hull	City Council
		NFM	Heathrow Airport	Airline & BAA Ops
		NFM	Ipswich	Ports Police
		NFM	Nationwide	British Rail
		NFM	Brae N, S	Marathon
		NFM	St. Fergus	Shell
		NFM	Glasgow	Prince's Sq. SCS
		NFM	Gatwick Airport	Ground Repeater
		NFM	Jersey Airport	Ground Repeater
453.4250	453.4250	NFM	Clyde A	BP
		NFM	Magnus	BP
453.4250	459.9250	NFM	Buchan	BP
		NFM	Magnus	BP
		NFM	Alba Chevron	FSU Maintenance

Base	Mobile	Mode	Location	User and Notes
		NFM	Humberside	Conoco Oil Refinery
		NFM	Swansea	DVLA
		NFM	Middlesborough	British Steel Security
		NFM	Gatwick Airport	Ground Repeater
		NFM	Heathrow Airport	Ground Repeater
		NFM	Swansea City	DVLA Security
453.4500	453.4500	NFM	Dunlin	Shell
		NFM	Guernsey	HM Customs & Excise
		NFM	Cardiff	Inland Revenue Security
		NFM	Cowley	Rover Plant Channel 3
		NFM	Guernsey	Customs & Excise
		NFM	Nationwide	BAA Police
		NFM	Stoke-on-Trent	Police
		NFM	Llantrisant	Royal Mint Security
		NFM	Leicester	Haymarket Centre Security
		NFM	Gatwick Airport	Ground Repeater
		NFM	Heathrow Airport	Ground Repeater
453.4625	459.9625	NFM	Nationwide	Inland Revenue Security
		NFM	Brighton	Inland Revenue Security
453.4750	453.4750	NFM	Stansted Airport	Security
		NFM	Manchester	Manchester Univ. Security
		NFM	Guernsey	HM Customs Surveillance
		NFM	Peterborough	Football Ground Control
		NFM	Manchester	Arndale SCS
		NFM	Swindon	Austin Rover Security
		NFM	Newcastle	Metro Centre
		NFM	Grimsby	Council
		NFM	Bishopton	Compaq Security
453.4750	460.7750	NFM	Nationwide	CAA Ground Movements
		NFM	Gatwick Airport	Airline & BAA Ops
		NFM	Luton Airport	Arrivals/Departures Ch 3
		NFM	Flint	CBM Security
453.4750	459.9750	NFM	Buchan	BP
		NFM	Murchison	Conoco
453.4875	459.9875	NFM	East Midlands Airport	Airport Fire
453.5000	460.0000	NFM	Nationwide	British Rail Security
		NFM	Sheffield	Council Markets Security
		NFM	Stansted Airport	Central Telephone
		NFM	Heathrow Airport	British Midland
		NFM	Tyne & Wear	Metro
		NFM	Heathrow Airport	Airline & BAA Ops
		NFM	Gatwick Airport	Airline & BAA Ops
		NFM	Stansted Airport	Airline & BAA Ops
		NFM	Eider	Shell
		NFM	Newport	BR Security
		NFM	Southampton	Sealink
		NFM	Folkestone	Stena Sealink
		NFM	Belfast	Castlecourt SCS

Base	Mobile	Mode	Location	User and Notes
453.5250	453.5250	NFM	Nigg Bay	Oil Terminal Security
		NFM	Alba Chevron	ANP East Crane
		NFM	Ninian North	Chevron
453.5250	460.0250	NFM	East Midlands Airport	Airport Fire
		NFM	Hull	City Council Housing
		NFM	Ipswich	British Rail
		NFM	Jersey	Harbour Ch 2
		NFM	Leicester	Leicester Poly. Security
		NFM	Nationwide	British Rail Transport Police
		NFM	Brighton	British Rail Transport Police
		NFM	Ellesmere Port	Shell Security
		NFM	Leicester	Polytechnic Security
		NFM	East Midlands Airport	Fire Channel 1
453.5500	460.0500	NFM	Aberdeen	British Rail
		NFM	Bedford	British Rail
		NFM	Birmingham	British Rail New Street
		NFM	Bletchley	British Rail Bletchley Yard
		NFM	Brentwood	British Rail Shenfield
		NFM	Brighton	British Rail
		NFM	Brighton	British Rail (Brighton Depot)
		NFM	Cardiff	British Rail
		NFM	Cardiff	British Rail (DMU Shunters)
		NFM	Carlisle	British Rail
		NFM	Chester	British Rail
		NFM	Clapham	British Rail
		NFM	Clapham Junction Yard	British Rail
		NFM	Coventry	British Rail
		NFM	Crewe	British Rail
		NFM	Doncaster	British Rail
		NFM	East Croydon	British Rail
		NFM	Edinburgh	British Rail Waverley
		NFM	Ely	British Rail
		NFM	Glasgow	BR Glasgow Queen Street
		NFM	Harwich	British Rail Parkeston Yard
		NFM	Hull	British Rail Hull Paragon
		NFM	Ipswich	British Rail
		NFM	Leeds	British Rail
		NFM	Leicester	British Rail
		NFM	London	British Rail (Cannon Street)
		NFM	London	British Rail (East Croydon)
		NFM	London	British Rail (Fenchurch St)
		NFM	London	British Rail (Ilford Car Sheds)
		NFM	London	British Rail (Liverpool Street)
		NFM	London	British Rail (Paddington)
		NFM	London	British Rail (Slade Green)
		NFM	London	British Rail (Waterloo)
		NFM	London	British Rail (Wimbledon Park
		NFM	Manchester	British Rail(icadilly)

Base	Mobile	Mode	Location	User and Notes
		NFM	Nationwide	British Rail Stations Ch1
		NFM	Newcastle	Railway Station
		NFM	Norwich	British Rail
		NFM	Norwich	British Rail (Crown Point)
		NFM	Penzance	British Rail
		NFM	Preston	British Rail
		NFM	Reading	British Rail
		NFM	Salford	British Rail
		NFM	Selhurst Junction	British Rail
		NFM	Sheffield	British Rail
		NFM	Shrewsbury	British Rail
		NFM	Slade Green Depot	British Rail
		NFM	Stansted Airport	British Rail
		NFM	Stratford-Upon-Avon	British Rail
		NFM	Wigan	British Rail
		NFM	Woking	British Rail
		NFM	Wolverhampton	British Rail
		NFM	York	British Rail
		NFM	Nottingham	City Council
		NFM	Alba	Chevron ANP Construction
		NFM	Ninian South	Chevron
		NFM	Cardiff	Great Western Railway
		NFM	Blackpool	British Rail
453.5500	453.5500	NFM	North-West	BR Track Workers Ch 1
453.5625	460.0625	NFM	Nationwide	British Rail
453.5750	460.0750	NFM	Felixstowe	Freightliners
		NFM	Nationwide	British Airways
		NFM	Worksop	Tesco
		NFM	Humberside	Conoco Oil Refinery
		NFM	Nationwide	National Power
		NFM	Felixstowe	Freightliners
		NFM	Buchan	BP
		NFM	Magnus	BP
453.5875	460.0875	NFM	Newcastle	Data Link
453.6000	453.6000	NFM	Tartan	Texaco
453.6000	460.1000	NFM	Cowley	Rover Assembly
		NFM	Glasgow	PMR
		NFM	Nationwide	Bus Inspectors
		NFM	Prestatyn	Ship Technicians
		NFM	Humberside	County Council
		NFM	Heathrow Airport	Airline & BAA Ops
		NFM	N W Hutton	Amoco
		NFM	Newport	Godings Steel Holdings
		NFM	Gatwick Airport	Ground Repeater
		NFM	Stansted Airport	Ground Repeater
		NFM	Heathrow Airport	Ground Repeater
453.6250	460.1250	NFM	Jersey	British Airways Handling
		NFM	Alba	Chevron FSU General Ops

Base	Mobile	Mode	Location	User and Notes
		NFM	Immingham	Tioxide Chemicals
		NFM	Swansea Docks	Cargo Handlers
453.6500	453.6500	NFM	Leman AK	Shell
453.6500	453.6500	NFM	Tartan	Texaco
453.6500	460.1500	NFM	Newport	Godings Workers Handhelds
		NFM	Edinburgh	Lothian Regional Transport
		NFM	Heathrow Airport	Airline & BAA Ops
		NFM	Newmarket	Police
		NFM	Leicester	Fosse Park Car Park Security
		NFM	York	York Council Car Parks
453.6750	460.1750	NFM	Edinburgh	Lothian Regional Transport
		NFM	London	Docklands Light Railway
		NFM	Stallingbough	SCM
453.7000	460.2000	NFM	Dover	Eastern Docks Port Ops
		NFM	Coventry	Dunlop Security
		NFM	Hull	Corp. Transport
		NFM	Newcastle	The Metro Centre Paging
		NFM	Gatwick Airport	Airline & BAA Ops
		NFM	Middlesborough	Cleveland Centre Security
		NFM	Stockport	Merseybus Inspectors
453.7000	453.7000	NFM	Alba Chevron	FSU Crane Operations
		NFM	Ninian North	Chevron
		NFM	North Cormorant	Shell
453.7125	453.7125	NFM	Immingham	Conoco Oil Maintainance
453.7250	460.7250	NFM	Manchester	Hospital Porters
		NFM	West Midlands	Engineering Town Planning
453.7250	460.2250	NFM	Morecambc Bay	BGE&P
		NFM	Alba Chevron	ANP Production - Mobiles
		NFM	Ninian Central	Chevron
453.7500	460.2500	NFM	Aberdeen/Dyce Airport	Staff
		NFM	Bournemouth	Repeater
		NFM	Manchester	Shopping Centre Security
453.7500	453.7500	NFM	Brighton	Conference Centre
		NFM	Gatwick Airport	Airline & BAA Ops
		NFM	Lomond	Amoco CTCSS 131.8 Hz
		NFM	NW Hutton	Amoco
		NFM	North Everest	Amoco CTCSS 131.8 Hz
		NFM	Oldham	The Spindlers Security
		NFM	Brighton	American Express
		NFM	Wiltshire	Great Western Security
		NFM	Gloucestershire	Great Western Security
		NFM	Newport	Godings Security
		NFM	North West	PMR
453.7500	459.5750	NFM	Bacton	Amoco
453.7750	453.7750	NFM	Stansted Airport	Light Railway
453.7750	460.2750	NFM	Culham	UKAEA
		NFM	Cambridge	City Centre Security
		NFM	Hatfield	Galleria SCS

Base	Mobile	Mode	Location	User and Notes
		NFM	Maureen	Phillips Telemetry
		NFM	Runcorn	Shopping Centre Security
		NFM	Southampton	Hospital Transport Ch 2
		NFM	Northampton	Grosvenor Centre Security
		NFM	Northampton	C & A Security
		NFM	Northampton	Debenhams Security
		NFM	Leicester	Fosse Park Shop Security
		NFM	Birkenhead	Pyramid SCS
		NFM	Stansted Airport	Ground Repeater
		NFM	Gatwick Airport	Ground Repeater
		NFM	Heathrow Airport	Ground Repeater
		NFM	Newcastle Airport	Airline Ops
		NFM	Liverpool	St Johns SCS
453.8000	460.3000	NFM	Newmarket	The Jockey Club
		NFM	Brighton	Brighton & Hove Bus Co.
		NFM	Heathrow Airport	Airline & BAA Ops
		NFM	Lomond	Amoco
		NFM	North Everest	Amoco
		NFM	Ninian South	Chevron
		NFM	Tem	Shell
		NFM	Gatwick Airport	Ground Repeater
453.8000	453.8000	NFM	Lomond	Amoco
		NFM	North Everest	Amoco
453.8250	453.8250	NFM	Lomond	Amoco CTCSS 131.8 Hz
		NFM	North Everest	Amoco CTCSS 131.8 Hz
453.8500	453.8500	NFM	Forties E	BP
453.8250	460.3250	NFM	Ipswich	Cranfield Bros.
		NFM	New Holland	Howarth Timber
		NFM	Heathrow Airport	Ground Repeater
		NFM	Bury	Premier Cars
453.8500	460.3500	NFM	Aberdeen	Hospital
		NFM	Norwich	Norwich & Norfolk Hospital
		NFM	Stansted Airport	Catering
		NFM	Gatwick Airport	Ground Ops
		NFM	Bellingham	ICI
		NFM	Norfolk	Norwich & Norfolk Hospital
		NFM	Forties E	BP
		NFM	Brighton	Buses
		NFM	Merseyside	Merseyside Electric
		NFM	Hampshire	Buses
		NFM	Newport	Docks
		NFM	Bealieu	Motor Museum Security
		NFM	Newmarket	Security
		NFM	Wirral	Merseybus Inspectors
		NFM	Gatwick Airport	Ground Repeater
		NFM	Stansted Airport	Ground Repeater
		NFM	Heathrow Airport	Ground Repeater
		NFM	Luton Airport	Car Parks Ch 6

Base	Mobile	Mode	Location	User and Notes
		NFM	Rochdale	Queensway Private Hire
		NFM	Belfast	Ulsterbus
453.8750	460.3750	NFM	Aberdeen/Dyce Airport	Staff
		NFM	Edinburgh	Lothian Regional Transport
		NFM	Luton Airport	Monarch Airlines
		NFM	Manchester	Freightliners Supervisors
		NFM	Heathrow Airport	Airline & BAA Ops
		NFM	Gatwick Airport	Airline & BAA Ops
		NFM	Alba	Chevron Field Safety
		NFM	Ninian Central	Chevron
		NFM	Luton Airport	Airline Ops Ch 4
453.9000	453.9000	NFM	Cormorant A	Shell
453.9000	460.4000	NFM	Ashford	British Rail
		NFM	Birmingham	British Rail International
		NFM	Derby	British Rail
		NFM	Doncaster	British Rail
		NFM	Edinburgh	British Rail Haymarket Depot
		NFM	Gatwick	British Rail (Gatwick Airport)
		NFM	Glasgow	BR Glasgow Central
		NFM	Guildford	British Rail
		NFM	Hoo Junction Deport	British Rail
		NFM	Hull	British Rail Paragon Sig Box
		NFM	Liverpool	British Rail Lime Street
		NFM	London	British Rail (Barking)
		NFM	London	British Rail (Charing Cross)
		NFM	London	British Rail (Euston)
		NFM	London	British Rail (Kings Cross)
		NFM	London	British Rail (Victoria)
		NFM	London	British Rail (Waterloo City)
		NFM	London	British Rail (Willesden Yard)
		NFM	Manchester	British Rail (Heaton Depot)
		NFM	Nationwide	British Rail Stations
		NFM	Norwich	British Rail (Crown Point)
		NFM	Nottingham	British Rail
		NFM	Perth	British Rail
		NFM	Peterborough	British Rail
		NFM	Reading	British Rail
		NFM	Ramsgate	British Rail Station & Depot
		NFM	Watford	British Rail (Watford Junc)
		NFM	Killingholme	British Rail/Oil Refineries
		NFM	Birmingham	Trackman Ch 2
		NFM	Newport	BR Porters
		NFM	Thames	BR Turbo Workshop
		NFM	Barry	Docks Security
453.9175		NFM	Machynlleth	British Rail
453.9250	460.4250	NFM	Stansted Airport	Loading
		NFM	London	Docklands Light Railway
		NFM	County Durham	Security Firm

Base	Mobile	Mode	Location	User and Notes
		NFM	Swindon	Austin Rover Security
		NFM	Gatwick Airport	Airline & BAA Ops
		NFM	Heathrow Airport	Airline & BAA Ops
		NFM	Stansted Airport	Airline & BAA Ops
		NFM	Forties E	BP
		NFM	Newport	Patent Office Security
		NFM	Leicester	Shires Centre Security Ch 1
453.9375	460.4375	NFM	Edinburgh	ScotRail Data Links
		NFM	Glasgow	ScotRail Data Links
		NFM	Perth	ScotRail Data Links
453.9500	460.4500	NFM	Alba	Chevron ANP Maintenance
		NFM	Ninian Central	Chevron
		NFM	Brae North	Marathon
		NFM	Newport	Spencer & Llanwern Docks
		NFM	Humberside	Conoco Oil Refinery
453.9625	460.5625	NFM	London	London Taxis
453.9750	460.4750	NFM	Cowley	Rover Security Channel 7
		NFM	Luton	Vauxhall Motors
		NFM	Stansted Airport	UL Leisure
		NFM	Heathrow Airport	Airline & BAA Ops
		NFM	Stansted Airport	Air UK
		NFM	Forties F	BP
		NFM	Bath	University Security
		NFM	Liverpool	John Moore University Sec.
		NFM	Stansted Airport	Airline Flight Despatch
		NFM	Liverpool	University Security

454.0250 - 454.8250 MHz   PRIVATE RADIO PAGING SYSTEMS 25 kHz

Base	Mobile	Mode	Location	User and Notes
454.0250		NFM	Nationwide	Hospital Voice Paging
		NFM	London	US Embassy
		NFM	Newcastle	Hospital Emerg. Paging
		NFM	Nationwide	Medical Voice Paging
		NFM	Birmingham	QE Hospital Pagers
454.0250	454.0250	NFM	Ninian North	Chevron
		NFM	Claymore A	Elf Enterprise
		NFM	Piper	Elf Enterprise
454.0500	454.0500	NFM	Ninian North	Chevron
		NFM	Claymore A	Elf Enterprise
		NFM	Piper	Elf Enterprise
454.0750		NFM	Bacton	Amoco Paging System
454.0750	447.5750	NFM	Nationwide	Aircall Voice Paging
454.1000		NFM	Whiston	Hospital Voice Paging
		NFM	Birmingham	Hospital Paging
454.1000	454.1000	NFM	Brent B	Shell
454.1250	454.1250	NFM	Ninian North	Chevron
		NFM	Claymore A	Elf Enterprise
		NFM	Piper	Elf Enterprise
454.1625	454.1625	NFM	Ninian Central	Chevron

Base	Mobile	Mode	Location	User and Notes
454.1750		NFM	Nationwide	Hospital Voice Paging
		NFM	Newcastle	Hospital Emerg. Paging
		NFM	Sheffield	R. Hallamshire Hosp Pager
		NFM	Cambridge	Addenbrookes Hosp. Paging
		NFM	Stevenage	Lister Hospital Pagers
454.1750	454.1750	NFM	Ninian South	Chevron
454.2000		NFM	Nationwide	Medical Pagers
		NFM	Derbyshire	Centracom Doctors Paging
		NFM	Manchester	Hospital Pager
454.2500		NFM	Milton Keynes	Hospital Pagers
454.2750	454.2750	NFM	Alba Chevron	ANP West Crane
		NFM	Ninian South	Chevron
		NFM	Claymore A	Elf Enterprise
		NFM	Piper	Elf Enterprise
454.3000		NFM	Edinburgh Airport	Radiopagers Channel 9
454.3125	454.3125	NFM	Nationwide	Ligier Formula One Team
454.3125	459.3125	NFM	Castle Donington	Grand Prix Team
454.3250		NFM	Oxford	Medical Paging
		NFM	County Durham	Hospital Emerg. Paging
454.3250	454.3250	NFM	Claymore A	Elf Enterprise
		NFM	Piper	Elf Enterprise
454.3250		NFM	Basildon	Hospital Data/Paging
454.3500	454.3500	NFM	Ninian Central	Chevron
454.3750		NFM	Jersey	King Street Dept Store
454.4000		NFM	Gatwick Airport	Airline & BAA Ops
454.4000	454.4000	NFM	Alba	Chevron ANP Drilling
		NFM	Ninian South	Chevron
454.4000	468.4000	NFM	Forties A	BP
454.4250	454.4250	NFM	Ninian Central	Chevron
454.4500	454.4500	NFM	Claymore A	Elf Enterprise
		NFM	Piper	Elf Enterprise
454.4750		NFM	Southampton	AirCall Pagers
454.4750	468.4250	NFM	Anglia	Anglia TV O/B
454.5000	454.5000	NFM	Nationwide	UK Atomic Energy Authority
454.5250	468.5250	NFM	Anglia	Anglia TV O/B
454.5500		NFM	London	Taxis
454.5750		NFM	Guernsey	HM Customs
454.5750	460.0750	NFM	Magnus	BP
454.6250		NFM	Newport	Royal Gwent Hospital Pagers
454.6750		NFM	Nationwide	Hutchison Paging
		NFM	Nationwide	Millicomm Paging
454.6875		NFM	Heathrow Airport	Airline & BAA Ops
454.7000		NFM	Bromley	Bromley Health Pagers
454.7500		NFM	Jersey Airport	British Airways
454.7750		NFM	Hull	Air Call Paging
		NFM	Nationwide	AirCall Paging
454.8000		NFM	Southampton	Meridian Pagers
454.8250		NFM	Nationwide	Page Boy Paging

Base	Mobile	Mode	Location	User and Notes
		NFM	Machynlleth	Hospital Paging
454.8500		NFM	Glasgow	Paging

454.8500 - 454.9750 MHz   Limited MoD & PMR Alloactions

Base	Mobile	Mode	Location	User and Notes
454.8500	454.8500	NFM	Wimbledon	BR Driver Only Operations
		NFM	Stevenage	BR Driver Only Operations
454.8750	454.8750	NFM	Baldock	British Rail
454.8875	454.8875	NFM	Gidea Park	BR Driver Only Operations
		NFM	Reedham	BR Driver Only Operations
		NFM	Waterloo	BR Driver Only Operations
		NFM	Liverpool	BR Driver Only Operations
		NFM	Bishopton	BR Driver Only Operations
		NFM	Heathrow Airport	Iberia
454.9000	454.9000	NFM	Alexandra Palace	BR Driver Only Operations
		NFM	Stratford	BR Driver Only Operations
		NFM	Selhurst	BR Driver Only Operations
454.9250	454.9250	NFM	Threebridges	BR Driver Only Operations
		NFM	Heathrow Airport	Airline & BAA Ops
		NFM	Hitchin	British Rail
454.9375	454.9375	NFM	Threebridges	BR Driver Only Operations
		NFM	Motherwell	BR Driver Only Operations
454.9500	454.9500	NFM	Burgess Hill	BR Driver Only Operations
454.9625	454.9625	NFM	Victoria	BR Driver Only Operations
		NFM	Motherwell	BR Driver Only Operations
454.9750	454.9750	NFM	Redhill	BR Driver Only Operations
		NFM	Victoria	BR Driver Only Operations
		NFM	Jordanhil1	BR Driver Only Operations
		NFM	Letchworth	British Rail
454.9875	454.9875	NFM	Motherwell	BR Driver Only Operations
		NFM	Stoke On Trent	Stoke City Video Surveilance
454.9925		NFM	Edinburgh	Grampian TV O/B Talkback
		NFM	Glasgow	Grampian TV O/B Talkback
		NFM	Perth	Grampian TV O/B Talkback
454.99375		NFM	Nationwide	ITV O/B
		NFM	East Anglia	Anglia TV Talkback
454.9950		NFM	Liverpool	Granada TV Talkback

455.0000 - 467.7500 MHz   Irish Police Base 25kHz

455.0000 - 455.4500 MHz   BBC TV O/B Talkback & Formula One Racing

Base	Mobile	Mode	Location	User and Notes
455.0000		WFM	Nationwide	Central TV O/B
		NFM	Southampton	Meridian TV O/B
455.0000	469.0000	NFM	Dublin	Police O
455.0125	468.0500	NFM	Jersey	Channel TV O/B
455.0125		NFM	Wales	S4C O/B Unit
		NFM	Nationwide	Ozi TV O/B
455.0250		WFM	Nationwide	Central TV O/B

Base	Mobile	Mode	Location	User and Notes
455.0250	469.0250	NFM	Dublin	Police O
455.03125		NFM	London	Independant TV Talkback
455.0500	469.0500	NFM	Dublin	Police O
455.0625		NFM	Dorset	2CR Eye-In-The-Sky
		NFM	Stoke on Trent	Signal Radio O/B Link
		NFM	London	BBC South East
		NFM	Southampton	Ocean Sound Helo
455.0750		NFM	London	Capital Radio Flying Eye
455.0750	469.0750	NFM	Dublin	Police O
455.0940		WFM	Nationwide	CTV Outside Broadcast
455.1000		NFM	Nottingham	BBC Radio Nottingham
455.1000	469.1000	NFM	Dublin	Police O
455.10625		WFM	London	BBC-TV London Marathon
455.1250	468.3900	NFM	Jersey	Channel TV O/B
455.1250	469.1250	NFM	Dublin	Police T (Traffic)
455.1250		NFM	Liverpool	Granada TV Talkback
455.1320		NFM	Edinburgh	Grampian TV O/B Talkback
		NFM	Glasgow	Grampian TV O/B Talkback
		WFM	Perth	Grampian TV O/B Talkback
455.1326		NFM	Nationwide	BBC TV Sports Commentary
455.1375		WFM	Nationwide	CTV Outside Broadcast
		NFM	Newcastle Airport	Stores
455.1500		NFM	Heathrow Airport	Met. Police (Hunter Delta)
		NFM	Manchester	Piccadilly Eye in the Sky
455.1500	469.1500	NFM	Dublin	Police T (Traffic)
		NFM	Anglia	Anglia TV Studio Producer
455.1625		NFM	Dorset	2CR O/B Feeder
		NFM	London	BBC South East
		NFM	Manchester	Radio Piccadilly Eye In Sky
		NFM	Stoke on Trent	Signal Radio O/B Link
		NFM	Milton Keynes	Chilton Radio OB
		NFM	Birmingham	BRMB/Extra AM Flying Eye
		NFM	Oxfordshire	Chilton Radio Heli Traffic Rep
455.1750	469.1750	NFM	Dublin	Police W
455.1875		NFM	Stoke on Trent	Stock City O/B Microphones
455.2000		WFM	Nationwide	Central TV O/B
		NFM	Newmarket	Channel 4 Racing O/B
		NFM	Nationwide	Radio Investigations Service
455.2000	469.2000	NFM	Dublin	Police N
455.2250		WFM	Nationwide	Central TV O/B
		NFM	Newmarket	Channel 4 Racing O/B
		NFM	Nationwide	Radio Investigations Service
455.2250	469.2250	NFM	Dublin	Police F
455.2350		NFM	Grand Prix Circuits	Ferrari Team Voice Link
455.2375		NFM	Nuneaton	George Elliot Hosp. Pagers
455.2400		WFM	Leicester	BBC East Midlands O/B
		NFM	Leicester	BBC Midlands O/B
455.2437	468.1687	NFM	Belfry (Ryder Cup)	BBC TV

Base	Mobile	Mode	Location	User and Notes
455.2500		NFM	Nationwide	Radio Investigations Service
		NFM	Manchester	ITN O/B Studio Link
		NFM	Burnley	Granada TV OB
455.2500	469.2500	NFM	Dublin	Police F
455.2562	468.1937	NFM	Nationwide	BBC TV O/B Talkback
455.26875		WFM	London	BBC-TV London Marathon
455.2750	469.2750	NFM	Dublin	Police P
455.2800		WFM	Leicester	BBC East Midlands O/B
		WFM	Portsmouth	BBC1 OB
		NFM	Leicester	BBC Midlands O/B
455.2812	468.2937	NFM	Belfry (Ryder Cup)	BBC TV
455.2850		NFM	Edinburgh	BBC Scotland O/B
		NFM	Glasgow	BBC Scotland O/B
		WFM	Perth	BBC Scotland O/B
455.2875		NFM	Goodwood	BBC Glorious Goodwood
455.3000	469.3000	NFM	Dublin	Police M
455.3120		WFM	Salisbury	BBC Wiltshire Sound
455.3125		NFM	Nationwide	BBC Radio 1 O/B
		WFM	Jersey	BBC Jersey O/B
		NFM	Belfry (Ryder Cup)	BBC Radio 5
455.3125	469.1125	WFM	Salisbury	BBC Wiltshire Sound
455.3125	455.3125	NFM	Nationwide	BBC Radio 1 O/B
455.3250	469.3250	NFM	Gairloch	Police
		NFM	Dublin	Police L/B/A
455.3500	469.3500	NFM	Inverness	Police
		NFM	Dublin	Police G
455.3625		NFM	Nationwide	BBC Radio 1 O/B
		WFM	Jersey	BBC Jersey O/B
		NFM	Belfry (Ryder Cup)	BBC Radio 5
		NFM	Carlisle	BBC Radio Cumbria OB
455.3625	455.3625	NFM	Nationwide	BBC Radio 1 O/B
455.3650		WFM	Hampshire	BBC Radio Solent Radio Car
455.3750	469.3750	NFM	Garve	Police
		NFM	Dublin	Police G
455.3750		NFM	RAF Fairford	IAT Emergency Control
455.39375		NFM	Nationwide	BBC TV O/B Talkback
		NFM	Belfry (Ryder Cup)	BBC TV
455.4000		NFM	Farnborough (RAE Airfield)	BBC Talkback
455.4000	469.4000	NFM	Dublin	Police E
455.41875		NFM	Belfry (Ryder Cup)	BBC TV
455.4250	469.4250	NFM	Strathclyde	Police
		NFM	Dublin	Police A
455.4250		NFM	S Cumbria	Data Link
455.43125		NFM	Belfry (Ryder Cup)	BBC TV
455.4375	455.4375	NFM	Preston	Radio Lancashire O/B
455.4450		NFM	Leicester	Radio Leicester O/B Ch 2
455.4500	469.4500	NFM	Applecross	Police
		NFM	Dublin	Police B

Base	Mobile	Mode	Location	User and Notes
455.4625	469.9000	NFM	London	BBC Eastenders Production

455.4750 - 455.9750 MHz   PMR AIRPORT SECURITY & GROUND REPEATERS

Base	Mobile	Mode	Location	User and Notes
455.4750		NFM	Gatwick Airport	Tower Re-Broardcast
		NFM	Woodford Airfield	Crash Ops
455.4750	460.7750	NFM	Birmingham Airport	Ground Staff
		NFM	Birmingham Airport	Ground Repeater
455.4750	469.4750	NFM	Dublin	Police B
455.4875	461.7875	NFM	Bournemouth Airport (Hurn)	Tower
		NFM	East Midlands Airport	Ground
		NFM	London Heathrow	Armed Police (Hunter Delta)
		NFM	Liverpool Airport	Apron Supervisor
		NFM	Heathrow Airport	Police (Hunter Delta)
		NFM	Bournmouth Airport	Tower Repeater
455.5000		NFM	Guernsey Airport	Tower Rebroadcast
		NFM	Guernsey Airport	Ground Repeater
455.5000	460.8000	NFM	RAF Fairford	IAT Medical Control
455.5000	469.5000	NFM	Dublin	Police J
455.5125	455.5125	NFM	Nationwide	Transport Police (Bravo Xray)
455.5125		NFM	Duxford	Data Link
		NFM	Victoria	BR Driver Only Operation
		NFM	Cranfield Airport	Fire Services
455.5250	455.5250	NFM	Nationwide	HM Customs & Excise
455.5250	460.8250	NFM	Bristol Airport	HM Customs & Excise
		NFM	Coventry Airport	Fire Service
		NFM	East Midlands Airport	Fire Service
		NFM	London Heathrow	Tower Rebroadcast
		NFM	Manchester Airport	Ops 3
		NFM	Nationwide	Airport Customs
		NFM	Heathrow Airport	Tower Rebroadcast
455.5250	469.5250	NFM	Dublin	Police R
455.5250	461.1750	NFM	Cranfield Airfield	Fire & Security
455.5375		NFM	RAF Fairford	IAT
		NFM	London Bridge	BR Driver Only Operation
		NFM	Luton Airport	Maintenance
455.5375	460.5375	NFM	Birmingham Airport	Ground Control
455.5500	461.2000	NFM	Stansted Airport	Ground Re-Broadcast
455.5500	461.8500	NFM	Leeds Airport	Security/Fire
		NFM	Heathrow Airport	Tower Rebroadcast
		NFM	Stansted Airport	Tower Repeater
		NFM	Heathrow Airport	Ground Repeater
		NFM	Manchester Airport	Tower Repeater
455.5500	469.5500	NFM	Dublin	Police K
455.5625	455.5625	NFM	Stansted Airport	Crash Vehicles
455.5750	461.2250	NFM	London Heathrow	Security
		NFM	RAF Fairford	IAT Barriers
		NFM	Various Airports	Fire Services

Base	Mobile	Mode	Location	User and Notes
		NFM	Birmingham Airport	Fire
		NFM	BAe Woodford	Tower Link
		NFM	Heathrow Airport	Passport Control
		NFM	Woodford Airfield	Tower-Ground
455.5750	469.5750	NFM	Dublin	Police H
455.5875		NFM	Wimbeldon	BR Driver Only Operation
		NFM	Liverpool	BR Driver Only Operation
455.6000	455.6000	NFM	Jersey Aiport	Securicor
		NFM	Blackpool Airport	Ground
		NFM	East Midlands Airport	Security
		NFM	Filton (BAe)	Security
		NFM	Gatwick Airport	Airline & BAA Ops
455.6000	460.9000	NFM	East Midlands Airport	Terminal Security
455.6000	469.0000	NFM	Forties C	BP
455.6000	469.6000	NFM	Dublin	Police H
455.6125	461.9125	NFM	London Heathrow	Ground
		NFM	RAF Fairford	IAT
		NFM	Leeds Bradford Airport	Ground Staff/Fire
455.6250	460.9250	NFM	Nationwide	Red Devil Parachute Team
		NFM	Jersey	Airport Ground
		NFM	Prestwick Airport	Ground Ops Link
		NFM	Glasgow Airport	Cargo Handlers
455.6250	469.6250	NFM	Dublin	Police C
455.6375	460.9375	NFM	RAF Fairford	IAT Transport Control
		NFM	Stansted Airport	Maintenance
		NFM	Heathrow Airport	Airline & BAA Ops
		NFM	Liverpool Airport	Ground Movement Control
		NFM	Gatwick Airport	Crash Ops
		NFM	Luton Airport	Crash Ops Ch 2
455.6500	460.8500	NFM	Birmingham Airport	Airway Crossing/Security
		NFM	MoD Airfields	Fire Control
		NFM	Stansted Airport	Airline & BAA Ops
		NFM	Newcastle Airport	Grass Cutting
		NFM	Stansted Airport	Crash Ops
		NFM	Heathrow Airport	Crash Ops
		NFM	Birmingham Airport	Tower Repeater
		NFM	Manchester Airport	Ground Repeater
		NFM	RAF Fairford	IAT Fire Control
455.6500	469.6500	NFM	Dublin	Police U
455.6750	455.6750	NFM	Norwich	HM Customs & Excise
455.6750	469.6750	NFM	Dublin	Police D
455.6875	460.9875	NFM	Ronaldsway Airport	Tower-Ground
455.7000	461.0000	NFM	Birmingham Airport	Apron
		NFM	RAF Fairford	IAT Engineering
		NFM	Gatwick Airport	BAA Ops
		NFM	Heathrow Airport	Tower Rebroadcast
		NFM	Cardiff	Airport Security
		NFM	Hawarden Airfield	Ground

Base	Mobile	Mode	Location	User and Notes
		NFM	Edinburgh Airport	PMR Channel 5
		NFM	Bournmouth Airport	Ground Services
		NFM	Edinburgh Airport	Channel 25
		NFM	Gatwick Airport	Ground Repeater
		NFM	Heathrow Airport	Tower Repeater
		NFM	Birmingham Airport	Apron Ch 4
455.7125	461.0125	NFM	Bedford (MoD Airfield)	Ground
		NFM	London Heathrow	Weather Information Relay
		NFM	East Midlands Airport	Fire Service
		NFM	London Docklands	Ground Control
		NFM	Manchester Airport	Ground Handling
455.7250	461.0250	NFM	London Heathrow	Armed Police
		NFM	Nationwide	Airport Tower Rebroadcasts
		NFM	Edinburgh Airport	Channel 23
455.7250	469.7250	NFM	Dublin	Police W/N/T
455.7250	461.0250	NFM	Edinburgh Airport	PMR Channel 3
		NFM	Heathrow Airport	Police (Hunter Delta)
		NFM	Woodford Airfield	Fuel & Maintenance
455.7375	461.0375	NFM	RAF Fairford	IAT Speedbird
		NFM	Gatwick Airport	BAA Ops
		NFM	Coventry Airport	Ground Ops
		NFM	Manchester Airport	Coach Ops
		NFM	Newcastle Airport	Tower
		NFM	RAE Farnborough	Maintenance/Fuel
		NFM	Newcastle Airport	Tower Repeater
455.7500	469.7500	NFM	Dublin	Police D/U/C
455.7500	461.0500	NFM	Newcastle Airport	Tower Repeater
455.7625	461.0625	NFM	Birmingham Airport	Ground Staff
		NFM	RAF Fairford	IAT (Zodiac Base)
		NFM	Liverpool Airport	Security
455.7750	455.7750	NFM	Nationwide	HM Customs (Airports)
455.7750	461.0750	NFM	Gatwick	Ground Control Link
		NFM	London Heathrow	Armed Police
		NFM	Edinburgh Airport	PMR Channel 2
		NFM	Edinburgh Airport	Channel 22
		NFM	Heathrow Airport	Ground Repeater
455.7750	469.7750	NFM	Dublin	Police R/H/J/K
455.7875	461.0875	NFM	Bedford (MoD Airfield)	Ground
		NFM	Manchester Airport	Car Park Security
		NFM	Manchester Airport	Ground Repeater
455.8000	461.1000	NFM	RAF Fairford	IAT Emergency Control
		NFM	Weston-super-Mare	Airport Security
		NFM	Birmingham Airport	Baggage Handlers
455.8000	469.8000	NFM	Dublin	Police E/B/A
455.8125	461.1125	NFM	Aberdeen/Dyce Airport	Ground
		NFM	London Heathrow	Ground
		NFM	Stansted Airport	Security Ops
		NFM	Newcastle Airport	Baggage Handling

Base	Mobile	Mode	Location	User and Notes
		NFM	Manchester Airport	Ground Handling
		NFM	Edinburgh Airport	PMR Channel 4
		NFM	Heathrow Airport	Seagull & Checker
455.8250	461.1250	NFM	Nationwide	HM Customs (Airport)
		NFM	Stansted Airport	Tower
		NFM	Birmingham Airport	Maglev
		NFM	Birmingham Airport	Maintenance
		NFM	Luton Airport	MacAlpine Aviation
		NFM	Luton Airport	Ground Movements Ch1
		NFM	Luton Airport	Magec Ops
		NFM	RAF Fairford	IAT Message Centre
		NFM	Gatwick Airport	Data
		NFM	Birmingham Airport	Maglev
		NFM	East Midlands Airport	Maintenance
455.8250	469.8250	NFM	Dublin	Police L/M/G/P
455.8375	461.1375	NFM	Glasgow Airport	Baggage Handlers
		NFM	Liverpool Airport	Fire Control
		NFM	Edinburgh Airport	PMR Channel 1
		NFM	Lydd Airfield	Ground Repeater
455.8500	455.8500	NFM	Nationwide	HM Customs (Airport)
455.8500	461.1500	NFM	RAF Fairford	IAT Security Control
		NFM	Gatwick Airport	Baggage Handlers
		NFM	Woodford Airfield	VIP & Crew Bus

455.8750 - 456.0000 MHz   EMERGENCY SERVICES 12.5 KHZ NFM

Base	Mobile	Mode	Location	User and Notes
455.8750	461.1750	NFM	London Heathrow	Approach
455.9250		NFM	London Heathrow	Airline & BAA Ops
455.9625	425.4375	NFM	Yorkshire	Fruit Lorries
455.9875	455.9875	NFM	Edinburgh	Fire Brigade
		NFM	Glasgow	Fire Brigade
		NFM	Scotland	Fire Brigade Channel 7
		NFM	Leeds	Fire/Police Inter Agency
		NFM	West Yorkshire	Fire/Police Inter Agency
		NFM	Nationwide	Interagency Liaison
455.9875	462.5375	NFM	Nationwide	Interagency Liaison
		NFM	Nationwide	Airfield Fire Channel 7
455.9875	455.9875	NFM	Nationwide	Airfield Fire Channel 8

456.0000 - 457.0000 MHz   TRANSPORT, SECURITY 12.5 KHZ
(SPLIT + 5.5 MHZ) FORMULA ONE RACING
TEAM LINKS

Base	Mobile	Mode	Location	User and Notes
456.0000	456.0000	NFM	Jersey	Securicor Handhelds
		NFM	Heathrow Airport	Airline & BAA Ops
		NFM	St. Fergus	Shell
		NFM	Southampton	Securicor
456.0250	461.5250	NFM	Aberdeen	PMR
		NFM	Gatwick	Security
		NFM	Manchester	Airport Ground Services

Base	Mobile	Mode	Location	User and Notes
		NFM	Nottingham	Streamline Taxis
		NFM	Stansted Airport	Aviation Traders
		NFM	Nationwide	Simply Red Crew
		NFM	London	Haileys Toy Shop Security
		NFM	Dover Harbour	Police
		NFM	Swansea	Quadrant SCS
		NFM	Blackpool	Spectrum Security
		NFM	Immingham	DFDS Transport
		NFM	Middlesborough	ICI Leeks
		NFM	Heathrow Airport	Ground Repeater
456.0375	461.0375	NFM	Stansted Airport	Air UK Flight Despatch
456.0500	456.0500	NFM	Brent D	Shell
456.0500	456.0500	NFM	N. Cormorant	Shell
		NFM	Bristol	UKAEA Power Station Sec.
		NFM	Heathrow Airport	Airline & BAA Ops
		NFM	Rough A	BGE&P
		NFM	Brac South	Marathon
		NFM	Grays Thurrock	Council Refuse Collection
		NFM	Blackpool	Trams
		NFM	Birmingham	Flightlink Coaches
456.0625	461.0625	NFM	Heathrow Airport	Airline & BAA Ops
456.0750	461.5750	NFM	Belfast	City Hospital Security
		NFM	Heathrow Airport	Airline & BAA Ops
456.0875	461.5875	NFM	Jersey	Airport Ground Services
		NFM	Nationwide	National Power
456.1000	461.6000	NFM	England	CEGB
		NFM	Heathrow Airport	Airline & BAA Ops
		NFM	Rough A	BGE&P
		NFM	Brae S	Marathon
		NFM	Southampton	National Power
		NFM	Manchester Airport	Tugs
456.1250	461.6250	NFM	Birmingham	City Council
		NFM	London	Trunked PMR
		NFM	Nationwide	Simply Red Crew
		NFM	Salford	Hospital Trust Managers.
		NFM	Magnus	BP Sulair
		NFM	The Port of Heysham	Isle of Man Steam Packet
		NFM	Cemaes Bay	Wylfa Power Station
		NFM	Edinburgh	United Artist Cable Layers
456.1375	461.6375	NFM	Newcastle Airport	Stores Department
		NFM	London	Vediotron Ltd
456.1500	461.6500	NFM	Manchester	Sub Station Audio Alarm
		NFM	London	London Electric
456.1525	456.1525	NFM	Dover Harbour	Police
456.1625	461.6625	NFM	London	Victoria Coach Station
		NFM	London	London Electric
456.1750	461.6750	NFM	Calverton	National Coal Board
		NFM	Dungeness	Power Station

Base	Mobile	Mode	Location	User and Notes
		NFM	Nationwide	National Power Operations
		NFM	Alwyn	Total
456.1875	461.6875	NFM	London	Electricity Board Engineers
		NFM	Morecambe	Voice Alarm
456.2000	456.2000	NFM	Auk	Shell PMR
		NFM	Brent A	Shell PMR
		NFM	Dunlin	Shell PMR
456.2000	461.7000	NFM	Berkeley	BNFL Command & Control
		NFM	Leicester	British Gas Security
		NFM	Belfast	CityBus Channel 1
456.2125	461.7250	NFM	London	Electricity Board Engineers
		NFM	Surrey	Electricity Board Engineers
456.2250	461.7250	NFM	Morecambe	Data Link
		NFM	Nationwide	National Power Mainten.
		NFM	Rough A	BGE&P
		NFM	Dunfin	Shell
456.2375	461.7375	NFM	London	London Electric
456.2500	461.7500	NFM	Berkeley	BNFL Command & Control
		NFM	Manchester	BR Transport Police
456.2625	461.7625	NFM	Heathrow Airport	Airline & BAA Ops
		NFM	Canvey Island	British Gas
456.2750	461.7750	NFM	Dungeness	Power Station
		NFM	Nationwide	National Power Operations
		NFM	London	London Electric
		NFM	Brent D	Shell PMR
		NFM	N Cormorant	Shell PMR
456.3000	461.8000	NFM	Easington	British Gas Terminal
		NFM	Heathrow Airport	Airline & BAA Ops
		NFM	Brae N	Marathon
		NFM	Barrow	VSEL Security
456.3125	461.8125	NFM	London	Eastern Electricity
456.3250	461.8250	NFM	Dungeness	Power Station
		NFM	Heathrow Airport	General Purpose Channel
		NFM	Brent B	Shell PMR
		NFM	Cormorant A	Shell PMR
456.3375	461.8375	NFM	Nationwide	British Rail Transport Police
456.3500	461.8500	NFM	Aberdeen	City Buses
		NFM	Brighton	Royal Pavillion
		NFM	Eastbourne	City Buses
		NFM	Gatwick	Cleaners & Cargo Loaders
		NFM	Moray Firth	Beatrice Bravo Platform
		NFM	Nottingham	City Engineers
		NFM	Saltend	BP Oil Refinery
		NFM	Heathrow Airport	Airline & BAA Ops
456.3500	462.8500	NFM	Billingham	ICI
456.3500	456.3500	NFM	Beatrice B	BP
456.3750	461.8375	NFM	Nationwide	British Transport Police Ch 2
		NFM	Doncaster	British Transport Police

Base	Mobile	Mode	Location	User and Notes
		NFM	Exeter	British Transport Police
		NFM	Sheffield	British Transport Police
		NFM	London	Tower of London
		NFM	London	Docks Light Railvay Ch 10
		NFM	London	Westminster Abbey
		NFM	Cleveland	DSS Dole Frauds Ch 8
456.4000	456.4000	NFM	Nationwide	Royal Mail Police
		NFM	M1	Bullion Movements
456.4000	456.4000	NFM	Nationwide	BR Royal Mail Police
		NFM	Blackpool Airport	CAA Repeater
		NFM	Luton Airport	Customs
		NFM	Manchester Airport	Customs
		NFM	Martlesham Heath	British Telecom
		NFM	Nationwide	HM Customs (Airport)
		NFM	Nationwide BR Stations	Post Offices
		NFM	Sheffield	City Buses
		NFM	Thornton	ICI Emergency
		NFM	Cleveland	DSS Dole Frauds Ch 9
456.4250	456.4250	NFM	Nationwide	BR Trans. Police Ops Ch. 3
456.4250	461.9250	NFM	Birmingham	BR Transport Police
		NFM	Doncaster	BR Transport Police
		NFM	Edinburgh	British Transport Police
		NFM	Gatwick	Ground Control Link
		NFM	Glasgow	BR Transport Police
		NFM	Liverpool	British Transport Police
		NFM	London	British Transport Police (LT)
		NFM	Sheffield	Council Works Department
		NFM	Hull	Docks Police
		NFM	Heathrow Airport	Airline & BAA Ops
456.4500	456.4500	NFM	Dunlin	Shell
456.4500	461.9500	NFM	Aberdeen	City Buses
		NFM	Nottingham	Traffic Light Repairs
		NFM	Thamesmead	Caretakers & Lift Ops
		NFM	Nationwide	BRTP National Channel
		NFM	SMV	BP
		NFM	Bacton	Phillips
		NFM	Brent B	Shell PMR
		NFM	Cormorant A	Shell PMR
		NFM	Sullom Voe	Shell
		NFM	Brighton	Buses
		NFM	Newcastle Airport	Airport Security
		NFM	Leicester	City Council Cleansing
		NFM	IWM Duxford	Security
		NFM	Bury	Council
456.4625	461.9625	NFM	Cleethorpes	Ross Young Fish Factory
456.4750	461.9750	NFM	Birmingham	Safari Park Control
		NFM	Nationwide	Independent Coach Ops
		NFM	Wilton	ICI Fire & Security

Base	Mobile	Mode	Location	
		NFM	Luton	
		NFM	Heathrow Airport	A
		NFM	Gatwick Airport	Air
		NFM	Glasgow Airport	Bag
		NFM	Thistle A	BP
		NFM	Grimsby	Appleb
		NFM	Leicester	Security
		NFM	Heathrow Airport	Ground R
		NFM	Edinburgh	St James Ce security
		NFM	Clayton	Maynes Buses
456.5000	456.5000	NFM	Bristol	Police Link
456.5000	462.0000	NFM	Stockport	TNT Carriers
		NFM	Dungeness	Power Station
		NFM	Gatwick	Aircraft Tugs
		NFM	Nationwide	HM Customs & Excise
		NFM	Nationwide	Federal Express
		NFM	Immingham	Tor Line Docks
		NFM	Heathrow Airport	Airline & BAA Ops
		NFM	Immingham	Exxtor Shipping
		NFM	N Welsh Coast	ESSO Rig
		NFM	Leicester	Woods Coaches Ch2
		NFM	Preston	Skips & Bottle Banks
		NFM	Liverpool	Dockside Crane Control
		NFM	IWM Duxford	Management/Maintenance
		NFM	Norwich Airport	Ground Movements
		NFM	Middleton	Diamond Cars
456.5250	462.0250	NFM	Brent C	Shell PMR
		NFM	Gatwick	Aircraft Tugs
		NFM	Ipswich	Port Authority
		NFM	Nationwide	HM Customs & Excise
		NFM	Sheffield	Sheffield University Ch A
		NFM	Stansted Airport	Telephone Ops
		NFM	Billingham	ICI
		NFM	Gateshead	Metro Centre Security
		NFM	Salisbury	Hospital Emergency/Security
		NFM	Saltend	BP Oil Refinery
		NFM	Immingham	Docks/Repairs
		NFM	Ipswich	Ports Police
		NFM	Stoke-on-Trent	Police
		NFM	Leicester	LCFC Stewards
		NFM	Stansted Airport	Ground Repeater
		NFM	Bristol Airport	Ground Repeater
		NFM	Birmingham Airport	Ops
456.5500	461.0500	NFM	Filton (BAe)	Security
		NFM	Gatwick	Ground Control Link
		NFM	Nottingham	Cap Count Victoria Centre
		NFM	Nottinghamshire	Lex Wilkinson
		NFM	Perth	Perth Cable Company

		Mode	Location	User and Notes
		NFM	Stirling	Hydro Electric Engineers
		NFM	Heathrow Airport	Aircraft Maintanence
		NFM	Hull	University Security
		NFM	Morecambe	Parcel Service
		NFM	Poole	Borough Council
		NFM	Newcastle	Eldon SCS
		NFM	Heathrow Airport	Airline & BAA Ops
		NFM	Brighton	Royal Sussex County Hospital
		NFM	Stoke-on-Trent	Potteries Shopping Centre
		NFM	Bristol	Federal Express
		NFM	Lancashire	24Hr Vehicle Recovery
		NFM	Gatwick Airport	Ground Repeater
		NFM	Heathrow Airport	Ground Repeater
		NFM	Bristol Filton	Security
456.5750	456.5750	NFM	Nationwide	D.O.T Motorcycle Tests
		NFM	Newtown	MotorcycleTests
456.5750	462.0750	NFM	Beeston	Boots
		NFM	Jersey	Servisair Handling
		NFM	Hull	Hull University
		NFM	Immingham	APT
		NFM	Brighton	British Home Stores Security
		NFM	Dimlington	BP
		NFM	Easington	BP
		NFM	Miller	BP
		NFM	Auk	Shell PMR
		NFM	Brent A	Shell PMR
		NFM	Dunlin	Shell PMR
		NFM	Brighton	Store Detectives
		NFM	Bristol	Poly-Tech Security
		NFM	Ashford	Learner Motor Cycles
		NFM	Southampton	ESSO Fawley (CCR3)
		NFM	Heathrow Airport	Ground Repeater
		NFM	Swansea	Motorcycle Training
456.6000	456.6000	NFM	Maureen	Phillips
456.6000	462.1000	NFM	Maureen	Phillips
		NFM	Alwyn	Total
		NFM	Aberdeen/Dyce Airport	Loading
		NFM	Leicester	Shires SCS
		NFM	Saltend	BP Oil Refinery
		NFM	Thornton	ICI
		NFM	Manchester Airport	Aircraft Cleaners
		NFM	Aberdeen Airport	Ground Repeater
		NFM	Bristol Filton	Ground Repeater
		NFM	Belfast Airport	Tower
		NFM	Cardiff	RadioNet Shop Security
456.6125	462.1125	NFM	Newcastle Airport	Tower
456.6150		NFM	Grand Prix Circuits	Ferrari Team Voice Link
456.6250	462.1250	NFM	Oxford	Clarendon Centre

Base	Mobile	Mode	Location	User and Notes
		NFM	Birmingham	Birmingham Univ. Security
		NFM	Warwick	Warwick University Security
		NFM	Gatwick	Ground Control Link
		NFM	Peterborough	Security Company
		NFM	Brent C	Shell PMR
		NFM	Jersey Airport	Ground
		NFM	Fulmar A	Shell PMR
		NFM	Croydon	Drummond SCS
		NFM	Cleethorpes	Ross Young Fish Factory
		NFM	Southampton	ESSO Fawley
		NFM	Gatwick Airport	Ground Repeater
		NFM	IWM Duxford	Fire Control
		NFM	London	Victoria Coach Station
456.6300	456.6300	NFM	N. Cormorant	Shell
456.6500	462.1500	NFM	Manchester Airport	Ground Control
		NFM	Sheffield	Meadowhall Centre (Zero)
		NFM	Stansted Airport	Long Term Car Park
		NFM	Heathrow Airport	Ground Staff Terminal 1
		NFM	Hull	North Sea Ferries Ch 1
		NFM	Heathrow Airport	Airline & BAA Ops
		NFM	Gatwick Airport	Airline & BAA Ops
		NFM	Miller	BP
		NFM	Sheffield	Meadowhall SCS
		NFM	Nuneaton	Retail Security Link
		NFM	Gatwick	Aviation Fuel
		NFM	Southampton	ESSO Fawley (PET-M)
		NFM	Edinburgh Airport	PMR Channel 6
		NFM	Glasgow Airport	Ground
		NFM	Sandwich	Pfizers
456.6625	462.1625	NFM	Newcastle Airport	Stand Services
456.6750	462.1750	NFM	Aberdeen/Dyce Airport	Staff
		NFM	London	North Thames Electricity
		NFN	Nottingham	J. Player & Son
		NFM	Oldbury	BNFL Backup Channel
		NFM	Woburn	Woburn Abbey Wildlife Park
		NFM	Billingham	ICI
		NFM	Manchester	City Centre Car Clamping
		NFM	Heathrow Airport	Airline & BAA Ops
		NFM	Miller	BP
		NFM	Brent D	Shell
		NFM	Cormorant N	Shell
		NFM	Stoke-on-Trent	Police
		NFM	Manchester	Paramedic Teams
		NFM	Warton	Fence Security
		NFM	Southampton	ESSO Fawley (Lubes)
		NFM	Liverpool	Medic Control
		NFM	Heathrow Airport	Air France Passenger Serv.
		NFM	Aberdeen Airport	Ground Repeater

Base	Mobile	Mode	Location	User and Notes
456.6875	456.6875	NFM	Morecambe	Parcel Service
456.7000	456.7000	NFM	Brent C	Shell
		NFM	Fulmar A	Shell
456.7000	456.2000	NFM	Nationwide	Marconi Communications
		NFM	Nationwide	Motorola
		NFM	London	BR Signal Engineers
		NFM	Lancaster	Lancaster University Security
456.7000	462.2000	NFM	Perth	Car Park Security
		NFM	Grays	Lakeside Centre Car Park
		NFM	Saltend	BP Oil Refinery
		NFM	Great Coates	Courtaulds
		NFM	Lancaster	University
		NFM	Killingholme	Lindsey Oil Refinery
		NFM	Southampton	ESSO Fawley (RED) Fire
		NFM	Heathrow Airport	Ground Repeater
456.7250	462.2250	NFM	Cowley	Rover Plant Channel 5
		NFM	Ulverston	Glaxo UK
		NFM	Gatwick	Avionics Maintenance
		NFM	Hull	North Sea Passenger Ferries
		NFM	Nationwide	UHF Demo Channel Ch 99
		NFM	Stevenston	ICI Security and Fire Service
		NFM	Peterborough	City Council
		NFM	Luton Airport	Maintenance Engineers
		NFM	Hull	North Sea Ferries Ch 2
		NFM	Heathrow Airport	Airline & BAA Ops
		NFM	Gatwick Airport	Airline & BAA Ops
		NFM	SMV	BP
		NFM	Peterborough	County Council
		NFM	Canvey Island	Texaco Oil Refinery
		NFM	Southend-on-Sea	Store Security
		NFM	Jersey	Dock Crane Operators
		NFM	Southampton	ESSO Fawley (OMES)
		NFM	Luton Airport	Maintenance Engineers
		NFM	Swansea Docks	Shipping Pilots
		NFM	Edinburgh	Herriot Watt Univ. Security
456.7500	462.2500	NFM	Aberdeen/Dyce Airport	Loading
		NFM	Barrow	VSEL Fire & Nuclear Incid.
		NFM	Glasgow Airport	Cargo Handlers
		NFM	London	Bexley Heath SCS
		NFM	Skelmersdale	Town Centre Security
		NFM	Aberdeen Airport	Ground Repeater
456.7750	462.2750	NFM	Blackpool	Blackpool Pleasure Beach
		NFM	Glasgow	Police
		NFM	Harwich	Trinity House
		NFM	Millbrook	Test Track
		NFM	Redditch	King Fisher Shopping Centre
		NFM	Hull	Docks Cranes/Loading
		NFM	Heathrow Airport	Airline & BAA Ops

Base	Mobile	Mode	Location	User and Notes
		NFM	Gatwick Airport	Airline & BAA Ops
		NFM	Dyce	BP
		NFM	Nuneaton	George Elliot Hosp. Security
		NFM	Southampton	ESSO Fawley (Chemicals)
		NFM	Leicester	Area Traffic Control
		NFM	Eastham	Manchester Ship Canal
		NFM	Gatwick Airport	Ground Repeater
		NFM	Heathrow Airport	Kuwaiti Airlines
456.8000	456.8000	NFM	Ninian Central	Chevron Drilling
		NFM	Ninian South	Chevron Drilling
456.8000	462.3000	NFM	Beeston	Boots
		NFM	Guernsey	Beau Sejour Leisure Centre
		NFM	Nottingham	Queen's Medical Centre
		NFM	London	Harrods Shop Security
		NFM	Brent B	Shell PMR
		NFM	Cormorant A	Shell PMR
		NFM	Fulmar A	Shell PMR
		NFM	Heathrow Airport	Security
		NFM	Luton Airport	Security Ch 7
456.8000	462.1000	NFM	Gatwick	Aviation Fuel
		NFM	Guildford	Army & Navy Stores
456.8250	462.3250	NFM	Bath	University Security
		NFM	Billingham	ICI
		NFM	Boscombe	Chase Manhatten Bank
		NFM	Brighton	Sussex University Security
		NFM	Dover	Coastguard Cliff Rescue
		NFM	Heathrow Airport	Airline & BAA Ops
		NFM	Immingham	BSC
		NFM	Manchester Airport	Airline Ops
		NFM	Nationwide	NCB & Docks
		NFM	Nottingham	Patent Brick
		NFM	Sandwich	Pfizers
		NFM	Southampton	ESSO Fawley CCR1
		NFM	St Helens	Pilkingtons Security
		NFM	Stansted Airport	Telephone Ops
		NFM	Tamworth	Borough Council
		NFM	Woburn	Woburn Abbey Wildlife Park
456.8500	462.3500	NFM	Aberdeen	PMR
		NFM	Cowley	Rover Plant
		NFM	Nottingham	Mapperly Hospital
		NFM	Stansted Airport	Airport Buses
		NFM	Tilbury	Docks Security
		NFM	Heathrow Airport	Airline & BAA Ops
		NFM	Stansted Airport	Long Term Car Park
		NFM	Manchester	Taxis
		NFM	Coventry	Community Nurses
		NFM	Skelmersdale	Taxis
		NFM	Wansford	Nene Valley Railway

Base	Mobile	Mode	Location	User and Notes
		NFM	Manchester	Taxis
		NFM	Wigan	Taxis
456.8625	462.3625	NFM	Woodford	British Aerospace
		NFM	River Thames	Ship On-Board Comms
		NFM	Woodford Airfield	BAe Security
		NFM	London	Wembley Stadium VIP
		NFM	Edinburgh	Teviot House Security
		NFM	Nationwide	Short Term Hire
456.8750	462.3750	NFM	Gatwick	Handling
		NFM	Grays	Lakeside Centre Security
		NFM	Guernsey	Esso
		NFM	Nottingham	Esso Colwick
		NFM	Stevenston	ICI Acid Plant Maintenance
		NFM	Southampton	Docks
		NFM	Auk	Shell PMR
		NFM	Brent A	Shell PMR
		NFM	Dunlin	Shell MR
		NFM	Lancashire	Vanguard Couriers
		NFM	Southampton	ESSO Fawley Jetty
		NFM	N Welsh Coast	ESSO Rig
		NFM	Birmingham Airport	Ops
456.9000	462.4000	NFM	Barrow	VSEL Works Security Control
		NFM	Leeds/Bradford	Brown Cleaning Co.
		NFM	East Midlands Airport	Servisair
		NFM	Heathrow Airport	Tower Rebroadcast
		NFM	Gatwick Airport	Airline & BAA Ops
		NFM	Newcastle Airport	Refuelling
		NFM	Bournemouth	Bournemouth Zoo
		NFM	Glasgow Airport	Ops
		NFM	Liverpool Airport	Servisair
		NFM	Manchester Airport	Push Back Tugs
		NFM	Manchester Airport	Airline Ops
		NFM	Edinburgh Airport	Baggage Handlers
456.9250	462.4250	NFM	Cowley	Rover Plant Channel 6
		NFM	Nationwide	BAA Airport Security
		NFM	Nationwide	Power Station Security
		NFM	Nationwide	UHF Demonstration Channel
		NFM	Ealing	Shopping Centre
		NFM	Wigan	Galleries SCS
		NFM	Blackpool	Store Detectives
		NFM	Heathrow Airport	Ground Repeater
		NFM	London	Wembley Stadium VIP
		NFM	Nationwide	Short Term Hire
456.9500	462.4500	NFM	Bournemouth	Repeater
		NFM	Heathrow Airport	Airline & BAA Ops
		NFM	Gatwick Airport	Airline & BAA Ops
		NFM	Southampton	ESSO Fawley Chemicals
		NFM	Liverpool	City Centre Shops Security

Base	Mobile	Mode	Location	User and Notes
		NFM	Halewood	Ford Plant Shop Stewards
		NFM	Heathrow Airport	Virgin Airlines
		NFM	Birmingham Airport	Ops
		NFM	Liverpool	Cherry Tree SCS
456.9750	456.4750	NFM	Stansted Airport	Stansted Cars
		NFM	Aberdeen	PMR
		NFM	Leamington Spa	British Leyland
		NFM	Nationwide	Bus & Coach Operators
		NFM	Nationwide	Formula One Racing Team
		NFM	Scotland	Scottish HydroElectric
		NFM	Flitwick	Buffalo Bus Co.
		NFM	Humberside	Appleby's Coaches
		NFM	Newport	New Borough Transport
		NFM	Newcastle Airport	Brittania Airways
		NFM	Leicester	Woods Coaches Ch1
		NFM	Rochdale	Buses
456.9875	462.4875	NFM	Tunbrigde Wells	Tour de France Barriers
		NFM	Jersey	Community Repeater
		NFM	Heathrow Airport	Airline & BAA Ops
		NFM	Brighton	Royal Sussex County Hospital
		NFM	SE Sussex	Security Patrol
		NFM	IWM Duxford	Car Parks
		NFM	Nationwide	Short Term Hire

457.0000 - 457.2500 MHz   EMERGENCY SERVICES 12.5 kHz NFM

457.0000 - 457.5000 MHz   UHF FIRE MOBILE LINKS 12.5 kHz SIMPLEX & DUPLEX BASE (SPLIT + 5.5 MHz) SCOTTISH HYDROELECTRIC FORMULA ONE RACING TEAM LINKS

Base	Mobile	Mode	Location	User and Notes
457.0000	457.0000	NFM	England & Wales	Police Channel 93
457.0125	457.0125	NFM	Edinburgh	Fire Brigade
		NFM	Glasgow	Fire Brigade
457.0125	462.5125	NFM	London	Fire Brigade
457.0250		NFM	Nationwide	Minardi Formula One Voice
457.0250	462.5250	NFM	Gairloch	Hydro Electric
457.0375	462.5375	NFM	London	Fire Brigade
457.0375	457.0375	NFM	Cumbria	Fire Brigade Portables
		NFM	Edinburgh	Fire Brigade
		NFM	Glasgow	Fire Brigade
		NFM	Perth	Fire Brigade Tender
		NFM	Merseyside	Fire Brigade Ch 1
		NFM	Nationwide	Airfield Fire Channel 1
		NFM	Dyfed	Fire Motorola Ascom Ch 1
457.0500		NFM	Nationwide	Minardi Formula One Voice
457.0500	457.0500	NFM	England & Wales	Police Channel 91
457.0750	462.5750	NFM	Achanshellach	Hydro Electric Board
		NFM	Heathrow Airport	Airline & BAA Ops

Base	Mobile	Mode	Location	User and Notes
457.0750	462.5750	NFM	Ninian South	Chevron Back-up to Ninian N
457.0875	462.5875	NFM	Edinburgh	Fire Brigade
		NFM	Glasgow	Fire Brigade
		NFM	London	Fire Brigade
		NFM	Dyfed	Fire Motorola Ascom Ch 2
457.1000	462.6000	NFM	Gairloch	Hydro Electric
		NFM	Loch A'Burra	Scottish Hydro Electric
		NFM	England & Wales	Police Channel 92
457.1250		NFM	Heathrow Airport	Airline & BAA Ops
457.1375	457.1375	NFM	Edinburgh	Fire Brigade
		NFM	Glasgow	Fire Brigade
		NFM	Gatwick Airport	Fire Brigade
457.1375	462.6375	NFM	London	Fire Brigade
457.1500	462.6500	NFM	England & Wales	Police Channel 95
457.1875	457.1875	NFM	Edinburgh	Fire Brigade
		NFM	Glasgow	Fire Brigade
		NFM	Perth	Fire Brigade Chief Fire Officer
		NFM	Perth	Fire Brigade Handhelds
457.1875	462.6875	NFM	London	Fire Brigade
457.2000	457.2500	NFM	England & Wales	Police Channel 94
457.2000	462.7000	NFM	Nationwide	NCB Mine Rescue
457.2125		NFM	Heathrow Airport	Airline & BAA Ops
457.2250		NFM	Ipswich	Data Traffic
457.2375	457.2375	NFM	Cumbria	Fire Brigade Portables
		NFM	Edinburgh	Fire Brigade
		NFM	Glasgow	Fire Brigade
		NFM	London	Fire Brigade
457.2500	457.2500	NFM	England & Wales	Police Channel 96
457.3125		NFM	Grand Prix Circuits	Ligier Team Voice Link
457.3250		NFM	Glasgow	SkyTV Ibrox Park
457.3500	462.8500	NFM	Gairloch	Hydro Electric
		NFM	Nationwide	AA UHF Mobiles
457.3750	462.8750	NFM	Gairloch	Hydro Electric
		NFM	Inverness	Automobile Association
457.3875	462.8875	NFM	Heathrow Airport	Airline & BAA Ops
		NFM	Dyfed	Fire Motorola Ascom Ch 3
457.4000	462.9000	NFM	Yorkshire	Ambulance Service
		NFM	Humberside	Ambulance Service
457.4250	462.9250	NFM	Yorkshire	Ambulance Service
		NFM	Humberside	Ambulance Service
		NFM	Norfolk	Ambulance Service
		NFM	Suffolk	Ambulance Service
		NFM	Cambridgeshire	Ambulance Service
457.4500	462.9500	NFM	Gairloch	Hydro Electric
		NFM	Cleveland	Ambulance Service
		NFM	Cumbria	Ambulance Service
		NFM	Durham	Ambulance Service
		NFM	Northumbria	Ambulance Service

Base	Mobile	Mode	Location	User and Notes
457.4750	462.9750	NFM	Garve	Scottish Roads
		NFM	Norfolk	Ambulance Service
		NFM	Suffolk	Ambulance Service
		NFM	Cambridgeshire	Ambulance Service

457.50625 - 458.49375 MHz   FIXED SCAN LINKS & SHIP BOARD HANDHELD
TRANSCEIVERS 6.25 kHz (SPLIT + 5.5 MHz)

Base	Mobile	Mode	Location	User and Notes
457.5000	463.0000	NFM	Norfolk	Ambulance Service
		NFM	Suffolk	Ambulance Service
		NFM	Cambridgeshire	Ambulance Service
457.5250		NFM	Maritime	Ship Communications
457.5250	457.5250	NFM	Nationwide	BT Marine Cable Laying
		NFM	Frigg Field	Elf
		NFM	Balmor-al	Sun Oil Portables
		NFM	Mid Staffordshire	Ambulance Service
		NFM	Salop	Ambulance Service
		NFM	South Warwickshire	Ambulance Service
		NFM	Worcestershire	Ambulance Service
457.5312	463.0312	NFM	Maritime	Ship Portable Ch 3
457.5437	463.0437	NFM	Maritime	Ship Portable Ch 4
457.5500	457.5500	NFM	Maritime	Ship Communications
		NFM	Nationwide	BT Marine Cable Laying
		NFM	Morecambe	Data Link
		NFM	Newmarket	Scan Data Link
		NFM	Frigg Field	Elf
		NFM	Balmoral	Sun Oil Portables
		NFM	Southampton	P&O Marine
457.5562	463.0562	NFM	Nationwide	Channel 5
457.5625		NFM	Newmarket	Data Link
457.5687	463.0687	NFM	Nationwide	Channel 6
457.5750		NFM	Maritime	Ship Communications
457.5750	457.5750	NFM	Balmoral	Sun Oil
		NFM	Mid Staffordshire	Ambulance Service
		NFM	Salop	Ambulance Service
		NFM	South Warwickshire	Ambulance Service
		NFM	Worcestershire	Ambulance Service
457.5750	467.5750	NFM	Lolair	BP
		NFM	Ffigg Field	Elf
457.5750	467.5750	NFM	Balmoral	Sun Oil
		NFM	Southampton	P&O Marine
457.5812	463.0812	NFM	Nationwide	Channel 7
457.5937	463.0937	NFM	Nationwide	Channel 8
457.6000		NFM	Maritime	Ship Communications
457.6000	463.1000	NFM	Garve	Scottish Roads
457.6062	463.1062	NFM	Nationwide	Channel 9
457.6187	463.1187	NFM	Nationwide	Channel 10
457.6250	463.1250	NFM	Gatwick	Police M2KB (GatPol)
		NFM	Wales	Ambulance Service

Base	Mobile	Mode	Location	User and Notes
457.63125	463.1312	NFM	Nationwide	Channel 11
457.6375	457.63755	NFM	Cumbria	Fire Brigade Portables
457.64375	463.14375	NFM	Nationwide	Channel 12
457.6500		NFM	Newmarket	Digital Paging
457.65625	463.15625	NFM	Nationwide	Channel 13
457.6625		NFM	Newcastle	Data Link
457.66875	463.16875	NFM	Nationwide	Channel 14
457.6750		NFM	Newmarket	Data Link
457.68125	463.18125	NFM	Nationwide	Channel 15
457.69375	463.19375	NFM	Nationwide	Channel 16
457.7000	463.2000	NFM	Ullapool	Scottish Roads
457.70625	463.20625	NFM	Nationwide	Channel 17
457.70625	463.20625	NFM	Nationwide	Channel 25
457.71575	463.31875	NFM	Nationwide	Channel 26
457.71875	463.21875	NFM	Nationwide	Channel 18
457.7250	463.2250	NFM	Gairloch	Scottish Roads
		NFM	Cleveland	Ambulance Service
		NFM	Cumbria	Ambulance Service
		NFM	Durham	Ambulance Service
		NFM	Northumbria	Ambulance Service
457.73125	463.23125	NFM	Nationwide	Channel 19
457.74375	463.24375	NFM	Nationwide	Channel 20
457.7500		NFM	Wales	Ambulance Service
457.75625	463.25625	NFM	Nationwide	Channel 21
457.7625		NFM	Stirling	Data Link
457.7687	463.26875	NFM	Nationwide	Channel 22
457.77500	463.27500	NFM	Fulmar FSU	Shell Telemetry
		NFM	Norfolk	Ambulance Service
		NFM	Suffolk	Ambulance Service
		NFM	Cambridgeshire	Ambulance Service
457.78125	463.28125	NFM	Nationwide	Channel 23
457.79375	463.29375	NFM	Nationwide	Channel 24
457.83125	463.33125	NFM	Nationwide	Channel 27
457.84375	463.34375	NFM	Nationwide	Channel 28
457.85000	463.35000	NFM	Viking Field	Conoco Telemetry
457.85625	463.35625	NFM	Nationwide	Channel 29
457.86875	463.36876	NFM	Nationwide	Channel 30
457.87500	463.37500	NFM	Buchan	BP
457.87500	463.37500	NFM	Forties	BP to Forties D
457.88125	463.38125	NFM	Nationwide	Channel 31
457.89375	463.39375	NFM	Nationwide	Channel 32
457.90625	463.40625	NFM	Nationwide	Channel 33
457.91875	463.41875	NFM	Nationwide	Channel 34
457.9250	463.4250	NFM	Nationwide	Short Term Hire Equipment
457.93125	463.43125	NFM	Nationwide	Channel 35
457.9375		NFM	Stirling	Data Link
457.94375	463.44376	NFM	Nationwide	Channel 36
457.9500		NFM	Newcastle	Data Link

Base	Mobile	Mode	Location	User and Notes
457.95625	463.45625	NFM	Nationwide	Channel 37
457.95625	463.48125	NFM	Nationwide	Channel 39
457.96875	463.46875	NFM	Nationwide	Channel 38
457.9750	463.4750	NFM	Norfolk	Ambulance Service
		NFM	Suffolk	Ambulance Service
		NFM	Cambridgeshire	Ambulance Service
457.99375	463.49375	NFM	Nationwide	Channel 40
458.0000		NFM	Lincoln	Data Link
458.00625	463.50625	NFM	Nationwide	Channel 41
458.0250		NFM	Newcastle	Data Link
		NFM	North Bedfordshire	Ambulance Service
		NFM	East Hertfordshire	Ambulance Service
458.03125	463.53125	NFM	Nationwide	Channel 43
458.04375	463.54375	NFM	Nationwide	Channel 44
458.05000	463.55000	NFM	Beryl A	Mobil Telemetry
458.0500		NFM	Lincoln	Health Authority
		NFM	Derbyshire	Ambulance Service
		NFM	Leicestershire	Ambulance Service
		NFM	Lincolnshireshire	Ambulance Service
		NFM	Nottinghamshire	Ambulance Service
		NFM	South Yorkshire	Ambulance Service
		NFM	Avon	Ambulance Service
		NFM	Cornwall	Ambulance Service
		NFM	Devon	Ambulance Service
		NFM	Gloucester	Ambulance Service
		NFM	Scilly Isles	Ambulance Service
		NFM	Somerset	Ambulance Service
458.05625	463.55625	NFM	Nationwide	Channel 45
458.06875	463.56875	NFM	Nationwide	Channel 46
458.08125	463.58125	NFM	Nationwide	Channel 47
458.09376	463.59375	NFM	Nationwide	Channel 46
458.10625	463.60625	NFM	Nationwide	Channel 49
458.11875	463.61875	NFM	Nationwide	Channel so
458.1250		NFM	Cleveland	Ambulance Service
		NFM	Cumbria	Ambulance Service
		NFM	Durham	Ambulance Service
		NFM	Northumbria	Ambulance Service
458.13125	463.63125	NFM	Nationwide	Channel 51
458.14375	463.64475	NFM	Nationwide	Channel 52
458.1500		NFM	Mid Staffordshire	Ambulance Service
		NFM	Salop	Ambulance Service
		NFM	South Warwickshire	Ambulance Service
		NFM	Worcestershire	Ambulance Service
458.15625	463.65625	NFM	Nationwide	Channel 53
458.16875	463.66875	NFM	Nationwide	Channel 54
458.1750	463.6750	NFM	Lea Valley	Water Board
		NFM	Yorkshire	Ambulance Service
		NFM	Humbershire	Ambulance Service

Base	Mobile	Mode	Location	User and Notes
		NFM	Mid Staffordshire	Ambulance Service
		NFM	Salop	Ambulance Service
		NFM	South Warwickshire	Ambulance Service
		NFM	Worcestershire	Ambulance Service
		NFM	Wales	Ambulance Service
458.18125	463.68125	NFM	Nationwide	Channel 55
458.19375	463.69375	NFM	Nationwide	Channel 56
458.20625	463.70625	NFM	Nationwide	Channel 57
458.21875	463.71875	NFM	Nationwide	Channel 58
458.22500	463.72500	NFM	Dunlin A	Shell
		NFM	Norfolk	Ambulance Service
		NFM	Suffolk	Ambulance Service
		NFM	Cambridgeshire	Ambulance Service
458.23125	463.73125	NFM	Nationwide	Channel 59
458.24375	463.74375	NFM	Nationwide	Channel 60
458.2500		NFM	Yorkshire	Ambulance Service
		NFM	Humbershire	Ambulance Service
458.25625	463.75625	NFM	Nationwide	Channel 61
458.26875	463.76875	NFM	Nationwide	Channel 62
458.2750	463.7750	NFM	Oxford	Ambulance Service
458.27500	462.77500	NFM	Murchison	Conoco
458.28125	463.76125	NFM	Nationwide	Channel 63
458.29375	463.79375	NFM	Nationwide	Channel 64
458.30625	463.80625	NFM	Nationwide	Channel 65
458.31875	463.81875	NFM	Nationwide	Channel 66
458.32500	463.82500	NFM	Murchison	Conoco
		NFM	Cleveland	Ambulance Service
		NFM	Cumbria	Ambulance Service
		NFM	Durham	Ambulance Service
		NFM	Northumbria	Ambulance Service
		NFM	North Bedfordshire	Ambulance Service
		NFM	East Hertfordshire	Ambulance Service
		NFM	Mid Essex	Ambulance Service
		NFM	Eastbourne	Ambulance Service
		NFM	Medway	Ambulance Service
		NFM	Kent	Ambulance Service
		NFM	Mid Surrey	Ambulance Service
		NFM	West Sussex	Ambulance Service
458.33125	463.83125	NFM	Nationwide	Channel 67
458.34376	463.54375	NFM	Nationwide	Channel 68
458.3500	463.8500	NFM	Lea Valley	Water Board
		NFM	Cleveland	Ambulance Service
		NFM	Cumbria	Ambulance Service
		NFM	Durham	Ambulance Service
		NFM	Northumbria	Ambulance Service
458.35625	463.85625	NFM	Nationwide	Channel 69
458.3625		NFM	Morecambe	Data Link
		NFM	Dundee	Data Link

Base	Mobile	Mode	Location	User and Notes
458.36876	463.86875	NFM	Nationwide	Channel 70
458.3750		NFM	Newcastle Airport	Internal Paging
458.38176	463.87125	NFM	Nationwide	Channel 71
458.39375	463.89375	NFM	Nationwide	Channel 72
458.40625	463.90625	NFM	Nationwide	Channel 73
458.41875	463.91875	NFM	Nationwide	Channel 74
458.41875	463.90625	NFM	Alba FSU	Chevron Shuttle Green
458.41875	463.91875	NFM	Cormorant A	Shell
		NFM	Loading Buoy	Shell Kittiwake
458.4250		NFM	North Bedfordshire	Ambulance Service
		NFM	East Hertfordshire	Ambulance Service
		NFM	Mid Essex	Ambulance Service
		NFM	Eastbourne	Ambulance Service
		NFM	Medway	Ambulance Service
		NFM	Kent	Ambulance Service
		NFM	Mid Surrey	Ambulance Service
		NFM	West Sussex	Ambulance Service
458.43125	463.93125	NFM	Nationwide	Channel 75
458.43125	463.93125	NFM	Loading Buoy	Shell Tanker (Kittiwake)
458.44375	463.94375	NFM	Nationwide	Channel 76
458.45000	463.95000	NFM	Dunlin A	Shell
458.45625	463.95625	NFM	Nationwide	Channel 77
458.45625	463.90625	NFM	Alba	ANP Chevron Data
458.46875	463.96875	NFM	Nationwide	Channel 78
458.4750		NFM	Wales	Ambulance Service
458.48125	463.98125	NFM	Nationwide	Channel 79
458.49375	463.99375	NFM	Nationwide	Channel 80

458.5000 - 459.0000 MHz **UHF LOW POWER DEVICES**

Base	Mobile	Mode	Location	User and Notes
458.5000 - 459.5000 MHz			**UHF REMOTE CONTROLLED MODEL BAND**	
458.5000		NFM	Nationwide	Telemetry
		NFM	Nationwide	UHF Demo Channel
458.5125		NFM	Nationwide	Telemetry

Base	Mobile	Mode	Location	User and Notes
458.5125 - 459.4875 MHz			**LOW POWER PAGING**	
458.5250		NFM	Jersey	Paging Les Platons
		NFM	Morecambe	Data Link
		NFM	Jersey	BGS Seismic Telemetry
458.5375		NFM	Chichester	J Sainsbury Inventory Data
458.5500		NFM	Nationwide	BBC O/B Link (OL-94)
458.5500	458.5000	NFM	Edinburgh Airport	Telemetry Channel 8
458.5750		NFM	Nationwide	BBC O/B Link (OL-94)
		NFM	Jersey	Paging Beaumont
458.6000		NFM	Jersey	Paging Rozel Area
458.6250		NFM	Nationwide	BBC O/B Link (OL-94)
458.6500		NFM	Nationwide	Telemetry
		NFM	Nationwide	Telemetry

Base	Mobile	Mode	Location	User and Notes
458.6750		NFM	Jersey	BGS Seismic Telemetry
458.6750		NFM	Nationwide	Shell Geophysical
458.7000		NFM	Nationwide	Telemetry
458.7250		NFM	Jersey	Paging Queens Valley Dam
458.7250		NFM	Jersey	BGS Seismic Telemetry
458.8000		NFM	Jersey	BGS Seismic Telemetry
458.8250		NFM	Nationwide	Fixed Alarm Paging
458.8375		NFM	Nationwide	Mobile Alarm Paging
458.8500		NFM	Jersey	Paging Queens Valley Area
		NFM	Magnus	BP Paging-Base
458.9000		NFM	Nationwide	Car Theft Alarm Paging
458.9750	458.9750	NFM	Statfjord A	Mobil
459.0000		NFM	Nationwide	Medical & Biological Telem.
459.0000	459.0000	NFM	Statfjord A	Mobil
459.0250		NFM	Jersey	Paging Queens Valley East
		NFM	Jersey	BGS Seismic Telemetry
459.0250	459.02500	NFM	Statfjord A	Mobil
459.0500		NFM	Murchison	Conoco
459.0750	453.47500	NFM	Buchan	BP
459.0750	453.47500	NFM	Murchison	Conoco
459.0750	459.07500	NFM	Statfjord B	Mobil
459.1000	459.1000	NFM	Statfjord B	Mobil
459.1050		NFM	Nationwide	Betacom Cordless phones
459.1250	161.0000	NFM	Nationwide	Paging
459.1250	459.1250	NFM	Statfjord B	Mobil
459.1250		NFM	Newcastle Airport	Brittania Cleaners
459.1500		NFM	Jersey	Paging Fort Regent
459.1500	161.0250	NFM	Nationwide	Marina Paging
459.1500	459.1500	NFM	Stattjord C	Mobil
459.1750		NFM	Heysham	Pontins Holiday Camp Sec.
		NFM	Perth	Paging
459.2000	459.2000	NFM	Statfjord C	Mobil
459.2000		NFM	Leicester	Mackro Centre paging
459.2500	161.0500	NFM	Nationwide	Paging
		NFM	Earls Court	Voice Pagers
459.2500	459.2500	NFM	Statfjord C	Mobil
459.2500	459.2500	NFM	Edda	Phillips
459.2750	459.2750	NFM	Statijord A	Mobil Tanker
459.3000		NFM	London	Two Way Tone Paging
459.3000	459.3000	NFM	West Yorkshire	Ambulance Hand Held
459.3250	161.0125	NFM	Nationwide	Paging
459.3250	459.3250	NFM	Scarborough	Voice Paging
459.3250		NFM	Romford	Tesco Staff Paging
		NFM	Heysham Power Station	Ops
		NFM	Alba	ANP Chevron Paging
		NFM	Newcastle Airport	Passanger Control
459.3500	161.0250	NFM	Nationwide	Paging
		NFM	Brae South	Marathon Paging

Base	Mobile	Mode	Location	User and Notes
		NFM	Brett 2,1 A	Mobil Paging
459.3750	161.0375	NFM	Dumfries	Gates Rubber Company
459.3750	161.0375	NFM	Nationwide	Paging
459.3750		NFM	Romford	BAC Staff Paging
459.3750	469.3750	NFM	Statfjord C	Mobil A.L.P.
459.3750	161.0375	NFM	Basildon	Hospital Porters Paging
		NFM	Thornton	Multitone ICI
		NFM	Wirral	Mobil Oil Security
459.4000	161.0500	NFM	Nationwide	Paging
		NFM	Earls Court	Voice Pagers
459.4000	459.4000	NFM	Ekofisk Senter	Phillips
		NFM	Newcastle Airport	British Airways
459.4250	161.0625	NFM	London	BBC Bush House Pagers
459.4250	469.4250	NFM	Statfjord B	Mobil
459.4250	459.4250	NFM	Clyde A	BP Paging
		NFM	Heysham Power Station	Ops
459.4500	161.1000	NFM	Nationwide	Paging
459.4500	459.4500	NFM	Statfjord C	Mobil
		NFM	Heysham Power Station	Ops
459.4750	161.1125	NFM	Nationwide	Paging
		NFM	Luton	Arndale Shopping Centre
		NFM	Romford	BHS Staff Paging
		NFM	Wirral	Sainsbury's

459.5000 - 460.5000 MHz   AMBULANCE HANDSETS AND VARIOUS PMR
USERS MOBILE 12.5 kHz (SPLIT-5.5 MHz)
FORMULA ONE RACING TEAM LINKS

Base	Mobile	Mode	Location	User and Notes
459.5000	459.5000	NFM	Blackpool	Tower Ascent
		NFM	Albuskjell A	Phillips
459.5000	469.5000	NFM	Statfjord A	Mobil A.L.P.
459.5250		NFM	Stansted Airport	Telephone Ops
459.5250	453.0250	NFM	Beatrice A	BP
		NFM	Beryl B	Mobil Temp. Const. Facility
459.5250	459.5250	NFM	Albuskjell F	Phillips
459.5250	469.5250	NFM	Statfjord B	Mobil A. L. P.
459.5500	453.0500	NFM	Alba	Chevron ANP PABX
459.5750	453.0750	NFM	Bacton	Amoco
459.5750		NFM	Frigg Field	Total
459.5750	459.5750	NFM	Montrose Basin	Rangers
459.6000	453.1000	NFM	Beatrice B	BP
		NFM	Clyde A	BP
		NFM	Heather A	Unocol
459.6000		NFM	Frigg Field	Total
459.6250	453.1250	NFM	Viking Field	Conoco
		NFM	Frigg Field	Total
459.6500	453.1500	NFM	Nottingham	Boots Broadmarch SCS
459.6500		NFM	Frigg Field	Total
459.6750		NFM	Frigg Field	Total

Base	Mobile	Mode	Location	User and Notes
459.6750	453.1750	NFM	Bacton	Shell
		NFM	Indc J	Shell
		NFM	Inde K	Shell
		NFM	Leman B	Shell
		NFM	St. Fergus	Shell
459.7000	459.7000	NFM	Magnus	BP
		NFM	Frigg Field	Total
		NFM	Bristol	HTV Television
		NFM	Gatwick Airport	Ground Repeater
459.7250	453.2250	NFM	England & Wales	Police and Fire Channel
		NFM	Ninian South	Chevron
		NFM	Eider	Shell
459.7250	459.7250	NFM	Guernsey	Fuel Supplies
		NFM	Tor	Phillips
459.7250		NFM	Frigg Field	Total
459.7500	459.7500	NFM	Murchison	Conoco
		NFM	Brae South	Marathon
		NFM	Ekofisk Center	Phillips To Ekofisk B
459.7750	453.2750	NFM	Nationwide	Ambulance UHF to VHF
		NFM	Nationwide	Philips Security
		NFM	Jersey	Ambulance Service
		NFM	Leman BH	Shell Portables
459.7750	459.7750	NFM	Eldfisk B	Phillips To Ekofisk- Center
		NFM	Cormorant A	Shell
		NFM	Jersey	Ambulance Service
459.7750		NFM	Frigg Field	Total
459.8000	459.8000	NFM	Magnus	BP
		NFM	Brae South	Marathon
		NFM	Ekofisk Senter	Phillips
		NFM	Frigg Field	Total
459.8250		NFM	West Yorkshire	Ambulance Service
		NFM	Hampshire	Ambulance Pagers
459.8375		NFM	Swindon	Brunel Security
459.8500	453.3500	NFM	Nationwide	Ambulance UHF to VHF
459.8500	459.8500	NFM	Jersey	Alpha Airport Catering
		NFM	Morecambe Bay	BGE&P
		NFM	Murchison	Conoco
		NFM	Brae South	Marathon
		NFM	Swindon	Brunel Security
459.8750		NFM	Salisbury	Hospital Security
459.9000	453.4000	NFM	Ninian North	Chevron
		NFM	Brae N, S	Marathon
		NFM	St. Fergus	Shell
459.9250	453.4250	NFM	Buchan	BP
		NFM	Magnus	BP
		NFM	Alba	Chevron FSU Maintenance
459.9500	453.4500	NFM	Gatwick	Messages for Captains
		NFM	Bournmouth Airport	Ground Services

Base	Mobile	Mode	Location	User and Notes
		NFM	Jersey	Customs & Excise
459.9500	459.9500	NFM	Morecambe Bay	BGE&P
459.9750	453.4750	NFM	Buchan	BP
		NFM	Mutchison	Conoco
		NFM	Dorset	BP Wytch Farm
459.9750	459.9750	NFM	St. Fergus	Shell
460.0000	453.5000	NFM	Eider	Shell
460.0150	453.5250	NFM	Ninian North	Chevron
460.0250	453.6250	NFM	Morecambe Bay	BGE&P
460.0500	453.5500	NFM	Alba	Chevron ANP Construction
		NFM	Ninian South	Chevron
460.0750	453.5750	NFM	Buchan	BP
		NFM	Magnus	BP
460.0750	460.0750	NFM	Morecambe Bay	BGE&P
460.1000	453.6000	NFM	Bedford	Debenhams Security
		NFM	Birmingham	Debenhams Security
		NFM	Cambridge	Debenhams Security
		NFM	Derby	Debenhams Security
		NFM	Folkestone	Debenhams Security
460.1000	460.1000	NFM	Plymouth	Debenhams Security
		NFM	Tartan	Texaco
460.1000	453.6000	NFM	N W Hutton	Amoco
460.1125		NFM	London	British Rail (Richmond)
		NFM	Newcastle Airport	Passenger Information
460.12500	453.62500	NFM	Alba	Chevron FSU General Ops
460.1250		NFM	Swansea	University Security
		NFM	Swansea	University Security
460.1500	460.1500	NFM	TCM	Shell
460.1500		NFM	Brent C	Shell
460.2000	453.7000	NFM	Ninian North	Chevron
460.2000	460.1000	NFM	Eider	Shell
460.2000		NFM	Leman A	Shell Portables
460.2250	453.7000	NFM	Ninian North	Chevron
460.2250	453.7250	NFM	Isle Of Grain	Oil
		NFM	Morecambe Bay	BGE&P
		NFM	Alba	Chevron ANP Production
460.2500	453.7500	NFM	Nottingham	Formans
460.2500		NFM	Bradford	Allied Colloids Chemicals
460.2750		NFM	Culham	UKAEA Laboratory Fire
460.2750	453.7750	NFM	Maureen	Phillips Telemetry
460.3000		NFM	Newmarket	Community Repeater
460.3000	453.8000	NFM	Lomond	Amoco
		NFM	North Evercst	Amoco
		NFM	Ninian South	Chervon
		NFM	TCM	Shell
460.3250		NFM	Grand Prix Circuits	Lotus Team Voice Link
460.3250	460.3250	NFM	Plymouth	Dedenhams Maintenance
460.3500		NFM	County Durham	Taxis

Base	Mobile	Mode	Location	User and Notes
460.3500	453.8500	NFM	Magnus	BP
		NFM	Forties E	BP
460.3500	460.8500	NFM	TCM	Shell
460.3500		NFM	Bradford	Allied Colloids Chemicals
460.3750	453.8750	NFM	Alba	Chevron Field Safety
		NFM	Ninian Central	Chevron
460.4000	453.9000	NFM	Bristol	BR Bristol Temple Meads
		NFM	Doncaster	BR Doncater Yard
		NFM	London	British Rail (Euston)
		NFM	London	British Rail (Gatwick Airport)
		NFM	London	British Rail (Hornsey Depot)
		NFM	London	British Rail (Marylebone)
		NFM	London	British Rail (Victoria)
460.4000		NFM	Brent C	Shell
460.4250	453.9250	NFM	Magnus	BP
		NFM	Forties E	BP
460.4500	453.9500	NFM	Alba	Chevron ANP Maintenance
		NFM	Ninian Central	Chevron
		NFM	Brae North	Marathon
		NFM	Ninian Central	Chevron
		NFM	Brae North	Marathon
		NFM	Glasgow	Virgin Records Security
460.4750	453.9750	NFM	Magnus	BP
		NFM	Forties F	BP

460.5000 - 461.5000 MHz　　UHF POINT TO POINT LINKS 25 kHz
(SPLIT +6.5MHz)

Base	Mobile	Mode	Location	User and Notes
460.50625	467.00625	NFM	Nationwide	Sky TV O/B Talkback
		NFM	Belfry (Ryder Cup)	US TV Talkback
460.53125		NFM	Castle Donington	US TV Talkback
460.5500	467.0500	NFM	Jersey Airport	Air Traffic Control Link
		NFM	Kent	Southern Gas
		NFM	Nationwide	Sky TV Talkback
		NFM	Nationwide	Sky TV OB
460.5625		NFM	Falkirk	Police (G)
460.56875	467.06875	NFM	Castle Donington	Japanese TV Talkback
460.5750		NFM	Nationwide	Sky TV OB
		NFM	Wales	BBC Wales Talkback
		NFM	North Bedfordshire	Ambulance Service
		NFM	East Hertfordshire	Ambulance Service
		NFM	Avon	Ambulance Service
		NFM	Cornwall	Ambulance Service
		NFM	Devon	Ambulance Service
		NFM	Gloucester	Ambulance Service
		NFM	Scilly Isles	Ambulance Service
		NFM	Somerset	Ambulance Service
460.58125		NFM	Castle Donington	Japanese TV Talkback
		NFM	Belfry (Ryder Cup)	German TV Talkback

Base	Mobile	Mode	Location	User and Notes
460.58375		NFM	Nationwide	Sky TV OB Talkback
460.5875		NFM	Wales	BBC Wales Talkback
460.59375		NFM	Belfry (Ryder Cup)	US TV Talkback
460.6000		NFM	West Berkshire	Ambulance Service
		NFM	Buckinghamshire	Ambulance Service
		NFM	Northamptonshire	Ambulance Service
		NFM	Oxford	Ambulance Service
460.61875	467.11875	NFM	Belfry (Ryder Cup)	German TV Talkback
460.62500	460.62500	NFM	Statfjord A,B,C	Mobil
460.6250		NFM	Wales	BBC Wales Announcer
		NFM	Cleveland	Ambulance Service
		NFM	Cumbria	Ambulance Service
		NFM	Durham	Ambulance Service
		NFM	Northumbria	Ambulance Service
		NFM	West Berkshire	Ambulance Service
		NFM	Buckinghamshire	Ambulance Service
		NFM	Northamptonshire	Ambulance Service
		NFM	Oxford	Ambulance Service
460.64375		NFM	Belfry (Ryder Cup)	US TV Talkback
460.6500		NFM	Wales	Ambulance Service
460.6750	467.1750	NFM	Silverstone	French TV Talkback
		NFM	Cleveland	Ambulance Service
		NFM	Cumbria	Ambulance Service
		NFM	Durham	Ambulance Service
		NFM	Northumbria	Ambulance Service
		NFM	Yorkshire	Ambulance Service
		NFM	Humbershire	Ambulance Service
460.6875		NFM	Wales	BBC Wales Studio Cont.
460.7000		NFM	Dublin	Fire Service
460.70625		NFM	Nationwide	Sky TV Talkback
460.7250		NFM	Nationwide	Sky TV OB
		NFM	Avon	Ambulance Service
		NFM	Cornwall	Ambulance Service
		NFM	Devon	Ambulance Service
		NFM	Gloucester	Ambulance Service
		NFM	Scilly Isles	Ambulance Service
		NFM	Somerset	Ambulance Service
460.74375		NFM	Nationwide	BBC TV OB Production
460.7500		NFM	Cleveland	Ambulance Service
		NFM	Cumbria	Ambulance Service
		NFM	Durham	Ambulance Service
		NFM	Northumbria	Ambulance Service
460.7875	467.2875	NFM	Nationwide	National Air Traffic Service
		NFM	Poole	Point-to-Point Link
460.8500	460.3500	NFM	TCM	Shell
460.9250	460.9250	NFM	Newcastle Airport	Airport Mobiles
460.9250		NFM	Newcastle Airport	Airport Mobiles
460.9500	460.9500	NFM	Edinburgh Airport	PMR Channel 7

Base	Mobile	Mode	Location	User and Notes
461.0000	467.5000	NFM	Filton (BAe)	Ground Crews
461.0000	455.7000	NFM	Edinburgh Airport	PMR Channel 15
461.0000	461.0000	NFM	Edinburgh Airport	Channel 35
		NFM	Nationwide	RAF Falcons Display Team
461.0250	467.5250	NFM	Nationwide	National Air Traffic Service
		NFM	Easington	BP To West Sole A
		NFM	Cardiff	Air Traffic Control
461.0250	455.7250	NFM	Edinburgh Airport	PMR Channel 13
461.0250	461.0250	NFM	Edinburgh Airport	Channel 33
461.0500	467.5500	NFM	Fulmar A	Shell
461.0750	467.5750	NFM	Easington	BP To West Sole A
461.0750	455.7750	NFM	Edinburgh Airport	PMR Channel 12
461.0750	461.0750	NFM	Edinburgh Airport	Channel 32
461.1000	467.6000	NFM	Fulmar A	Shell
		NFM	Newcastle Airport	Tower & Following
461.1125		NFM	Newcastle Airport	Luggage Control
461.1625		NFM	Newcastle Airport	Baggage Handing
461.1750	467.6750	NFM	Gt. Yarmouth	Phillips To Hewett
461.2000		NFM	London Heathrow	Ground Staff
461.2625		NFM	Nationwide	Motorola Radios Ch 1
461.2750	461.2750	NFM	Brerit A	Shell
		NFM	Brent B	Shell
		NFM	Brent D	Shell
		NFM	Brent Spar	Shell
		NFM	Cleveland	Ambulance Service
		NFM	Cumbria	Ambulance Service
		NFM	Durham	Ambulance Service
		NFM	Northumbria	Ambulance Service
		NFM	North Bedfordshire	Ambulance Service
		NFM	East Hertfordshire	Ambulance Service
		NFM	Mid Essex	Ambulance Service
		NFM	Eastbourne	Ambulance Service
		NFM	Medway	Ambulance Service
		NFM	Kent	Ambulance Service
		NFM	Mid Surrey	Ambulance Service
		NFM	West Sussex	Ambulance Service
		NFM	Mid Staffordshire	Ambulance Service
		NFM	Salop	Ambulance Service
		NFM	South Warwickshire	Ambulance Service
		NFM	Worcestershire	Ambulance Service
		NFM	Yorkshire	Ambulance Service
		NFM	Humbershire	Ambulance Service
		NFM	Wales	Ambulance Service
461.2875	461.2875	NFM	Guernsey	Brock Fireworks
		NFM	Guernsey	Performing Arts Handhelds

461.3000 - 461.4875 MHZ   PMR SIMPLEX

Base	Mobile	Mode	Location	User and Notes
461.3000	461.3000	NFM	Nationwide	Motorola Radios Ch 2

Base	Mobile	Mode	Location	User and Notes
		NFM	North Bedfordshire	Ambulance Service
		NFM	East Hertfordshire	Ambulance Service
		NFM	Mid Essex	Ambulance Service
		NFM	Eastbourne	Ambulance Service
		NFM	Medway	Ambulance Service
		NFM	Kent	Ambulance Service
		NFM	Mid Surrey	Ambulance Service
		NFM	West Sussex	Ambulance Service
		NFM	West Berkshire	Ambulance Service
		NFM	Buckinghamshire	Ambulance Service
		NFM	Northamptonshire	Ambulance Service
		NFM	Oxford	Ambulance Service
		NFM	Yorkshire	Ambulance Service
		NFM	Humbershire	Ambulance Service
461.3125	461.3125	NFM	Nationwide	TNT Loaders Channel 1
		NFM	Ashford	County Square Security
461.3250	461.3250	NFM	Jersey	General Hospital
		NFM	West Berkshire	Ambulance Service
		NFM	Buckinghamshire	Ambulance Service
		NFM	Northamptonshire	Ambulance Service
		NFM	Oxford	Ambulance Service
461.3375	461.3375	NFM	Nationwide	TNT Loaders Channel 2
		NFM	Nationwide	TNT Security
		NFM	Widnes	Widnes Leisure Centre
		NFM	West Berkshire	Ambulance Service
		NFM	Buckinghamshire	Ambulance Service
		NFM	Northamptonshire	Ambulance Service
		NFM	Oxford	Ambulance Service
461.3500	461.3500	NFM	Jersey	Builders (On-Site Radios)
461.3625	461.3625	NFM	Ashford	Shop Security
461.3750	467.8750	NFM	Brent B	Shell
		NFM	West Berkshire	Ambulance Service
		NFM	Buckinghamshire	Ambulance Service
		NFM	Northamptonshire	Ambulance Service
		NFM	Oxford	Ambulance Service
461.4000		NFM	Jersey	PMR
461.4250	467.9250	NFM	Gatwick Airport	Cellular Link
461.4250		NFM	Brent D	Shell
461.4250	467.9250	NFM	Auk A	Shell To ELSBM
461.4500	461.4500	NFM	Jersey	C.A. Mauger Builders
461.4500		NFM	Ashford	Shop Security
461.4625		NFM	Hull	Princes Quay SCS
461.4625	467.9625	NFM	Nationwide	DSS
		NFM	Nationwide	National Audit Office
		NFM	Nationwide	Dept. of Employment
		NFM	West Drayton	Heathrow Sterling Hotel
		NFM	Walthamstow	Hawker Siddeley
		NFM	East Ham, London	Borough of Newham

Base	Mobile	Mode	Location	User and Notes
		NFM	Dagenham	Ford Motor Co.
		NFM	London	Odeon Cinemas Ltd.
		NFM	Lewisham	Lewisham College
461.4750	467.9750	NFM	Auk A	Shell To ELSBM
461.4750	461.4750	NFM	Nationwide	Marks & Spencer Security
		NFM	Nationwide	Motorola Radios Ch 3
		NFM	West Berkshire	Ambulance Service
		NFM	Buckinghamshire	Ambulance Service
		NFM	Northamptonshire	Ambulance Service
		NFM	Oxford	Ambulance Service
		NFM	Wales	Ambulance Service
461.4875	461.4875	NFM	Nationwide	Motorola Radios Ch 4

461.5000 - 462.5000 MHz   PMR UHF BAND BASE 12.5 KHZ (SPLIT-5.5 MHZ) FORMULA ONE RACING TEAM LINKS

Base	Mobile	Mode	Location	User and Notes
461.5000	456.0000	NFM	Leicester	City Council Repairs
		NFM	Southampton	Group 4 Security
461.5000	456.0000	NFM	Penzance	BR Repairs
461.5250	461.5250	NFM	Nationwide	Simply Red Crew
461.5250	456.0250	NFM	Alwyn	Total
461.5500	456.0500	NFM	Rough A	BGE&P
		NFM	Brae South	Marathon
461.5500	461.5500	NFM	Rough B	BGE&P
		NFM	Alwyn	Total
		NFM	Jersey	La Collette Power Station
461.5750	456.0750	NFM	Nationwide	NCB Security
		NFM	Nationwide	Simply Red Crew
		NFM	Bath	SW Electricity Disconnect.
461.6000	456.1000	NFM	Brae S	Marathon
461.6000	461.6000	NFM	Rough B	BGE&P
461.6250	461.6250	NFM	Nationwide	Simply Red Crew
461.6250	456.1150	NFM	Magnus	BP Sulair
461.6750	456.1750	NFM	Alwyn	Total
461.7000		NFM	Dunlin A	Shell
461.7000	461.7000	NFM	MCP-01	Total
461.7250	401.7215	NFM	Rough B	BGE&P
461.7750	456.2500	NFM	Nottingham	Esso Colwick
461.7750	456.2750	NFM	Brent D	Shell PMR
		NFM	Cormorant N	Shell PMR
461.8000	456.3000	NFM	Brae North	Marathon
461.8500	456.3500	NFM	Nottingham	Technical Services
461.9000	456.4000	NFM	Nationwide	HM Customs Covert Reptr
461.9000	461.9000	NFM	Nationwide	HM Customs Surveillance
		NFM	Alwyn	Total
461.9250	461.9250	NFM	Nationwide	British Telecom Security
		NFM	Thistle A	BP
		NFM	Manchester	British Rail Security

Base	Mobile	Mode	Location	User and Notes
461.9500	456.4500	NFM	Duxford Aerodrome	Imperial War Museum Sec.
		NFM	SMV	BP
		NFM	Brent B	Shell PMR
		NFM	Cormorant A	Shell PMR
		NFM	Sullom Voe	Shell
461.9750	456.4750	NFM	Thistle A	BP
461.9750	461.9750	NFM	Thistle A	BP
462.0000	456.5000	NFM	Duxford Aerodrome	Imperial War Museum Gnd
		NFM	Nationwide	Securicor Datatrak System
462.0125		NFM	London	Taxis
462.0250	456.5250	NFM	Brent C	Shell PMR
		NFM	London	Taxis
462.0500		NFM	London, Oxford St	John Lewis
462.0500	462.0500	NFM	Thistle A	BP
		NFM	Peterborough	Tesco's
462.0750	456.5750	NFM	Darlington	BP
		NFM	Easington	BP
		NFM	Miller	BP
		NFM	Auk	Shell PMR
		NFM	Brent A	Shell PMR
		NFM	Dunlin	Shell PMR
462.0750	462.0750	NFM	Buchan	BP
462.0750	453.5750	NFM	Heathrow	BP Oil
462.0950		NFM	Girton	Tarmac Quarries
462.1000	456.6000	NFM	Nationwide	Visual Comm. Systems
		NFM	Alwyn	Total
462.1000	462.1000	NFM	Welton	BP
462.1250	456.6250	NFM	Duxford Aerodrome	Imperial War Museum Fire
		NFM	Brent C	Shell PMR
462.1250	456.6215	NFM	Fulmar A	Shell PMR
462.1250	462.1250	NFM	St. Fergus/Peterhead	Total
462.1500	456.6500	NFM	Miller	BP
		NFM	Edinburgh Airport	PMR Channel 16
462.1750	456.6750	NFM	Miller	BP
		NFM	Brent D	Shell PMR
		NFM	Cormorant N	Shell PMR
		NFM	Heathrow Airport	Ground Staff
462.2000	462.2000	NFM	Auk	Shell PMR
462.2250		NFM	Hull	Docks
462.2250	456.7250	NFM	SMV	BP
462.2250	456.2250	NFM	Miller	BP
462.2500	462.2500	NFM	Blackpool	Security
		NFM	Heathrow Airport	Ground Staff
		NFM	Peterborough	Marks & Spencer Security
		NFM	Bournmouth	Marks & Spencer Security
462.2750	462.2750	NFM	Blackpool	Pleasure Beach Patrol
		NFM	Hull	Container Terminal
462.2750	456.7750	NFM	Dyce	BP

Base	Mobile	Mode	Location	User and Notes
462.3000	462.3000	NFM	Blackpool	Security Town Centre
462.3000	456.8000	NFM	Brent B	Shell PMR
		NFM	Cormorant A	Shell PMR
		NFM	Fulmar	Shell PMR
462.3000	462.3000	NFM	MCP-01	Total
		NFM	St. Fergus	Total
		NFM	Slough	Coopers-Payen Ltd Security
462.3250	456.8250	NFM	Ipswich	Port Authority Channel 4
462.3250		NFM	London	Earls Court/Olympia Sec.
462.3625	462.3625	NFM	Jersey	PMR
		NFM	Nationwide	Short Term Hire
462.3750	456.8750	NFM	Auk	Shell PMR
		NFM	Brent A	Shell PMR
		NFM	Dunlin	Shell PMR
		NFM	Peterborough	Boots Security
462.4000	456.9000	NFM	Alwyn	Total
462.4000	462.4000	NFM	SMV	BP
		NFM	St. Fergus	Total
		NFM	Chelmsford	Town Centre Security
462.4250	456.9250	NFM	Grand Prix Circuits	Lotus Team Voice Link
462.4250	462.4250	NFM	Nationwide	Simply Red Crew
		NFM	Bristol	Zoo
		NFM	London	TV Programme 'The Bill'
		NFM	Jersey	Short Term Hire Radios
		NFM	Welton	BP
		NFM	Southend-on-Sea	Victoria Circus Precinct Sec
		NFM	Nationwide	Short Term Hire
462.4750	456.9750	NFM	Nationwide	Short Term Hire Equipment
		NFM	Montrose Docks	Piggings
		NFM	Shire Oaks	Shire Oaks Colliery NCB Sec
		NFM	St. Fergus	Shell
462.4750	462.4750	NFM	London	TV Programme 'The Bill'
		NFM	Ashford	Shop Security
		NFM	Jersey	Short Term Hire Radios
462.4875	462.4875	NFM	Brighton	Marina Asda Supermarket
		NFM	Jersey	Short Term Hire Radios
		NFM	Nationwide	Short Term Hire

462.5000 - 462.7500 MHz   **EMERGENCY SERVICES 12.5 kHz NFM**

Base	Mobile	Mode	Location	User and Notes
462.5750	457.0750	NFM	Aberdeen	Hydro Electric
		NFM	Ninian North Chevron	Back-up to Ninian S
462.6250	462.6250	NFM	Nationwide	Red Devils Parachute Team
462.6500	466.5500	NFM	Poole	Police
462.7750		NFM	Ipswich	Data Traffic
462.7750	458.2750	NFM	Murchison	Conoco DKN
462.8500		NFM	Merseyside	Haulage
462.9250		NFM	Norfolk	Ambulance Service
		NFM	Suffolk	Ambulance Service

Base	Mobile	Mode	Location	User and Notes
		NFM	Cambridgeshire	Ambulance Service
462.9500		NFM	Cleveland	Ambulance Service
		NFM	Cumbria	Ambulance Service
		NFM	Durham	Ambulance Service
		NFM	Northumbria	Ambulance Service
		NFM	East Dorset	Ambulance Service
		NFM	Hampshire	Ambulance Service
		NFM	Isle of Wight	Ambulance Service
462.9750		NFM	Norfolk	Ambulance Service
		NFM	Suffolk	Ambulance Service
		NFM	Cambridgeshire	Ambulance Service
463.0000 - 464.0000 MHz			**UHF TELEMETRY LINKS NFM**	
463.0500		NFM	West Berkshire	Ambulance Service
		NFM	Buckinghamshire	Ambulance Service
		NFM	Northamptonshire	Ambulance Service
		NFM	Oxford	Ambulance Service
463.0625		NFM	Manchester	Cabin Hire
463.0750		NFM	Norfolk	Ambulance Service
		NFM	Suffolk	Ambulance Service
		NFM	Cambridgeshire	Ambulance Service
463.1000		NFM	Cleveland	Ambulance Service
		NFM	Cumbria	Ambulance Service
		NFM	Durham	Ambulance Service
		NFM	Northumbria	Ambulance Service
		NFM	Wales	Ambulance Service
463.1500		NFM	Cleveland	Ambulance Service
		NFM	Cumbria	Ambulance Service
		NFM	Durham	Ambulance Service
		NFM	Northumbria	Ambulance Service
		NFM	Wales	Ambulance Service
463.2250		NFM	Wales	Ambulance Service
463.2500		AM	Birmingham Airport	HM Customs
		NFM	Norfolk	Ambulance Service
		NFM	Suffolk	Ambulance Service
		NFM	Cambridgeshire	Ambulance Service
463.2750	457.7750	NFM	Fulmar	FSU Shell Telemetry
463.3500	457.8500	NFM	Viking Field	Conoco
463.3750	463.3750	NFM	Nationwide	Polly Peck Co
463.3750	457.8750	NFM	ESV III	BP
		NFM	Forties D	BP To Forties Kiwi
463.5000		NFM	East Dorset	Ambulance Service
		NFM	Hampshire	Ambulance Service
		NFM	Isle of Wight	Ambulance Service
463.5250		NFM	Norfolk	Ambulance Service
		NFM	Suffolk	Ambulance Service
		NFM	Cambridgeshire	Ambulance Service
		NFM	Cleveland	Ambulance Service

Base	Mobile	Mode	Location	User and Notes
		NFM	Cumbria	Ambulance Service
		NFM	Durham	Ambulance Service
		NFM	Northumbria	Ambulance Service
463.3750	463.3750	NFM	Buchan	BP
463.5500		NFM	Wales	Ambulance Service
463.6000		NFM	East Dorset	Ambulance Service
		NFM	Hampshire	Ambulance Service
		NFM	Isle of Wight	Ambulance Service
		NFM	Wales	Ambulance Service
463.6250		NFM	Cleveland	Ambulance Service
		NFM	Cumbria	Ambulance Service
		NFM	Durham	Ambulance Service
		NFM	Northumbria	Ambulance Service
		NFM	East Dorset	Ambulance Service
		NFM	Hampshire	Ambulance Service
		NFM	Isle of Wight	Ambulance Service
463.6500		NFM	North Bedfordshire	Ambulance Service
		NFM	East Hertfordshire	Ambulance Service
		NFM	Mid Essex	Ambulance Service
		NFM	Eastbourne	Ambulance Service
		NFM	Medway	Ambulance Service
		NFM	Kent	Ambulance Service
		NFM	Mid Surrey	Ambulance Service
		NFM	West Sussex	Ambulance Service
463.7000		NFM	Mid Staffordshire	Ambulance Service
		NFM	Salop	Ambulance Service
		NFM	South Warwickshire	Ambulance Service
		NFM	Worcestershire	Ambulance Service
463.7250	458.2250	NFM	Murchison	Conoco
		NFM	Brent A	Shell PLIS Backup-Dunlin A
		NFM	Brent B	Shell PLIS Backup-Dunlin A
		NFM	Brent C	Shell PLIS Backup-Dunlin A
		NFM	Brent D	Shell
		NFM	Brent Spar	Shell
		NFM	Cormorant A	Shell
		NFM	N. Cormorant	Shell
463.7500		NFM	East Dorset	Ambulance Service
		NFM	Hampshire	Ambulance Service
		NFM	Isle of Wight	Ambulance Service
		NFM	Mid Staffordshire	Ambulance Service
		NFM	Salop	Ambulance Service
		NFM	South Warwickshire	Ambulance Service
		NFM	Worcestershire	Ambulance Service
463.8250	458.3250	NFM	Murchison	Conoco
		NFM	Cleveland	Ambulance Service
		NFM	Cumbria	Ambulance Service
		NFM	Durham	Ambulance Service
		NFM	Northumbria	Ambulance Service

Base	Mobile	Mode	Location	User and Notes
		NFM	Wales	Ambulance Service
463.8500		NFM	Liverpool	Brookside Studio
		NFM	Cleveland	Ambulance Service
		NFM	Cumbria	Ambulance Service
		NFM	Durham	Ambulance Service
		NFM	Northumbria	Ambulance Service
		NFM	Wales	Ambulance Service
463.9000		NFM	North Bedfordshire	Ambulance Service
		NFM	East Hertfordshire	Ambulance Service
		NFM	Mid Essex	Ambulance Service
		NFM	Eastbourne	Ambulance Service
		NFM	Medway	Ambulance Service
		NFM	Kent	Ambulance Service
		NFM	Mid Surrey	Ambulance Service
		NFM	West Sussex	Ambulance Service
463.90625	458.45625	NFM	Alba	FSU Chevron To ANP, FSD
463.91875	458.41875	NFM	Kittiwake	Shell Loading Buoy
		NFM	Stadfill	Shell Cormorant A
463.9250		NFM	Cleveland	Ambulance Service
		NFM	Cumbria	Ambulance Service
		NFM	Durham	Ambulance Service
		NFM	Northumbria	Ambulance Service
463.93125	458.43125	NFM	Kittiwake Tanker	Shell Loading Buoy
463.9500	458.4500	NFM	Murchison	Conoco
		NFM	Brent A	Shell
		NFM	Brent B	Shell PEL Backup-Dunlin A
		NFM	Brent C	Shell PEL Back-up-Dunlin A
		NFM	Brent D	Shell PEL Backup-Dunlin A
		NFM	Brent Spar	Shell
		NFM	Cormorant N	Shell
		NFM	North Bedfordshire	Ambulance Service
		NFM	East Hertfordshire	Ambulance Service
		NFM	Mid Essex	Ambulance Service
		NFM	Eastbourne	Ambulance Service
		NFM	Medway	Ambulance Service
		NFM	Kent	Ambulance Service
		NFM	Mid Surrey	Ambulance Service
		NFM	West Sussex	Ambulance Service
		NFM	East Dorset	Ambulance Service
		NFM	Hampshire	Ambulance Service
		NFM	Isle of Wight	Ambulance Service
		NFM	Mid Staffordshire	Ambulance Service
		NFM	Salop	Ambulance Service
		NFM	South Warwickshire	Ambulance Service
		NFM	Worcestershire	Ambulance Service
463.9750		NFM	Mid Staffordshire	Ambulance Service
		NFM	Salop	Ambulance Service
		NFM	South Warwickshire	Ambulance Service

Base	Mobile	Mode	Location	User and Notes
		NFM	Worcestershire	Ambulance Service
463.9875		NFM	London	Dispatch Company

464.0000 - 465.0000 MHz   BRITISH TELECOM LINKS NFM
(SPLIT-14.0 MHz)

Base	Mobile	Mode	Location	User and Notes
464.0250		NFM	N. Cormorant	Shell
		NFM	Edinburgh	Police (Easter Road)
464.0500	450.0500	NFM	London	Notting Hill Carnival 6
464.0750	450.0750	NFM	Edinburgh	Police Tynecastle
464.1250	450.1250	NFM	London	Notting Hill Carnival 5
464.1250	464.1250	NFM	Bishop Auckland	Police Footbal Security
464.1750	450.1750	NFM	London	Notting Hill Carnival 1
464.3500	450.3500	NFM	Edinburgh	Police Special Events
464.4000	450.4000	NFM	Edinburgh	Police Special Events
464.4275		NFM	Yorkshire	Yorkshire TV O/B
464.4500	450.4500	NFM	Edinburgh	Police Special Events
464.5000	450.5000	NFM	Edinburgh	Police Special Events
464.6625		NFM	London	Dispatch Company
464.6750	450.6750	NFM	Edinburgh	Police Special Events
464.7500	450.7500	NFM	Edinburgh	Police Special Events
464.7750	450.7750	NFM	Edinburgh	Police Special Events

465.0000 - 467.0000 MHz   POLICE PR BASE & REPEATER SYSTEM
(SCOTLAND, LIMITED USE IN ENGLAND)

Base	Mobile	Mode	Location	User and Notes
465.0000	451.0000	NFM	Edinburgh	Police
		NFM	Lothian and Borders	Police (E) East Lothian
465.0000		NFM	Musselburgh	Police
465.0250	451.0250	NFM	Lothian and Borders	Police (N) East Lothian
465.0500	451.0500	NFM	Lothian and Borders	Police
		NFM	Dalkeith	Police
465.1000	451.1000	NFM	Broxburn	Police (F)
		NFM	Newtown	Police
465.1000	465.1000	NFM	Nationwide	RAF Falcons Para. Team
465.1250	451.1250	NFM	Edinburgh	Police
		NFM	Dalkeith	Police
465.1500	451.1500	NFM	South Queensferry	Police (F)
465.2000		NFM	Merseyside	Police (Encrypted)
465.2350		NFM	Grand Prix Circuits	Ferrari Team Voice Link
465.2500	451.2500	NFM	Edinburgh	Police (CV) Corstorphine
465.2750	451.2750	NFM	Edinburgh	Police (CH) Westerhailes
		NFM	Edinburgh	Police
465.3000	451.3000	NFM	Fife	Police
465.3250	451.3250	NFM	Hawick	Police
		NFM	Edinburgh	Police
465.4250	451.4250	NFM	Fife	Police
465.4250		NFM	Gloucester	Gloucester Cathedral
465.4750	451.4750	NFM	Brechin	Police
		NFM	Montrose	Police

Base	Mobile	Mode	Location	User and Notes
465.6000	451.6000	NFM	Bonnyrigg	Police
		NFM	Glasgow	Police
		NFM	Larkhall	Police
465.6000	451.6000	NFM	Pennicook	Police
465.6250	451.6250	NFM	Edinburgh	Police Special Events
		NFM	Glasgow	Police Special Events
		NFM	Perth	Police Special Events
465.6250	451.7250	NFM	London	Notting Hill Carnival 8
465.6250	466.5250	NFM	Hove	Police
		NFM	Edinburgh	Special Events
465.6500	465.6500	NFM	Glasgow	Police
465.6500	451.6500	NFM	Hamilton	Police
465.6750	451.6750	NFM	Edinburgh	Police Special Events
		NFM	Glasgow	Police Special Events
		NFM	Perth	Police Special Events
		NFM	Perth	Party Conference
465.6750	451.7750	NFM	London	Notting Hill Carnival 4
465.7000	451.7000	NFM	Motherwell	Police
		NFM	Glasgow	Police
465.7250	451.7250	NFM	Edinburgh	Police Hibernian FC
		NFM	Edinburgh	Police Special Events
		NFM	Glasgow	Police Special Events
		NFM	Perth	Police Special Events
		NFM	Perth	Party Conference
		NFM	Edinburgh	Police (ZH)
465.7500	451.7500	NFM	Wishaw	Police
465.7500	451.8500	NFM	London	Notting Hill Carnival 3
465.7750	451.7750	NFM	Edinburgh	Police Special Events
		NFM	Glasgow	Police Special Events
		NFM	Perth	Police Special Events
		NFM	Perth	Party Conference
		NFM	Yorkshire	Police Command Vehicle
465.8000	451.8000	NFM	Edinburgh	Police
		NFM	Dunbar	Police
465.8750	465.8750	NFM	Midlands	Police Helicopter (Air 1)
465.9000	465.9000	NFM	West Midlands	Police Helicopter Ch 2
465.9250	451.8250	NFM	Glasgow Airport	Police
466.0250	452.0250	NFM	Stirling	Police
466.0750		NFM	Nationwide	Hutchison Paging
466.2500	452.2500	NFM	Aberdeen	Police
		NFM	Ayr	Police
		NFM	Dumfries and Galloway	Police
		NFM	Edinburgh	Police Firearms Support
		NFM	Edinburgh St Leonards	Div HQ Channel 2
		NFM	Glasgow	Police Firearms Support
		NFM	Lanark	Police
		NFM	Dalkeith	Police
		NFM	Edinburgh	Police Div HQ (B)

Base	Mobile	Mode	Location	User and Notes
466.2750	452.2750	NFM	Aberdeen	Police
		NFM	Ayr	Traffic Wardens (TW)
		NFM	Dumfries and Galloway	Police
		NFM	Edinburgh	Police (C) Edinburgh Tattoo
		NFM	Edinburgh	Police Special Events
		NFM	Edinburgh	Traffic Wardens (TW /TM)
		NFM	Glasgow	Police Special Events
		NFM	Glasgow	Traffic Wardens (TW)
		NFM	Lanark	Traffic Wardens (TW)
		NFM	Perth	Police (Racecourse Control)
		NFM	Perth	Police Special Events
		NFM	Perth	Traffic Wardens (TW)
466.3000	452.3000	NFM	Fife	Traffic Wardens
466.3250	452.3250	NFM	Dumbarton	Police (L)
		NFM	Edinburgh	Police Oxgangs (CO)
		NFM	Edinburgh	Police Westerhailes (CH)
466.3500	451.3500	NFM	Glasgow	Police (E)
466.3500	452.4250	NFM	London	Notting Hill Carnival 7
466.3750	452.3750	NFM	Edinburgh	Police
		NFM	Glasgow	Police Barrhead (K)
466.4000	451.4000	NFM	Aberdeen	HMP Aberdeen
		NFM	Dumfries	HM Prison
		NFM	Edinburgh	HMP Saughton
		NFM	Forfar	HMP Noranside
		NFM	Glasgow	HMP Barlinnie
		NFM	Lothian and Borders	Police (E)
		NFM	Lothian and Borders	Police East Lothian (E)
		NFM	Merseyside	Police (Encrypted)
		NFM	Perth	HMP Friarton
		NFM	Stirling	HMP Corinton Vale
		NFM	St Andrews	Traffic Wardens
466.4250	452.4250	NFM	Various Areas	Police
		NFM	Edinburgh	Police
		NFM	Peebles	Police
466.4500	452.4500	NFM	Dundee	Police (ZS)
		NFM	Glasgow	Police North (C)
466.4500	452.5500	NFM	London	Notting Hill Carnival 2
466.4750	452.4750	NFM	Dumfries and Galloway	Police
466.5000	452.5000	NFM	Alloa	Police
		NFM	Arbroath	Police
		NFM	Argyll	Police (A)
		NFM	Dumfries and Galloway	Police
		NFM	Edinburgh	Police
		NFM	Forfar	Police
		NFM	Glasgow	Police Central (A)
		NFM	Perth	Police (W)
		NFM	Stirling	Police
466.5250	452.5250	NFM	Edinburgh	Police

Base	Mobile	Mode	Location	User and Notes
		NFM	Perth	Police St. Johnstone FC
		NFM	Selkirk	Police
		NFM	Edinburgh	Police City Centre
466.5500	452.5500	NFM	Argyll	Police (B)
		NFM	Glasgow	Police West (B)
		NFM	Inverness	Police
		NFM	Irvine	Police Pocket Phones (U)
		NFM	Kilbirnie	Police Pocket Phones (G)
		NFM	Killwinning	Police (U)
		NFM	Kilmarnock	Police Pocket Phones (U)
		NFM	Stirling	Police
466.5750	452.5750	NFM	Edinburgh	Police West End Div HQ (C)
		NFM	Edinburgh	Police 'C' Div HQ
466.6000	452.6000	NFM	Aberdeen	Police
		NFM	Angus	Police
		NFM	Cupar	Police
		NFM	Glasgow	Police Easterhill (D)
		NFM	Kilmarnock	Police
466.6150		NFM	Grand Prix Circuits	Ferrari Team Voice Link
466.6250	452.6250	NFM	Aberdeen	Police
		NFM	Edinburgh	Police Gayfield (BG)
		NFM	Thurso	Police (M2URCE)
		NFM	Fort William	Police
		NFM	Edinburgh	Police Garfield (BH)
466.6500	452.6500	NFM	Aberdeen	Police
		NFM	Ayr	Police (R)
		NFM	Ballater	Police (UBK5)
		NFM	Edinburgh	Police Drylaw (DR)
		NFM	Glasgow	Police Killpatrick (M)
		NFM	Glasgow	Police South/East (F)
		NFM	Edinburgh	Police Royston (Encrypted)
466.6750	452.6750	NFM	Portobello	Police (DJ & DN)
466.6750		NFM	Edinburgh	Police Portobello
466.7000	452.7000	NFM	Ayr	Police (X)
		NFM	Musselburgh	Police
		NFM	Strathclyde	Police Helicopter
		NFM	Musselburgh	Police (Spare)
466.7250	452.7250	NFM	Livingstone	Police (F)
466.7500	452.7500	NFM	Central Scotland	Police
		NFM	Glasgow	Police Ibrox (G)
		NFM	Stirling	Police
		NFM	Falkirk	Police
466.7750	452.7750	NFM	Glasgow	Police Hamilton (Q)
		NFM	Hamilton	Police Pocket Phones (Q)
466.8000	452.8000	NFM	Edinburgh	Police Firearms Support
		NFM	Glasgow	Police Firearms Support
466.8000	452.9000	NFM	Truleigh Hill	Fire Brigade
466.8250	452.8250	NFM	Lanark	Police (N)

Base	Mobile	Mode	Location	User and Notes
		NFM	Leith	Police (D) Division HQ
		NFM	Edinburgh	Police Leith
466.8750	466.8750	NFM	Nationwide	Simply Red Crew
466.8750	452.9000	NFM	Truleigh Hill	Fire Brigade
466.8750	452.8750	NFM	Galashiels	Police
466.9000	452.9000	NFM	Edinburgh	Police Firearms Support
		NFM	Glasgow	Police Firearms Support
		NFM	Nationwide	Simply Red Crew
466.9750		NFM	Enniskillen	Military Data Link
467.0000 - 467.8250 MHz			**UHF POINT TO POINT SIMPLEX LINKS SHIP**	
467.0250		NFM	Hereford	Ambulance Service
		NFM	Mid Staffordshire	Ambulance Service
		NFM	Salop	Ambulance Service
		NFM	South Warwickshire	Ambulance Service
		NFM	Worcestershire	Ambulance Service
467.0500	460.5500	NFM	Jersey	ATC Link
467.0500	460.5500	NFM	Guernsey	ATC Link
		NFM	Wales	Ambulance Service
467.1250		NFM	Cleveland	Ambulance Service
		NFM	Cumbria	Ambulance Service
		NFM	Durham	Ambulance Service
		NFM	Northumbria	Ambulance Service
467.1500		NFM	Cleveland	Ambulance Service
		NFM	Cumbria	Ambulance Service
		NFM	Durham	Ambulance Service
		NFM	Northumbria	Ambulance Service
467.2000		NFM	Dublin	Fire Service
467.2250		NFM	Avon	Ambulance Service
		NFM	Cornwall	Ambulance Service
		NFM	Devon	Ambulance Service
		NFM	Gloucester	Ambulance Service
		NFM	Scilly Isles	Ambulance Service
		NFM	Somerset	Ambulance Service
467.2500		NFM	Cleveland	Ambulance Service
		NFM	Cumbria	Ambulance Service
		NFM	Durham	Ambulance Service
		NFM	Northumbria	Ambulance Service
		NFM	Wales	Ambulance Service
467.3000		NFM	Nationwide	BBC Radio 5 O/B
467.3500		NFM	Wirral	Emergency Doctors
467.42375		NFM	London	BBC Radio 5 Talkback
467.4250		NFM	London	BBC Radio Engineers
467.4750		NFM	Burnley	Granada TV OB
		NFM	Wales	Ambulance Service
467.49375		NFM	London	Carlton TV Talkback
467.49375		NFM	London	ITV Weather
467.5250	467.5250	NFM	Nationwide	Ship Communications

Base	Mobile	Mode	Location	User and Notes
467.5250	457.5250	NFM	Nationwide	Ship Communications
467.5250	461.0250	NFM	West Sole A	BP To Easington
467.5500	467.5500	NFM	Nationwide	Ship Communications
467.5500	461.0500	NFM	Brent A	Stiell
467.5500	467.5500	NFM	Heather A	Unocol
		NFM	Thistle A	BP
467.5750	467.5750	NFM	Nationwide	Ship Communications
		NFM	Thistle A	BP
		NFM	Balmoral	Sun Oil Portablcs
		NFM	Montrose Docks	Big Orange XVIII
467.5750	461.0750	NFM	West Sole A	BP To Easington
467.5750	457.5750	NFM	Folair	BP Repeater
467.5750		NFM	Belfast	Downtown Radio O/B
467.6000	457.6000	NFM	Nationwide	Ship Communications
467.6125		WFM	Salisbury	Spire FM O/B
467.6250	461.1250	NFM	Fulmar	FSU Shell
467.6625		NFM	Coventry	Mercia Sound O/B
467.6625	467.6125	NFM	London	Capital Radio Flying Eye
467.6750	467.6750	NFM	Nationwide	Ship Communications
467.6750	461.1750	NFM	Hewett	Phillips To Gt Yarmouth
467.7125		WFM	Berkshire	Radio 210 O/B
		WFM	Hampshire	Radio 210 O/B
		NFM	Swansea	Swansea Sound O/B
467.7250	462.2500	NFM	Castle Donington	Grand Prix Team
		NFM	Nationwide	Grand Prix Benneton Team
467.7500	467.7500	NFM	Nationwide	Ship Communications
467.7500		NFM	Dublin	Police L/M/G/P
467.7750	467.7750	NFM	Nationwide	Ship Communications
467.7750		NFM	Brent A	Shell
		NFM	Wales	Ambulance Service
467.8000	467.8000	NFM	Nationwide	Ship Communications
		NFM	Wales	Ambulance Service
467.8250 - 468.0000 MHz			**UHF POINT TO POINT LINKS (SPLIT 6.0 MHZ)**	
467.8250	467.8250	NFM	Nationwide	Ship Communications
		NFM	Wales	Ambulance Service
467.8750	461.8750	NFM	Nationwide	Pye Telecom Mobiles
467.8750		NFM	Brent A	Shell
467.8750	461.3750	NFM	Brent Spar	Shell
467.8750	461.3750	NFM	Fulmar A	Shell To Auk-A
467.9000		NFM	Wales	Ambulance Service
467.9150		NFM	N. Cormorant	Shell
467.9250	461.9250	NFM	Nationwide	Pye Telecom Mobiles
467.9250	461.4250	NFM	E.L.S.B.M.	Shell To Auk-A
		NFM	Wales	Ambulance Service
467.9500	462.9500	NFM	Castle Donington	Grand Prix Team
467.9500	461.9500	NFM	Derby	County Council
467.9500		NFM	Dublin	Police L/M/G/P

Base	Mobile	Mode	Location	User and Notes
467.9750	461.4750	NFM	E.L.S.B.M.	Shell To Auk-A
468.0000 - 468.3500 MHz			**PMR Reserve 25 kHz O/B Talkback**	
468.0000	141.0000	NFM	London	LWT
468.0250		NFM	London	Police Dartford Tunnel
468.0250	468.0250	NFM	Ninian South	Chevron
468.0500		NFM	Jersey	Channel TV Talkback
468.0500	468.0500	NFM	Ninian South	Chevron
468.0625		NFM	East Sussex	Fire Brigade
468.0750		NFM	Kent	Invicta Radio
468.0875	141.1800	NFM	Leicester	Sunrise Radio O/B
		NFM	Kent	Heli-Teli Radio Uplink
		NFM	Tayside	Radio Tay Talkback
		NFM	Leicester	Sunrise Radio O/B
468.1250	468.1250	NFM	Ninian South	Chevron
468.13675		NFM	London	Spectrum Radio Flying Eye
468.1375	468.1375	NFM	Sussex	Local Radio Flying Eye
468.1375	141.0875	NFM	Manchester	Key 103 Eye in the Sky
468.1500		NFM	Castle Donington	Italian TV Talkback
		NFM	Nationwide	BBC Radio 1 Roadshow
468.1625	468.1625	NFM	Ninian South	Chevron
468.2500		NFM	Nationwide	BBC Radio 1 O/B
468.2750		NFM	Nationwide	BBC Radio 1 O/B
		NFM	Stanstead Airport	Police
468.3125		NFM	Gatwick	Police M2KB (GatPol)
		NFM	Newmarket	Community Repeater
468.3500 - 469.4750 MHz			**Outside Broadcast Talkback**	
468.3500	468.3500	NFM	Ninian South	Chevron
468.3750	468.3750	NFM	Nationwide	ITV Cameras
468.3900		NFM	Jersey	Channel TV Talkback
468.4000	454.4000	NFM	Forties A	BP
468.4250	468.4250	NFM	England	Central TV Base Link Input
		NFM	Ninian South	Chevron
468.4625	468.4625	NFM	Inverness	Moray Firth Radio O/B
468.4750	468.4750	NFM	Nationwide	IBA Riggers
468.5000	468.5000	NFM	Nationwide	ITV O/B
469.0000 - 469.8250 MHz			**Irish Police Mobiles 25kHz**	
469.0000	455.6000	NFM	Forties C	BP
469.0125	469.0125	NFM	Shropshire	BBC Radio Shropshire O/B
		NFM	Humberside	BBC Radio Humberside
		NFM	Berkshire	BBC Radio Berks Radio Car
469.0625	469.0625	NFM	Nationwide	BBC Radio 5 O/B
469.1125		NFM	London	BBC Radio 5 Talkback
		NFM	London	Choice FM Flying Eye
		NFM	London	Jazz FM Flying Eye
		NFM	London	Star FM Flying Eye

Base	Mobile	Mode	Location	User and Notes
		NFM	Lincoln	BBC Radio Lincs O/B
		NFM	York	BBC Radio York
469.2125	469.2125	NFM	Nationwide	BBC Radio 5 O/B
469.2400	469.2400	NFM	London	Executive Buses
469.2625		NFM	London	LBC FM Flying Eye
469.3125	469.3125	NFM	East Sussex	Radio Mercury
469.3625	469.3625	NFM	Glasgow	Radio Clyde Helicopter
		WFM	Berkshire	Radio 210 O/B
		WFM	Hampshire	Radio 210 O/B
		NFM	Swansea	Swansea Sound O/B
469.36975		NFM	Essex	BBC Radio Essex Flying Eye
469.4125	469.4125	NFM	Essex	Saxon Radio
		NFM	London	LBC Aircraft Downlink
469.4625	141.1875	NFM	Cowley	Fox FM Flying Eye
		NFM	London	Kiss FM Flying Eye
		NFM	Kent	Invicta Heli-Radio Uplink
469.5750		NFM	Doncaster	Continental Landscapes Ltd
469.7500	469.7500	NFM	EkoFisk-B	Phillips
		NFM	Castle Donington	French TV Talkback

469.8750 - 470.0000 MHz **EMERGENCY SERVICES NFM**

470.0000 - 582.0000 MHz **UK TV CHANNELS (SOUND/VIDEO) LOCAL RADIO TALKBACK AND THEATRE RADIOMICROPHONES (10mW MAX)**

Base	Mobile	Mode	Location	User and Notes
470.5065		NFM	Nationwide	British Telecom
474.0500		NFM	Norwich	Anglia TV Ch 1
474.1000		NFM	Norwich	Anglia TV Ch 2
474.2000		NFM	Norwich	Anglia TV Ch 3
474.4000		NFM	Norwich	Anglia TV Ch 4
476.4750		NFM	London	Capital Radio Flying Eye
477.2500	471.2500	WFM	Nationwide	Channel 21
		WFM	Edinburgh	Channel 4
		WFM	St. Peter Port, Guernsey	BBC 1
		WFM	Milton Keynes	Channel 4
		WFM	Cahir	RTE 1
		WFM	Ballybofey	RTE 1
		WFM	Stranolar	RTE 1
		WFM	Newcastle	BBC 1
		WFM	Gosport	Channel 4
		WFM	Calne	BBC 1
478.0000		NFM	London	Radio London
478.7000		NFM	Nationwide	Theatre Radiomicrophone
479.6500		NFM	Nationwide	Theatre Radiomicrophone
480.2000		NFM	Nationwide	Theatre Radiomicrophone
480.4000		NFM	Nationwide	Theatre Radiomicrophone
485.2500	479.2500	WFM	Nationwide	Channel 22
		WFM	Plymouth	BBC 1

Base	Mobile	Mode	Location	User and Notes
		WFM	Kerry	RTE 1
		WFM	Malin	RTE 1
488.8250		NFM	London	Talking Clock
493.2500	487.2500	WFM	Nationwide	Channel 23
		WFM	Jersey	ITV
		WFM	Crystal Palace	Thames TV
		WFM	Dingle	RTE 1
		WFM	Donegal	RTE 1
497.5000		NFM	Nationwide	Theatre Radiomicrophone
497.7000		NFM	Nationwide	Theatre Radiomicrophone
498.4800		NFM	Nationwide	Theatre Radiomicrophone
498.7800		NFM	Nationwide	Theatre Radiomicrophone
498.8250		NFM	Newmarket	Channel 4
499.6100		NFM	Nationwide	Theatre Radiomicrophone

Base	Mobile	Mode	Location	User and Notes
500.0000		AM	Nationwide	NATO Mayday Discreet
500.2800		NFM	Nationwide	Theatre Radiomicrophone
501.2500	495.2500	WFM	Nationwide	Channel 24
		WFM	Lancashire	ITV
		WFM	St. Peter Port	ITV
		WFM	Edinburgh	ITV
		WFM	Sandy Heath	Anglia TV
		WFM	Cahir	Network 2
501.2750		WFM	Newcastle	Tyne Tees
501.3000		WFM	Gosport	BBC 2
		WFM	Calne	BBC 2
502.4400		NFM	Nationwide	Theatre Radiomicrophone
502.6900		NFM	Nationwide	Theatre Radiomicrophone
503.2500	509.2500	WFM	Nationwide	Channel 25
506.8500		WFM	Glasgow	BBC 1
509.2500		WFM	Kerry	Network 2
		WFM	Malin	Network 2
		WFM	Plymouth	Westcountry TV Sound
511.2500	517.2500	WFM	Nationwide	Channel 26
		WFM	Gorey, Jersey	BBC 2
		WFM	Dingle	Network 2
		WFM	Donegal	Network 2
519.2500	525.2500	WFM	Nationwide	Channel 27
		WFM	Lancashire	BBC 2
		WFM	St. Peter Port	BBC 2
		WFM	Edinburgh	BBC2
		WFM	Clonmel	RTE 1
		WFM	Gosport	ITV
		WFM	Calne	HTV
527.2500	533.2500	WFM	Nationwide	Channel 28
		WFM	Plymouth	BBC 2
541.2500	535.2500	WFM	Nationwide	Channel 29
		WFM	Gorey, Jersey	C 4
		WFM	Co. Cork	RTE 1
		WFM	Dublin	RTE 1
549.2590	543.2500	WFM	Nationwide	Channel 30
		WFM	Bandon	RTE 1
		WFM	Knockmoyle	RTE 1
		WFM	Youghal	RTE 1
557.2500	551.2500	WFM	Nationwide	Channel 31
		WFM	Lancashire	BBC 1
		WFM	St. Peter Port	C4
		WFM	Clonmel	Network 2
		WFM	Ballybofey	Network 2
		WFM	Stranolar	Network 2
		WFM	Edinburgh	BBC 1
		WFM	Gosport	BBC 1
		WFM	Calne	Channel 4

Base	Mobile	Mode	Location	User and Notes
565.2500	559.2500	WFM	Nationwide	Channel 32
		WFM	Plymouth	Channel 4
573.2500	567.2500	WFM	Nationwide	Channel 33
		WFM	Co. Cork	Network 2
		WFM	Dublin	Network 2
581.2500	575.2500	WFM	Nationwide	Channel 34
		WFM	Bandon	Network 2
		WFM	Knockmoyle	Network 2
		WFM	Youghal	Network 2
583.6900		NFM	Nationwide	Theatre Radiomicrophone
584.1500		NFM	Nationwide	Theatre Radiomicrophone

590.0000 - 598.0000 MHz   CIVIL & DEFENCE RADAR

598.0000 - 606.0000 MHz   FUTURE TV CHANNEL 5 ALLOCATION

606.0000 - 614.0000 MHz   RADIO ASTRONOMY

614.0000 - 854.0000 MHz   UK WFM TV CHANNELS (SOUND/VIDEO)

Base	Mobile	Mode	Location	User and Notes
621.2500	615.2500	WFM	Nationwide	Channel 39
		WFM	Perth	BBC 1
		WFM	Cork City	RTE 1
		WFM	Glenbeigh	RTE 1
		WFM	Bantry	RTE 1
629.2500	623.2500	WFM	Nationwide	Channel 40
		WFM	Newmarket	ITV
		WFM	Torteval, Guernsey	BBC 2
		WFM	Longford	RTE 1
		WFM	Dunquin	RTE 1
637.2500	631.2500	WFM	Nationwide	Channel 41
		WFM	Fremont, Jersey	ITV
645.2500	639.2500	WFM	Nationwide	Channel 42
		WFM	Perth	ITV
		WFM	Glenbeigh	Network 2
653.2500	647.2500	WFM	Nationwide	Channel 43
		WFM	Longford	Network 2
		WFM	Dunquin	Network 2
661.2500	655.2500	WFM	Nationwide	Channel 44
		WFM	Newmarket	BBC 2
		WFM	Fremont, Jersey	BBC 2
669.2500	663.2500	WFM	Nationwide	Channel 45
		WFM	Perth	BBC 2
677.2500	671.2500	WFM	Nationwide	Channel 46
		WFM	Newmarket	C4
		WFM	Torteval, Guernsey	ITV
685.2500	679.2500	WFM	Nationwide	Channel 47
		WFM	Fremont, Jersey	C4
693.2500	687.2500	WFM	Nationwide	Channel 48

Base	Mobile	Mode	Location	User and Notes
		WFM	Les Touillets, Guernsey	BBC 2
		WFM	Limerick City	RTE 1
701.2500	695.2500	WFM	Nationwide	Channel 49
		WFM	Perth	C4
		WFM	Cork City	Network 2
		WFM	Bantry	Network 2
709.2500	703.2500	WFM	Nationwide	Channel 50
		WFM	Newmarket	BBC 1
		WFM	Torteval, Guernsey	BBC 1
717.2500	711.2500	WFM	Nationwide	Channel 51
		WFM	Fremont Point	BBC 1
725.2500	719.2500	WFM	Nationwide	Channel 52
		WFM	Les Touillets	C4
		WFM	Louth	RTE 1
		WFM	Limerick City	Network 2
733.2500	727.2500	WFM	Nationwide	Channel 53
		WFM	Inistioge	RTE 1
741.2500	735.2500	WFM	Nationwide	Channel 54
		WFM	Gorey, Jersey	BBC 1
		WFM	Les Touillets, Guernsey	ITV
749.2500	743.2500	WFM	Nationwide	Channel 55
		WFM	St. Helier, Jersey	BBC2
		WFM	Crosshaven	RTE 1
757.2500	751.2500	WFM	Nationwide	Channel 56
		WFM	Les Touillets, Guernsey	BBC 1
		WFM	Louth	Network 2
765.2500	759.2500	WFM	Nationwide	Channel 57
		WFM	Inistioge	Network 2
773.2500	767.2500	WFM	Nationwide	Channel 58
		WFM	Alderney	BBC1
781.2500	775.2500	WFM	Nationwide	Channel 59
		WFM	St. Helier, Jersey	ITV
		WFM	Crosshaven	Network 2
789.2500	783.2500	WFM	Nationwide	Channel 60
		NFM	Nationwide	BBC O/B (OL-94)
785.7500		NFM	Nationwide	BBC O/B (OL-94)
787.2500		NFM	Nationwide	BBC O/B (OL-94)
789.2500		WFM	Oxford	Central TV
797.2500	791.2500	WFM	Nationwide	Channel 61
		WFM	Alderney	ITV
		WFM	Carlingford	RTE 1
805.2500	799.2500	WFM	Nationwide	Channel 62
		WFM	St. Helier, Jersey	BBC2
813.2500	807.2500	WFM	Nationwide	Channel 63
821.2500	815.2500	WFM	Nationwide	Channel 64
		WFM	Alderney	BBC2
829.2500	823.2500	WFM	Nationwide	Channel 65
		WFM	St. Helier, Jersey	C4

Base	Mobile	Mode	Location	User and Notes
837.2500	831.2500	WFM	Nationwide	Channel 66
		WFM	Guernsey, Torteval	C4
845.2500	839.2500	WFM	Nationwide	Channel 67
		WFM	Carlingford	Network 2
846.0000			RAF Boulmer	R80 Defence Radar
853.2500	847.2500	WFM	Nationwide	Channel 68
		WFM	Alderney	C4
854.5000		WFM	Sutton Coldfield	BBC O/B Link

854.7500 - 855.2500 MHz   RADIO MICROPHONES

Base	Mobile	Mode	Location	User and Notes
854.7500		WFM	Nationwide	Channel 1
854.7750		WFM	Nationwide	Channel 2
854.8000		WFM	Nationwide	Channel 3
854.8250		WFM	Nationwide	Channel 4
854.8500		WFM	Nationwide	Channel 5
854.8750		WFM	Nationwide	Channel 6
854.9000		WFM	Nationwide	Channel 7
854.9250		WFM	Nationwide	Channel 8
854.9500		WFM	Nationwide	Channel 9
854.9750		WFM	Nationwide	Channel 10
855.0000		WFM	Nationwide	Channel 11
855.0250		WFM	Nationwide	Channel 12
855.0500		WFM	Nationwide	Channel 13
855.0750		WFM	Nationwide	Channel 14
855.1000		WFM	Nationwide	Channel 15
855.1250		WFM	Nationwide	Channel 16
855.1500		WFM	Nationwide	Channel 17
855.1750		WFM	Nationwide	Channel 18
855.2000		WFM	Nationwide	Channel 19
855.2250		WFM	Nationwide	Channel 20
859.8000		WFM	Sutton Coldfield	BBC O/B Link

860.2500 - 860.7500 MHz   RADIO MICROPHONES

Base	Mobile	Mode	Location	User and Notes
860.2500		WFM	Nationwide	Channel 1
860.2750		WFM	Nationwide	Channel 2
860.3000		WFM	Nationwide	Channel 3
860.3250		WFM	Nationwide	Channel 4
860.3500		WFM	Nationwide	Channel 5
860.3750		WFM	Nationwide	Channel 6
860.4000		WFM	Nationwide	Channel 7
860.4250		WFM	Nationwide	Channel 8
860.4500		WFM	Nationwide	Channel 9
860.4750		WFM	Nationwide	Channel 10
860.5000		WFM	Nationwide	Channel 11
860.5250		WFM	Nationwide	Channel 12
860.5500		WFM	Nationwide	Channel 13
860.5750		WFM	Nationwide	Channel 14
860.6000		WFM	Nationwide	Channel 15

Base	Mobile	Mode	Location	User and Notes
860.6250		WFM	Nationwide	Channel 16
860.6500		WFM	Nationwide	Channel 17
860.6750		WFM	Nationwide	Channel 18
860.7000		WFM	Nationwide	Channel 19
860.7250		WFM	Nationwide	Channel 20

862.0000 - 864.0000 MHz			MOBILE EMERGENCY SERVICES & FUTURE CT2 DIGITAL PHONES	
863.0000 - 864.0000 MHz			LAND MOBILE EXPERIMENTAL USE	
864.0000 - 868.0000 MHz			CT2 DIGITAL PHONES (30 x 100 kHz CHANNELS)	
868.0000 - 869.9750 MHz			DEREGULATED BAND FOR LOW POWER DEVICES & FUTURE CT2 DIGITAL PHONES	
870.0250		NFM	Bournemouth	BBC O/B Link
870.0000 - 872.0000 MHz			MINISTRY OF DEFENCE (SPLIT + 45 MHz)	
872.0000 - 904.9875 MHz			UHF ETACS CELLULAR TELEPHONE MOBILES	
875.0000		WFM	Nationwide	WFM BBC Music Link
880.0000		WFM	Nationwide	WFM BBC Music Link
888.0000 - 889.0000 MHz			LOW POWER DEVICES	
888.0000 - 890.0000 MHz			FUTURE DSRR (76 x 25 kHz CHANNELS)	
890.0000 - 915.0000 MHz			TACS AND GSM MOBILES	
915.0000 - 920.0000 MHz			POSSIBLE FUTURE ISM	
905.0000 - 915.0000 MHz			PAN EUROPEAN DIGITAL CELLULAR SERVICE MOBILES	
914.0125 - 914.9875 MHz			NEW CYBERNET/UNIDEN CORDLESS TELEPHONES HANDSET	
915.0000 - 917.0000 MHz			MINISTRY OF DEFENCE (SPLIT - 45 MHz)	
917.0125 - 949.9875 MHz			UHF CELLULAR ETACS (EXTENDED TOTAL ACCESS COMMUNICATIONS SYSTEM) TELEPHONE NODES	
917.0125	872.0125	NFM	Durham	Vodafone Channel 1329
917.0375	872.0375	NFM	Central Scotland	Vodafone Channel 1330
917.0625	872.0625	NFM	North Yorkshire	Vodafone Channel 1331
917.0875	872.0875	NFM	Cumbria	Vodafone Channel 1332
		NFM	Lancashire	

Base	Mobile	Mode	Location	User and Notes
		NFM	Edinburgh	
		NFM	Central Scotland	
917.1625	872.1625	NFM	Edinburgh	Vodafone Channel 1335
		NFM	North Yorkshire	
917.2125	872.2125	NFM	Durham	Vodafone Channel 1337
		NFM	North Yorkshire	
917.2625	872.2625	NFM	Durham	Vodafone Channel 1339
917.3125	872.3125	NFM	Edinburgh	Vodafone Channel 1341
		NFM	Ferrybridge	
917.3375	872.3375	NFM	Chathill	Vodafone Channel 1342
917.3625	872.3625	NFM	Newmarket	Vodafone Channel 1343
917.3875	872.3875	NFM	Ferrybridge	Vodafone Channel 1344
		NFM	Perth	
		NFM	North Yorkshire	
917.4125	872.4125	NFM	Cumbria	Vodafone Channel 1345
		NFM	Lancashire	
917.4375	872.4375	NFM	Central Scotland	Vodafone Channel 1346
917.4625	872.4625	NFM	Newmarket	Vodafone Channel 1347
917.4875	872.4875	NFM	Nationwide	Vodafone Channel 1348
		NFM	Newcastle	
917.5125	872.5125	NFM	Nationwide	Vodafone Channel 1349
		NFM	Edinburgh	
917.5375	872.5375	NFM	Nationwide	Vodafone Channel 1350
		NFM	Durham	
917.5625	872.5625	NFM	Nationwide	Vodafone Channel 1351
		NFM	Central Scotland	
917.5875	872.5875	NFM	Nationwide	Vodafone Channel 1352
		NFM	North Yorkshire	
917.6125	872.6125	NFM	Nationwide	Vodafone Channel 1353
		NFM	Cumbria	
		NFM	Lancashire	
		NFM	Central Scotland	
		NFM	Edinburgh	
917.6875	872.6875	NFM	Nationwide	Vodafone Channel 1356
		NFM	Edinburgh	
		NFM	North Yorkshire	
917.7375	872.7375	NFM	Nationwide	Vodafone Channel 1358
		NFM	Durham	
917.7375	872.7375	NFM	North Yorkshire	
917.7875	872.7875	NFM	Nationwide	Vodafone Channel 1360
		NFM	Durham	
917.8375	872.8375	NFM	Nationwide	Vodafone Channel 1362
		NFM	Edinburgh	
917.8625	872.8625	NFM	Nationwide	Vodafone Channel 1363
		NFM	Chathill	
		NFM	Edinburgh	
917.8875	872.8875	NFM	Nationwide	Vodafone Channel 1364
		NFM	Newmarket	

Base	Mobile	Mode	Location	User and Notes
917.9125	872.9125	NFM	Nationwide	Vodafone Channel 1365
		NFM	Perth	
		NFM	Lauder	
		NFM	North Yorkshire	
917.9375	872.9375	NFM	Nationwide	Vodafone Channel 1366
		NFM	Cumbria	
		NFM	Lancashire	
917.9625	872.9625	NFM	Nationwide	Vodafone Channel 1367
		NFM	Central Scotland	
918.0125	873.0125	NFM	Nationwide	Vodafone Channel 1369
		NFM	Newcastle	
918.0375	873.0375	NFM	Nationwide	Vodafone Channel 1370
		NFM	Edinburgh	
918.0625	873.0625	NFM	Nationwide	Vodafone Channel 1371
		NFM	Durham	
918.0875	873.0875	NFM	Nationwide	Vodafone Channel 1372
		NFM	Central Scotland	
918.1125	873.1125	NFM	Nationwide	Vodafone Channel 1373
		NFM	North Yorkshire	
918.1375	873.1375	NFM	Nationwide	Vodafone Channel 1374
		NFM	Cumbria	
		NFM	Edinburgh	
		NFM	Lancashire	
		NFM	Central Scotland	
918.2125	873.2125	NFM	Nationwide	Vodafone Channel 1377
		NFM	Edinburgh	
		NFM	North Yorkshire	
918.2625	873.2625	NFM	Nationwide	Vodafone Channel 1379
		NFM	Durham	
		NFM	North Yorkshire	
918.3125	873.3125	NFM	Nationwide	Vodafone Channel 1381
		NFM	Durham	
918.3625	873.3625	NFM	Nationwide	Vodafone Channel 1383
		NFM	Edinburgh	
918.3875	873.3875	NFM	Nationwide	Vodafone Channel 1384
		NFM	Edinburgh	
		NFM	Chathill	
918.4125	873.4125	NFM	Nationwide	Vodafone Channel 1385
		NFM	Newmarket	
918.4375	873.4375	NFM	Nationwide	Vodafone Channel 1386
		NFM	Ferrybridge	
		NFM	Perth	
		NFM	North Yorkshire	
918.4875	873.4875	NFM	Nationwide	Vodafone Channel 1388
		NFM	Central Scotland	
918.5125	873.5125	NFM	Nationwide	Vodafone Channel 1389
		NFM	Newmarket	
918.5375	873.5375	NFM	Nationwide	Vodafone Channel 1390

Base	Mobile	Mode	Location	User and Notes
		NFM	Newcastle	
918.5625	873.5625	NFM	Nationwide	Vodafone Channel 1391
		NFM	Edinburgh	
918.5875	873.5875	NFM	Nationwide	Vodafone Channel 1392
		NFM	Durham	
918.6125	873.6125	NFM	Nationwide	Vodafone Channel 1393
		NFM	Central Scotland	
918.6375	873.6375	NFM	Nationwide	Vodafone Channel 1394
		NFM	North Yorkshire	
918.6625	873.6625	NFM	Nationwide	Vodafone Channel 1395
		NFM	Cumbria	
		NFM	Lancashire	
		NFM	Central Scotland	
		NFM	Edinburgh	
918.7375	873.7375	NFM	Nationwide	Vodafone Channel 1398
		NFM	Edinburgh	
		NFM	North Yorkshire	
918.7875	873.7875	NFM	Nationwide	Vodafone Channel 1400
		NFM	Durham	
918.7875	873.7875	NFM	North Yorkshire	
918.8375	873.8375	NFM	Nationwide	Vodafone Channel 1402
		NFM	Durham	
918.8875	873.8875	NFM	Nationwide	Vodafone Channel 1404
		NFM	Edinburgh	
918.9125	873.9125	NFM	Nationwide	Vodafone Channel 1405
		NFM	Chathill	
918.9375	873.9375	NFM	Nationwide	Vodafone Channel 1406
		NFM	Newmarket	
918.9625	873.9625	NFM	Nationwide	Vodafone Channel 1407
		NFM	North Yorkshire	
919.0125	874.0125	NFM	Nationwide	Vodafone Channel 1409
		NFM	Central Scotland	
919.0625	874.0625	NFM	Nationwide	Vodafone Channel 1411
		NFM	Newcastle	
919.0875	874.0875	NFM	Nationwide	Vodafone Channel 1412
919.1125	874.1125	NFM	Nationwide	Vodafone Channel 1413
		NFM	Durham	
919.1375	874.1375	NFM	Nationwide	Vodafone Channel 1414
		NFM	Central Scotland	
919.1625	874.1625	NFM	Nationwide	Vodafone Channel 1415
		NFM	North Yorkshire	
919.1875	874.1875	NFM	Nationwide	Vodafone Channel 1416
		NFM	Cumbria	
		NFM	Lancashire	
		NFM	Central Scotland	
919.2375	874.2375	NFM	Nationwide	Vodafone Channel 1418
		NFM	Edinburgh	
		NFM	Ferrybridge	

Base	Mobile	Mode	Location	User and Notes
919.2625	874.2625	NFM	Nationwide	Vodafone Channel 1419
		NFM	Edinburgh	
		NFM	North Yorkshire	
919.3125	874.3125	NFM	Nationwide	Vodafone Channel 1421
		NFM	Durham	
		NFM	North Yorkshire	
919.3625	874.3625	NFM	Nationwide	Vodafone Channel 1423
		NFM	Durham	
919.4125	874.4125	NFM	Nationwide	Vodafone Channel 1425
		NFM	Edinburgh	
919.4375	874.4375	NFM	Nationwide	Vodafone Channel 1426
		NFM	Chathill	
		NFM	Edinburgh	
919.4625	874.4625	NFM	Nationwide	Vodafone Channel 1427
		NFM	Newmarket	
919.4875	874.4875	NFM	Nationwide	Vodafone Channel 1428
		NFM	Ferrybridge	
		NFM	North Yorkshire	
919.5375	874.5375	NFM	Nationwide	Vodafone Channel 1430
		NFM	Central Scotland	
919.5625	874.5625	NFM	Nationwide	Vodafone Channel 1431
		NFM	Newmarket	
919.5875	874.5875	NFM	Nationwide	Vodafone Channel 1432
		NFM	Newcastle	
919.6125	874.6125	NFM	Nationwide	Vodafone Channel 1433
		NFM	Edinburgh	
919.6375	874.6375	NFM	Nationwide	Vodafone Channel 1434
		NFM	Durham	
919.6625	874.6625	NFM	Nationwide	Vodafone Channel 1435
		NFM	Central Scotland	
919.6875	874.6875	NFM	Nationwide	Vodafone Channel 1436
		NFM	North Yorkshire	
919.7125	874.7125	NFM	Nationwide	Vodafone Channel 1437
		NFM	Cumbria	
		NFM	Lancashire	
		NFM	Central Scotland	
		NFM	Edinburgh	
919.7625	874.7625	NFM	Nationwide	Vodafone Channel 1439
		NFM	Ferrybridge	
919.7875	874.7875	NFM	Nationwide	Vodafone Channel 1440
		NFM	Edinburgh	
		NFM	North Yorkshire	
919.8375	874.8375	NFM	Nationwide	Vodafone Channel 1442
		NFM	Durham	
		NFM	North Yorkshire	
919.8875	874.8875	NFM	Nationwide	Vodafone Channel 1444
		NFM	Durham	
919.9125	874.9125	NFM	Nationwide	Vodafone Channel 1445

Base	Mobile	Mode	Location	User and Notes
919.9375	874.9375	NFM	Nationwide	Vodafone Channel 1446
		NFM	Edinburgh	
		NFM	Ferrybridge	
919.9625	874.9625	NFM	Nationwide	Vodafone Channel 1447
		NFM	Chathill	
919.9875	874.9875	NFM	Nationwide	Vodafone Channel 1448
		NFM	Newmarket	
920.0125	875.0125	NFM	Nationwide	Vodafone Channel 1449
		NFM	Perth	
		NFM	North Yorkshire	
920.0625	875.0625	NFM	Nationwide	Vodafone Channel 1451
		NFM	Central Scotland	
920.0875	875.0875	NFM	Nationwide	Vodafone Channel 1452
		NFM	Newmarket	
920.1125	875.1125	NFM	Nationwide	Vodafone Channel 1453
		NFM	Newcastle	
920.1375	875.1375	NFM	Nationwide	Vodafone Channel 1454
		NFM	Edinburgh	
920.1625	875.1625	NFM	Nationwide	Vodafone Channel 1455
		NFM	Durham	
920.1875	875.1875	NFM	Nationwide	Vodafone Channel 1456
		NFM	Central Scotland	
920.2125	875.2125	NFM	Nationwide	Vodafone Channel 1457
		NFM	North Yorkshire	
920.2375	875.2375	NFM	Nationwide	Vodafone Channel 1458
		NFM	Cumbria	
		NFM	Edinburgh	
		NFM	Lancashire	
		NFM	Central Scotland	
920.3125	875.3125	NFM	Nationwide	Vodafone Channel 1461
		NFM	Edinburgh	
		NFM	North Yorkshire	
920.3625	875.3625	NFM	Nationwide	Vodafone Channel 1463
		NFM	Durham	
		NFM	North Yorkshire	
920.4125	875.4125	NFM	Nationwide	Vodafone Channel 1465
		NFM	Durham	
920.4625	875.4625	NFM	Nationwide	Vodafone Channel 1467
		NFM	Edinburgh	
920.4875	875.4875	NFM	Nationwide	Vodafone Channel 1468
		NFM	Chathill	
920.5375	875.5375	NFM	Nationwide	Vodafone Channel 1470
		NFM	Perth	
		NFM	North Yorkshire	
920.5875	875.5875	NFM	Nationwide	Vodafone Channel 1472
		NFM	Central Scotland	
920.6125	875.6125	NFM	Nationwide	Vodafone Channel 1473
		NFM	Newmarket	

Base	Mobile	Mode	Location	User and Notes
920.6375	875.6375	NFM	Nationwide	Vodafone Channel 1474
		NFM	Newcastle	
920.6625	875.6625	NFM	Nationwide	Vodafone Channel 1475
		NFM	Edinburgh	
920.6875	875.6875	NFM	Nationwide	Vodafone Channel 1476
		NFM	Durham	
920.7125	875.7125	NFM	Nationwide	Vodafone Channel 1477
		NFM	Central Scotland	
920.7375	875.7375	NFM	Nationwide	Vodafone Channel 1478
		NFM	North Yorkshire	
920.7625	875.7625	NFM	Nationwide	Vodafone Channel 1479
		NFM	Cumbria	
		NFM	Edinburgh	
		NFM	Lancashire	
		NFM	Central Scotland	
920.8375	875.8375	NFM	Nationwide	Vodafone Channel 1482
		NFM	Edinburgh	
		NFM	North Yorkshire	
920.8875	875.8875	NFM	Nationwide	Vodafone Channel 1484
		NFM	Durham	
		NFM	North Yorkshire	
920.9375	875.9375	NFM	Nationwide	Vodafone Channel 1486
		NFM	Durham	
920.9875	875.9875	NFM	Nationwide	Vodafone Channel 1488
		NFM	Edinburgh	
921.0125	876.0125	NFM	Nationwide	Vodafone Channel 1489
		NFM	Chathill	
921.0625	876.0625	NFM	Nationwide	Vodafone Channel 1491
		NFM	Perth	
		NFM	North Yorkshire	
921.1125	876.1125	NFM	Nationwide	Vodafone Channel 1493
		NFM	Central Scotland	
921.1375	876.1375	NFM	Nationwide	Vodafone Channel 1494
		NFM	Newmarket	
921.1625	876.1625	NFM	Nationwide	Vodafone Channel 1495
921.1625	876.1625	NFM	Newcastle	
921.1875	876.1875	NFM	Nationwide	Vodafone Channel 1496
		NFM	Edinburgh	
921.2125	876.2125	NFM	Nationwide	Vodafone Channel 1497
		NFM	Durham	
921.2375	876.2375	NFM	Nationwide	Vodafone Channel 1498
		NFM	Central Scotland	
921.2625	876.2625	NFM	Nationwide	Vodafone Channel 1499
		NFM	North Yorkshire	
921.2875	876.2875	NFM	Nationwide	Vodafone Channel 1500
		NFM	Cumbria	
		NFM	Lancashire	
		NFM	Edinburgh	

Base	Mobile	Mode	Location	User and Notes
		NFM	Central Scotland	
921.3625	876.3625	NFM	Nationwide	Vodafone Channel 1503
		NFM	Edinburgh	
		NFM	North Yorkshire	
921.4125	876.4125	NFM	Nationwide	Vodafone Channel 1505
		NFM	Durham	
		NFM	North Yorkshire	
921.4625	876.4625	NFM	Nationwide	Vodafone Channel 1507
		NFM	Durham	
921.5125	876.5125	NFM	Nationwide	Vodafone Channel 1509
		NFM	Edinburgh	
921.5375	876.5375	NFM	Nationwide	Vodafone Channel 1510
		NFM	Chathill	
921.5875	876.5875	NFM	Nationwide	Vodafone Channel 1512
		NFM	Perth	
		NFM	North Yorkshire	
921.6375	876.6375	NFM	Nationwide	Vodafone Channel 1514
		NFM	Central Scotland	
921.6625	876.6625	NFM	Nationwide	Vodafone Channel 1515
		NFM	Newmarket	
921.6875	876.6875	NFM	Nationwide	Vodafone Channel 1516
		NFM	Newcastle	
921.7125	876.7125	NFM	Nationwide	Vodafone Channel 1517
		NFM	Edinburgh	
921.7375	876.7375	NFM	Nationwide	Vodafone Channel 1518
		NFM	Durham	
921.7625	876.7625	NFM	Nationwide	Vodafone Channel 1519
		NFM	Central Scotland	
921.7875	876.7875	NFM	Nationwide	Vodafone Channel 1520
		NFM	North Yorkshire	
921.8125	876.8125	NFM	Nationwide	Vodafone Channel 1521
		NFM	Cumbria	
		NFM	Edinburgh	
		NFM	Lancashire	
		NFM	Central Scotland	
921.8875	876.8875	NFM	Nationwide	Vodafone Channel 1524
		NFM	Edinburgh	
		NFM	North Yorkshire	
921.9375	876.9375	NFM	Nationwide	Vodafone Channel 1526
		NFM	Durham	
		NFM	North Yorkshire	
921.9875	876.9875	NFM	Nationwide	Vodafone Channel 1528
		NFM	Durham	
922.0375	877.0375	NFM	Nationwide	Vodafone Channel 1530
		NFM	Edinburgh	
922.0625	877.0625	NFM	Nationwide	Vodafone Channel 1531
		NFM	Chathill	
922.0875	877.0875	NFM	Nationwide	Vodafone Channel 1532

Base	Mobile	Mode	Location	User and Notes
922.1125	877.1125	NFM	Nationwide	Vodafone Channel 1533
		NFM	North Yorkshire	
		NFM	Perth	
922.1625	877.1625	NFM	Nationwide	Vodafone Channel 1535
		NFM	Central Scotland	
922.2125	877.2125	NFM	Nationwide	Vodafone Channel 1537
		NFM	Newcastle	
922.2375	877.2375	NFM	Nationwide	Vodafone Channel 1538
		NFM	Edinburgh	
922.2625	877.2625	NFM	Nationwide	Vodafone Channel 1539
		NFM	Durham	
922.2875	877.2875	NFM	Nationwide	Vodafone Channel 1540
		NFM	Central Scotland	
922.3125	877.3125	NFM	Nationwide	Vodafone Channel 1541
		NFM	North Yorkshire	
922.3375	877.3375	NFM	Nationwide	Vodafone Channel 1542
		NFM	Cumbria	
		NFM	Lancashire	
		NFM	Edinburgh	
		NFM	Central Scotland	
922.4125	877.4125	NFM	Nationwide	Vodafone Channel 1545
		NFM	Edinburgh	
		NFM	North Yorkshire	
922.4625	877.4625	NFM	Nationwide	Vodafone Channel 1547
		NFM	Durham	
		NFM	North Yorkshire	
922.5125	877.5125	NFM	Nationwide	Vodafone Channel 1549
		NFM	Durham	
922.5625	877.5625	NFM	Nationwide	Vodafone Channel 1551
		NFM	Edinburgh	
922.5875	877.5875	NFM	Nationwide	Vodafone Channel 1552
		NFM	Chathill	
922.6375	877.6375	NFM	Nationwide	Vodafone Channel 1554
		NFM	Perth	
		NFM	North Yorkshire	
922.6875	877.6875	NFM	Nationwide	Vodafone Channel 1556
		NFM	Central Scotland	
922.7375	877.7375	NFM	Nationwide	Vodafone Channel 1558
		NFM	Newcastle	
922.7625	877.7625	NFM	Nationwide	Vodafone Channel 1559
		NFM	Edinburgh	
922.7875	877.7875	NFM	Nationwide	Vodafone Channel 1560
		NFM	Durham	
922.8125	877.8125	NFM	Nationwide	Vodafone Channel 1561
		NFM	Central Scotland	
922.8375	877.8375	NFM	Nationwide	Vodafone Channel 1562
		NFM	North Yorkshire	
922.8625	877.8625	NFM	Nationwide	Vodafone Channel 1563

Base	Mobile	Mode	Location	User and Notes
		NFM	Edinburgh	
		NFM	Central Scotland	
922.9375	877.9375	NFM	Nationwide	Vodafone Channel 1566
		NFM	Edinburgh	
		NFM	North Yorkshire	
922.9875	877.9875	NFM	Nationwide	Vodafone Channel 1568
		NFM	Durham	
		NFM	North Yorkshire	
923.0375	878.0375	NFM	Nationwide	Vodafone Channel 1570
		NFM	Durham	
923.0875	878.0875	NFM	Nationwide	Vodafone Channel 1572
		NFM	Edinburgh	
923.1125	878.1125	NFM	Nationwide	Vodafone Channel 1573
		NFM	Chathill	
923.1625	878.1625	NFM	Nationwide	Vodafone Channel 1575
		NFM	Perth	
		NFM	North Yorkshire	
923.2125	878.2125	NFM	Nationwide	Vodafone Channel 1577
		NFM	Central Scotland	
923.2625	878.2625	NFM	Nationwide	Vodafone Channel 1579
		NFM	Newcastle	
923.2875	878.2875	NFM	Nationwide	Vodafone Channel 1580
		NFM	Edinburgh	
923.3125	878.3125	NFM	Nationwide	Vodafone Channel 1581
		NFM	Durham	
923.3375	878.3375	NFM	Nationwide	Vodafone Channel 1582
		NFM	Central Scotland	
923.3625	878.3625	NFM	Nationwide	Vodafone Channel 1583
		NFM	North Yorkshire	
923.3875	878.3875	NFM	Nationwide	Vodafone Channel 1584
		NFM	Central Scotland	
923.4625	878.4625	NFM	Nationwide	Vodafone Channel 1587
		NFM	Edinburgh	
		NFM	North Yorkshire	
923.5125	878.5125	NFM	Nationwide	Vodafone Channel 1589
		NFM	Durham	
		NFM	North Yorkshire	
923.5625	878.5625	NFM	Nationwide	Vodafone Channel 1591
		NFM	Durham	
923.6125	878.6125	NFM	Nationwide	Vodafone Channel 1593
		NFM	Edinburgh	
		NFM	Ferrybridge	
923.6375	878.6375	NFM	Nationwide	Vodafone Channel 1594
		NFM	Chathill	
923.6875	878.6875	NFM	Nationwide	Vodafone Channel 1596
		NFM	Perth	
		NFM	North Yorkshire	
923.7125	878.7125	NFM	Nationwide	Vodafone Channel 1597

Base	Mobile	Mode	Location	User and Notes
923.7375	878.7375	NFM	Nationwide	Vodafone Channel 1598
		NFM	Central Scotland	
923.7875	878.7875	NFM	Nationwide	Vodafone Channel 1600
		NFM	Newcastle	
923.8125	878.8125	NFM	Nationwide	Vodafone Channel 1601
		NFM	Edinburgh	
923.8375	878.8375	NFM	Nationwide	Vodafone Channel 1602
		NFM	Durham	
923.8625	878.8625	NFM	Nationwide	Vodafone Channel 1603
		NFM	Central Scotland	
923.8875	878.8875	NFM	Nationwide	Vodafone Channel 1604
		NFM	North Yorkshire	
923.9125	878.9125	NFM	Nationwide	Vodafone Channel 1605
		NFM	Edinburgh	
		NFM	Central Scotland	
923.9875	878.9875	NFM	Nationwide	Vodafone Channel 1608
		NFM	Edinburgh	
		NFM	North Yorkshire	
924.0375	879.0375	NFM	Nationwide	Vodafone Channel 1610
		NFM	Durham	
		NFM	North Yorkshire	
924.0875	879.0875	NFM	Nationwide	Vodatone Channel 1612
		NFM	Durham	
924.1375	879.1375	NFM	Nationwide	Vodafone Channel 1614
		NFM	Edinburgh	
924.1625	879.1625	NFM	Nationwide	Vodafone Channel 1615
		NFM	Chathill	
924.2125	879.2125	NFM	Nationwide	Vodafone Channel 1617
		NFM	Ferrybridge	
		NFM	Perth	
		NFM	North Yorkshire	
924.2625	879.2625	NFM	Nationwide	Vodafone Channel 1619
		NFM	Central Scotland	
924.3125	879.3125	NFM	Nationwide	Vodafone Channel 1621
		NFM	Newcastle	
924.3375	879.3375	NFM	Nationwide	Vodafone Channel 1622
		NFM	Edinburgh	
924.3625	879.3625	NFM	Nationwide	Vodafone Channel 1623
		NFM	Durham	
924.3875	879.3875	NFM	Nationwide	Vodafone Channel 1624
		NFM	Central Scotland	
924.4125	879.4125	NFM	Nationwide	Vodafone Channel 1625
		NFM	North Yorkshire	
924.4375	879.4375	NFM	Nationwide	Vodafone Channel 1626
		NFM	Edinburgh	
		NFM	Central Scotland	
924.5125	879.5125	NFM	Nationwide	Vodafone Channel 1629
		NFM	Edinburgh	

Base	Mobile	Mode	Location	User and Notes
		NFM	North Yorkshire	
924.5625	879.5625	NFM	Nationwide	Vodafone Channel 1631
		NFM	Durham	
		NFM	North Yorkshire	
924.6125	879.6125	NFM	Nationwide	Vodafone Channel 1633
		NFM	Durham	
924.6625	879.6625	NFM	Nationwide	Vodafone Channel 1635
		NFM	Edinburgh	
924.6875	879.6875	NFM	Nationwide	Vodafone Channel 1636
		NFM	Chathill	
924.7375	879.7375	NFM	Nationwide	Vodafone Channel 1638
		NFM	Ferrybridge	
		NFM	Perth	
		NFM	North Yorkshire	
924.7875	879.7875	NFM	Nationwide	Vodafone Channel 1640
		NFM	Central Scotland	
924.8375	879.8375	NFM	Nationwide	Vodafone Channel 1642
		NFM	Newcastle	
924.8625	879.8625	NFM	Nationwide	Vodafone Channel 1643
		NFM	Edinburgh	
924.8875	879.8875	NFM	Nationwide	Vodafone Channel 1644
		NFM	Durham	
924.9125	879.9125	NFM	Nationwide	Vodafone Channel 1645
		NFM	Central Scotland	
924.9375	879.9375	NFM	Nationwide	Vodafone Channel 1646
		NFM	North Yorkshire	
924.9625	879.9625	NFM	Nationwide	Vodafone Channel 1647
		NFM	Central Scotland	
928.3875	883.3875	NFM	Nationwide	Cellnet Channel 1784
		NFM	Newmarket	

933.0000 MHz   RADIO LOCATION DEVICES

933.0125 - 934.9875 MHz   PROPOSED LOWER POWER BUSINESS "SHORT RANGE RADIO" NETWORK

934.0125 - 934.9875 MHz   UHF CB BAND

Base	Mobile	Mode	Location	User and Notes
934.0125	934.0125	NFM	Nationwide	Channel 1
934.0625	934.0625	NFM	Nationwide	Channel 2
934.1125	934.1125	NFM	Nationwide	Channel 3
934.1625	934.1625	NFM	Nationwide	Channel 4
934.2125	934.2125	NFM	Nationwide	Channel 5
934.2625	934.2625	NFM	Nationwide	Channel 6
934.3125	934.3125	NFM	Nationwide	Channel 7
934.3625	934.3625	NFM	Nationwide	Channel 8
934.4125	934.4125	NFM	Nationwide	Channel 9
934.4625	934.4625	NFM	Nationwide	Channel 10
934.5125	934.5125	NFM	Nationwide	Channel 11

Base	Mobile	Mode	Location	User and Notes
934.5625	934.5625	NFM	Nationwide	Channel 12
934.6125	934.6125	NFM	Nationwide	Channel 13
934.6625	934.6625	NFM	Nationwide	Channel 14
934.7125	934.7125	NFM	Nationwide	Channel 15
934.7625	934.7625	NFM	Nationwide	Channel 16
934.8125	934.8125	NFM	Nationwide	Channel 17
934.8625	934.8625	NFM	Nationwide	Channel 18
934.9125	934.9125	NFM	Nationwide	Channel 19
934.9625	934.9625	NFM	Nationwide	Channel 20
935.0000 - 950.0000 MHz				**UHF CELLULAR RADIO TELEPHONES (CELLNET & VODAFONE) REPEATER SITES**
935.0625	890.0625	NFM	Nationwide	Vodafone Channel 3
		NFM	Edinburgh	
935.1375	890.1375	NFM	Nationwide	Vodafone Channel 6
		NFM	Galway	Eirean Telecom
935.1875	890.1875	NFM	Nationwide	Vodafone Channel 8
		NFM	Galway	Eirean Telecom
		NFM	West Perthshire	
935.2125	890.2125	NFM	Nationwide	Vodafone Channel 9
		NFM	Lauder	
		NFM	Newmarket	
935.2375	890.2375	NFM	Nationwide	Vodafone Channel 10
		NFM	Ballinrobe	Eirean Telecom
		NFM	Perth	Vodafone
935.2625	890.2625	NFM	Nationwide	Vodafone Channel 11
		NFM	Galway	Eirean Telecom
935.2875	890.2875	NFM	Nationwide	Vodafone Channel 12
		NFM	West Perthshire	
935.3125	890.3125	NFM	Nationwide	Vodafone Channel 13
		NFM	Galway	Eirean Telecom
935.3375	890.3375	NFM	Nationwide	Vodafone Channel 14
		NFM	West Perthshire	
935.3625	890.3625	NFM	Nationwide	Vodafone Channel 15
		NFM	Edinburgh	Vodafone
935.3875	890.3875	NFM	Nationwide	Vodafone Channel 16
935.4125	890.4125	NFM	Nationwide	Vodafone Channel 17
		NFM	Lauder	
935.4375	890.4375	NFM	Nationwide	Vodafone Channel 18
		NFM	Castlebar	Eirean Telecom
935.4625	890.4625	NFM	Nationwide	Vodafone Channel 19
		NFM	Edinburgh	Vodafone
935.5625	890.5625	NFM	Nationwide	Vodafone Channel 23
		NFM	Nationwide	Vodafone Data Control
		NFM	Bath	Vodafone
		NFM	West Perthshire	
935.5875	890.5875	NFM	Nationwide	Vodafone Channel 24
		NFM	Nationwide	Vodafone Data Control

Base	Mobile	Mode	Location	User and Notes
		NFM	North Yorkshire	Vodafone
		NFM	Durham	
935.6125	890.6125	NFM	Nationwide	Vodafone Channel 25
		NFM	Nationwide	Vodafone Data Control
		NFM	Belfast	
935.6375	890.6375	NFM	Nationwide	Vodafone Channel 26
		NFM	Nationwide	Vodafone Data Control
		NFM	Bath	
		NFM	Larne	
		NFM	Durham	
935.6625	890.6625	NFM	Nationwide	Vodafone Channel 27
		NFM	Nationwide	Vodafone Data Control
		NFM	Galway	Eirean Telecom
935.6875	890.6875	NFM	Nationwide	Vodafone Channel 28
		NFM	Nationwide	Vodafone Data Control
		NFM	Edinburgh	
935.7125	890.7125	NFM	Nationwide	Vodafone Channel 29
		NFM	Nationwide	Vodafone Data Control
		NFM	Chathill	
		NFM	West Perthshire	
935.7375	890.7375	NFM	Nationwide	Vodafone Channel 30
		NFM	Nationwide	Vodafone Data Control
		NFM	Lauder	
		NFM	Newmarket	
935.7625	890.7625	NFM	Nationwide	Vodafone Channel 31
		NFM	Perth	Vodafone Data Control
		NFM	North Yorkshire	
935.7875	890.7875	NFM	Nationwide	Vodafone Channel 32
		NFM	Nationwide	Vodafone Data Control
		NFM	Belfast	
935.8125	890.8125	NFM	Nationwide	Vodafone Channel 33
		NFM	Nationwide	Vodafone Data Control
		NFM	Central Scotland	
		NFM	Galway	Eirean Telecom
		NFM	Lauder	
935.8375	890.8375	NFM	Nationwide	Vodafone Channel 34
		NFM	Nationwide	Vodafone Data Control
		NFM	Dundee	
		NFM	West Perthshire	
935.8625	890.8625	NFM	Nationwide	Vodafone Channel 35
		NFM	Nationwide	Vodafone Data Control
		NFM	Ferrybridge	
		NFM	Newcastle	
935.8875	890.8875	NFM	Nationwide	Vodafone Channel 36
		NFM	Nationwide	Vodafone Data Control
		NFM	Edinburgh	
		NFM	Enniskillen	
		NFM	Ferrybridge	

Base	Mobile	Mode	Location	User and Notes
		NFM	West Perthshire	
935.9125	890.9125	NFM	Nationwide	Vodafone Channel 37
		NFM	Nationwide	Vodafone Data Control
		NFM	Edinburgh	
		NFM	Durham	
		NFM	Bath	
935.9375	890.9375	NFM	Nationwide	Vodafone Channel 38
		NFM	Nationwide	Vodafone Data Control
		NFM	Central Scotland	
		NFM	Chesterfield	
		NFM	Lauder	
935.9625	890.9625	NFM	Nationwide	Vodafone Channel 39
		NFM	Nationwide	Vodafone Data Control
		NFM	Castlebar	Eirean Telecom
		NFM	Edinburgh	
		NFM	North Yorkshire	
935.9875	890.9875	NFM	Nationwide	Vodafone Channel 40
		NFM	Nationwide	Vodafone Data Control
		NFM	Central Scotland	
		NFM	Chesterfield	
		NFM	Cumbria	
		NFM	Lancashire	
936.0125	891.0125	NFM	Nationwide	Vodafone Channel 41
		NFM	Nationwide	Vodafone Data Control
		NFM	Galway	Eirean Telecom
936.0375	891.0375	NFM	Nationwide	Vodafone Channel 42
		NFM	Nationwide	Vodafone Data Control
936.0625	891.0625	NFM	Nationwide	Vodafone Channel 43
		NFM	Chesterfield	
		NFM	Edinburgh	Vodafone Data Control
		NFM	North Yorkshire	
936.1125	891.1125	NFM	Nationwide	Vodafone Channel 45
		NFM	Edinburgh	
936.1875	891.1875	NFM	Nationwide	Vodafone Channel 48
		NFM	Tayside	
		NFM	Galway	Eirean Telecom
936.2125	891.2125	NFM	Nationwide	Vodafone Channel 49
		NFM	Edinburgh	
936.2375	891.2375	NFM	Nationwide	Vodafone Channel 50
		NFM	Galway	Eirean Telecom
936.2625	891.2625	NFM	Nationwide	Vodafone Channel 51
		NFM	Newmarket	
936.2875	891.2875	NFM	Nationwide	Vodafone Channel 52
		NFM	Ballinrobe	Eirean Telecom
		NFM	Ferrybridge	
936.3125	891.3125	NFM	Nationwide	Vodafone Channel 53
		NFM	Galway	Eirean Telecom
936.3375	891.3375	NFM	Nationwide	Vodafone Channel 54

Base	Mobile	Mode	Location	User and Notes
936.3625	891.3625	NFM	Nationwide	Vodafone Channel 55
		NFM	Galway	Eirean Telecom
936.3875	891.3875	NFM	Nationwide	Vodafone Channel 56
		NFM	Bath	
		NFM	West Perthshire	
936.4125	891.4125	NFM	Nationwide	Vodafone Channel 57
		NFM	Edinburgh	
936.5125	891.5125	NFM	Nationwide	Vodafone Channel 61
		NFM	Edinburgh	
936.6375	891.6375	NFM	Nationwide	Vodafone Channel 66
		NFM	Edinburgh	
936.6875	891.6875	NFM	Nationwide	Vodafone Channel 68
		NFM	Bath	
936.7375	891.7375	NFM	Nationwide	Vodafone Channel 70
		NFM	Edinburgh	
		NFM	Ferrybridge	
936.7625	891.7625	NFM	Nationwide	Vodafone Channel 71
		NFM	West Perthshire	
936.8125	891.8125	NFM	Nationwide	Vodafone Channel 73
		NFM	Ferrybridge	
		NFM	Perth	
936.8375	891.8375	NFM	Nationwide	Vodafone Channel 74
		NFM	Galway	Eirean Telecom
936.8875	891.8875	NFM	Nationwide	Vodafone Channel 76
		NFM	Galway	Eirean Telecom
936.9375	891.9375	NFM	Nationwide	Vodafone Channel 78
		NFM	Edinburgh	
937.0375	892.0375	NFM	Nationwide	Vodafone Channel 82
		NFM	Edinburgh	
937.0625	892.0625	NFM	Nationwide	Vodafone Channel 83
		NFM	Galway	Eirean Telecom
937.1625	892.1625	NFM	Nationwide	Vodafone Channel 87
		NFM	Edinburgh	
937.2625	892.2625	NFM	Nationwide	Vodafone Channel 91
		NFM	Edinburgh	
937.2875	892.2875	NFM	Nationwide	Vodafone Channel 92
		NFM	West Perthshire	
937.3125	892.3125	NFM	Nationwide	Vodafone Channel 93
		NFM	Lauder	
937.3375	892.3375	NFM	Nationwide	Vodafone Channel 94
		NFM	Ferrybridge	
		NFM	Perth	
937.4125	892.4125	NFM	Nationwide	Vodafone Channel 97
		NFM	Galway	Eirean Telecom
937.4375	892.4375	NFM	Nationwide	Vodafone Channel 98
		NFM	West Perthshire	
937.4625	892.4625	NFM	Nationwide	Vodafone Channel 99
		NFM	Edinburgh	

Base	Mobile	Mode	Location	User and Notes
937.5125	892.5125	NFM	Nationwide	Vodafone Channel 101
		NFM	West Perthshire	
937.5625	892.5625	NFM	Nationwide	Vodafone Channel 103
		NFM	Edinburgh	
937.5875	892.5875	NFM	Nationwide	Vodafone Channel 104
		NFM	West Perthshire	
937.6625	892.6625	NFM	Nationwide	Vodafone Channel 107
		NFM	West Perthshire	
937.7875	892.7875	NFM	Nationwide	Vodafone Channel 112
		NFM	Ferrybridge	
937.8625	892.8625	NFM	Nationwide	Vodafone Channel 115
		NFM	Ballinrobe	Eirean Telecom
		NFM	Ferrybridge	
		NFM	Perth	
937.8875	892.8875	NFM	Nationwide	Vodafone Channel 116
		NFM	Galway	Eirean Telecom
937.9375	892.9375	NFM	Nationwide	Vodafone Channel 118
		NFM	Galway	Eirean Telecom
937.9875	892.9875	NFM	Nationwide	Vodafone Channel 120
		NFM	Edinburgh	
938.0125	893.0125	NFM	Nationwide	Vodafone Channel 121
		NFM	West Perthshire	
938.0375	893.0375	NFM	Nationwide	Vodafone Channel 122
		NFM	Ferrybridge	
938.0875	893.0875	NFM	Nationwide	Vodafone Channel 124
		NFM	Edinburgh	
938.1125	893.1125	NFM	Nationwide	Vodafone Channel 125
		NFM	Galway	Eirean Telecom
938.1375	893.1375	NFM	Nationwide	Vodafone Channel 126
938.1625	893.1625	NFM	Nationwide	Vodafone Channel 127
938.1875	893.1875	NFM	Nationwide	Vodafone Channel 128
		NFM	West Perthshire	
938.2125	893.2125	NFM	Nationwide	Vodafone Channel 129
		NFM	Edinburgh	
938.3125	893.3125	NFM	Nationwide	Vodafone Channel 133
		NFM	Edinburgh	
938.3875	893.3875	NFM	Nationwide	Vodafone Channel 136
		NFM	Ballinrobe	Eirean Telecom
		NFM	Ferrybridge	
938.4125	893.4125	NFM	Nationwide	Vodafone Channel 137
		NFM	Galway	Eirean Telecom
938.4625	893.4625	NFM	Nationwide	Vodafone Channel 139
		NFM	Dundee	
938.5125	893.5125	NFM	Nationwide	Vodafone Channel 141
		NFM	Edinburgh	
938.5375	893.5375	NFM	Nationwide	Vodafone Channel 142
		NFM	West Perthshire	
938.5625	893.5625	NFM	Nationwide	Vodafone Channel 143

Base	Mobile	Mode	Location	User and Notes
938.5875	893.5875	NFM	Nationwide	Vodafone Channel 144
		NFM	Castlebar	Eirean Telecom
938.6125	893.6125	NFM	Nationwide	Vodafone Channel 145
		NFM	Edinburgh	
938.6375	893.6375	NFM	Nationwide	Vodafone Channel 146
		NFM	Galway	Eirean Telecom
		NFM	West Perthshire	
938.6625	893.6625	NFM	Nationwide	Vodafone Channel 147
		NFM	Castlebar	Eirean Telecom
		NFM	West Perthshire	
938.7375	893.7375	NFM	Nationwide	Vodafone Channel 150
		NFM	Edinburgh	
938.7875	893.7875	NFM	Nationwide	Vodafone Channel 152
		NFM	Perth	
938.8375	893.8375	NFM	Nationwide	Vodafone Channel 154
		NFM	Edinburgh	
938.8625	893.8625	NFM	Nationwide	Vodafone Channel 155
938.8875	893.8875	NFM	Nationwide	Vodafone Channel 156
938.9125	893.9125	NFM	Nationwide	Vodafone Channel 157
		NFM	Ballinrobe	Eirean Telecom
		NFM	Perth	
		NFM	Ferrybridge	
938.9375	893.9375	NFM	Nationwide	Vodafone Channel 158
		NFM	Galway	Eirean Telecom
938.9875	893.9875	NFM	Nationwide	Vodafone Channel 160
		NFM	Galway	Eirean Telecom
939.0375	894.0375	NFM	Nationwide	Vodafone Channel 162
		NFM	Edinburgh	
939.1375	894.1375	NFM	Nationwide	Vodafone Channel 166
		NFM	Edinburgh	
939.1625	894.1625	NFM	Nationwide	Vodafone Channel 167
		NFM	Galway	Eirean Telecom
939.2625	894.2625	NFM	Nationwide	Vodafone Channel 171
		NFM	Edinburgh	
939.3125	894.3125	NFM	Nationwide	Vodafone Channel 173
		NFM	Larne	
939.3375	894.3375	NFM	Nationwide	Vodafone Channel 174
		NFM	Galway	Eirean Telecom
939.3625	894.3625	NFM	Nationwide	Vodafone Channel 175
		NFM	Edinburgh	
939.3875	894.3875	NFM	Nationwide	Vodafone Channel 176
		NFM	Galway	Eirean Telecom
939.4375	894.4375	NFM	Nationwide	Vodafone Channel 178
		NFM	Ballinrobe	Eirean Telecom
		NFM	Ferrybridge	
939.4625	894.4625	NFM	Nationwide	Vodafone Channel 179
		NFM	Galway	Eirean Telecom
939.4875	894.4875	NFM	Nationwide	Vodafone Channel 180

Base	Mobile	Mode	Location	User and Notes
939.6875	894.6875	NFM	Nationwide	Cellnet Channel 188
		NFM	Galway	Eirean Telecom
939.7625	894.7625	NFM	Nationwide	Cellnet Channel 191
		NFM	Perth	
939.8125	894.8125	NFM	Nationwide	Cellnet Channel 193
		NFM	Ferrybridge	
		NFM	Newmarket	
		NFM	West Perthshire	
939.8625	894.8625	NFM	Nationwide	Cellnet Channel 195
		NFM	Edinburgh	
		NFM	Perth	
939.8875	894.8875	NFM	Nationwide	Cellnet Channel 196
		NFM	Lauder	
939.9125	894.9125	NFM	Nationwide	Cellnet Channel 197
		NFM	Galway	Eirean Telecom
939.9625	894.9625	NFM	Nationwide	Cellnet Channel 199
		NFM	Ballinrobe	Eirean Telecom
939.9875	894.9875	NFM	Nationwide	Cellnet Channel 200
		NFM	Galway	Eirean Telecom
940.0125	895.0125	NFM	Nationwide	Cellnet Channel 201
		NFM	Edinburgh	
940.0375	895.0375	NFM	Nationwide	Cellnet Channel 202
		NFM	Galway	Eirean Telecom
		NFM	Lauder	
		NFM	West Perthshire	
940.2125	895.2125	NFM	Nationwide	Cellnet Channel 209
		NFM	Galway	Eirean Telecom
940.2375	895.2375	NFM	Nationwide	Cellnet Channel 210
		NFM	Dundee	
940.3625	895.3625	NFM	Nationwide	Cellnet Channel 215
		NFM	Perth	
940.3875	895.3875	NFM	Nationwide	Cellnet Channel 216
		NFM	Galway	Eirean Telecom
940.4125	895.4125	NFM	Nationwide	Cellnet Channel 217
		NFM	Dundee	
		NFM	Newmarket	
940.4375	895.4375	NFM	Nationwide	Cellnet Channel 218
		NFM	Galway	Eirean Telecom
940.4625	895.4625	NFM	Nationwide	Cellnet Channel 219
		NFM	Perth	
940.4875	895.4875	NFM	Nationwide	(Not Used) Channel 220
		NFM	Ballinrobe	Eirean Telecom
940.5375	895.5375	NFM	Nationwide	Vodafone Channel 222
		NFM	Lauder	
940.5625	895.5625	NFM	Nationwide	Vodafone Channel 223
		NFM	Galway	Eirean Telecom
940.6125	895.6125	NFM	Nationwide	Vodafone Channel 225
		NFM	West Perthshire	Vodafone

Base	Mobile	Mode	Location	User and Notes
940.6375	895.6375	NFM	Nationwide	Vodafone Channel 226
		NFM	Dundee	
940.6875	895.6875	NFM	Nationwide	Vodafone Channel 228
		NFM	Castlebar	Eirean Telecom
940.7125	895.7125	NFM	Nationwide	Vodafone Channel 229
		NFM	Edinburgh	
940.7375	895.7375	NFM	Nationwide	Vodafone Channel 230
		NFM	Galway	Eirean Telecom
		NFM	West Perthshire	
940.8375	895.8375	NFM	Nationwide	Vodafone Channel 234
		NFM	Edinburgh	
940.9375	895.9375	NFM	Nationwide	Vodafone Channel 238
		NFM	Edinburgh	
941.0125	896.0125	NFM	Nationwide	Vodafone Channel 241
		NFM	Galway	Eirean Telecom
941.0375	896.0375	NFM	Nationwide	Vodafone Channel 242
		NFM	Galway	Eirean Telecom
941.0625	896.0625	NFM	Nationwide	Vodafone Channel 243
		NFM	Edinburgh	
		NFM	Perth	
941.0875	896.0875	NFM	Nationwide	Vodafone Channel 244
		NFM	Galway	Eirean Telecom
941.1375	896.1375	NFM	Nationwide	Vodafone Channel 246
		NFM	Newmarket	
941.2125	896.2125	NFM	Nationwide	Vodafone Channel 249
		NFM	Ballinrobe	Eirean Telecom
941.2375	896.2375	NFM	Nationwide	Vodafone Channel 250
		NFM	Edinburgh	
941.2625	896.2625	NFM	Nationwide	Vodafone Channel 251
		NFM	Galway	Eirean Telecom
941.3125	896.3125	NFM	Nationwide	Vodafone Channel 253
		NFM	Galway	Eirean Telecom
941.5125	896.5125	NFM	Nationwide	Vodafone Channel 261
		NFM	West Perthshire	
941.5375	896.5375	NFM	Nationwide	Vodafone Channel 262
		NFM	Ferrybridge	
941.5625	896.5625	NFM	Nationwide	Vodafone Channel 263
		NFM	Galway	Eirean Telecom
		NFM	Perth	
941.6125	896.6125	NFM	Nationwide	Vodafone Channel 265
		NFM	Newmarket	
		NFM	West Perthshire	Vodafone
941.6625	896.6625	NFM	Nationwide	Vodafone Channel 267
		NFM	Edinburgh	
		NFM	Perth	
941.7875	896.7875	NFM	Nationwide	Vodafone Channel 272
		NFM	Galway	Eirean Telecom
941.8375	896.8375	NFM	Nationwide	Vodafone Channel 274

Base	Mobile	Mode	Location	User and Notes
		NFM	Dundee	
		NFM	Edinburgh	
941.8875	896.8875	NFM	Nationwide	Vodafone Channel 276
		NFM	Ferrybridge	
941.9625	896.9625	NFM	Nationwide	Vodafone Channel 279
		NFM	Galway	Eirean Telecom
942.0375	897.0375	NFM	Nationwide	Vodafone Channel 282
		NFM	Dundee	
942.0875	897.0875	NFM	Nationwide	Vodafone Channel 284
		NFM	Galway	Eirean Telecom
942.1625	897.1625	NFM	Nationwide	Vodafone Channel 287
		NFM	Perth	
942.2125	897.2125	NFM	Nationwide	Vodafone Channel 289
		NFM	Ferrybridge	
942.2625	897.2625	NFM	Nationwide	Vodafone Channel 291
		NFM	Edinburgh	
		NFM	Perth	
942.3625	897.3625	NFM	Nationwide	Vodafone Channel 295
		NFM	Larne	
942.4375	897.4375	NFM	Nationwide	Vodafone Channel 298
		NFM	Dundee	
		NFM	Edinburgh	
942.4875	897.4875	NFM	Nationwide	Vodafone Channel 300
		NFM	Galway	Eirean Telecom
942.5375	897.5375	NFM	Nationwide	Cellnet Channel 302
		NFM	Galway	Eirean Telecom
942.5625	897.5625	NFM	Nationwide	Cellnet Channel 303
		NFM	Perth	
942.6125	897.6125	NFM	Nationwide	Cellnet Channel 305
		NFM	Galway	Eirean Telecom
942.7625	897.7625	NFM	Nationwide	Cellnet Channel 311
		NFM	Perth	
942.8125	897.8125	NFM	Nationwide	Cellnet Channel 313
		NFM	West Perthshire	
942.8375	897.8375	NFM	Nationwide	Cellnet Channel 314
		NFM	Galway	Eirean Telecom
942.8625	897.8625	NFM	Nationwide	Cellnet Channel 315
		NFM	Edinburgh	
942.9625	897.9625	NFM	Nationwide	Cellnet Channel 319
		NFM	Perth	
943.0625	898.0625	NFM	Nationwide	Cellnet Channel 323
		NFM	Newcastle	
		NFM	Edinburgh	Cellnet Data Control
943.0875	898.0875	NFM	Nationwide	Cellnet Channel 324
		NFM	Five Oaks, Jersey	Cellnet Data Control
943.1125	898.1125	NFM	Nationwide	Cellnet Channel 325
		NFM	Nationwide	Cellnet Data Control
		NFM	Durham	

Base	Mobile	Mode	Location	User and Notes
943.1375	898.1375	NFM	Nationwide	Cellnet Channel 326
		NFM	Guernsey	Cellnet Data Control
		NFM	Guernsey (Bailiwick)	
		NFM	Newcastle	
		NFM	Cumbria	
		NFM	Galway	Eirean Telecom
		NFM	Lancashire	
943.1625	898.1625	NFM	Nationwide	Cellnet Channel 327
		NFM	Nationwide	Cellnet Data Control
943.1875	898.1875	NFM	Nationwide	Cellnet Channel 328
		NFM	Ferrybridge	
		NFM	Galway	Eirean Telecom
943.2125	898.2125	NFM	Nationwide	Cellnet Channel 329
		NFM	Nationwide	Cellnet Data Control
		NFM	Lauder	
		NFM	Woodseats	
		NFM	La Chasse, St. Ouen, Jersey	
943.2375	898.2375	NFM	Nationwide	Cellnet Channel 330
		NFM	Nationwide	Cellnet Data Control
		NFM	Guernsey (Bailiwick)	
943.2625	898.2625	NFM	Nationwide	Cellnet Channel 331
		NFM	Nationwide	Cellnet Data Control
		NFM	Gorey	
943.2875	898.2875	NFM	Nationwide	Cellnet Channel 332
		NFM	Guernsey	Cellnet Data Control
		NFM	Guernsey (Bailiwick)	
		NFM	Newmarket	
		NFM	Durham	
943.3125	898.3125	NFM	Nationwide	Cellnet Channel 333
		NFM	Nationwide	Cellnet Data Control
		NFM	Dundee	
943.3375	898.3375	NFM	Nationwide	Cellnet Channel 334
		NFM	Chesterfield	
		NFM	Edinburgh	
		NFM	Lauder	
		NFM	Alderney	
943.3625	898.3625	NFM	Nationwide	Cellnet Channel 335
		NFM	Perth	
943.3875	898.3875	NFM	Nationwide	Cellnet Channel 336
		NFM	Fort Road, Guernsey	
		NFM	Edinburgh	
		NFM	Stranraer	
943.4125	898.4125	NFM	Nationwide	Cellnet Channel 337
		NFM	Nationwide	Cellnet Data Control
		NFM	Central Scotland	
943.4375	898.4375	NFM	Nationwide	Cellnet Channel 338
		NFM	Nationwide	Cellnet Data Control
		NFM	Chathill	

Base	Mobile	Mode	Location	User and Notes
943.4625	898.4625	NFM	Nationwide	Cellnet Channel 339
		NFM	Nationwide	Cellnet Data Control
		NFM	Fort Regent, Jersey	
943.4875	898.4875	NFM	Nationwide	Cellnet Channel 340
		NFM	Nationwide	Cellnet Data Control
		NFM	Chesterfield	
943.5125	898.5125	NFM	Nationwide	Cellnet Channel 341
		NFM	Nationwide	Cellnet Data Control
		NFM	Chesterfield	
		NFM	Les Touillets, Guernsey	
943.5375	898.5375	NFM	Nationwide	Cellnet Channel 342
		NFM	Nationwide	Cellnet Data Control
943.5625	898.5625	NFM	Nationwide	Cellnet Channel 343
		NFM	Nationwide	Cellnet Data Control
		NFM	Larne	
943.6375	898.6375	NFM	Nationwide	Cellnet Channel 346
		NFM	Edinburgh	
		NFM	Newmarket	
943.6875	898.6875	NFM	Nationwide	Cellnet Channel 348
		NFM	Galway	Eirean Telecom
943.7875	898.7875	NFM	Nationwide	Cellnet Channel 352
		NFM	Perth	
943.8000	898.8000	WFM	Red Houses, Jersey	GSM
943.8125	898.8125	NFM	Nationwide	Cellnet Channel 353
		NFM	Lauder	
943.9625	898.9625	NFM	Nationwide	Channel 359 Data Control
		NFM	Perth	
		NFM	Stranraer	
944.0125	899.0125	NFM	Nationwide	Cellnet Channel 361
		NFM	Dundee	
944.0625	899.0625	NFM	Nationwide	Cellnet Channel 363
		NFM	Perth	
944.1125	899.1125	NFM	Nationwide	Cellnet Channel 365
		NFM	Dundee	
944.1375	899.1375	NFM	Nationwide	Cellnet Channel 366
		NFM	Larne	
944.1875	899.1875	NFM	Nationwide	Cellnet Channel 368
		NFM	Enniskillen	
944.2375	899.2375	NFM	Nationwide	Cellnet Channel 370
		NFM	West Perthshire	
944.3875	899.3875	NFM	Nationwide	Cellnet Channel 376
		NFM	Galway	Eirean Telecom
		NFM	Perth	
944.4000	899.4000	WFM	St. John's Village, Jersey	GSM
944.4375	899.4375	NFM	Nationwide	Cellnet Channel 378
		NFM	Dundee	
		NFM	West Perthshire	
944.4625	899.4625	NFM	Nationwide	Cellnet Channel 379

Base	Mobile	Mode	Location	User and Notes
944.4875	899.4875	NFM	Nationwide	Cellnet Channel 380
		NFM	West Perthshire	
944.5125	899.5125	NFM	Nationwide	Cellnet Channel 381
		NFM	West Perthshire	
944.5625	899.5625	NFM	Nationwide	Cellnet Channel 383
		NFM	Perth	
944.6125	899.6125	NFM	Nationwide	Cellnet Channel 385
		NFM	West Perthshire	
944.6625	899.6625	NFM	Nationwide	Cellnet Channel 387
		NFM	Edinburgh	
		NFM	Perth	
944.8375	899.8375	NFM	Nationwide	Cellnet Channel 394
		NFM	Edinburgh	
944.9875	899.9875	NFM	Nationwide	Cellnet Channel 400
		NFM	Perth	
945.0375	900.0375	NFM	Nationwide	Cellnet Channel 402
		NFM	Dundee	
945.1125	900.1125	NFM	Nationwide	Cellnet Channel 405
		NFM	Dundee	
945.1625	900.1625	NFM	Nationwide	Cellnet Channel 407
		NFM	Perth	
945.2625	900.2625	NFM	Nationwide	Cellnet Channel 411
		NFM	Perth	
945.6375	900.6375	NFM	Nationwide	Cellnet Channel 426
		NFM	West Perthshire	
945.6875	900.6875	NFM	Nationwide	Cellnet Channel 428
		NFM	West Perthshire	
945.7625	900.7625	NFM	Nationwide	Cellnet Channel 431
		NFM	Perth	
945.8125	900.8125	NFM	Nationwide	Cellnet Channel 433
		NFM	West Perthshire	
945.8625	900.8625	NFM	Nationwide	Cellnet Channel 435
		NFM	Perth	
946.0125	901.0125	NFM	Nationwide	Cellnet Channel 441
		NFM	Edinburgh	
946.1125	901.1125	NFM	Nationwide	Cellnet Channel 445
		NFM	West Perthshire	
946.1875	901.1875	NFM	Nationwide	Cellnet Channel 448
		NFM	Perth	
946.2375	901.2375	NFM	Nationwide	Cellnet Channel 450
		NFM	Dundee	
		NFM	West Perthshire	
946.2625	901.2625	NFM	Nationwide	Cellnet Channel 451
		NFM	West Perthshire	
946.2875	901.2875	NFM	Nationwide	Cellnet Channel 452
		NFM	West Perthshire	
946.3625	901.3625	NFM	Nationwide	Cellnet Channel 455
		NFM	Ferrybridge	

Base	Mobile	Mode	Location	User and Notes
		NFM	Perth	
946.4625	901.4625	NFM	Nationwide	Cellnet Channel 459
		NFM	Perth	
946.5125	901.5125	NFM	Nationwide	Vodafone Channel 461
		NFM	Edinburgh	
946.6000	901.6000	WFM	La Chasse, Jersey	GSM
946.6125	901.6125	NFM	Nationwide	Vodafone Channel 465
		NFM	West Perthshire	
946.7375	901.7375	NFM	Nationwide	Vodafone Channel 470
		NFM	Edinburgh	
946.8000	901.8000	WFM	St Helier, Jersey	GSM
946.8375	901.8375	NFM	Nationwide	Vodafone Channel 474
		NFM	Edinburgh	
946.8875	901.8875	NFM	Nationwide	Vodafone Channel 476
		NFM	Newmarket	
946.9125	901.9125	NFM	Nationwide	Vodafone Channel 477
		NFM	Perth	
947.0375	902.0375	NFM	Nationwide	Vodafone Channel 482
		NFM	Edinburgh	
947.1625	902.1625	NFM	Nationwide	Vodafone Channel 487
		NFM	West Perthshire	Vodafone
947.2625	902.2625	NFM	Nationwide	Vodafone Channel 491
		NFM	Edinburgh	
947.3625	902.3625	NFM	Nationwide	Vodafone Channel 495
		NFM	Edinburgh	
947.4125	902.4125	NFM	Nationwide	Vodafone Channel 497
		NFM	Lauder	
947.5875	902.5875	NFM	Nationwide	Vodafone Channel 504
		NFM	West Perthshire	Vodafone
947.6625	902.6625	NFM	Nationwide	Vodafone Channel 507
		NFM	Edinburgh	
947.8875	902.8875	NFM	Nationwide	Vodafone Channel 516
		NFM	Edinburgh	
947.9375	902.9375	NFM	Nationwide	Vodafone Channel 518
		NFM	Lauder	
		NFM	Newmarket	
947.9625	902.9625	NFM	Nationwide	Vodafone Channel 519
		NFM	Perth	
948.1875	903.1875	NFM	Nationwide	Vodafone Channel 528
		NFM	Edinburgh	
948.4125	903.4125	NFM	Nationwide	Vodafone Channel 537
		NFM	Edinburgh	
948.4625	903.4625	NFM	Nationwide	Vodafone Channel 539
		NFM	Perth	
948.4875	903.4875	NFM	Nationwide	Vodafone Channel 540
		NFM	Perth	
948.9375	903.9375	NFM	Nationwide	Vodafone Channel 558
		NFM	Edinburgh	

Base	Mobile	Mode	Location	User and Notes
948.9625	903.9625	NFM	Nationwide	Vodafone Channel 559
		NFM	West Perthshire	
949.0375	904.0375	NFM	Nationwide	Cellnet Channel 562
		NFM	Lauder	
		NFM	West Perthshire	
949.2375	904.2375	NFM	Nationwide	Cellnet Channel 570
		NFM	Dundee	
949.4125	904.4125	NFM	Nationwide	Cellnet Channel 577
		NFM	West Perthshire	
949.4875	904.4875	NFM	Nationwide	Cellnet Channel 580
		NFM	Tayside	
949.7125	904.7125	NFM	Nationwide	Cellnet Channel 589
		NFM	Edinburgh	
949.9125	904.9125	NFM	Nationwide	Cellnet Channel 597
		NFM	Dundee	

950.0000 - 960.0000 MHz			PAN EUROPEAN DIGITAL CELLULAR SERVICE	
950.0000	905.0000	WFM	Steam Museum, Jersey	GSM
950.8000	905.8000	WFM	St Helier, Jersey	GSM
		WFM	Gorey, Jersey	GSM
951.2000	906.2000	WFM	Rozel Hill, Jersey	GSM
		WFM	Five Oaks, Jersey	GSM
951.6000	906.6000	WFM	Five Oaks, Jersey	GSM
952.0000	907.0000	WFM	Queen's Valley, Jersey	GSM
952.6000	907.6000	WFM	St Helier, Jersey	GSM
952.8000	907.8000	WFM	St Peter, Jersey	GSM
953.0000	908.0000	WFM	Les Platons, Jersey	GSM
953.4000	908.4000	WFM	First Tower, Jersey	GSM
		WFM	St Ouen's Bay, Jersey	GSM
953.8000	908.8000	WFM	Ouaisne, Jersey	GSM
954.8000	909.8000	WFM	St Helier, Jersey	GSM

959.0125 - 959.9875 MHz			NEW CYBERNET/UNIDEN CORDLESS TELEPHONE BASE	
959.0125	914.0125	NFM	Nationwide	Channel 1
959.0250	914.0250	NFM	Nationwide	Channel 2
959.0375	914.0375	NFM	Nationwide	Channel 3
959.0500	914.0500	NFM	Nationwide	Channel 4
959.0625	914.0625	NFM	Nationwide	Channel 5
959.0750	914.0750	NFM	Nationwide	Channel 6
959.0875	914.0875	NFM	Nationwide	Channel 7
959.1000	914.1000	NFM	Nationwide	Channel 8
959.1125	914.1125	NFM	Nationwide	Channel 9
959.1250	914.1250	NFM	Nationwide	Channel 10
959.1375	914.1375	NFM	Nationwide	Channel 11
959.1500	914.1500	NFM	Nationwide	Channel 12
959.1625	914.1625	NFM	Nationwide	Channel 13
959.1750	914.1750	NFM	Nationwide	Channel 14

Base	Mobile	Mode	Location	User and Notes
959.1875	914.1875	NFM	Nationwide	Channel 15
959.2000	914.2000	NFM	Nationwide	Channel 16
959.2125	914.2125	NFM	Nationwide	Channel 17
959.2250	914.2250	NFM	Nationwide	Channel 18
959.2375	914.2375	NFM	Nationwide	Channel 19
959.2500	914.2500	NFM	Nationwide	Channel 20
959.2625	914.2625	NFM	Nationwide	Channel 21
959.2750	914.2750	NFM	Nationwide	Channel 22
959.2875	914.2875	NFM	Nationwide	Channel 23
959.3000	914.3000	NFM	Nationwide	Channel 24
959.3125	914.3125	NFM	Nationwide	Channel 25
959.3250	914.3250	NFM	Nationwide	Channel 26
959.3375	914.3375	NFM	Nationwide	Channel 27
959.3500	914.3500	NFM	Nationwide	Channel 28
959.3625	914.3625	NFM	Nationwide	Channel 29
959.3750	914.3750	NFM	Nationwide	Channel 30
959.3875	914.3875	NFM	Nationwide	Channel 31
959.4000	914.4000	NFM	Nationwide	Channel 32
959.4125	914.4125	NFM	Nationwide	Channel 33
959.4250	914.4250	NFM	Nationwide	Channel 34
959.4375	914.4375	NFM	Nationwide	Channel 35
959.4500	914.4500	NFM	Nationwide	Channel 36
959.4625	914.4625	NFM	Nationwide	Channel 37
959.4750	914.4750	NFM	Nationwide	Channel 38
959.4875	914.4875	NFM	Nationwide	Channel 39
959.5000	914.5000	NFM	Nationwide	Channel 40
959.5125	914.5125	NFM	Nationwide	Channel 41
959.5250	914.5250	NFM	Nationwide	Channel 42
959.5375	914.5375	NFM	Nationwide	Channel 43
959.5500	914.5500	NFM	Nationwide	Channel 44
959.5625	914.5625	NFM	Nationwide	Channel 45
959.5750	914.5750	NFM	Nationwide	Channel 46
959.5875	914.5875	NFM	Nationwide	Channel 47
959.6000	914.6000	NFM	Nationwide	Channel 48
959.6125	914.6125	NFM	Nationwide	Channel 49
959.6250	914.6250	NFM	Nationwide	Channel 50
959.6375	914.6375	NFM	Nationwide	Channel 51
959.6500	914.6500	NFM	Nationwide	Channel 52
959.6625	914.6625	NFM	Nationwide	Channel 53
959.6750	914.6750	NFM	Nationwide	Channel 54
959.6875	914.6875	NFM	Nationwide	Channel 55
959.7000	914.7000	NFM	Nationwide	Channel 56
959.7125	914.7125	NFM	Nationwide	Channel 57
959.7250	914.7250	NFM	Nationwide	Channel 58
959.7375	914.7375	NFM	Nationwide	Channel 59
959.7500	914.7500	NFM	Nationwide	Channel 60
959.7625	914.7625	NFM	Nationwide	Channel 61
959.7750	914.7750	NFM	Nationwide	Channel 62

Base	Mobile	Mode	Location	User and Notes
959.7875	914.7875	NFM	Nationwide	Channel 63
959.8000	914.8000	NFM	Nationwide	Channel 64
959.8125	914.8125	NFM	Nationwide	Channel 65
959.8250	914.8250	NFM	Nationwide	Channel 66
959.8375	914.8375	NFM	Nationwide	Channel 67
959.8500	914.8500	NFM	Nationwide	Channel 68
959.8625	914.8625	NFM	Nationwide	Channel 69
959.8750	914.8750	NFM	Nationwide	Channel 70
959.8875	914.8875	NFM	Nationwide	Channel 71
959.9000	914.9000	NFM	Nationwide	Channel 72
959.9125	914.9125	NFM	Nationwide	Channel 73
959.9250	914.9250	NFM	Nationwide	Channel 74
959.9375	914.9375	NFM	Nationwide	Channel 75
959.9500	914.9500	NFM	Nationwide	Channel 76
959.9625	914.9625	NFM	Nationwide	Channel 77
959.9750	914.9750	NFM	Nationwide	Channel 78
959.9875	914.9875	NFM	Nationwide	Channel 79
960.0000 - 1215.0000 MHz			DME AERONAUTICAL RADIO NAVIGATION AND TRANSPONDER EQUIPMENT	
962.0000	1025.0000	AM	Nationwide	DME Channel 1X Not Used
963.0000	1026.0000	AM	Nationwide	DME Channel 2X Not Used
964.0000	1027.0000	AM	Nationwide	DME Channel 3X Not Used
965.0000	1028.0000	AM	Nationwide	DME Channel 4X Not Used
966.0000	1029.0000	AM	Nationwide	DME Channel 5X Not Used
967.0000	1030.0000	AM	Nationwide	DME Channel 6X Not Used
968.0000	1031.0000	AM	Nationwide	DME Channel 7X Not Used
969.0000	1032.0000	AM	Nationwide	DME Channel 8X Not Used
970.0000	1033.0000	AM	Nationwide	DME Channel 9X Not Used
971.0000	1034.0000	AM	Nationwide	DME Channel 10X Not Used
972.0000	1035.0000	AM	Nationwide	DME Channel 11X Not Used
973.0000	1036.0000	AM	Nationwide	DME Channel 12X Not Used
974.0000	1037.0000	AM	Nationwide	DME Channel 13X Not Used
975.0000	1038.0000	AM	Nationwide	DME Channel 14X Not Used
976.0000	1039.0000	AM	Nationwide	DME Channel 15X Not Used
977.0000	1040.0000	AM	Nationwide	DME Channel 16X Not Used
978.0000	1041.0000	AM	Nationwide	DME Ch 17X (108.00 MHz)
		AM	RAF Greenham Common	TACAN
979.0000	1042.0000	AM	Nationwide	DME Ch 18X (108.10 MHz)
		AM	Dundee Airport	DME
		AM	RAF Cottesmore	TACAN
980.0000	1043.0000	AM	Nationwide	DME Ch 19X (108.20 MHz)
		AM	Boscombe Down (MoD)	TACAN
981.0000	1044.0000	AM	Nationwide	DME Ch 20X (108.30 MHz)
982.0000	1045.0000	AM	Nationwide	DME Ch 21X (108.40 MHz)
		AM	RAF Valley	TACAN
983.0000	1046.0000	AM	Nationwide	DME Ch 22X (108.50 MHz)
		AM	Sumburgh Airport	DME

Base	Mobile	Mode	Location	User and Notes
		AM	Teesside Airport	DME
984.0000	1047.0000	AM	Nationwide	DME Ch 23X (108.60 MHz)
		AM	Kirkwall Airport	DME
985.0000	1048.0000	AM	Nationwide	DME Ch 24X (108.70 MHz)
		AM	Newton Point	TACAN
986.0000	1049.0000	AM	Nationwide	DME Ch 25X (108.80 MHz)
		AM	Weathersfield	TACAN
987.0000	1050.0000	AM	Nationwide	DME Ch 26X (108.90 MHz)
		AM	Edinburgh Airport	DME
		AM	Ventnor	TACAN
988.0000	1051.0000	AM	Nationwide	DME Ch 27X (109.00 MHz)
		AM	RAF Alconbury	TACAN
989.0000	1052.0000	AM	Nationwide	DME Ch 28X (109.10 MHz)
990.0000	1053.0000	AM	Nationwide	DME Ch 29X (109.20 MHz)
		AM	Inverness Airport	DME
990.0000	1053.0000	AM	Swansea Aerodrome	DME
991.0000	1054.0000	AM	Nationwide	DME Ch 30X (109.30 MHz)
		AM	RAF Wattisham	TACAN
992.0000	1055.0000	AM	Nationwide	DME Ch 31X (109.40 MHz)
		AM	Barrow Airport	DME
993.0000	1056.0000	AM	Nationwide	DME Ch 32X (109.50 MHz)
		AM	London Heathrow	DME
		AM	Manchester Airport	DME
		AM	Plymouth Airport	DME
994.0000	1057.0000	AM	Nationwide	DME Ch 33X (109.60 MHz)
		AM	RAF Linton-on-Ouse	TACAN
		AM	RAF Odiham	TACAN
995.0000	1058.0000	AM	Nationwide	DME Ch 34X (109.70 MHz)
996.0000	1059.0000	AM	Nationwide	DME Ch 35X (109.80 MHz)
		AM	RAF Kinloss	TACAN
997.0000	1060.0000	AM	Nationwide	DME Ch 36X (109.90 MHz)
		AM	Warton (MoD)	DME
998.0000	1061.0000	AM	Nationwide	DME Ch 37X (110.00 MHz)
999.0000	1062.0000	AM	Nationwide	DME Ch 38X (110.10 MHz)
		AM	Birmingham Airport	DME
1000.0000	1063.0000	AM	Nationwide	DME Ch 39X (110.20 MHz)
		AM	RAF Lakenheath	TACAN
1001.0000	1064.0000	AM	Nationwide	DME Ch 40X (110.30 MHz)
1002.0000	1065.0000	AM	Nationwide	DME Ch 41X (110.40 MHz)
		AM	Bournemouth Airport	DME
1003.0000	1066.0000	AM	Nationwide	DME Ch 42X (110.50 MHz)
		AM	RAF Leuchars	TACAN
		AM	Stansted Airport	DME
1004.0000	1067.0000	AM	Nationwide	DME Ch 43X (110.60 MHz)
		AM	Cardiff Airport	DME
		AM	Carlisle Airport	DME
		AM	London Heathrow	DME
1005.0000	1068.0000	AM	Nationwide	DME Ch 44X (110.70 MHz)

Base	Mobile	Mode	Location	User and Notes
1006.0000	1069.0000	AM	Nationwide	DME Ch 45X (110.80 MHz)
1007.0000	1070.0000	AM	Nationwide	DME Ch 46X (110.90 MHz)
		AM	Gatwick	DME
		AM	Jersey Airport	DME
		AM	Ronaldsway	DME
1008.0000	1071.0000	AM	Nationwide	DME Ch 47X (111.00 MHz)
		AM	RNAS Yeovilton	TACAN
1009.0000	1072.0000	AM	Nationwide	DME Ch 48X (111.10 MHz)
1010.0000	1073.0000	AM	Nationwide	DME Ch 49X (111.20 MHz)
1011.0000	1074.0000	AM	Nationwide	DME Ch 50X (111.30 MHz)
		AM	London Heathrow	DME
1012.0000	1075.0000	AM	Nationwide	DME Ch 51X (111.40 MHz)
		AM	RAF Binbrook	TACAN
		AM	RAF Coningsby	TACAN
1013.0000	1076.0000	AM	Nationwide	DME Ch 52X (111.50 MHz)
		AM	London Docklands	DME
		AM	Newcastle Airport	DME
		AM	RAF Fairford	TACAN
1014.0000	1077.0000	AM	Nationwide	DME Ch 53X (111.60 MHz)
		AM	RAF Chivenor	TACAN
1015.0000	1078.0000	AM	Nationwide	DME Ch 54X (111.70 MHz)
1016.0000	1079.0000	AM	Nationwide	DME Ch 55X (111.80 MHz)
1017.0000	1080.0000	AM	Nationwide	DME Ch 56X (111.90 MHz)
		AM	RAF Brize Norton	TACAN
1018.0000	1081.0000	AM	Nationwide	DME Ch 57X (112.00 MHz)
1019.0000	1082.0000	AM	Nationwide	DME Ch 58X (112.10 MHz)
		AM	Pole Hill	DME
1020.0000	1083.0000	AM	Nationwide	DME Ch 59X (112.20 MHz)
		AM	Ronaldsway	DME
1021.0000	1084.0000	AM	Nationwide	DME Ch 60X (112.30 MHz)
1022.0000	1085.0000	AM	Nationwide	DME Ch 61X Not Used
1023.0000	1086.0000	AM	Nationwide	DME Ch 62X Not Used
1024.0000	1087.0000	AM	Nationwide	DME Ch 63X Not Used
1025.0000	1088.0000	AM	Nationwide	DME Ch 64X Not Used
1026.0000	1089.0000	AM	Nationwide	DME Ch 65X Not Used
1027.0000	1090.0000	AM	Nationwide	DME Ch 66X Not Used
1028.0000	1091.0000	AM	Nationwide	DME Ch 67X Not Used
1029.0000	1092.0000	AM	Nationwide	DME Ch 68X Not Used
1030.0000	1090.0000	AM	Nationwide	Transponder Interrog./Reply
1030.0000	1093.0000	AM	Nationwide	DME Ch 69X Not Used
1031.0000	1094.0000	AM	Nationwide	DME Ch 70X (112.30 MHz)
1032.0000	1095.0000	AM	Nationwide	DME Ch 71X (112.40 MHz)
1033.0000	1096.0000	AM	Nationwide	DME Ch 72X (112.50 MHz)
		AM	St Abbs	DME
1034.0000	1097.0000	AM	Nationwide	DME Ch 73X (112.60 MHz)
		AM	RAF St Mawgan	TACAN
1035.0000	1098.0000	AM	Nationwide	DME Ch 74X (112.70 MHz)
		AM	Berry Head	DME

Base	Mobile	Mode	Location	User and Notes
		AM	Donegal Aerodrome	DME
1036.0000	1099.0000	AM	Nationwide	DME Ch 75X (112.80 MHz)
		AM	Gamston Aerodrome	DME
1037.0000	1100.0000	AM	Nationwide	DME Ch 76X (112.90 MHz)
1038.0000	1101.0000	AM	Nationwide	DME Ch 77X (113.00 MHz)
1039.0000	1102.0000	AM	Nationwide	DME Ch 78X (113.10 MHz)
		AM	Strumble	DME
1040.0000	1103.0000	AM	Nationwide	DME Ch 79X (113.20 MHz)
		AM	Warton (MoD)	TACAN
1041.0000	1104.0000	AM	Nationwide	DME Ch 80X (113.30 MHz)
1042.0000	1105.0000	AM	Nationwide	DME Ch 81X (113.40 MHz)
1043.0000	1106.0000	AM	Nationwide	DME Ch 82X (113.50 MHz)
1044.0000	1107.0000	AM	Nationwide	DME Ch 83X (113.60 MHz)
		AM	London Heathrow	DME
		AM	Wick Aerodrome	TACAN
1045.0000	1108.0000	AM	Nationwide	DME Ch 84X (113.70 MHz)
		AM	RAF Upper Heyford	TACAN
1046.0000	1109.0000	AM	Nationwide	DME Ch 85X (113.80 MHz)
		AM	Talla	DME
1047.0000	1110.0000	AM	Nationwide	DME Ch 86X (113.90 MHz)
		AM	Ottringham	DME
1048.0000	1111.0000	AM	Nationwide	DME Ch 87X (114.00 MHz)
		AM	Midhurst	DME
1049.0000	1112.0000	AM	Nationwide	DME Ch 88X (114.10 MHz)
		AM	Wallasey	DME
1050.0000	1113.0000	AM	Nationwide	DME Ch 89X (114.20 MHz)
		AM	Land's End Airport	DME
1051.0000	1114.0000	AM	Nationwide	DME Ch 90X (114.30 MHz)
		AM	Aberdeen/Dyce Airport	DME
1052.0000	1115.0000	AM	Nationwide	DME Ch 91X (114.40 MHz)
		AM	Benbecula Airport	TACAN
1053.0000	1116.0000	AM	Nationwide	DME Ch 92X (114.50 MHz)
		AM	Koksijde	DME
1054.0000	1117.0000	AM	Nationwide	DME Ch 93X (114.60 MHz)
1055.0000	1118.0000	AM	Nationwide	DME Ch 94X (114.70 MHz)
1056.0000	1119.0000	AM	Nationwide	DME Ch 95X (114.80 MHz)
		AM	RAF Sculthorpe	TACAN
1057.0000	1120.0000	AM	Nationwide	DME Ch 96X (114.90 MHz)
		AM	Vallafield	TACAN
1058.0000	1121.0000	AM	Nationwide	DME Ch 97X (115.00 MHz)
		AM	Stornoway Airport	TACAN
1059.0000	1122.0000	AM	Nationwide	DME Ch 98X (115.10 MHz)
		AM	Biggin Hill	DME
1060.0000	1123.0000	AM	Nationwide	DME Ch 99X (115.20 MHz)
		AM	Dean Cross	DME
1061.0000	1124.0000	AM	Nationwide	DME Ch 100X (115.30 MHz)
		AM	Ockham	DME
1062.0000	1125.0000	AM	Nationwide	DME Ch 101X (115.40 MHz)

Base	Mobile	Mode	Location	User and Notes
		AM	Glasgow Airport	DME
1063.0000	1126.0000	AM	Nationwide	DME Ch 102X (115.50 MHz)
1064.0000	1127.0000	AM	Nationwide	DME Ch 103X (115.60 MHz)
		AM	Lambourne	DME
1065.0000	1128.0000	AM	Nationwide	DME Ch 104X (115.70 MHz)
		AM	Stoke on Trent	DME
1066.0000	1129.0000	AM	Nationwide	DME Ch 105X (115.80 MHz)
1067.0000	1130.0000	AM	Nationwide	DME Ch 106X (115.90 MHz)
		AM	RAF Mildenhall	TACAN
1068.0000	1131.0000	AM	Nationwide	DME Ch 107X (116.00 MHz)
		AM	RAF Machrihanish	TACAN
1069.0000	1132.0000	AM	Nationwide	DME Ch 108X (116.10 MHz)
		AM	RAF Church Fenton	TACAN
1070.0000	1133.0000	AM	Nationwide	DME Ch 109X (116.20 MHz)
		AM	Blackbushe Aerodrome	DME
1071.0000	1134.0000	AM	Nationwide	DME Ch 110X (116.30 MHz)
1072.0000	1135.0000	AM	Nationwide	DME Ch 111X (116.40 MHz)
		AM	Daventry	DME
1073.0000	1136.0000	AM	Nationwide	DME Ch 112X (116.50 MHz)
		AM	RAF Coltishall	TACAN
1074.0000	1137.0000	AM	Nationwide	DME Ch 113X (116.60 MHz)
		AM	RAF Brawdy	TACAN
1075.0000	1138.0000	AM	Nationwide	DME Ch 114X (116.70 MHz)
1076.0000	1139.0000	AM	Nationwide	DME Ch 115X (116.80 MHz)
1077.0000	1140.0000	AM	Nationwide	DME Ch 116X (116.90 MHz)
1078.0000	1141.0000	AM	Nationwide	DME Ch 117X (117.00 MHz)
		AM	Seaford	DME
1079.0000	1142.0000	AM	Nationwide	DME Ch 118X (117.10 MHz)
1080.0000	1143.0000	AM	Nationwide	DME Ch 119X (117.20 MHz)
1081.0000	1144.0000	AM	Nationwide	DME Ch 120X (117.30 MHz)
		AM	Detling	DME
1082.0000	1145.0000	AM	Nationwide	DME Ch 121X (117.40 MHz)
		AM	Connaught Airport	DME
		AM	RAF Cranwell	TACAN
1083.0000	1146.0000	AM	Nationwide	DME Ch 122X (117.50 MHz)
		AM	Brookmans Park	DME
		AM	Turnberry	DME
1084.0000	1147.0000	AM	Nationwide	DME Ch 123X (117.60 MHz)
		AM	RAF Wittering	TACAN
1085.0000	1148.0000	AM	Nationwide	DME Ch 124X (117.70 MHz)
		AM	Oxford/Kidlington	DME
		AM	Tiree	DME
1086.0000	1149.0000	AM	Nationwide	DME Ch 125X (117.80 MHz)
1087.0000	1150.0000	AM	Nationwide	DME Ch 126X (117.90 MHz)
		AM	Mayfield	DME
1088.0000	1025.0000	AM	Nationwide	DME Channel 1Y Not Used
1089.0000	1026.0000	AM	Nationwide	DME Channel 2Y Not Used
1090.0000	1027.0000	AM	Nationwide	DME Channel 3Y Not Used

Base	Mobile	Mode	Location	User and Notes
1091.0000	1028.0000	AM	Nationwide	DME Channel 4Y Not Used
1092.0000	1029.0000	AM	Nationwide	DME Channel 5Y Not Used
1093.0000	1030.0000	AM	Nationwide	DME Channel 6Y Not Used
1094.0000	1031.0000	AM	Nationwide	DME Channel 7Y Not Used
1095.0000	1032.0000	AM	Nationwide	DME Channel 8Y Not Used
1096.0000	1033.0000	AM	Nationwide	DME Channel 9Y Not Used
1097.0000	1034.0000	AM	Nationwide	DME Channel 10Y Not Used
1098.0000	1035.0000	AM	Nationwide	DME Channel 11Y Not Used
1099.0000	1036.0000	AM	Nationwide	DME Channel 12Y Not Used
1100.0000	1037.0000	AM	Nationwide	DME Channel 13Y Not Used
1101.0000	1038.0000	AM	Nationwide	DME Channel 14Y Not Used
1102.0000	1039.0000	AM	Nationwide	DME Channel 15Y Not Used
1103.0000	1040.0000	AM	Nationwide	DME Channel 16Y Not Used
1104.0000	1041.0000	AM	Nationwide	DME Ch 17Y (108.05 MHz)
		AM	Lydd Airport	DME
1105.0000	1042.0000	AM	Nationwide	DME Ch 18Y (108.15 MHz)
		AM	Blackpool Airport	DME
1106.0000	1043.0000	AM	Nationwide	DME Ch 19Y (108.25 MHz)
1107.0000	1044.0000	AM	Nationwide	DME Ch 20Y (108.35 MHz)
1108.0000	1045.0000	AM	Nationwide	DME Ch 21Y (108.45 MHz)
1109.0000	1046.0000	AM	Nationwide	DME Ch 22Y (108.55 MHz)
1110.0000	1047.0000	AM	Nationwide	DME Ch 23Y (108.65 MHz)
1111.0000	1048.0000	AM	Nationwide	DME Ch 24Y (108.75 MHz)
		AM	Humberside Airport	DME
1112.0000	1049.0000	AM	Nationwide	DME Ch 25Y (108.85 MHz)
1113.0000	1050.0000	AM	Nationwide	DME Ch26Y (108.95 MHz)
1113.0000	1050.0000	AM	Woodford	DME
1114.0000	1051.0000	AM	Nationwide	DME Ch 27Y (109.05 MHz)
		AM	Yeovil Aerodrome	DME
1115.0000	1052.0000	AM	Nationwide	DME Ch 28Y (109.15 MHz)
		AM	Luton Airport	DME
1116.0000	1053.0000	AM	Nationwide	DME Ch 29Y (109.25 MHz)
1117.0000	1054.0000	AM	Nationwide	DME Ch 30Y (109.35 MHz)
1118.0000	1055.0000	AM	Nationwide	DME Ch 31Y (109.45 MHz)
1119.0000	1056.0000	AM	Nationwide	DME Ch 32Y (109.55 MHz)
1120.0000	1057.0000	AM	Nationwide	DME Ch 33Y (109.65 MHz)
1121.0000	1058.0000	AM	Nationwide	DME Ch 34Y (109.75 MHz)
1122.0000	1059.0000	AM	Nationwide	DME Ch 35Y (109.85 MHz)
		AM	Fair Oaks Aerodrome	DME
1123.0000	1060.0000	AM	Nationwide	DME Ch36Y (109.95 MHz)
1124.0000	1061.0000	AM	Nationwide	DME Ch 37Y (110.05 MHz)
1125.0000	1062.0000	AM	Nationwide	DME Ch 38Y (110.15 MHz)
1126.0000	1063.0000	AM	Nationwide	DME Ch39Y (110.25 MHz)
1127.0000	1064.0000	AM	Nationwide	DME Ch 40Y (110.35 MHz)
1128.0000	1065.0000	AM	Nationwide	DME Ch 41Y (110.45 MHz)
1129.0000	1066.0000	AM	Nationwide	DME Ch 42Y (110.55 MHz)
1130.0000	1067.0000	AM	Nationwide	DME Ch 43Y (110.65 MHz)
1131.0000	1068.0000	AM	Nationwide	DME Ch 44Y (110.75 MHz)

Base	Mobile	Mode	Location	User and Notes
1132.0000	1069.0000	AM	Nationwide	DME Ch 45Y (110.85 MHz)
1133.0000	1070.0000	AM	Nationwide	DME Ch 46Y (110.95 MHz)
1134.0000	1071.0000	AM	Nationwide	DME Ch 47Y (111.05 MHz)
1135.0000	1072.0000	AM	Nationwide	DME Ch 48Y (111.15 MHz)
1136.0000	1073.0000	AM	Nationwide	DME Ch 49Y (111.25 MHz)
1137.0000	1074.0000	AM	Nationwide	DME Ch 50Y (111.35 MHz)
		AM	Southend Airport	DME
1138.0000	1075.0000	AM	Nationwide	DME Ch 51Y (111.45 MHz)
1139.0000	1076.0000	AM	Nationwide	DME Ch 52Y (111.55 MHz)
1140.0000	1077.0000	AM	Nationwide	DME Ch 53Y (111.65 MHz)
1141.0000	1078.0000	AM	Nationwide	DME Ch 54Y (111.75 MHz)
		AM	Liverpool Airport	DME
1142.0000	1079.0000	AM	Nationwide	DME Ch 55Y (111.85 MHz)
1143.0000	1080.0000	AM	Nationwide	DME Ch 56Y (111.95 MHz)
1144.0000	1081.0000	AM	Nationwide	DME Ch 57Y (112.05 MHz)
1145.0000	1082.0000	AM	Nationwide	DME Ch 58Y (112.15 MHz)
1146.0000	1083.0000	AM	Nationwide	DME Ch 59Y (112.25 MHz)
1147.0000	1084.0000	AM	Nationwide	DME Channel 60Y Not Used
1148.0000	1085.0000	AM	Nationwide	DME Channel 61Y Not Used
1149.0000	1086.0000	AM	Nationwide	DME Channel 62Y Not Used
1150.0000	1087.0000	AM	Nationwide	DME Channel 63Y Not Used
1151.0000	1088.0000	AM	Nationwide	DME Channel 64Y Not Used
1152.0000	1089.0000	AM	Nationwide	DME Channel 65Y Not Used
1153.0000	1090.0000	AM	Nationwide	DME Channel 66Y Not Used
1154.0000	1091.0000	AM	Nationwide	DME Channel 67Y Not Used
1155.0000	1092.0000	AM	Nationwide	DME Channel 68Y Not Used
1156.0000	1093.0000	AM	Nationwide	DME Channel 69Y Not Used
1157.0000	1094.0000	AM	Nationwide	DME Ch 70Y (112.35 MHz)
1158.0000	1095.0000	AM	Nationwide	DME Ch 71Y (112.45 MHz)
1159.0000	1096.0000	AM	Nationwide	DME Ch 72Y (112.55 MHz)
1160.0000	1097.0000	AM	Nationwide	DME Ch 73Y (112.65 MHz)
1161.0000	1098.0000	AM	Nationwide	DME Ch 74Y (112.75 MHz)
1162.0000	1099.0000	AM	Nationwide	DME Ch 75Y (112.85 MHz)
1163.0000	1100.0000	AM	Nationwide	DME Ch 76Y (112.95 MHz)
1164.0000	1101.0000	AM	Nationwide	DME Ch 77Y (113.05 MHz)
1165.0000	1102.0000	AM	Nationwide	DME Ch 78Y (113.15 MHz)
1166.0000	1103.0000	AM	Nationwide	DME Ch 79Y (113.25 MHz)
1167.0000	1104.0000	AM	Nationwide	DME Ch 80Y (113.35 MHz)
1168.0000	1105.0000	AM	Nationwide	DME Ch 81Y (113.45 MHz)
1169.0000	1106.0000	AM	Nationwide	DME Ch 82Y (113.55 MHz)
		AM	Manchester Airport	DME
1170.0000	1107.0000	AM	Nationwide	DME Ch 83Y (113.65 MHz)
		AM	Honiley	DME
1171.0000	1108.0000	AM	Nationwide	DME Ch 84Y (113.75 MHz)
		AM	Bovingdon	DME
1172.0000	1109.0000	AM	Nationwide	DME Ch 85Y (113.85 MHz)
1173.0000	1110.0000	AM	Nationwide	DME Ch 86Y (113.95 MHz)
1174.0000	1111.0000	AM	Nationwide	DME Ch 87Y (114.05 MHz)

Base	Mobile	Mode	Location	User and Notes
1175.0000	1112.0000	AM	Nationwide	DME Ch 88Y (114.15 MHz)
1176.0000	1113.0000	AM	Nationwide	DME Ch 89Y (114.25 MHz)
1177.0000	1114.0000	AM	Nationwide	DME Ch90Y (114.35 MHz)
		AM	Compton	DME
1178.0000	1115.0000	AM	Nationwide	DME Ch 91Y (114.45 MHz)
1179.0000	1116.0000	AM	Nationwide	DME Ch 92Y (114.55 MHz)
		AM	Clacton Aerodrome	DME
1180.0000	1117.0000	AM	Nationwide	DME Ch 93Y (114.65 MHz)
1181.0000	1118.0000	AM	Nationwide	DME Ch 94Y (114.75 MHz)
1182.0000	1119.0000	AM	Nationwide	DME Ch 95Y (114.85 MHz)
1183.0000	1120.0000	AM	Nationwide	DME Ch 96Y (114.95 MHz)
		AM	Dover	DME
1184.0000	1121.0000	AM	Nationwide	DME Ch 97Y (115.05 MHz)
1185.0000	1122.0000	AM	Nationwide	DME Ch 98Y (115.15 MHz)
1186.0000	1123.0000	AM	Nationwide	DME Ch 99Y (115.25 MHz)
1187.0000	1124.0000	AM	Nationwide	DME Ch 100Y (115.35 MHz)
1188.0000	1125.0000	AM	Nationwide	DME Ch 101Y (115.45 MHz)
1189.0000	1126.0000	AM	Nationwide	DME Ch 102Y (115.55 MHz)
		AM	Gloucester Airport	DME
1190.0000	1127.0000	AM	Nationwide	DME Ch 103Y (115.65 MHz)
1191.0000	1128.0000	AM	Nationwide	DME Ch 104Y (115.75 MHz)
1192.0000	1129.0000	AM	Nationwide	DME Ch 105Y (115.85 MHz)
1193.0000	1130.0000	AM	Nationwide	DME Ch 106Y (115.95 MHz)
1194.0000	1131.0000	AM	Nationwide	DME Ch 107Y (116.05 MHz)
1195.0000	1132.0000	AM	Nationwide	DME Ch 108Y (116.15 MHz)
1196.0000	1133.0000	AM	Nationwide	DME Ch 109Y (116.25 MHz)
		AM	Barkway	DME
1197.0000	1134.0000	AM	Nationwide	DME Ch 110Y (116.35 MHz)
1198.0000	1135.0000	AM	Nationwide	DME Ch 111Y (116.45 MHz)
1199.0000	1136.0000	AM	Nationwide	DME Ch 112Y (116.55 MHz)
1200.0000	1137.0000	AM	Nationwide	DME Ch 113Y (116.65 MHz)
1201.0000	1138.0000	AM	Nationwide	DME Ch 114Y (116.75 MHz)
		AM	Cambridge Airport	DME
1202.0000	1139.0000	AM	Nationwide	DME Ch 115Y (116.85 MHz)
1203.0000	1140.0000	AM	Nationwide	DME Ch 116Y (116.95 MHz)
1204.0000	1141.0000	AM	Nationwide	DME Ch 117Y (117.05 MHz)
1205.0000	1142.0000	AM	Nationwide	DME Ch 118Y (117.15 MHz)
1206.0000	1143.0000	AM	Nationwide	DME Ch 119Y (117.25 MHz)
1207.0000	1144.0000	AM	Nationwide	DME Ch 120Y (117.35 MHz)
		AM	Sumburgh Airport	DME
1208.0000	1145.0000	AM	Nationwide	DME Ch 121Y (117.45 MHz)
		AM	Brecon	DME
1209.0000	1146.0000	AM	Nationwide	DME Ch 122Y (117.55 MHz)
1210.0000	1147.0000	AM	Nationwide	DME Ch 123Y (117.65 MHz)
1211.0000	1148.0000	AM	Nationwide	DME Ch 124Y (117.75 MHz)
1212.0000	1149.0000	AM	Nationwide	DME Ch 125Y (117.85 MHz)
1213.0000	1150.0000	AM	Nationwide	DME Ch 126Y (117.95 MHz)

Base	Mobile	Mode	Location	User and Notes
1215.0000 - 1365.0000 MHz			DEFENCE AND CIVIL RADAR SYSTEMS	
1215.0000 - 1240.0000 MHz			SATELLITE NAVIGATION SYSTEMS	
1227.6000		NFM	Nationwide	Military GPS Navstar
1240.0000 - 1296.0000 MHz			RADIO LOCATION AND SATELLITE POSITIONING SYSTEMS	
1246.0000		NFM	Nationwide	Military Glonass Ch 0
1246.4375		NFM	Nationwide	Military Glonass Ch 1
1246.8750		NFM	Nationwide	Military Glonass Ch 2
1247.3125		NFM	Nationwide	Military Glonass Ch 3
1247.7500		NFM	Nationwide	Military Glonass Ch 4
1248.1875		NFM	Nationwide	Military Glonass Ch 5
1248.6250		NFM	Nationwide	Military Glonass Ch 6
1249.0625		NFM	Nationwide	Military Glonass Ch 7
1249.5000		NFM	Nationwide	Military Glonass Ch 8
1249.9375		NFM	Nationwide	Military Glonass Ch 9
1250.3750		NFM	Nationwide	Military Glonass Ch 10
1250.8125		NFM	Nationwide	Military Glonass Ch 11
1251.2500		NFM	Nationwide	Military Glonass Ch 12
1251.6875		NFM	Nationwide	Military Glonass Ch 13
1252.1250		NFM	Nationwide	Military Glonass Ch 14
1252.5625		NFM	Nationwide	Military Glonass Ch 15
1253.0000		NFM	Nationwide	Military Glonass Ch 16
1253.4375		NFM	Nationwide	Military Glonass Ch 17
1253.8750		NFM	Nationwide	Military Glonass Ch 18
1254.3125		NFM	Nationwide	Military Glonass Ch 19
1254.7500		NFM	Nationwide	Military Glonass Ch 20
1255.0000	1255.0000	WFM	Nationwide	Amateur TV
1255.1875		NFM	Nationwide	Military Glonass Ch 21
1255.6250		NFM	Nationwide	Military Glonass Ch 22
1256.0625		NFM	Nationwide	Military Glonass Ch 23
1256.5000		NFM	Nationwide	Military Glonass Ch 24
1260.0000		NFM	Nationwide	German Bugging Devices
1265.0000	1265.0000	WFM	Nationwide	Amateur TV
1296.0000 - 1325.0000 MHz			25 CM AMATEUR RADIO BAND	
1296.8000		CW	Farnborough	Beacon (GB3FRS)
1296.8100		CW	Orpington	Beacon (GB3NWK)
1296.8300		CW	Martlesham Heath	Beacon (GB3MHL)
1296.8600		CW	St Austell	Beacon (GB3MCB)
1296.8900		CW	Dunstable	Beacon (GB3DUN)
1296.9000		CW	Newport	Beacon (GB3IOW)
1296.9100		CW	Clee Hill	Beacon (GB3CLE)
1296.9700		CW	Hastings	Beacon (GB3ESB)
1296.9900		CW	Edinburgh	Beacon (GB3EDN)
1297.0000	1291.0000	NFM	Nationwide	Amateur Repeater Ch RM0

Base	Mobile	Mode	Location	User and Notes
		NFM	Bolton	Repeater (GB3MC)
		NFM	Bushey Heath	Repeater (GB3BH)
		NFM	Norwich	Repeater (GB3NO)
1297.0250	1291.0250	NFM	Nationwide	Amateur Repeater Ch RM1
1297.0500	1291.0500	NFM	Nationwide	Amateur Repeater Ch RM2
1297.0750	1291.0750	NFM	Nationwide	Amateur Repeater Ch RM3
		NFM	Barkway	Repeater (GB3PS)
		NFM	Crawley	Repeater (GB3CP)
		NFM	Stoke on Trent	Repeater (GB3SE)
1297.1000	1291.1000	NFM	Nationwide	Amateur Repeater Ch RM4
1297.1250	1291.1250	NFM	Nationwide	Amateur Repeater Ch RM5
		NFM	Bedford	Repeater (GB3BW)
1297.1500	1291.1500	NFM	Nationwide	Amateur Repeater Ch RM6
		NFM	Northampton	Repeater (GB3CN)
		NFM	Southampton	Repeater (GB3AD)
		NFM	Wolverhampton	Repeater (GB3MH)
1297.2250	1291.2250	NFM	Nationwide	Amateur Repeater Ch RM9
		NFM	Brighton	Repeater (GB3WX)
		NFM	Reading	Repeater (GB3RU)
1299.3750	1291.3750	NFM	Nationwide	Amateur Repeater Ch RM15
		NFM	Wakefield	Repeater (GB3WC)
1297.5000		NFM	Nationwide	Amateur Ch SM 20
1297.5250		NFM	Nationwide	Amateur Ch SM 21
1297.5500		NFM	Nationwide	Amateur Ch SM 22
1297.5750		NFM	Nationwide	Amateur Ch SM 23
1297.6000		NFM	Nationwide	Amateur Ch SM 24
1297.6250		NFM	Nationwide	Amateur Ch SM 25
1297.6500		NFM	Nationwide	Amateur Ch SM 26
1297.6750		NFM	Nationwide	Amateur Ch SM 27
1297.7000		NFM	Nationwide	Amateur Ch SM 28
1297.7250		NFM	Nationwide	Amateur Ch SM 29
1297.7500		NFM	Nationwide	Amateur Ch SM 30
1308.0000	1249.0000	NFM	Aldborough	Repeater (GB3EY)
		NFM	Bedford	Repeater (GB3BW)
		NFM	High Wycombe	Repeater (GB3HV)
		NFM	Wolverhampton	Repeater (GB3MM)
1311.5000	1276.5000	NFM	Bath	Repeater (GB3UT)
		NFM	Hastings	Repeater (GB3VI)
1316.0000	1249.0000	NFM	Brighton	Repeater (GB3VR)
		NFM	Chesterfield	Repeater (GB3TT)
		NFM	Fakenham	Repeater (GB3TN)
		NFM	Mereway	Repeater (GB3MV)
		NFM	Bristol	Repeater (GB3ZZ)
		NFM	Coventry	Repeater (GB3RT)
		NFM	Crawley	Repeater (GB3CT)
		NFM	Dunstable	Repeater (GB3TV)
		NFM	Glasgow	Repeater (GB3GT)
		NFM	Leicester	Repeater (GB3GV)

Base	Mobile	Mode	Location	User and Notes
		NFM	Madingley	Repeater (GB3PV)
		NFM	Nottingham	Repeater (GB3NW)
		NFM	Stoke on Trent	Repeater (GB3UD)
1325.0000 - 1400.0000 MHz			**POINT-TO-POINT DIGITAL MULTIPLEXED MICROWAVE LINKS**	
1328.0200		MUX	Poole	Bulbarrow Main Site
1331.2000		MUX	Poole	Bulbarrow Main Site
1334.0000		MUX	Poole	Bulbarrow Main Site
1400.0000 - 1427.0000 MHz			**RADIO ASTRONOMY**	
1427.0000 - 1429.0000 MHz			**SATELLITE UPLINKS**	
1429.0000 - 1450.0000 MHz			**MoD ALLOCATIONS**	
1450.0000 - 1530.0000 MHz			**POINT-TO-POINT DIGITAL MICROWAVE LINKS**	
1450.6000		MUX	Poole	Bulbarrow Main Site
1455.3500		NFM	Merseyside	Police DCR Link
1457.6400		MUX	Poole	70.8625 MHz Fire Brigade
1458.2475		NFM	Badminton	Palace Link
1459.1500		MUX	Poole	Microwave Link
1460.4300		MUX	Poole	Microwave Link
1461.6250		NFM	Wiltshire	Fire Brigade
1461.6400		MUX	Poole	Microwave Link
1466.8750	1529.3750	NFM	Nationwide	UK Test & Development
1467.1250	1529.6250	NFM	Nationwide	UK Test & Development
1468.7700		MUX	Poole	Microwave Link
1469.6800		MUX	Poole	171.2875 MHz Feeder
1470.3300		MUX	Poole	Bulbarrow Main Site
1472.0000		MUX	Poole	Corfe Castle
1472.6500		MUX	Poole	Microwave Link
1472.9875	1492.8500	NFM	Channel Islands	Aurigny Airlines Link
1473.1500		MUX	Poole	Bulbarrow Main Site
1492.3000		MUX	Poole	454.1 MHz Paging Feeder
1510.5250		MUX	Poole	Microwave Link
1575.4200		NFM	Nationwide	Civilian GPS Navstar
1602.0000		NFM	Nationwide	Civil Glonass Ch 0
1602.5625		NFM	Nationwide	Civil Glonass Ch 1
1603.1250		NFM	Nationwide	Civil Glonass Ch 2
1603.6785		NFM	Nationwide	Civil Glonass Ch 3
1604.2500		NFM	Nationwide	Civil Glonass Ch 4
1604.8125		NFM	Nationwide	Civil Glonass Ch 5
1605.3750		NFM	Nationwide	Civil Glonass Ch 6
1605.9375		NFM	Nationwide	Civil Glonass Ch 7
1606.5000		NFM	Nationwide	Civil Glonass Ch 8
1607.0625		NFM	Nationwide	Civil Glonass Ch 9
1607.6250		NFM	Nationwide	Civil Glonass Ch 10

Base	Mobile	Mode	Location	User and Notes
1608.1875		NFM	Nationwide	Civil Glonass Ch 11
1608.7500		NFM	Nationwide	Civil Glonass Ch 12
1609.3125		NFM	Nationwide	Civil Glonass Ch 13
1609.8750		NFM	Nationwide	Civil Glonass Ch 14
1610.4375		NFM	Nationwide	Civil Glonass Ch 15
1611.0000		NFM	Nationwide	Civil Glonass Ch 16
1611.5625		NFM	Nationwide	Civil Glonass Ch 17
1612.1250		NFM	Nationwide	Civil Glonass Ch 18
1612.6785		NFM	Nationwide	Civil Glonass Ch 19
1613.2500		NFM	Nationwide	Civil Glonass Ch 20
1613.8125		NFM	Nationwide	Civil Glonass Ch 21
1614.3750		NFM	Nationwide	Civil Glonass Ch 22
1614.9375		NFM	Nationwide	Civil Glonass Ch 23
1616.5000		NFM	Nationwide	Civil Glonass Ch 24

1670.0000 - 1675.0000 MHz   TERRESTRIAL FLIGHT TELEPHONE SYSTEM UPLINKS

Base	Mobile	Mode	Location	User and Notes
1691.0000		NFM	Nationwide	Meteosat Ch A1/GOES
1694.5000		NFM	Nationwide	Meteosat Ch A2/FAX
1698.0000		NFM	Nationwide	NOAA-10
1707.0000		NFM	Nationwide	NOAA-9, 11

1800.0000 - 1805.0000 MHz   TERRESTRIAL FLIGHT TELEPHONE SYSTEM DOWNLINKS

FREE Book for You!

These new guides list by county the radio frequencies used by the police in Britain, and now include the other emergency services. There are hundreds of frequencies, many have never been published before. The country is covered in four comprehensive parts: London, Southern England, Northern England, and Scotland and Wales.

All you have to do to receive your free copy is to send us 25 or more VHF/UHF frequencies and their users from your area. The frequencies must not be listed in any edition of *The UK Scanning Directory*, and must include location and user. It's that simple!

To get your free book set out your list under these headings:

Base Freq.	Mobile Freq.	Mode	Location	User & Notes

Good luck!

Important:
To qualify for your copy of the *UK Police Radio Guide,* please send the appropriate voucher which is on the last page, for the one you would like along with your frequency list. Please do not send photocopies of the voucher as only the original will be accepted.

Competition for a FREE copy of the 6th Edition!

The overwhelming number of contributions that have been received for the 5th Edition of *The UK Scanning Directory* has prompted the publisher to extend the bounds of the competition. Unlike previous, now *25 free copies* of the 6th Edition are being given away absolutely free.

All you have to do is send your list of previously unpublished frequencies to the editor, along with your name and address (anonymity is guaranteed to all), then your name will be entered into a prize draw to be drawn at the launch of the 6th Edition.

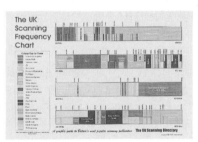

Shortwave Maritime Communications
by B. E. Richardson

Disasters are quite common, ships are blown onto rocks, run aground or are lost, and each month at least one super tanker breaks up and sinks. *Shortwave Maritime Communications* gives step-by-step instructions on how to monitor these incidents with all the shipping frequencies worldwide.

The book is laid out with both the beginner and the well-seasoned maritime radio enthusiast in mind, providing the most accurate and detailed information in an easy-to-use format. The first few chapters show in detail the various communication modes used by ships today, from Morse right through to Inmarsat. Each one begins with a bandplan of the mode to quickly and easily see where to tune and how the whole system operates. Two mammoth frequency lists include every coastal station from around the world together with the shore and corresponding ship's frequency, and are arranged not only by frequency but by station's name, mode and callsign. Regardless where in the world you live *Shortwave Maritime Communications* provides endless hours of enjoyment. (200 pages A4).

Price: £16.50 plus £1 UK postage. Overseas post add £2.50 for Europe (airmail) and sea mail worldwide, airmail outside Europe add £6.

Plug into your authoritative source.

The leading full-spectrum radio hobby magazine has now expanded to bring you even more frequencies and information. Shortwave listeners will discover more than twenty-five pages devoted to broadcasting schedules, international newscasts and propagation charts. Utility listeners are especially catered for with columns dedicated to military, maritime, aeronautical, RTTY etc. plus large frequency lists. Recent articles have covered the war in Bosnia, Shuttle and Ham Radio, Pirate Broadcasting v. Governments, Monitoring Cruise Ships and USF Global HF System. For reviews, features, listening tips and much more *Monitoring Times* is the one listening tool you can't afford to be without.

Prices include postage: Single issue £3.75 UK or £4 overseas. Subscriptions: 1 year £33.50 or £18.50 for 6 months in UK. Europe (airmail) and rest of the world by sea 1 year £39 or £21.50 for 6 issues. Ask for other airmail rates.

INTERPRODUCTS
8 Abbot Street, Perth, PH2 0EB, Scotland
Tel. & Fax: 01738-441199

ORDER FORM

To: **Interproducts**
8 Abbot Street
Perth,
PH2 0EB,
Scotland.

Tel. & Fax: 01738-441199
International: +44-1738-441199

Name:

Address:

Qty	Items	Each£	Postage£	Total£
		Total£		

UKSD5

I am enclosing a cheque/draft for £..........................

VISA

MasterCard

Please charge to my
credit card

Expiry date........................ Signature...

Books normally available from stock.

UK credit card orders under £10 have a services charge of 75p.

Please allow 2 weeks for delivery of orders.

ORDER FORM

To: **Interproducts**
    8 Abbot Street
    Perth,
    PH2 0EB,
    Scotland.

Tel. & Fax: 01738-441199
International: +44-1738-441199

Name:

Address:

Qty	Items	Each£	Postage£	Total£
		Total£		

UKSD5

I am enclosing a cheque/draft for £..........................

VISA

MasterCard

Please charge to my
credit card

Expiry date........................   Signature...

Books normally available from stock.

UK credit card orders under £10 have a services charge of 75p.

Please allow 2 weeks for delivery of orders.